Microbiology

An Introduction to Protists

Microbiology

An Introduction to Protists

J. S. Poindexter

New York University School of Medicine

THE MACMILLAN COMPANY, New York

Collier-Macmillan Limited, London

Frontispiece: The primitive, intranuclear mitotic apparatus of baker's
yeast, as seen in an electron micrograph of a freeze-
etched preparation of a dividing nucleus. (From Moor, H.,
1966. *J. Cell Biol.* **29**:153. By permission of The
Rockefeller University Press.)

The Macmillan Company
866 Third Avenue, New York, New York 10022

Collier-Macmillan Canada, Ltd., Toronto, Ontario

Library of Congress catalog card number: 74-113933
First Printing

The growing interest in microbes among persons who do not intend to pursue careers in microbiology is welcomed. Microbiology courses are now being offered to college students with some high school or college background in chemistry and general biology. This book is intended for use in such courses.

Most introductory microbiology courses are completed in one semester, but vary in content and emphasis. Although this book covers more material than is normally treated in one semester, portions can be used selectively and the material expanded by the instructor according to the character of his course and the needs, interests, and backgrounds of his students. In particular, the instructor may find that a group of protists especially relevant to his course has been treated briefly or not at all. Or he may feel that the background of his students in organic and physical chemistry is sufficient to make a more extensive treatment of biochemical phenomena meaningful to them. Or he and his students may enjoy historical anecdotes about discoveries and ideas in microbiology, or detailed verbalizations of reasoning processes using specific observations on protists; these topics are especially effective when presented orally.

Part 4 contains a large amount of descriptive information that it might be tempting to encourage students to memorize. The section is, however, intended primarily to inform students of the diversity among protists, and secondarily to illustrate phylogenetic relationships as inferred from properties of modern organisms whose ancestors have left only a trace of a fossil record.

For non-majors in particular, the principles rather than the details and terminology should be emphasized. Instructors who do not wish to present lengthy descriptions of the major groups of protists should nevertheless find this section useful when referring to selected organisms in discussions of phenomena observable in protists.

The author is deeply grateful to the many microbiologists who contributed illustrative material. Their generous response to requests for illustrations seems to be further evidence of the interest of these scientists in sharing their observations with a more general audience than that which reads research journals. Gratitude is also expressed to the societies and publishing companies who have permitted reproduction of copyrighted material.

As a specialist in only one group of protists, the author is indebted to the several persons who read and corrected the chapters in Part 4 dealing with protists with which they are especially familiar; and to E. B. Shirling, C. B. van Niel, and the late R. P. Hall, each of whom read and criticized the entire manuscript. It is hoped that the efforts of these critics are reflected in an accurate and informative introduction to the organisms which are our common interest.

J. S. P.

Contents

Part 1

The Scientific Study of Protists as Living Systems

Chapter 1

Natural Science and Protistology

Natural Science

A science is a system of propositions that are interrelated by rational implication. In a formal science, the system consists of two sets of propositions: the axioms, which are assumed to be true, and the theorems, which can be deduced[1] from the axioms. The truth of a theorem is tested by determining whether the theorem is deducible from an axiom(s) of the system. In a natural science, the system consists of a body of information accumulated by observation and a set of ideas formulated on the basis of observations and that lead to further observation and ideas. The ideas are tested for their truth (verifiability) by determining whether their predictions agree with observations of real phenomena. The several branches of natural science are differentiated by the phenomena with which they are concerned.

Theories in a natural science are the ideas that interrelate and explain observations. They are formulated empirically, i.e., by inductive inference from observations and measurements of natural, physically real phenomena. An induction is a generalization about a class inferred from observation of a particular member (or subgroup) of the class. It may be a broad generalization, i.e., one applicable not to every member of the class, but to a significant proportion of the members of the class; or a strict generalization, i.e., one applicable to the class without exception of any member. From a generalization, deductions may predict the characteristics of a particular system or phenomenon that has not previously been observed.

---

[1]The process of deduction is prescribed by the rules of logic; these rules may be found in an introductory textbook of logic and will not be presented here.

Since an inductive inference cannot, usually for practical reasons, be tested directly by observation, its reliability must be determined by other means. There are four fundamental criteria for evaluating an inductive inference; it is not sufficient that the inference meet one criterion—it must meet all four.

1. The greater the number of samples (particular instances) observed, the greater the reliability of the generalization; the sampling must be random and must reflect any stratification naturally present among the type of instance observed.

2. There must not be any contrary[2] observations.

3. The phenomenon observed must be non-variable.

4. The generalization must be independently confirmed by deduction from generalizations of greater scope, even though the other generalizations may also be inductions.

A generalization that meets all four criteria should have a high degree of probability, such that predictions (called hypotheses) deduced from it would be verifiable.

Useful hypotheses in a natural science are those that can be tested by observation; in this way, the theory is tested. Observation of a real phenomenon may be made naturally, i.e., under conditions not manipulated by the observer, or experimentally, i.e., under conditions determined by the observer. In an experiment, the observer controls all the factors that might influence the phenomenon. By allowing only one factor to vary independently of his control, but in such a way that he can observe or measure it, the observer can infer the kind and amount of influence exerted by that variable.

If an observation is predicted by the hypothesis, the hypothesis has been verified. If it is not predicted, the hypothesis is proved inadequate. Unexpected observations are sometimes called accidents in experimental science and, when pursued, may lead to generalizations more significant than the one that originally brought attention to the phenomenon. If the observations and the prediction of the hypothesis cannot both be true, the hypothesis is disproved; the hypothesis, the deductions that led to it, and the theory from which it was deduced must be re-examined and modified or discarded. A new explanation must be formulated.

Most of the natural sciences include formal branches that contribute theories through deductive reasoning and are, therefore, similar to formal sciences. Nevertheless, predictions of the propositions of a formal branch of a natural science must agree with the conclusions of the empiricists.

Ideas in Biology. Biology, the branch of natural science concerned with living systems, includes a few central theories and concepts from which the rationale for all natural and experimental observation is derived. Theories relevant to all types of living systems are described briefly on page 5.

---

[2]"Contraries" in formal reasoning are propositions that cannot simultaneously be true, although they may both be false.

1. Theory of Biogenesis. All life now in existence has arisen from other life. This is not contrary to the hypothesis that, at one time, life arose from inanimate materials.

2. The Cell Theory. All living systems are cellular; i.e., they are or are composed of cells. Further concepts of this theory are discussed in Chapter 4.

3. The Gene Theory. All heritable traits are transmitted by substantial units called genes. Heritable changes in traits occur only by changes in the genes.

4. Theory of Evolution by Natural Selection of Genetic Mutants and Recombinants. Differences between parent and offspring arise by changes in the genetic endowment between generations; these changes are due to alteration of genes or to reassortment of the genes from more than one parent to compose the endowment of the offspring. The traits and combinations of traits make an individual or group more or less fit to survive in its environment, and the individuals and groups with the advantageous traits survive and reproduce. The environment thereby naturally selects traits and combinations of traits. A corollary deducible from this theory states that in a constant environment (i.e., in the absence of change in selective pressures), the genetic composition (defined by the frequency of particular genes) of a population remains constant.

5. Theory of Monophylogeny. The descent of all modern living organisms can be traced to a single ancestral type (not necessarily a single ancestor). This theory has been formulated largely in the twentieth century as an interpretation of accumulating evidence that all living systems are fundamentally similar at the biochemical level.

6. Concept of Coordinated Metabolism. All chemical processes within a cell are integral parts of a whole that is directed by genetic material and results in expansion of the living system. This concept involves several others, e.g., enzymes, regulatory substances, gene products, coenzymes, metabolic intermediates, energy-storage substances. Many of these are discussed in Part 3.

7. Concept of Interdependent Communities. All living organisms that inhabit a common area are interdependent, mainly in the matters of their physical, spatial interactions and their cycling of foods. The only net input into a stable community is the energy of sunlight, which provides potential chemical energy through photosynthesis and kinetic energy for organisms that do not regulate their internal temperatures, and water (as rain or flowing water) with its solutes.

These theories and concepts are probably familiar to the reader from previous studies. They are presented here in a discussion of biologic reasoning as examples of the fruits of this reasoning. It is also important that the conceptual nature of much of the content of biology be re-emphasized, because "many scientific ideas have been so deeply embedded in our everyday view of the world that we find it difficult to draw the line between conceptual schemes and matters of fact" (Conant, p. 262).

Protistology[3]

Protistology, or microbiology, is the branch of biology that is concerned with protists. It consists of a body of systematized information about the characteristics and activities of protists and a set of generalizations and speculations concerning the various aspects of protistan existence—their history, their phylogenetic relationships, their effects on the animate and inanimate components of their environment, their structure and composition, the ways in which they respond to environmental changes, the mechanisms of their growth and reproduction and heredity, and the respective functions of their various components. Protistology parallels botany, which is concerned with plants, and zoology, which is concerned with animals.

These three branches of biology reflect the classification of living organisms in three kingdoms as proposed by E. Haeckel in 1866. The kingdoms Planta, Animalia, and Protista would accommodate, respectively, photosynthetic differentiated organisms, non-photosynthetic differentiated organisms, and undifferentiated organisms. By 1970, the kingdom Protista had not been officially adopted in biologic classification. At present, viruses, bacteria, algae, and fungi are classified as plants, and protozoa as animals. Some protists are classified both as plants and as animals. The content of this textbook anticipates that biologic classification will be revised to include the kingdom Protista, to accommodate bacteria, algae, fungi, and protozoa.

The kingdom Protista, as recognized unofficially at present, accommodates those organisms that are unicellular or, if multicellular, are not composed of differentiated tissues (see Chap. 9). Such organisms are referred to as "protists," "microorganisms," and "microbes." The latter two terms are more widely used, but they connote microscopic size. Because there are macroscopic as well as microscopic organisms without tissues, as well as differentiated organisms of microscopic size, it is generally preferable to refer to members of the kingdom as protists. (All three terms are used in this text, although usage of the latter two is reserved for reference to protists that are microscopic; the majority of protists are microscopic.)

It was essential to the development of microbiology that protists, particularly the microscopic ones, were recognized as living organisms fundamentally similar to plants and animals. In order to trace the recognition of protists as living organisms, it is necessary first to examine the criteria by which living organisms are recognized (Chap. 2).

[3]It seems to the author that the organization of a living system is far more significant than its size, and therefore that "protistology" is preferable to "microbiology." However, the latter term is traditional and more widely used.

Properties of
Living Systems

Two basic characteristics are common to all systems that biologists today unanimously regard as living organisms. The term "living" is used to refer to a system that can perpetuate its kind by **reproduction** and can expand by converting environmental substances into its own peculiar components, a capability referred to as **growth.**

The question of whether a system is living relates to the type of system, rather than to an individual system. According to the developmental pattern of a given type of living system, an individual may express only one of these properties at any particular time, or neither if it is in a dormant stage or senescent. An individual that is demonstrably capable of reproduction is referred to as **viable.** An individual is considered potentially capable of growth if it can be demonstrated (1) to be metabolically active or (2), if dormant, to possess certain properties known to be associated with reversible dormancy in that type of organism.

Growth

Growth,[1] in the biologic sense, refers to the sum of processes by which substances are taken from the environment into the system and converted there by chemical reactions into components of the system. This definition implies (1) that there is a boundary between the system's interior and its environment, and (2) that there are differences between the chemical composition of the system and that of its environment. The amount of conversion necessary is

[1]Part 3.

7

determined by the degree of these differences; some conversion invariably occurs during growth.

Most of the conversion reactions are accompanied by a change in the potential energy of participating molecules. Within the system, energy-yielding reactions supply energy for energy-consuming reactions; the ultimate source of energy, as of substances that are converted into components of the system, is the environment.

Reproduction

Reproduction[2] is the capability of a system to separate from itself some of its own substance which subsequently develops into an independent system of the same kind. Because sameness includes the capacity for reproduction, it follows that a system with this capability can give rise to an indefinite number of generations, and its descendants will continue to arise long after it has ceased to exist.

According to this definition, a system could not perpetuate itself by reproduction unless it could also grow. Without growth, each succeeding generation would be smaller; ultimately, a generation of offspring similar to the parents could not be produced, because at least one component could not be further subdivided.

At least some of the parental substance contributed to the progeny must contain the determinants of properties of the progeny, because it is generally the case that not all the characteristics are expressed in progeny simultaneously with their formation by a reproductive event. Because such determinants are substantial, they are susceptible to alteration in their chemical composition. When such alteration occurs, it may result in a change in the properties that the substance determines. Consequently, reproducing systems are mutable, and the changes are observed as differences between parent and offspring.

Other Properties

Certain other properties are exhibited by all known living organisms. These include cellular organization;[3] specific structural properties (chemical composition, internal organization, and shape) by which any one type of living organism may be distinguished from all others;[4] the ability to respond to environmental changes;[5] and the ability to effect changes in the environment.[6] Brief reflection on the fundamental properties of living organisms would allow one to predict these other properties, because they are implicit in the description of the basic

[2]Part 5, Chap. 19.
[3]Part 2.
[4]Part 4.
[5]Part 5, Chap. 18.
[6]Part 6.

properties, are necessary for them, or would be expected as consequences of them.

Many types of organisms also display one or both of two additional properties, although these are not universal among living organisms. The first of these is a maximum size among individuals of one type. The second is the ability to effect motion, either within the organism or of the organism and the environment relative to each other.

It might be noted that the two basic properties of living organisms, growth and reproduction, would be useful criteria of life in the search for extraterrestrial living systems. At present, criteria of chemical composition (particularly presence of nucleic acids) are proposed, but the findings of exploratory vehicles and instruments, especially if negative but also if positive, might prove misleading. In chemical and physical environments different from those afforded by earth, the chemical composition of growing, reproducing systems may have evolved differently.

Chapter 3

History of Recognition of Microscopic Organisms as Living Systems

The recognition that microscopic organisms were living required demonstration first that they existed and, further, that they perpetuated themselves by reproduction and grew by chemical interaction with their environment. The science of microbiology grew out of awareness of the existence of small organisms and, during the nineteenth century, from the polemics concerning the phenomena of natural transformations of organic materials (putrefactions and fermentations) and of communicable diseases.

Existence of Microorganisms

There is evidence that, at least from the time of Homer, man has suspected the existence of organisms too small to be visible to the human eye, but able to influence other organisms and inanimate materials. However, until late in the seventeenth century, there had been no more direct evidence for their existence than for that of any other invisible entity, such as an evil or beneficent spirit. Early in the seventeenth century, on the basis of optical principles already applied in the construction of telescopes, microscopes were developed that allowed visualization of very small particles. The first microscopes were employed mainly in the examination of animal parts, but one microscopist, Antony van Leeuwenhoek (1632–1723) of Delft, eventually turned his lenses on preparations containing microorganisms he could see. Prior to his studies, visualization of such creatures had not been reported.

Among the materials in which Leeuwenhoek observed microorganisms were waters from various sources (rain barrels, rivers, wells, the sea), spittle and teeth scrapings, peppercorn infusions (soakings), and naturally fermented materials such as vinegar. Most of the organisms he described in early letters to the Royal Society in London apparently were protozoa. In later reports, he described microbes that were surely bacteria, as evidenced mainly by their size, but also by their shape and movements. Leeuwenhoek's criterion of animation of a particle was its power of locomotion; he described a variety of globules and small bodies that he regarded as inanimate, but that were probably yeasts and non-motile bacteria.

The first confirmation of Leeuwenhoek's discovery of microscopic living organisms was reported in 1718 by L. Joblot (1645–1723), who had examined a variety of infusions of natural materials. Most of the microorganisms he described apparently were protozoa. He found that microorganisms did not appear in hay infusions that had been boiled and then left to stand in sealed vessels; microorganisms did appear in boiled infusions left open to air. He concluded that the "insects" or their eggs entered the infusions from the air.

Other microscopists of the eighteenth century observed microorganisms, but their descriptions were less detailed than those in the accounts of Leeuwenhoek and Joblot. J. T. Needham (1713–1781) found non-motile microbes that could grow and reproduce and concluded that locomotion was not a useful criterion of life in microorganisms.

Although there were disagreements among microscopists concerning the origin, form, and motility of microorganisms, the existence of such creatures was widely accepted among European scientists by the end of the eighteenth century. Any observer with a sufficiently powerful microscope could see them in a variety of natural materials, and they were known to be particularly numerous in decomposing organic materials.

Origin of Microorganisms

Reproducing organisms can arise, according to definition, from pre-existing organisms of the same kind. Whether they could arise from other sources had been speculated upon since the earliest recorded history. Mice, frogs, worms, bees, and other small animals were believed for a long time to arise either from parents or from materials such as stored grain, mud, and animal carcasses. (Plants and green organisms of all sizes were presumed to arise only from seeds.) Terms used to designate non-parental origin of animals included "spontaneous generation," "heterogenesis," and "abiogenesis."

Bio- Versus Abiogenesis. The notion of spontaneous generation, discredited for macroscopic organisms in the seventeenth century, was revitalized in the eighteenth century by the discovery of microorganisms. It seemed possible that such minute organisms could arise spontaneously. Several theoretic mechanisms by which microbes might be generated were proposed during the eighteenth and nineteenth centuries. The majority of these theories postulated the existence of a vital force. Proponents of the theories agreed that this vitality could be weakened or even destroyed by heat (just as the substance of a chicken's egg was irreversibly altered by heat), but they disagreed about the distribution of the vital force in nature.

Because microorganisms were most frequently observed in decomposing organic materials (including rotting foodstuffs, decaying animal carcasses, and diseased animal tissues), one group of theories held that organic material contained the vital force. This vitality was a property of organic molecules that could cause them to reorganize so that the matter was transformed (decomposed) and some of it was reorganized into minute living systems. Some theoreticians of this school believed that such systems, once organized, could subsequently perpetuate themselves by reproduction.

The second major group of theories located the vital force in the air. Most proponents held that this airborne vitality was non-substantial. With the discovery of oxygen in air and the demonstration of its necessity for animal existence, certain polemicists of this group asserted that the force invariably accompanied O_2. Exclusion of O_2, therefore, was exclusion of the vital force.

A third view held that microorganisms arose, like other living systems, only from parents or from seeds produced by parents, i.e., from pre-existing microorganisms. Proponents of this type of theory asserted that microbes and their seeds were ubiquitous, occurring in all types of natural materials and in air. Microbes were found in great numbers in decomposing materials because they caused the decomposition as they grew and multiplied. As this theory developed along with microscopic observations and experiments, it was further asserted that there were different kinds of microbes, and each kind gave rise only to its own kind.

Experiments performed during the nineteenth century finally provided sufficient evidence for biogenesis (origin in parents) to discredit abiogenesis (origin in non-living matter) of microscopic organisms. Resolution of the argument proceeded from experiments that demonstrated, in approximate chronologic order, that:

1. Non-motile globules in fermenting materials could reproduce.
2. The vital principle in air was particulate.
3. The vital particles in air had the same physical features (shapes, dimensions) as microorganisms that appeared in decomposing organic materials.
4. Microorganisms were necessary for organic transformations such as fermentations and were sufficient (other components of air were not necessary).
5. Microorganisms exhibited constant characteristics from generation to generation.

In 1836 C. Cagniard-Latour (1777–1859) and in 1837 T. Schwann (1810–1882) independently reported observations of reproduction of yeast globules in wine and grape juice. Cagniard-Latour described the formation of a small cell on the surface of a yeast globule; the two cells remained attached to each other for some time before becoming two separate globules. Schwann observed this budding process and also observed two other features of yeast development: the formation of chains of cells resulting from continued adherence of cells and buds through successive reproductive events, and formation of several cells within one cell (sporulation, known by that time to be a mechanism of reproduction in fungi). On the basis of these latter two characteristics, Schwann concluded that yeasts were a type of fungus that he called *Zuckerpilz* (sugar fungus). Other microscopists reported observations of yeast reproduction in 1837 and 1838, but many abiogenecists still held that this demonstrated only the biologic origin of yeasts and did not disprove the notion that they could also arise by spontaneous chemical processes.

In the late 1850's, H. G. F. Schroeder (1810–1885) and T. von Dusch (1824–1890) reported experiments in which they studied the role of air in initiating decomposition of organic materials. It was already established that decomposition could be prevented in many instances by heating the material and then excluding unheated air from it. (This method had already been adopted as a means of food preservation.) The abiogenecists explained that heating the material or the air destroyed its vital force, and that unheated air was necessary as a source of this force.

Schroeder and von Dusch boiled various materials in flasks to which unheated air was admitted through cotton wool. They found that the experimental material did not decompose when only filtered air was admitted, but decomposition followed whenever unfiltered air was admitted. (Schroeder further demonstrated that boiling was not sufficient to prevent decomposition of meat, milk, and egg yolk; it was necessary to heat these materials to about 130° C.) This implied that the "vital force" could be removed from air by passing it through the fine filter provided by a mass of cotton wool.

L. Pasteur (1822–1895) entered the controversy shortly after Schroeder and von Dusch's first reports, and in 1861 reported his direct observation of airborne particles that he believed were microorganisms. He drew air through a wad of heated gun cotton contained in a piece of glass tubing. The gun cotton was then transferred to a mixture of alcohol and ether, which dissolved the gun cotton, leaving undissolved the dust particles that had been trapped in the cotton. Microscopic observation of the insoluble materials revealed crystals and spherical and ovoid bodies morphologically indistinguishable from the spores of fungi or the cells of smaller microbes that had previously been described. In these and a few other types of experiments, Pasteur demonstrated that particles resembling microorganisms were present in air. He also found that air close to soil contained larger numbers of such particles than air farther from the ground.

He then proceeded to demonstrate that filters (of various materials; all were masses of small fibers) trapped the entities in air that could initiate fermentation of a boiled mixture containing sugar and nitrogenous materials extracted from yeasts. He found that this mixture would undergo fermentation in the absence of air if filters containing particles obtained from air were introduced into it. He thereby established that only the particles removed from air by filtration need be present for fermentation to occur.

In 1865, Pasteur demonstrated his experiments before the French Academy of Sciences. In the course of the demonstration, Pasteur added a new dimension to his experiments. He allowed unfiltered air to enter some of the flasks through a neck that had been drawn out in a sigmoid shape, but was not sealed, constricted, or plugged with a fibrous material. The path of air entering the flask was first downhill, then uphill, but otherwise unimpeded. By the time fermentations had begun and microorganisms had appeared in other flasks opened directly to air and then sealed or stoppered, the liquid in the gooseneck flasks was still unchanged. Pasteur then tilted one of the flasks so that fluid ran into the neck, then back into the flask. Fermentation began and microbes appeared in that flask within three days. Pasteur interpreted this as demonstration that the microorganisms present in air that entered the flask had settled in the crook of the neck. Only after they had been washed into the main part of the flask could they begin to grow and bring about fermentation.

The matter was generally considered settled by this demonstration, although a few critics of Pasteur's experiments and interpretations continued to propose an abiogenic origin of microorganisms for many years. Within a few years, however, so much more information concerning microorganisms was accumulated that their role as causes rather than results of fermentations and other organic transformations became clearly established.

The notion of spontaneous generation of self-perpetuating entities has not been conclusively disproved, nor has it been discarded. It is still considered possible that viruses arise or arose as maverick cell components; although viruses are not cellular organisms, they are infective agents that may elicit disease symptoms in their hosts, and the diseases they cause are communicable. The notion of abiogenesis has been forced down the scale of size and organizational complexity, from men to mice to fungi to bacteria to viruses, and is still invoked as the probable mechanism of ultimate natural origin of living systems on earth (see Chap. 4, for example).

Constancy of Characteristics. In regard to the fifth point concerning microbial existence that was demonstrated in the nineteenth century—that they exhibited constant, heritable characteristics—it must be pointed out that populations of microorganisms observed before the 1870's comprised mixtures of types of microbes. However, several observers had pointed out that particular types predominated in certain types of decomposing materials. Schwann had noted that different types of yeasts were present in beer and in wine. Pasteur had noted that the yeast that predominated when his sugar solution underwent conversion to alcohol was globular, whereas when lactic acid rather than alcohol appeared, the yeast (later recognized as a bacterium) was cylindric and much smaller. Pasteur further demonstrated that the lactic acid organism acidified and coagulated milk, but the globular organism did not.

On the basis of the opinion that there were various types of microorganisms, it was predicted that pure populations of individual types could be obtained. This was attempted unsuccessfully by several investigators, including Pasteur; it was accomplished in the late 1870's.

In 1875, O. Brefeld (1839–1925) succeeded in establishing a pure culture of a mold (fungus) by isolating a single spore from an isolated sporangium and transferring the spore to a sterile nutrient environment. In 1878, J. Lister (1827–1912) obtained a pure population of a milk-coagulating bacterium by diluting a suspension of bacteria so that there was less than one bacterium in a droplet. He placed droplets in portions of sterile milk; only one portion of milk, the one that had received a single cell, subsequently soured. A similar dilution technique was used by E. C. Hansen (1842–1909) in 1883 to obtain a pure culture of a yeast. Various other methods were developed, especially by investigators of disease-producing microorganisms. These pathologists learned by the 1870's that the tissues of healthy animals were usually free of protists; introduction of a mixed microbial population into the circulatory system of a healthy animal often resulted in disappearance from the bloodstream of all but one type of microbe, and that particular type multiplied in the bloodstream.

At the International Medical Congress in London in 1881, R. Koch (1843–1910) demonstrated a method of isolating bacterial types by streaking an inoculum (a sample of viable microorganisms) over the surface of a nutrient medium solidified with gelatin. This technique, described in detail in Chapter 11, has not been significantly modified since 1881. By this method, many types of bacteria were isolated within a few years, and the constancy of morphologic, colonial, and physiologic characteristics of the smallest microorganisms, bacteria, was soon obvious to all who worked with pure cultures.

Interaction of Microorganisms and Their Environment

One conclusion derived from studies related to the origin of microscopic organisms was that they were the cause, rather than a result, of decomposition of organic material. Pasteur, whose work on various fermentations included studies of the chemical changes as well as of the microbes present, demonstrated that the specific chemical transformation that occurred depended on the type of microbe that predominated in the fermenting mixture. Mainly as a consequence of Pasteur's work, it became clear that one activity of microorganisms was specific transformation of organic matter.

Two other activities of microbes were recognized during the nineteenth century. The first was their role as agents of communicable diseases, and the second was their role in the cycling of elements. Their relationship to diseases was elucidated during the years when very little of their influence on man's environment was appreciated, and the suggestion that these creatures caused diseases in humans and their crops and livestock was considered improbable—even ridiculous—by many nineteenth-century scientists, philosophers, religionists, and medical practitioners.

The recognition of their role in geochemical changes, although of greater importance to the welfare of all organisms, stimulated relatively little controversy. This lack of controversy was due in part to the rapidly increasing awareness of the capabilities of microscopic organisms in general, and in part to the smaller immediate effect of this discovery on man's welfare. On the other hand, the recognition of the role of microbes in communicable diseases immediately suggested means of prevention and of cure of such diseases. Implementation of these means made and is still making dramatic changes in agriculture and in the longevity, general health, and numbers of humans on earth (see Chap. 23).

Germ Theory of Disease. The doctrine that a particular disease was caused by a distinct agent was first set forth by P. F. Bretonneau (1778–1862). On the basis of his observations on the spread of typhoid fever and diphtheria and the clinical appearance of persons suffering from one or the other disease, he concluded that (1) the agent that caused typhoid fever was different from the one that caused diphtheria, and (2) each agent affected a specific part of the body. He did not, however, connect his etiologic agents with microorganisms, either by observation or by inference.

The first experimental demonstration that a microorganism was responsible for a disease was carried out by A. Bassi (1773–1856), who studied a disease of silkworms called muscardino or calcino. He first demonstrated that it was communicable by scratching a worm which was in the early stages of the disease with a sterile pin, then scratching a healthy worm with the same pin; the latter soon showed symptoms of the disease. After death from calcino, a worm became covered with a white crust, and Bassi showed that the disease was communicated from such a carcass to other worms by direct contact between them and by contamination of foods by the carcass. He examined worms in all stages of the disease and discovered that a fungus was growing in their tissues. He did not succeed (by 1837, his last report) in cultivating the fungus outside the host worms; this was accomplished later (1852) by Vittadini.

At about the same time (1837), A. Donné (1801–1878) reported his observations on syphilitic lesions. He regularly found minute vibrios (which were spirochetes) in the lesions of syphilis; such organisms were not present in normal smegma, or in non-syphilitic lesions. He also found that they were adversely affected, presumably killed, by vinegar. He attempted to induce syphilitic lesions in healthy persons by inoculating one leg of each subject with pus from a syphilis lesion and the other with vinegar-treated pus. He expected that only the untreated pus would evoke a vibrio-containing lesion. However, although he observed the predicted results in some cases, the vinegar treatment did not in every case prevent development of a syphilis lesion; and some persons did not develop lesions even in the area into which untreated pus had been introduced. Consequently, Donné could not demonstrate an invariable correlation between living vibrios and experimental syphilis, even though all naturally occurring syphilis lesions contained the vibrios.

Opponents of the idea that microorganisms caused communicable diseases first held that microbes were not associated with disease. In light of the work of Bassi and Donné in experimental disease, and of Cagniard-Latour and Schwann on reproduction in yeasts, this opinion was modified to the view that microorganisms arose spontaneously from transformation of diseased tissue, just as they arose from rotting vegetation, fermenting fruit juices, and decomposing meat. When other diseases, including potato blight, grape mildew, and pebrine in silkworms, were shown to result from experimental inoculation with particular fungi (the first two) or protozoa (the third), the view was further modified to allow that such organisms, once having arisen spontaneously in a diseased host, could transmit the disease to healthy organisms.

By 1850, the notion that disease-producing germs were responsible for the spread of diseases, if not also for the initial appearance of a disease in a population of humans, livestock, or agricultural plants, had become fairly widely accepted. It stimulated the search in medicine and plant pathology for microbial agents of disease. Most of the first few microorganisms that were shown to be pathogenic agents were fungi. The generalization that pathogens are fungi (from the observation that some fungi are pathogens) led to interpretation of disease-associated bacteria as stages in the life cycles of fungi.

As an immediate consequence of Koch's development of techniques for the isolation and pure cultivation of bacteria, several types of pathogenic bacteria were identified in the 1880's. During that decade, Koch and his co-workers isolated the bacteria of tuberculosis, cholera, typhoid fever, diphtheria, pneumonia, meningitis, gonorrhea, and tetanus, and streptococci and staphylococci associated with various diseases. They further demonstrated that these organisms alone were sufficient to cause the diseases with which they were associated.

Koch formulated a set of criteria by which the causative role of a given type of microorganism would be demonstrated.

Koch's postulates state that:
If a particular microorganism is the cause of a particular disease, then

    1. The microorganism will be found in all instances of the disease.

    2. The microorganism can be obtained in pure cultures in artificial media.

    3. The disease can be elicited in a healthy host by inoculation of the host with microorganisms from the pure cultures.

    4. The microorganism will multiply in and can be reisolated from the experimental host.

These criteria were met for each of the diseases studied in Koch's laboratory. Fulfillment of these criteria is still regarded as sufficient evidence that a given microorganism is the causative agent of a disease.

Geochemical Activities. By the late nineteenth century, it was known that one of the factors on which the development of agricultural plants depended was nitrogen. Leguminous plants that possessed nodules on their roots could utilize atmospheric nitrogen (N_2); this process was called N_2 fixation. All other agricultural plants required nitrogenous compounds (combined nitrogen) as their source of nitrogen for growth. Nitrates were the most suitable compounds, but soil could be enriched with nitrates by the addition of organic materials (plant or animal remains or animal excreta). As these materials decomposed, most of the nitrogen they contained was released as ammonia, which was subsequently converted to nitrate in the soil. The conversion of ammonia to nitrate was called nitrification.

In the 1880's, microscopic examination of root nodules of legumes revealed that they contained bacteria-like bodies ("bacteroids"). In 1888, M. W. Beijerinck (1851–1931) isolated these bacteria in pure culture. Their growth in artificial media required the presence of combined nitrogen. He demonstrated that when protist-free seeds of legumes were inoculated with these pure cultures, they regularly developed into nodulated plants. This practice is still employed in agriculture as a means of ensuring nodule development, which is essential for N_2 fixation by leguminous plants. Beijerinck also found that there were certain types of bacteria and blue-green algae that could utilize N_2 as the sole source of nitrogen for growth when not associated with leguminous plants.

The agent of nitrification was known to be inactivated by heat, a nineteenth-century criterion of life. S. Winogradsky (1856–1953) isolated this agent, and reported in 1890 that the "agent" was two types of bacteria: one type converted ammonia to nitrite; the other converted nitrite to nitrate. In his studies of these bacteria, he discovered that they could grow in an inorganic environment, without illumination. They employed oxidations of inorganic nitrogen compounds as their source of energy and CO_2 as their source of carbon.

Elucidation of the roles of bacteria and blue-green algae in N_2 fixation and of bacteria in nitrification implied that protists effected inorganic as well as organic transformations in nature. Pursuit of this implication led to the discovery of various roles of protists as geochemical agents (see Chap. 20).

Present Position of Microorganisms Among Living Systems

Morphologic, physiologic, and ecologic investigations have provided descriptive information from which the natural relationships of microorganisms among themselves and to larger organisms have been inferred. It is now believed that there is a close relationship between bacteria and algae, as evidenced by the existence of one group of protists, the blue-green algae. These algae exhibit biochemical and morphologic properties typical of other algae, but also exhibit characteristics of chemical composition, virus production, and intracellular organization otherwise known only in bacteria. Blue-green algae seem to represent the kind of organism that evolved from bacteria-like ancestors by acquisition of O_2-evolving photosynthesis, and from which other (higher) algae arose by increased complexity of intracellular organization.

One group of higher algae, the green algae, comprises organisms similar to green plants in biochemical properties and internal structure of their photosynthesizing cells; green plants have apparently descended from green alga-like ancestors principally by increased developmental complexity.

Green algae (and several other types of algae) also seem to have been the ancestors of at least some colorless (i.e., non-photosynthetic) protists. Some unicellular protists possess practically all the characteristics of known algal types except the capacity for photosynthesis. From such forms, possibly, a variety of non-photosynthetic protists (protozoa and perhaps also fungi) have descended.

The relationship between protists and animals is the least susceptible to interpretation. Some biologists suggest that animals have descended from protozoa-like ancestors, while others suspect a descent from fungus-like ancestors. Much of the evidence presented in support of either view is morphologic; biochemically, many animals seem as similar to some types of bacteria as to other protists.

The proposed descents of all protistan groups are still very largely presumptive. Presumably, some ancient types no longer exist and, because of their small size and relatively simple organization, left a fossil record that is almost unintelligible, although attempts to understand it continue.

Modern protists are distinguished from plants and animals not primarily on the basis of size, but according to features of internal organization. Whereas plants and animals in some stage of development possess lines of functionally specialized cells organized into tissues, this type of organization does not occur in protists. One of the principal differences between protists and non-protists, relevant to specialization of lines of cells, is the retention by practically every protistan cell of the capacity—under certain environmental conditions—to develop into a complete organism. This potential is apparently retained even by protistan cells that are, in the course of normal development, specialized for certain metabolic functions. In contrast, differentiation of a line of cells specialized as reproductive cells (germ plasm) is common among non-protists.

It is implicit in the distinction between protists and non-protists that the former group would include unicellular and colonial organisms. The distinction is made with regard to multicellular organisms in order to delimit the kingdom of undifferentiated organisms from higher forms, all of which are multicellular. There are types of protists that, because they exhibit a definite tendency toward functional specialization of cells with loss of reproductive potential, seem intermediate between protists and differentiated organisms. Whereas this might seem to reflect the inadequacy of the distinction between protists and non-protists, it is predictable from the theories of biologic evolution and of monophylogeny that there would be a continuous gradation in type among living systems, and that a potential for a given kind of change would be expressed in more than one kind of organism. Discontinuity arises only as a consequence of a geologic upheaval or some more subtle phenomenon that extinguishes a type of organism. Biologists anticipate difficulty in classifying organisms in discrete categories, but present opinion tends to regard tissue differentiation and photosynthetic capability as characteristics of primary significance in the evolutionary history of modern organisms.

Part **2**

Cellular Organization

Chapter 4

Organization and Chemical Composition of Cells

Organization

At some time, estimated at more than 4,000 million years ago, organic substances became organized into units each of which (1) was surrounded by a semipermeable boundary, (2) contained a substance that determined the chemical reactions within the boundary, and (3) was capable of reproducing. Such units were the primeval cells. Their descendants include the multitude of living systems now in existence.

The characteristics of modern cells are similar to those proposed for primeval cells. Each cell possesses a selectively permeable boundary, the **cell membrane;** a **nucleus** which determines chemical reactions by directing the synthesis of highly specific catalysts; the catalysts, called **enzymes;** and the ability to reproduce. Many modern cells also possess **walls,** which lie external to the semipermeable membrane. The basic unit common to all types of cells is the **protoplast:** the cell membrane and the components enclosed within it.

During the first half of the nineteenth century, several biologists—notably Dutrochet, Brown, Schleiden, Schwann, and Virchow—began to formulate the generalization now called the cell theory. In its present form, this theory states that all living systems are cells or are composed of cells and cell products, that all cells arise from pre-existing cells, that the activities of a multicellular organism are the sum of the activities of its component cells, and that all cells are basically similar in chemical composition and chemical activities.

Protistan cells are of two organizational types: **procaryotic** cells, which are the more primitive, and **eucaryotic** cells, which are more complex and are considered more advanced. The cells of plants and animals are eucaryotic. The two types of cells are distinguished primarily by the presence of a nuclear membrane only in eucaryotic cells. This primary differentiating characteristic is correlated with other differences in subcellular organization. Generally, eucaryotic cells are compartmentalized, with specific metabolic functions distributed among organelles composed of or bounded by membranes; membranous and membrane-delimited organelles are rudimentary, when present, in procaryotic cells.

Chemical Composition

The chemical composition of all types of protoplasts is similar with regard to the classes of compounds present and to the relative amounts and respective functions of compounds of each class. However, the variation in intramolecular structure, particularly of high molecular weight components of protoplasts, seems infinite. Each cell line, whether a genetically homogeneous population of unicellular organisms or a line of specialized cells within a multicellular, differentiated organism, synthesizes some large molecules that do not occur elsewhere in nature. Classes of substances found in living cells are described briefly in the following sections. The reader is referred to a biochemistry text for details of the structure and chemical properties of these materials.

Water and Other Inorganic Components. The major component of living cells is water, which accounts for approximately 75 per cent of the total mass of the cell. It serves as the medium in which soluble components are diffused, and it serves to hydrate large molecules whose functions depend on their configuration in space as well as their chemical composition. These configurations are maintained in large part by the interposition of water molecules among particular parts of the large molecules. The quantitative composition of cells is usually expressed as the proportion of the dry weight (i.e., of about 25 per cent of the total mass) accounted for by each component other than water.

Inorganic bases, acids, and salts usually account for less than 10 per cent of the dry weight of the cell. However, they are essential for maintenance of internal osmotic pressure, electrostatic balance, and pH; and specific ions, most of which are cations, are necessary for the activity of certain enzymes.

Organic Components of Protoplasts. The distinctive substances of living systems are, with few exceptions, organic chemicals, and carbon is the major elemental constituent of all protoplasts. An organic molecule contains at least one carbon atom in an oxidation state lower than that of the carbon atom of CO_2. The outer orbit of the carbon atom contains four electrons, which can be shared in different ways with other atoms, of carbon or of other elements. Consequently, carbon can form as great a variety of compounds as any other element on earth, or a greater variety.

Only a few classes of organic substances are common to all types of protoplasts, and their functions are similar in all cells. The principal constituents of cells are large molecules; they serve as structural components, reserve foods, enzymes, genetic material, and regulatory substances that determine the formation and activity of enzymes. The large molecules, called macromolecules, are polymers of smaller molecules, called subunits. The three predominant classes of macromolecules, their corresponding subunits, and the known functions of each class are indicated in Table 4-1. A fourth, heterogeneous class of large molecules, the lipids, is also present in all protoplasts; lipids function as structural components and as reserve foods. Complex macromolecules contain two or more types of subunits or polymers. Such substances include lipoproteins (lipid-protein complexes), nucleoproteins (nucleic acid–protein complexes), and mucopeptides (amino sugar–peptide complexes).

Most of the small molecules of a cell are present transiently as intermediates in sequences of chemical reactions or as potential subunits (precursors) for the construction of macromolecules. Some serve as cofactors for enzyme-catalyzed reactions; as the reaction proceeds, the cofactor participates by donating or receiving electrons or a chemical group to or from a reactant. The small molecules include sugars and other low molecular weight carbohydrates, amino acids and non-nitrogenous acids, vitamins and other enzyme cofactors, purine and pyrimidine bases and nucleosides, and phosphorylated derivatives of each of these substances.

Cell Wall Components. Cell walls are typically present in vegetative (growing) cells of bacteria, algae, fungi, and plants, and typically absent from vegetative cells of protozoa, slime protists, and animals. Dormant stages of protists possess

TABLE 4-1.   Predominant Classes of Macromolecules in Protoplasts

Class	Subunits	Known Functions of the Macromolecules
Proteins*	Amino acids	As enzymes As structural components† As reserve foods As pH buffers
Polysaccharides	Sugars, sugar acids, sugar alcohols, amino sugars (in mucopolysaccharides)	As structural components As reserve foods
Nucleic acids	Nucleotides‡	As genetic material§ As regulatory substances‖ As structural components‡

*Proteins are amino acid polymers of molecular weight greater than 5,000; smaller polymers are called (poly)peptides.

†Whether the proteins of eucaryotic chromosomes serve as structural components or play a role in heredity is uncertain.

‡A nucleotide contains a purine or pyrimidine base, a sugar—ribose in ribonucleic acid (RNA), deoxyribose in deoxyribonucleic acid (DNA)—and an orthophosphate group.

§DNA.

‖Soluble RNA's.

‡Insoluble RNA.

some kind of wall-like structure. Some protistan walls are composed of a single class of substance, e.g., cellulose in some green algae and silica in diatoms. However, walls are often composed of more than one substance; depending on the organism, the wall substances may be arranged in chemically homogeneous layers or intermingled in a single layer of heterogeneous composition.

All the wall substances are water-insoluble polymers. Some of the classes of compounds that occur in protistan walls and the major groups of protists in which each has been found, in either vegetative or dormant stages, are listed below.

Lipoprotein-lipopolysaccharide	Bacteria
Teichoic acids	Bacteria
Mucopeptide	Bacteria, blue-green algae
Cellulose	Higher algae, possibly some blue-green algae, fungi, slime protists, protozoa
Polyuronic acids	Higher algae
Pectins	Higher algae
Silica	Higher algae, protozoa
Chitins	Fungi, protozoa

Chapter 5

Procaryotic Cells

The cells of bacteria and blue-green algae are procaryotic. Until techniques for visualizing their subcellular components were developed in the mid-twentieth century, procaryotic cells were regarded as nearly structureless internally. Most bacterial cells are not more than two micrometers[1] in largest dimension; they were described as containing a structurally homogeneous protoplasm, which occasionally contained granules of reserve foods. Blue-green algal cells, generally several micrometers in shortest dimension, were described simply as containing a pigmented peripheral cytoplasm surrounding a central body. Finer structural details could not be distinguished.

By 1950, techniques had been developed in the use of the electron microscope[2] that made it possible to employ this high-resolution instrument in the examination of biologic specimens. Electron microscopy allows visualization of structures as small as a few tenths of a nanometer in thickness, whereas the light microscope does not allow visualization of components less than about 200 nm. Most of the internal structures of procaryotic cells and the details of eucaryotic subcellular organization have been described only in the past two decades.

A generalized procaryotic cell is diagrammed in Figure 5-1. The general

---

[1]Microscopic measurements in biology are expressed in metric units: meter (m), millimeter (mm; 0.001 m), micrometer (μm; 0.001 mm, 0.000001 m), nanometer (nm; 0.001 μm, 0.000001 mm, 0.000000001 m).

[2]The electron microscope employs a beam of electrons, rather than of light; image formation depends on differences in relative transparency to electrons among cell components. Salts of heavy metals, e.g., uranium and lead, which bind more readily to certain types of organic materials than to others, serve as "stains" that increase the electron opacity of the substances to which they bind and thereby increase the contrast among components of the cells.

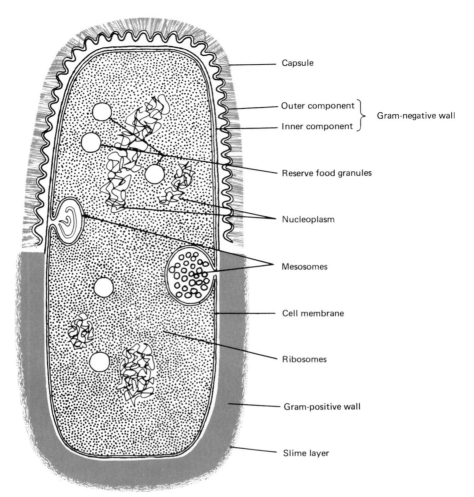

Capsule

Outer component ⎫
                 ⎬ Gram-negative wall
Inner component ⎭

Reserve food granules

Nucleoplasm

Mesosomes

Cell membrane

Ribosomes

Gram-positive wall

Slime layer

Figure 5-1   Diagram of a generalized bacterial cell, as a composite gram-negative and gram-positive bacterium.

Abbreviations used in figures in this chapter:

   CW, cell wall: *OC* and *IC,* outer and inner components, respectively; *OL, ML, IL,* outer, middle, and inner layers, respectively.

   CM, cell membrane; *Me,* mesosome; *PV,* photosynthetic vesicle; *PM,* photosynthetic membrane; *IM,* internal membrane, non-photosynthetic.

   R, ribosomes; *N,* nucleoplasm; *RFG,* reserve food granule; *SL,* slime layer; *Sh,* sheath; *F,* flagellum; *PP,* periplasm.

features of procaryotic cells are described below and illustrated in the electron micrographs of Figures 5-3 to 5-13.

Cell Membrane

The structure that forms the outer boundary of a protoplast is called the cell membrane. It is composed of phospholipoprotein. In the electron microscope, it appears in vertical section as a three-layered structure approximately 10 nm thick. The two outer layers are relatively dense to electrons when stained with heavy metals; the intermediate layer does not stain. This appearance is widely interpreted as indicated diagrammatically in Figure 5-2. The outer surfaces are believed to be composed of the protein portions of the lipoprotein molecules. The lipid portions of the molecules are believed to comprise the middle layer. This type of structure, called a **unit membrane,** is characteristic of most membranes in cells, including cell membranes and structures derived from them in procaryotic cells, and the cell membranes, nuclear membranes, endoplasmic reticulum, and the membranes of metabolically specialized subcellular organelles, vesicles, and flagella in eucaryotic cells. The exceptions are the single-layered membranes around reserve food deposits in some bacteria.

The cell membrane functions as the selectively permeable boundary of the protoplast. It is freely permeable to some low molecular weight, uncharged molecules such as certain sugars and other alcohols and impermeable to large molecules and most negatively charged small molecules. The movement of certain chemicals across the cell membrane apparently is mediated by transport catalysts, called permeases, included within the structure of or closely associated with the membrane. The existence of permeases has been postulated to account for the following observations regarding cell permeability: (1) some cells are permeable to substances that are excluded from other cells, although the chemical composition of their bounding membranes is similar; (2) cells can accumulate substances to concentrations higher than those in the extracellular milieu; (3) transport of some substances into cells requires energy; and (4) cells may become permeable to a substance they need for growth in one environment, but exclude it in environments where it is not needed for growth. Because their proposed function requires the integrity of the protoplast, permeases cannot be isolated from the membrane and identified as such; the evidence for their existence is circumstantial.

Certain catalytic activities in addition to selective permeability seem to be structurally associated with the cell membrane of procaryotic cells. (1) In bacteria capable of respiratory metabolism (see Chap. 10), the respiratory enzymes are typically inseparable from the cell membrane. (2) Some bacteria produce enzymes, e.g., those that catalyze digestion of insoluble materials, which are present only external to the membrane. These "exoenzymes" are

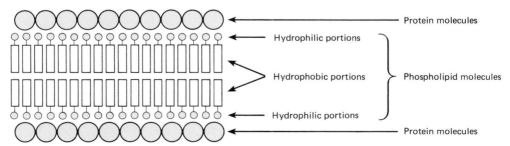

Current conception of unit membrane construction (diagrammatic).   Figure 5-2

apparently synthesized or assembled into active units on the outer surface of the membrane. This implies that catalysts that produce such enzymes are localized within the membrane. (3) Another function proposed for a cell membrane constituent is initiation of DNA synthesis, which is believed to occur on the inner surface of the procaryotic cell membrane.

In most bacteria, the cell membrane is the only membranous structure that can be visualized within the protoplast. However, organelles derived from the cell membrane occur in some bacteria; the most widely occurring type of cell-membrane-derived organelle is the mesosome.[3] A mesosome is an approximately spheric body consisting of membranes arranged concentrically or, less commonly, as tubes. In some bacteria, mesosomes seem to enhance respiratory capacity by increasing the amount of membrane in which the respiratory catalysts are situated. In all the bacteria in which they occur, mesosomes are topologically associated with the site of cell wall development during cell division. In endospore-forming bacteria (see Chap. 13), mesosomes are regularly seen in association with developing endospores. Presumably, they are active in synthesis, assembly, or translocation of components of walls or spores, and in this role may be analogous to the dictyosomes of plant and algal cells (see "Golgi Apparatus," Chap. 6).

Particularly elaborate membranous organelles occur in a few physiologic types of bacteria. An extensive, wandering membrane system occurs in free-living N_2-fixing bacteria, and membranes arranged in stacks occur in some nitrifying bacteria. All photosynthetic bacteria that have been examined contain internal membrane systems; these systems may be vesicles, stacks, or concentric layers of membranes, depending mainly on the genus. The vesicular organelles, which can be separated from other cell components, contain a much higher proportion of photosynthetic pigments and enzymes than the whole cells and are regarded as photosynthetic organelles.

Blue-green algal cells typically contain internal membrane systems which consist of parallel layers of membranes arranged either concentrically within the cell periphery (the "pigmented peripheral cytoplasm"; see above) or in groups through the cytoplasm. Analysis of fractions of such cells has revealed that the photosynthetic and the respiratory activities of blue-green algae are localized in membranes.

Cell Wall

Almost all procaryotic cells possess walls which are responsible for rigidity and for constancy of cell shape. Walls vary in fine structure among procaryotic organisms. In gram-negative bacteria,[4] there are two components separable by fractionation of the cell. The outer component is a flexible unit membrane which may appear smooth or wavy in profile and have vesicular outgrowths.

---

[3]This is only one of several names that have been used for these organelles; it is the oldest and most widely used.

[4]See Chap. 13 regarding the gram stain.

It is composed of lipoprotein, sometimes with lipopolysaccharide, and is 7.5 to 20 nm thick. The inner component is usually smooth in profile and up to about 2.5 nm in thickness. It is composed predominantly of mucopeptide and is responsible for the rigidity of the cell cortex. In many gram-negative bacteria it is quite thin, closely apposed to the cell membrane, and often indistinguishable in electron micrographs.

In gram-positive bacteria, the outer lipoprotein membrane does not occur. The rigid layer, which constitutes the entire cell wall, is typically much thicker (20 to 80 nm) than in gram-negative cells.

The walls of blue-green algae have not been studied so extensively as those of bacteria, and it is not yet possible to describe them generally. Some are single-layered structures approximately 20 nm thick. Others are multilayered and similar in organization to walls of gram-negative bacteria. A smooth-contoured layer of 10 to 20 nm thickness lies between the cell membrane and an outer unit membrane approximately 10 nm thick. The total thickness of 30 to 40 nm includes the two distinctive layers and intervening unstained spaces (layers?). The single-layered wall and the inner layer of the more elaborate type presumably are composed of mucopeptide, which has been found in all blue-green algal walls that have been analyzed chemically.

External to the walls of many bacteria and most blue-green algae is one or more layers of more or less cohesive slime. Bacterial slime may be poly-saccharide or, in a few types, polypeptide; thick layers of cohesive slime are designated capsules. The slime of blue-green algae is often pectic and may contain fibrils of cellulose. This slime may be copious and serve as a sheath enclosing a chain of cells, or as a matrix in which cells are embedded in colonies.

Nucleoplasm

The distinctive characteristic of procaryotic cells is the absence, throughout the cell cycle, of a membrane that separates the nuclear material from other cell components. The nucleoplasm nevertheless is contained as a discrete region that consists of fibrils in a matrix of as yet undetermined composition. The fibrils are a few tenths of a nanometer in diameter and in electron micrographs appear darkly stained with uranium; these properties (dimensions of the fibrils and binding of uranium ions) are exhibited by purified bacterial DNA. The fibrils are, accordingly, interpreted as the DNA of the cell. The microscopic appearance of DNA is similar in bacteria and blue-green algae and in extra-nuclear, DNA-containing organelles of eucaryotic cells.

Observations made with the aid of phase-contrast optics or chromatic staining procedures reveal usually one or at most two bodies of nucleoplasm in a bacterial cell. In electron micrographs of sections of some procaryotic cells, the nucleoplasm is seen as a single region. In most cases, however, the nucleoplasm occurs in patches and appears to be an irregularly lobed body.

Cytoplasmic Granules

One type of granular body occurs in all types of living cells; these are **ribosomes**—spheric bodies 10 to 20 nm in diameter, composed of about 60 per cent RNA and 40 per cent protein in procaryotic cells, and of about 50 per cent RNA and 50 per cent protein in (higher) eucaryotic cells. There may be thousands of ribosomes within a cell, occurring singly or in groups ("polyribosomes") of various sizes. There is considerable evidence that the polyribosomes in particular are the sites of synthesis of many (most?) enzymatically active proteins in the cell; it is possible that other proteins are synthesized on ribosomes.

Other cytoplasmic granules occur in different types of procaryotic cells or, in any one type of organism, in different environments. Two types of carbonaceous reserves are stored by bacteria; glycogen, a polysaccharide reserve, is stored as small granules scattered in the cytoplasm; poly-beta-hydroxybutyric acid, a lipid reserve, is stored as larger granules that in some bacteria are surrounded by single-layered membranes. A few bacteria can store both types of reserve substances, depending on the nutritional environment. Volutin granules, which occur in a wide variety of bacteria, are composed of polymetaphosphate; their role is interpreted as storage of phosphate. Granules of elemental sulfur are stored internally by large photosynthetic sulfur bacteria growing in the presence of sulfides; the sulfur is eventually oxidized to sulfate, which is excreted.

Blue-green algae often contain cytoplasmic crystals of unknown composition and function. Small granules usually located among the photosynthetic membranes are composed of cyanophycean starch, the polysaccharide reserve material peculiar to this group of organisms.

Spaces

The spaces among distinguishable protoplasmic components within a cell are probably occupied by an aqueous solution of low molecular weight substances. When cells are disrupted artificially, these materials are released into the medium and cannot be caused to sediment in two hours, even under centrifugal forces exceeding $100,000 \times g$. The substances dissolved in the cytoplasm include most of the inorganic components of the cell, the low molecular weight organic substances, and some of the macromolecules that are not built into large structures. These last include relatively small molecules of RNA that function in the cell as messengers of genetic information to sites of protein synthesis, RNA molecules that react with amino acids prior to their incorporation into proteins, and a number of enzymes involved in intermediary metabolism.

A second area occupied by components that cannot be visualized is the space between cell membrane and cell wall. This area, the periplasm, was at one time supposed to contain only molecules in transit between environment and protoplast. In the past few years, however, particular enzymes have been found to be localized in this region. They are generally hydrolytic enzymes that degrade large molecules or remove small groups, e.g., phosphate, from molecules to which the cell membrane is not permeable; the products of these enzymatic reactions may then diffuse or be transported into the protoplast.

Flagella

Blue-green algal cells do not possess flagella; the only flagella of procaryotic cells occur among bacteria. A typical bacterial flagellum is approximately 25 nm in diameter; its length varies among types of bacteria, but it is usually at least as long as the cell. It is a fibril composed of spheroid subunits aligned as a tightly wound helix. Each subunit is a protein molecule; the molecular composition varies somewhat in different bacteria, but molecular weights and physical properties are similar.

A bacterial flagellum arises just within the cell membrane and extends to the exterior through the membrane and cell wall. The base of the flagellum may be a hook-shaped swelling, a spool-shaped structure associated with other basal structures in a layer beneath the cell membrane, or a flattened, collar-like expansion. The hook type of basal structure has been observed in bacteria that bear a single polar flagellum or numerous, scattered flagella. The spool type has been observed in bacteria that bear tufts of flagella. The collar has been seen only in spirochetes. However, the basal structures of flagella of most types of bacteria have not yet been visualized.

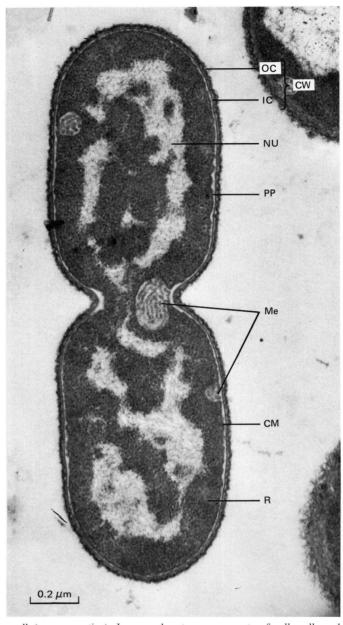

Figure 5-3 Dividing *Achromobacter* cell (gram negative). Inner and outer components of cell wall, and mesosomes. (See Fig. 5-1 for key to abbreviations.) (From Wiebe, W. J., and G. B. Chapman, 1968. *J. Bact.*, **95**:1874. By permission of the American Society for Microbiology.)

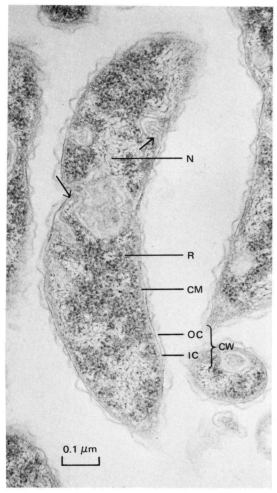

Dividing *Caulobacter* cell (gram negative). The arrows indicate sites of continuity between cell membrane and mesosomes.

Figure 5-4

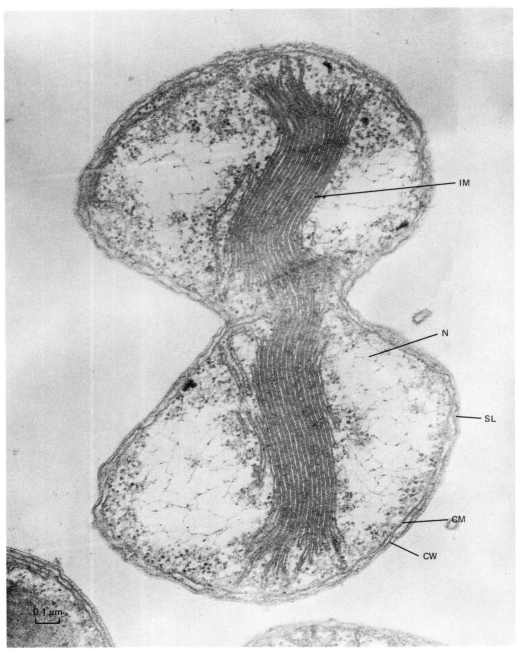

IM

N

SL

CM

CW

0.1 μm

Figure 5-5 Dividing *Nitrosocystis* cell (gram negative). Within the constricted equator, the stacks of internal membranes are separating. The inner component of the cell wall is not discernible in this marine (*N. oceanus*) bacterium. (From Remsen, C. C., F. W. Valois, and S. W. Watson, 1967. *J. Bact.*, **94:**422. By permission of the American Society for Microbiology.)

36

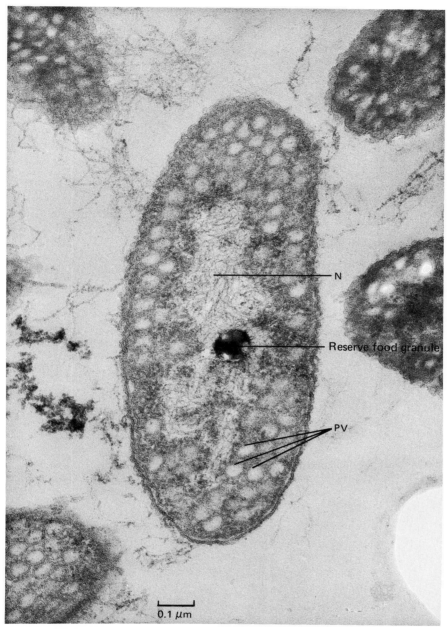

Rhodopseudomonas (gram negative) with numerous photosynthetic vesicles in extranucleoplasmic regions of the protoplast. (Courtesy of G. Cohen-Bazire.)

Figure 5-6

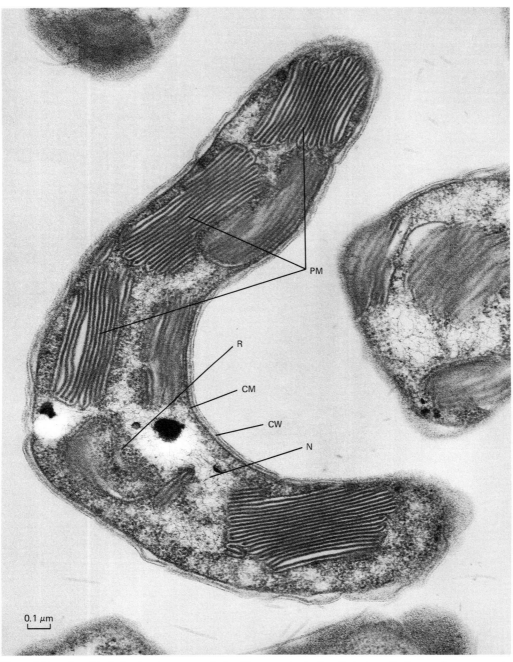

0.1 μm

Figure 5-7 *Ectothiorhodospira* (gram negative) with separate stacks of photosynthetic membranes, one to four double unit membrane complexes per group within a stack. (Courtesy of H. G. Trüper and S. W. Watson.)

38

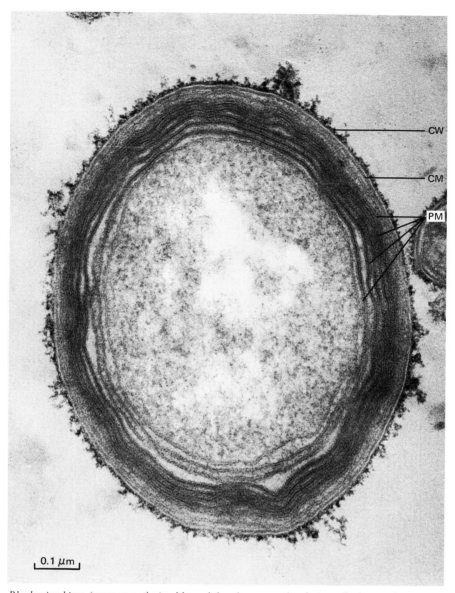

CW

CM

PM

0.1 μm

Rhodomicrobium (gram negative) with peripheral, concentric photosynthetic membranes; each layer is composed of a double unit membrane complex. (From Conti, S. F., and P. Hirsch, 1965, *J. Bact.*, **89:**503. By permission of the American Society for Microbiology.)

Figure 5-8

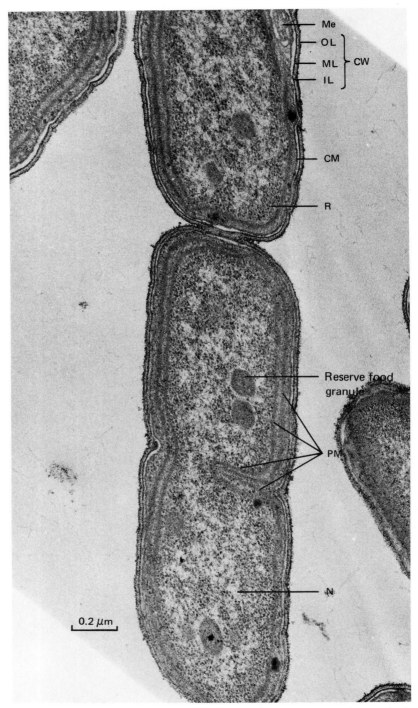

Figure 5-9 Portion of a filament of the blue-green alga *Anacystis,* with peripheral, concentric photosynthetic membranes that grow inward near the equator of the cell during cell division. (Courtesy of M. M. Allen.)

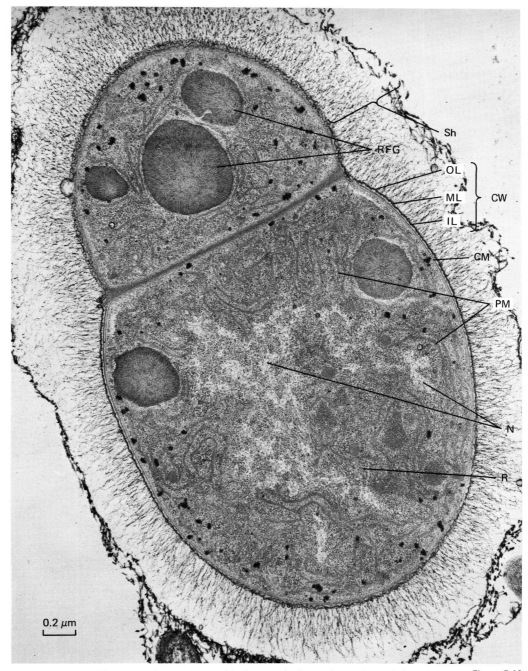

Divided cell of the blue-green alga *Anabaena* with photosynthetic membranes irregularly arranged. **Figure 5-10**
A thick, fibrous sheath lies external to the multilayered cell wall. (From Leak, L. V., 1967.
J. Ultrastructure Res., **21:**61. By permission of Academic Press, Inc.)

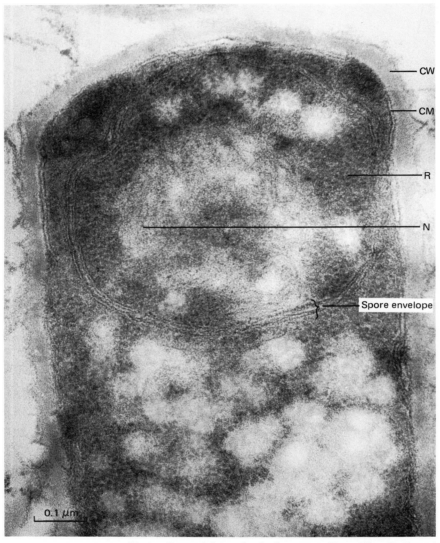

Figure 5-11   Portion of *Bacillus* (gram positive) cell containing a developing spore. (From Ellar, D. J., and D. G. Lundgren, 1966. *J. Bact.,* **92:**1748. By permission of the American Society for Microbiology.)

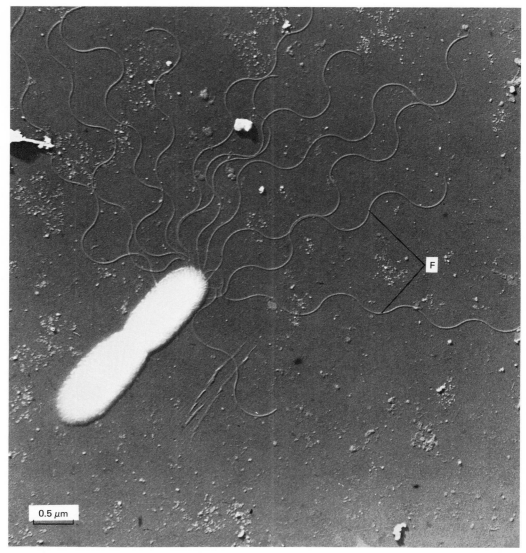

Acetomonas with a sparse tuft of polar flagella. (Courtesy of A. L. Houwink.)   **Figure 5-12**

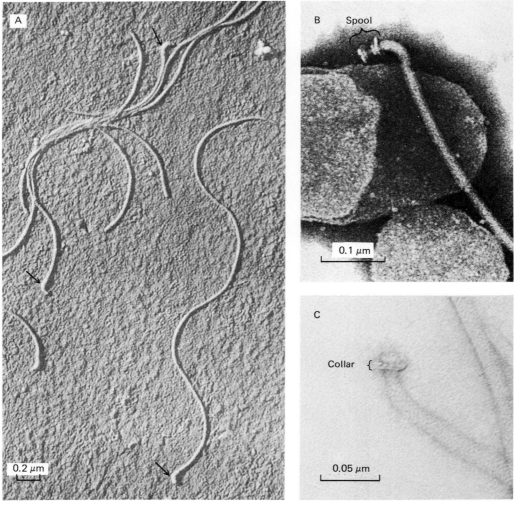

Figure 5-13   Basal structures of bacterial flagella. *A. Caulobacter* flagella with hook-shaped basal ends (arrows). *B. Rhodospirillum* flagellum with spool-shaped structure at the base. Subunits are visible within the flagellum. (From Cohen-Bazire, G., and J. London, 1967. *J. Bact.*, **94:**458. By permission of the American Society for Microbiology.) *C.* Portion of *Spirochaeta* flagellum with a collar-like structure at the base. (From Holt, S. C., and E. Canale-Parola, 1968. *J. Bact.*, **96:**822. By permission of the American Society for Microbiology.)

Chapter 6

Eucaryotic Cells

The cells of all organisms other than bacteria and blue-green algae are eucaryotic. During most or all of its reproductive cycle, a eucaryotic cell possesses a definite membranous envelope around the nucleoplasm; in plants and animals and some protists, the nuclear envelope disintegrates during nuclear division and a new envelope is resynthesized or reassembled around each daughter nucleus. The membrane-bounded nucleoplasm is called a nucleoplast or true nucleus. It is one of several membrane-delimited bodies that occur in eucaryotic cells.

A generalized eucaryotic cell is diagrammed in Figure 6-1. Structures characteristic of eucaryotic cells are described below and illustrated in the electron micrographs of Figures 6-2 to 6-16. Other specialized subcellular organelles, which are particularly numerous in protozoa, are described in relevant sections of Part 4. Because the cell membranes and ribosomes are basically the same in eucaryotic and procaryotic cells, they are not described again here (see Chap. 5).

Endoplasmic Reticulum

The endoplasmic reticulum is a cytoplasmic network of unit membranes continuous with the cell membrane. The amount of endoplasmic reticulum varies with the type of cell and with its physiologic state. The reticulum undergoes considerable change in appearance during the life of a cell and seems to serve a variety of functions, summarized below.

(1) The reticulum provides a mechanical barrier between subcellular organelles and maintains them in constant relative position. (2) It delimits channels within the cytoplasm through which small molecules can diffuse readily in only

45

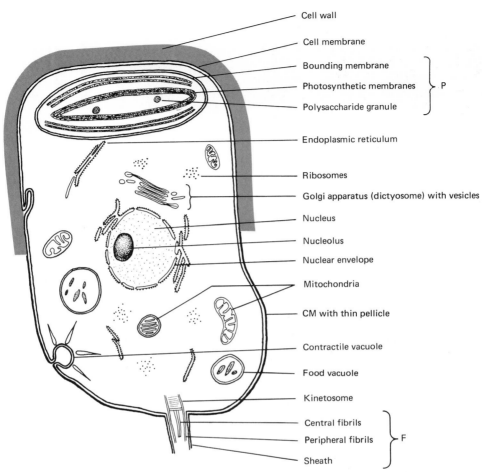

Cell wall

Cell membrane

Bounding membrane

Photosynthetic membranes

Polysaccharide granule

} P

Endoplasmic reticulum

Ribosomes

Golgi apparatus (dictyosome) with vesicles

Nucleus

Nucleolus

Nuclear envelope

Mitochondria

CM with thin pellicle

Contractile vacuole

Food vacuole

Kinetosome

Central fibrils

Peripheral fibrils

Sheath

} F

Figure 6-1   Diagram of a generalized eucaryotic cell as a composite alga and protozoon.
Abbreviations used in figures in this chapter:
   ER, endoplasmic reticulum; *D*, dictyosome; *M*, mitochondrion; *CM*, cell membrane;
N, nucleus; *Nl*, nucleolus; *NE*, nuclear envelope; *P*, photosynthetic organelle; *K*, kinetosome;
F, flagellum; *Ci*, cilium; *T*, microtubule; *R*, ribosome; *CW*, cell wall.

one or two directions, rather than randomly through the cytoplasm. (3) It is
a source of growing internal membranes from which other membranes of less
dynamic nature and more specific function can be derived. (4) By disintegrating
and reforming, it allows and then inhibits movement of other cytoplasmic
components. (5) It serves as a base to which ribosomes adhere and become
aligned and functional in protein synthesis as polyribosomes.

Golgi Apparatus

   The Golgi apparatus (or body or complex) is, like the endoplasmic reticulum,
a system of unit membranes. It is more discrete than the reticulum and suffi-

ciently large and compact to be discernible in the light microscope. Details of its internal construction can, however, be observed only with the electron microscope. The Golgi apparatus may consist of a group of vesicles or tubules or, in its most distinctive form (called a **dictyosome,** see Fig. 6-2*A*), of a short cylindric stack of membranes alternating with tubules and surrounded by a network of tubules from which vesicles arise. The dictyosome occurs as one form of the Golgi apparatus in animal cells and is the typical Golgi form in cells of photosynthetic organisms (both algae and plants).

Although the function(s) of the Golgi apparatus is not yet entirely clear, it has at least been clearly demonstrated that the apparatus serves to store (and possibly to concentrate) certain cell products, particularly proteins and cell wall materials. Such substances are contained within the vesicles released from the Golgi apparatus. The vesicles may then migrate to the periphery of the cell, where their membranes fuse with the cell membrane and their contents are released to the exterior of the protoplast. This is a (the?) means by which certain animal cells, such as in the pancreas, secrete hormones into the circulatory system and by which plant and algal cells transport cell wall materials to the cell surface.

Some of the vesicles released from the Golgi apparatus remain within the cell. These seem to be of two types: lysosomes and storage bodies. The lysosomes contain hydrolytic enzymes that can degrade the large molecules of the cells; their containment within vesicles prevents their destruction of cell components in a normal, growing cell. The enzymes are probably released when the cell dies; they would accelerate disintegration of the dead cell. Lysosomes also have been observed to associate and fuse with food vacuoles; apparently, the enzymes are released into the vacuoles to digest ingested foods. Storage bodies such as zymogen granules have been observed to arise from the Golgi apparatus. They store proteins produced at polyribosomes associated with the endoplasmic reticulum. Proteins are presumably not synthesized within the Golgi apparatus, since ribosomes are not associated with its membranes.

In many types of cells, the Golgi apparatus lies near the nucleus. Particularly in the dictyosome form, the Golgi apparatus seems to participate in cytoplasmic division, and it may disappear during nuclear division and reform as the protoplast divides. In flagellate algae, the Golgi apparatus may be located near the contractile vacuole; such a location suggests a role in excretion, but this has not been demonstrated.

Nuclei

The nucleoplasm of eucaryotic cells consists of DNA, basic proteins, and a mass of RNA called the **nucleolus.** The DNA is complexed with the basic proteins, which are of relatively low molecular weight. RNA may also be present in the nucleoproteins. In electron micrographs of intact nuclei, the nucleoproteins appear as strands larger in diameter than the DNA fibrils of procaryotic nucleoplasm. Prior to nuclear division, units of nucleoprotein become thick, dense, usually elongated bodies, which may be more than 1 μm in diameter. These are the **chromosomes,** whose number is constant within a species.[1] The nucleolus, which apparently participates in the synthesis of RNA, may change in shape and appearance as the cell grows. In most higher organisms, it disappears and reforms during nuclear division, but it persists and divides by elongation and constriction in many eucaryotic protistan cells.

The **nuclear envelope** (see Fig. 6-3A) is composed of two concentric unit membranes that are continuous with the endoplasmic reticulum, which in turn communicates with the cell membrane. Accordingly, all the major membranes of the cell are part of one membrane system. The nuclear envelope is porous, and the nucleoplasm and cytoplasm are in direct contact through the pores.

Mitochondria

Mitochondria occur in all types of eucaryotic cells except a few specialized cells of higher organisms and cells of certain protists while growing under anaerobic (O_2-free) conditions. A mitochondrion is a vesicular organelle (see Fig. 6-2B) constructed of a unit membrane whose inner layer forms folds ("cristae") within the vesicle. Spheroid bodies are attached by slender stalks to the surfaces of the cristae; the respiratory enzymes of the cell are localized in these bodies. The enzymes of systems by which organic acids are oxidized to CO_2 and H_2O are present in the lumen and membranes of the mitochondrion. Thus, the final steps in the oxidation of organic compounds occur in mitochondria, which thereby provide the cell with the energy obtained by respiratory metabolism of organic substrates.

The number of mitochondria varies from one to thousands per cell. Their shape is variable; it changes as small mitochondria elongate or fuse with each other, and as larger ones give rise to others by pinching off small portions. Mitochondria contain some DNA and can perpetuate themselves within the cell. There is some evidence that, at least in yeasts and possibly some lower plants, they can also arise by derivation from the cell membrane; this has been observed in yeast cells grown anaerobically as they adjust to aerobic conditions and change from fermentative to respiratory metabolism.

Photosynthetic Organelles

In all photosynthetic eucaryotic cells, the enzymes and pigments of photosynthetic metabolism are contained in discrete organelles. The fine structure of plant and algal organelles is somewhat different, and the description presented here refers mainly to algal organelles. Each of these structures is surrounded by a unit membrane and contains stacks of membranes. The surfaces of the internal membranes are covered with chlorophyll molecules. Other pigments have not been definitely located, but apparently reside in the matrix substance and/or the outer organellar membrane, since they may be present in incomplete organelles (proplastids; see below) that do not possess the internal stacks of membranes or chlorophyll. Certain of the photosynthetic

---

[1]In some animals, the number is different in males and females.

enzymes are localized in the organellar membranes, others in the matrix substance.

Some algae possess masses of pigmented granules called **stigmas.** There is usually one per cell and, except for the euglenids, the stigma typically lies just within the bounding membrane of the photosynthetic organelle; in euglenids, it lies outside the organelle. The stigma is involved in light source detection, apparently by shading a photoreceptor when it lies between the receptor and the light source. A second organelle often found within the photosynthetic organelle is the **pyrenoid,** a proteinaceous body that may function in conversion of organic products of photosynthesis into reserve foods.

The photosynthetic organelles of plants possess closely packed stacks of membranes among the internal membranes (see, e.g., Fig. 7-9C). These stacks, called grana, are especially active in photosynthesis. They have been seen in only one type of alga, the desmid group *Micrasterias*.

Photosynthetic organelles contain some DNA and can perpetuate themselves, usually by binary fission prior to reproduction of the cell (see Fig. 18-5). Cells can be caused to reduce their photosynthetic organelles to "proplastids," which lack internal membranes and chlorophyll. Functional organelles can be derived from proplastids by return of the cells to conditions favorable for photosynthesis (return from dark to light, removal of an inhibitor of photosynthesis, lowering of the incubation temperature). Photosynthetic cells can also be irreversibly bleached by treatments with various chemicals; such bleached cells invariably lack any remnant of the photosynthetic organellar system (except stigmas in some algae) and apparently cannot regenerate photosynthetic organelles from any other cell components.

Centrioles

The centriole is a cylindric body that, if present, is located in the cytoplasm. It is composed mainly of protein and also contains nucleic acid, at least some of which is DNA. The centriole is composed of nine groups of three fibrils arranged as a hollow tube with the long axes of the fibrils parallel to the long axis of the centriole (see Fig. 6-4A). Centrioles arise by division of pre-existing centrioles; their divisions regularly precede cell division so that a constant number (one or two per cell) is maintained.

Centrioles occur in animal cells and some eucaryotic protistan cells; among protists, their occurrence and functions are best documented for protozoa. In animal cells, the centrioles produce the asters and spindle fibers of the mitotic apparatus. In protozoa, the centrioles may produce fibers that participate in nuclear division, but a more common role is the production of flagella (or cilia). Both functions are served by the centrioles of some protozoa and fungi.

Flagella and Cilia

The flagella of all eucaryotic cells that have been examined with the electron microscope exhibit the same basic construction (see Fig. 6-5A). The outer surface of the flagellum is a unit membrane derived from the cell membrane.

Within the flagellar membrane, nine double fibrils lie parallel to the long dimension of the flagellum and approximately equally spaced or spaced as three triplets around the periphery. Two single fibrils, parallel to the others, lie along the center of the flagellum. This "nine plus two" construction is also observed in cilia, which differ structurally from flagella only by being shorter.

Two morphologic types of flagella are distinguished among eucaryotic protists. The "whiplash" type has a slender "end-piece" at the outer tip. Within the endpiece, there are fewer internal fibrils than in the main portion of the flagellum, because some of the fibrils are terminated before others. The "tinsel" type has numerous short, hairlike, lateral projections; these flagella usually end without a marked tapering. Cilia typically taper toward the distal end; internally, first the central and then the peripheral fibrils disappear as the diameter of the structure decreases.

The outer membrane of these organelles is composed of lipoprotein, and the internal fibrils are of protein, at least some of which is contractile. Waves of contraction pass along the fibrils and cause them to vibrate in directions and at speeds characteristic of the organism and its responses to environmental conditions. Movement of the flagella or cilia effects locomotion of the organism, or, in certain protozoa, effects movement of environmental liquid toward an area of the cell at which ingestion of food particles suspended in the liquid can occur.

Each flagellum arises from a basal body ("kinetosome") located just within the cell membrane. The structure of basal bodies varies somewhat, especially among protozoa, but all possess the nine groups of peripheral fibrils that are continuous through the flagellum. Apparently, the basal bodies of all protozoan (possibly of all eucaryotic) flagella are derived from centrioles, either within each reproductive cycle of the cell or as self-perpetuating descendants of centrioles. The flagellum develops by outgrowth of two of the fibrils of each peripheral triplet of the kinetosome. At the level of the cell membrane, the fibrils acquire a unit membrane sheath and the two central fibrils.

In algal cells, the basal portion of a flagellum may function as a photoreceptor. This seems to be true particularly of those basal bodies that give rise to rudimentary, short flagella or do not produce flagella; such bodies occur among euglenids and brown algae.

Microtubules

The fibrils that arise from centrioles are similar in size and construction to slender tubules that occur independently in the cytoplasm of many types of eucaryotic cells. These tubules may be 20 to nearly 100 nm in diameter, though usually less than 50 nm, and are of variable lengths. In cross-section, they are seen to be composed of 12 to 14 subunits (see Fig. 6-4B) evenly spaced in a circle within which there may be an additional, central subunit. The long dimensions of the subunits are not known; each may extend the entire length of the tubule, or they may be spheric.

Microtubules are apparently composed chiefly or entirely of protein. They are probably contractile and at present are regarded as a probable source of intracellular motion. This is inferred in part from their form and apparent composition, and in part from their distribution within the cell. In plant cells, they are abundant in the periphery of the protoplast, where the cytoplasm is especially mobile. Among protists, microtubules have been found in large numbers in the motile plasmodial stages of plasmodial slime protists, within which the protoplasm is in constant motion; in the tentacles of suctoreans, within which digestive enzymes are moved outward and food is moved inward toward the main part of the protoplast; just within the plastic pellicles of unicellular flagellates and ciliates (see Fig. 15-24); and in bundles called myonemes in sporozoa, which are motile protozoa that lack external organelles of locomotion and seem to move by a serpentine mechanism.

The spindle fibers of mitotic apparatus that arise from centrioles or from areas within the nuclear envelope, depending on the organism, are similar in construction to cytoplasmic microtubules, as are the internal fibrils of flagella. These two sets of fibrils are associated with and are probably responsible for motion—the migration of chromosomes and locomotion, respectively—and the function of microtubules in movement of protoplasm is in part ascribed to these fibrils by analogy with spindle and flagellar fibrils.

The principal type of motion that seems to involve microtubules is called protoplasmic streaming. This streaming is regarded as an intracellular circulatory system that serves to move nutrients throughout the cell and to transport waste materials from the sites of their formation to areas (such as near the cell membrane) or organelles (such as contractile vacuoles) from which they are excreted. Streaming can be readily observed in eucaryotic algae and protozoa, where protoplasm often moves in a constant direction, apparently along channels within the cytoplasm; in the plasmodia of slime protists, where a rhythmic reversal of the direction of streaming occurs; and in the hyphae of higher fungi, where the protoplasm moves predominantly toward the growing tip of the hypha. In the last case, however, it is not clear whether microtubules play an important role in the streaming; older portions of hyphae become highly vacuolated, and the development and expansion of the vacuoles could force the protoplasm toward the area where new cell wall formation allows expansion.

Whether protoplasmic streaming occurs in procaryotic cells is uncertain. It is possible that diffusion is sufficient to transport nutrients and waste products within the procaryotic cell, and that lack of an organized source of intracellular motion accounts in part for the limitation of maximum size of procaryotic cells (see Chap. 9).

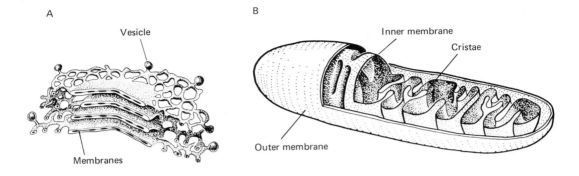

A

Vesicle

Membranes

B

Inner membrane

Cristae

Outer membrane

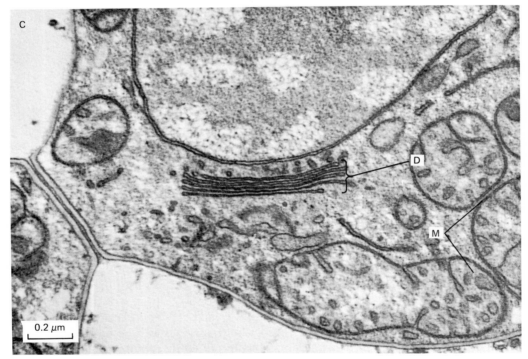

C

D

M

0.2 μm

Figure 6-2 Dictyosomes and mitochondria. *A*. Diagram of present conception of dictyosome construction. *B*. Diagram of a generalized mitochondrion. *C*. Portion of a cell of the fungus *Rhizidiomyces apophysatus*. (From Fuller, M. S., and R. Reichle, 1965. *Mycologia*, **57**:946. By permission of *Mycologia* and The New York Botanical Garden.)

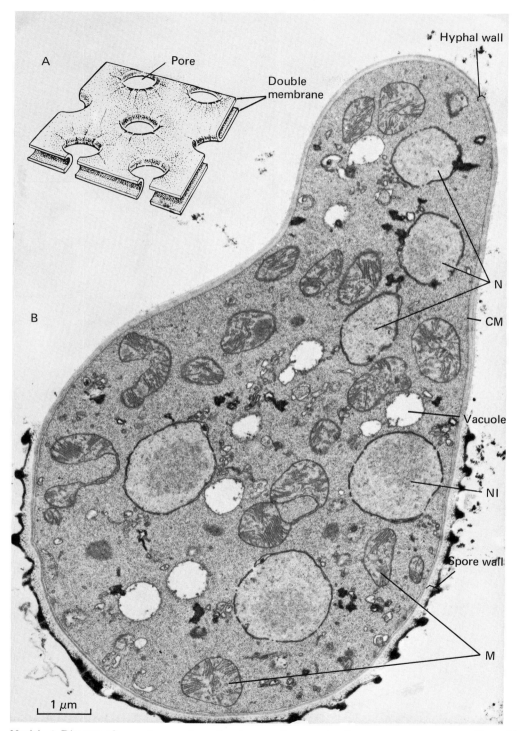

Nuclei. *A.* Diagram of present conception of nuclear envelope construction.
    B. Germinating sporangiospore of the fungus *Rhizopus stolonifer* with sections of six nuclei and numerous mitochondria. The spore wall is disrupted and the hyphal wall is constructed during germination. (From Buckley, P. M., N. F. Sommer, and T. T. Matsumoto, 1968. *J. Bact.,* **95**:2365. By permission of the American Society for Microbiology.)

Figure 6-3

A

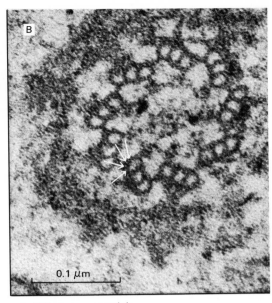

0.1 μm

Figure 6-4   Centrioles. *A.* Diagram of the arrangement of fibrils in a centriole.
        B. Cross-section of the organelle of the fungus *Catenaria anguillulae* which serves as centriole
(see Fig. 19-6) and as kinetosome. The subunits of the individual microtubules are visible
(arrows). (From Ichida, A. A., and M. S. Fuller, 1968. *Mycologia,* **60:**141. By permission of
Mycologia and The New York Botanical Garden.)

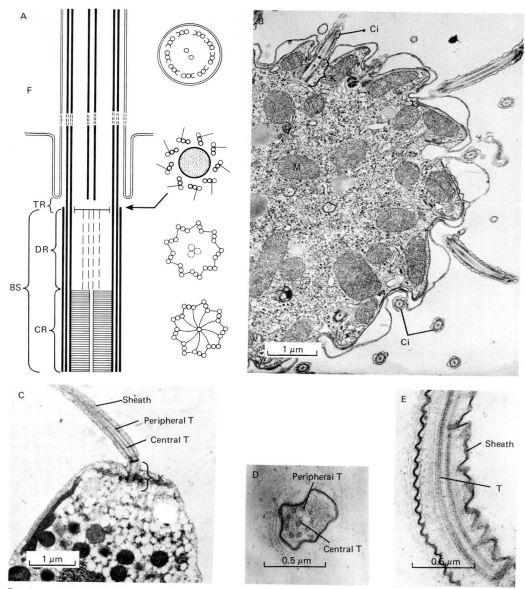

Basal structures of flagella and cilia. *A.* Diagram of current description of flagellum (cilium) construction. *Left:* longitudinal section, and *right:* transverse sections at four levels. *BS,* basal structure, including *CR,* the "cartwheel" region, and *DR,* the distal region, which in some organisms includes cylindric bodies in the interior. *TR,* region of transition from basal structure to flagellum proper; there is a transverse plate in this region. *F,* the flagellum proper, with nine pairs of peripheral fibrils, two central fibrils, and a membrane sheath that is continuous with the cell membrane. *B.* Portion of the ciliate protozoon *Tetrahymena pyriformis* containing longitudinal sections of proximal regions of cilia. (From Allen, R. D., 1967. *J. Protozool.,* **14:**553. By permission of The Society of Protozoologists and *The Journal of Protozoology.*)

C. Portion of a zoospore of the fungus *Monoblepharella* sp. with the basal structure and proximal region of the flagellum. (From Fuller, M. S., and R. E. Reichle, 1968. *Can. J. Botany,* **46:**279. By permission of the National Research Council of Canada.)

D. Transverse section of a flagellum of the euglenoid alga *Euglena gracilis. E.* Longitudinal section of a flagellum of the euglenoid alga *Euglena gracilis.* (*D* and *E* from Leedale, G. F., 1967. *Euglenoid Flagellates.* By permission of Prentice-Hall, Inc., Englewood Cliffs, N.J.)

Figure 6-5

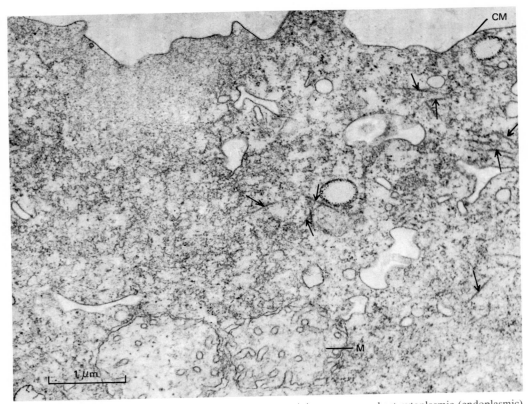

Figure 6-6   Portion of the protozoon *Amoeba proteus* containing numerous short cytoplasmic (endoplasmic) microtubules (arrows). These microtubules have been isolated from other cell components and demonstrated to be contractile. (From Schäfer-Danneel, S., 1967. Strukturelle und funktionelle Voraussetzungen für die Bewegung von *Amoeba proteus,* in *Zeit. f. Zellforsch. und mikroskop. Anat.,* **78**:441–62. By permission of Springer-Verlag, Berlin, Heidelberg, New York.)

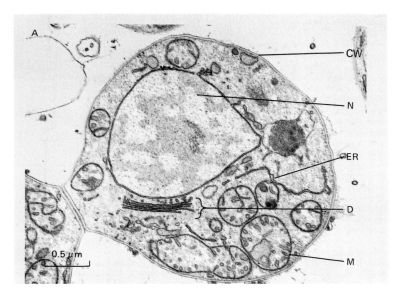

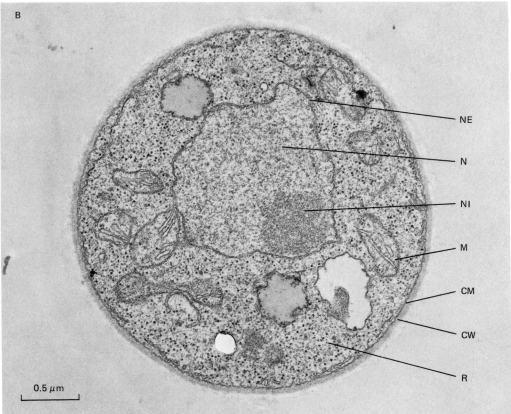

Sections of fungal cells. *A*. The entire cell of Fig. 6-2*C* (*Rhizidiomyces apophysatus*). (From Fuller, M. S., and R. Reichle, 1965. *Mycologia*, **57**:946. By permission of *Mycologia* and The New York Botanical Garden.) *B*. A unicellular fungus, *Cryptococcus neoformans*. (From Edwards, M. R., M. A. Gordon, E. W. Lapa, and W. C. Ghiorse, 1969. *J. Bact.*, **94**:766. By permission of the American Society for Microbiology.)

Figure 6-7

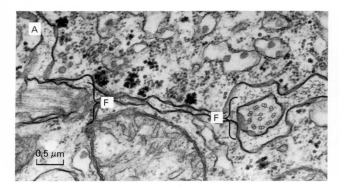

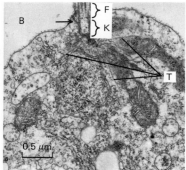

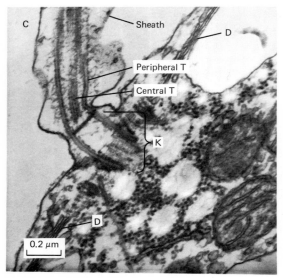

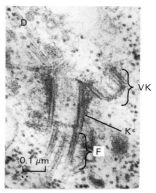

Figure 6-8   Fungal flagellar structures. *A. Blastocladiella emersonii* zoospore flagellum, transverse and longitudinal sections. (From Lessie, P. E., and J. S. Lovett, 1968. *Amer. J. Botany,* **55**:220. By permission of the Botanical Society of America and the *American Journal of Botany.*)

B. Zoospore kinetosome of *Rhizophydium sphaerotheca.* Microtubules are typically associated with the kinetosome, and the kinetosome is connected with the cell membrane (arrows).

C. Kinetosome and base of flagellum of *Monoblepharella* sp. zoospore. The small dictyosomes typically lie beside the kinetosomes. (*B* and *C* from Fuller, M. S., 1966. *Proc. XVIII Symp. Colston Res. Soc.,* p. 67. By permission of the Colston Research Society and Butterworths, publishers.)

D. Phlyctochytrium punctatum, which develops only one functional flagellum (*F*), but which contains a second, vestigial kinetosome (*VK*). It is believed that this type of fungus descended from a biflagellate type by reduction, specifically, by loss of the second flagellum (see also Fig. 6-12). (From Olson, L. W., and M. S. Fuller, 1968. "Ultrastructural Evidence for the Biflagellate Origin of the Uniflagellate Fungal Zoospore," in *Arch. f. Mikrobiol.* **62**:237–50. By permission of Springer-Verlag, Berlin, Heidelberg, New York.)

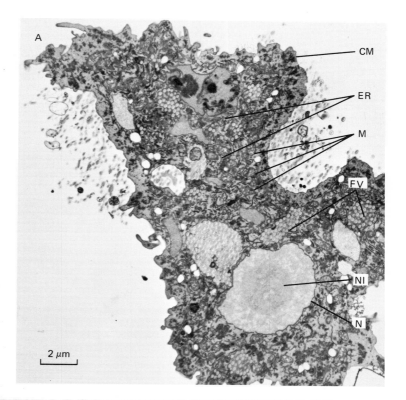

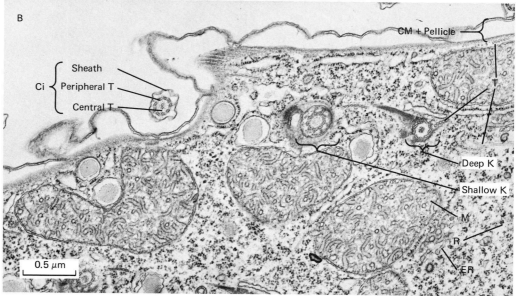

Sections of protozoan cells. *A. Acanthamoeba* sp. during ingestion of latex particles, seen within food vacuoles (FV). (From Korn, E. D., and R. A. Weisman, 1967. *J. Cell Biol.,* **34**:219. By permission of The Rockefeller University Press.) *B. Tetrahymena pyriformis.* The pellicle is multilayered, with the cell membrane fused with the innermost layer. In some specimens, including this one, the layers of the pellicle separate during preparation for electron microscopy. (From Allen, R. D., 1967. *J. Protozool.,* **14**:553. By permission of The Society of Protozoologists and *The Journal of Protozoology.*)

Figure 6-9

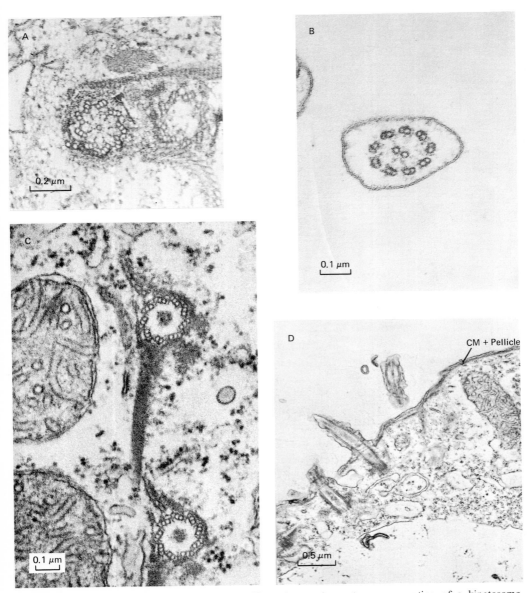

Figure 6-10   Protozoan locomotor organelles. *A. Tetramitus rostratus,* transverse section of a kinetosome. *B. Tetramitus rostratus,* transverse section of a flagellum. (*A* and *B* from Outka, D. E., and B. C. Kluss, 1967. *J. Cell Biol.,* **35:**323. By permission of The Rockefeller University Press.) *C. Tetrahymena pyriformis,* transverse sections of kinetosomes. (Courtesy of R. D. Allen.) *D. Tetrahymena pyriformis,* longitudinal sections of kinetosomes and basal portions of cilia. (From Allen, R. D., 1967. *J. Protozool.,* **14:**553. By permission of The Society of Protozoologists and *The Journal of Protozoology.*)

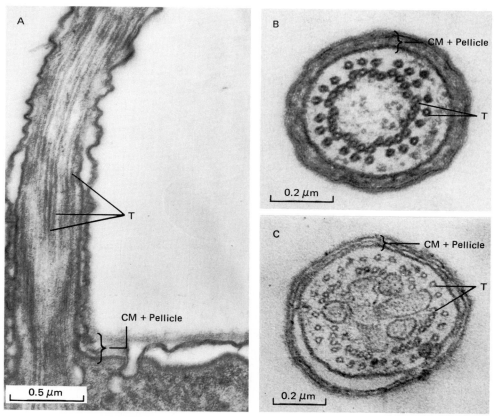

Sections of suctorean tentacles (*Tokophrya infusionum*). *A.* Lateral longitudinal section. *B.* Transverse section of tentacle at rest. *C.* Transverse section of tentacle during feeding. (From Rudzinska, M. A., 1965. *J. Cell Biol.*, **25**:459. By permission of The Rockefeller University Press.)

Figure 6-11

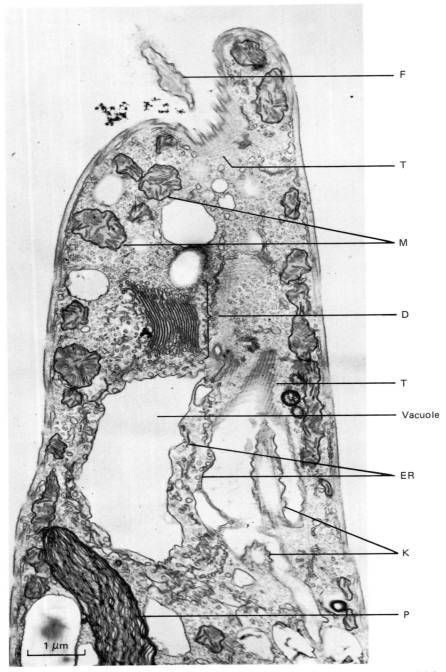

F

T

M

D

T

Vacuole

ER

K

P

1 µm

Figure 6-12 Longitudinal section of the anterior end of a cell of *Euglena gracilis*. One kinetosome is vestigial; only one flagellum emerges and functions in locomotion. (From Leedale, G. F., 1967. *Euglenoid Flagellates.* By permission of Prentice-Hall, Inc., Englewood Cliffs, N.J.)

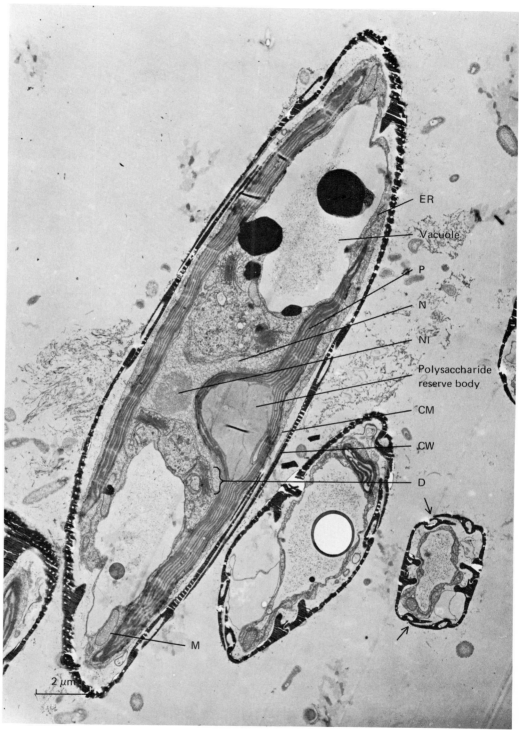

Sections of the diatom *Amphipleura pellucida.* Structures are labeled in the longitudinal section. **Figure 6-13**
The arrows indicate overlapping of wall portions ("valves"; see "Diatoms," Chap. 17) visible
in the transverse section. (From Stoermer, E. F., H. S. Pankratz, and C. C. Bowen, 1965. *Amer.
J. Botany,* **52:**1067. By permission of the *American Journal of Botany* and the Botanical Society
of America.)

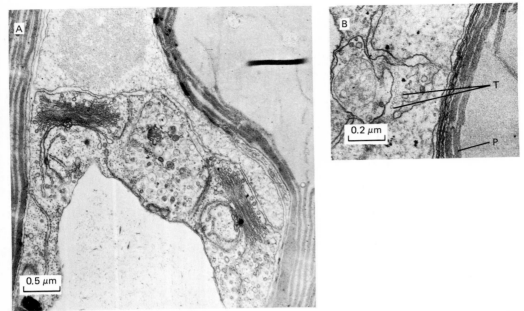

Figure 6-14   Details of *Amphipleura pellucida. A.* Portion of the longitudinal section of Figure 6-13 showing one of the pair of dictyosomes at higher magnification. *B.* Transverse section of microtubules within cytoplasm. (From Stoermer, E. F., H. S. Pankratz, and C. C. Bowen, 1965. *Amer. J. Botany,* **52:**1067. By permission of the *American Journal of Botany* and the Botanical Society of America.)

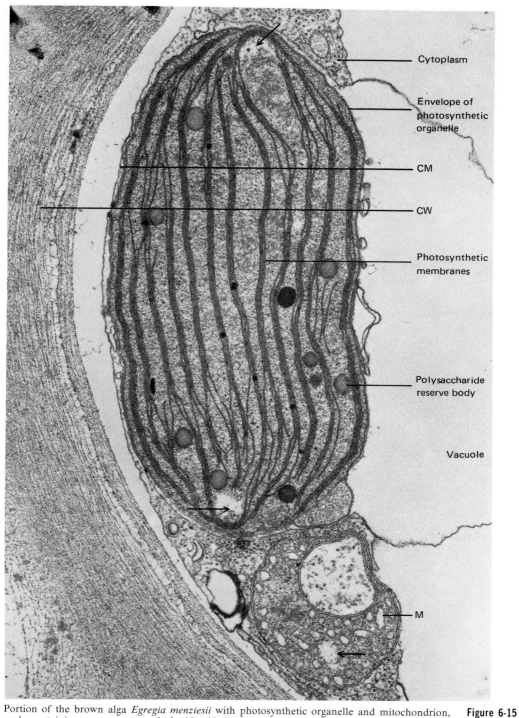

Labels on figure:
- Cytoplasm
- Envelope of photosynthetic organelle
- CM
- CW
- Photosynthetic membranes
- Polysaccharide reserve body
- Vacuole
- M

Figure 6-15

Portion of the brown alga *Egregia menziesii* with photosynthetic organelle and mitochondrion, each containing areas presumptively identified as sites of organellar DNA (arrows). (From Bisalputra, T., and A. A. Bisalputra, 1967. *J. Cell Biol.,* **33:**511. By permission of The Rockefeller University Press.)

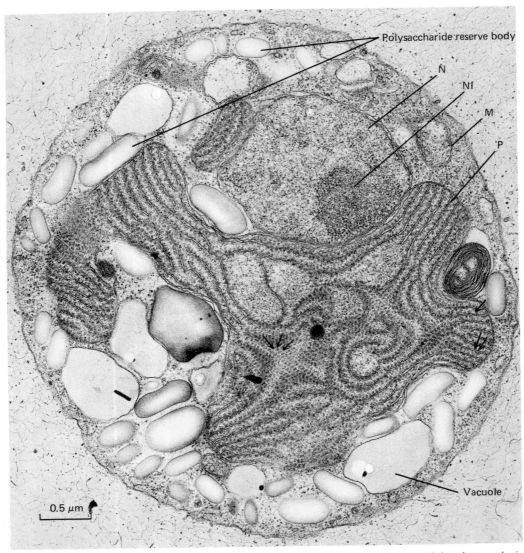

Polysaccharide reserve body

N

N1

M

P

Vacuole

0.5 μm

Figure 6-16 Section of the red alga *Porphyridium cruentum,* in which the membranes of the photosynthetic organelle are associated with regularly spaced granules (arrows) that apparently contain the phycobilin pigments (see Table 17-1). The nucleolus typically lies near the border of the nucleus adjacent to the photosynthetic organelle. (From Gantt, E., and S. F. Conti, 1965. *J. Cell Biol.,* **26:**365. By permission of The Rockefeller University Press.)

Viruses:
Infective Cell Products

Certain types of cells produce particulate entities capable of infecting other cells and inducing them to produce the same type of particle. These cell products are called viruses.

In its most complete form, a virus is a particle that is usually too small to be visualized in a light microscope, but can be seen with the electron microscope. It contains protein, one type of nucleic acid (RNA or DNA), and in some cases additional substances, usually lipids. This particle, called the **virion,** is the usual form of the virus that is released from cells and can infect other cells. Characteristics of the virion are used to distinguish various types of viruses (see Table 7-1).

Viruses exist in two other known forms: **vegetative form** and **provirus.** The vegetative form seems to consist only of nucleic acid, which is the virion component that must enter a cell in order for the cell to become capable of producing that virus. Copies of vegetative virus are synthesized within the cell during virus production. Provirus is the form present in cells that do not synthesize virions, but inherit the ability to do so without external infection by a virion. In some instances, provirus has been identified with a region of the cell genome that is a copy of the viral nucleic acid.[1] In others, both viral nucleic acid (unassociated with the cell's genome) and viral protein have been found in provirus-containing cells. In many instances, provirus has not been identified with a cell component.

---

[1]"Viral nucleic acid" refers to the minimal content of nucleic acid that is present in every infective virion of a virus. Nucleic acid of the cell in which the virion was produced may also be present in some of the infective particles of a virion population.

TABLE 7-1. Some Major Classes of Viruses Distinguished According to Virion Morphology and Nucleic Acid

Class	Shape of Capsid	Dimensions (nm)*	Nucleic Acid	Example†
Bacteriophages				
Filamentous phages	Helical	5.0–7.5 × 800–1,600	1s‡ DNA	ZJ/2
Tailless prismatic phages	Icosahedral or octahedral	20–25	1s DNA or 1s RNA	Phage 7s
Head-and-tail phages	Elongated, icosa-hedral, or octa-hedral	Variable§	2s DNA	Phage T4, phage lambda
Plant viruses‖				
Rod-shaped	Helical	16 × 300–10 × 800	1s RNA	Tobacco mosaic virus (TMV)
Prismatic	Icosahedral	28	1s RNA	Turnip yellow mosaic virus (TYMV)
	Icosahedral	70	2s RNA	Wound tumor virus
Animal viruses				
Adenoviruses	Icosahedral	60–90	2s DNA	Human type 7
Herpesviruses	Icosahedral	100; 180–200 with envelope‡	2s DNA	Herpes simplex
Reoviruses	Icosahedral	70	2s RNA	(Not illustrated)
Picornaviruses	Icosahedral	25–30	1s RNA	Poliovirus
Myxoviruses	Helical	9–10 × 600–800; 90–100 with envelope**	1s RNA	Influenza, vesicular stomatitis virus (VSV)
Poxviruses	(See text)	250–300††	2s DNA	Vaccinia

*Characteristic ranges; there is some variation within each class.
†See Figures 7-3 through 7-16.
‡1s: single nucleic acid molecules; 2s: nucleic acid molecules wound in pairs.
§The morphology of head-and-tail phages varies with regard to dimensions of head and of tail, to shape of the head, and to the presence of additional structures associated with the tail. The reader is referred to Bradley (1967) for a review of phage morphology.
‖Some plant viruses are transmitted among plants by insects, within which virus multiplication may occur.
‡Envelope apparently is derived from the nuclear membrane; contains lipid as well as protein.
**Envelope is derived from the cell membrane; contains lipid as well as protein.
††Envelope is not derived from cell components; contains protein only, not any lipid.

Discovery of Viruses and Distinction from Microorganisms

Because the relationships of some viruses to virus-producing organisms are similar to those of parasitic microorganisms to their hosts, viruses were long suspected of being microorganisms. Some viruses can cause diseases, and most viral diseases are communicable. The term "virus" was originally used to designate any infectious agent of disease; as the identification of some infectious agents with particular microorganisms (fungi, protozoa, or bacteria) was accomplished in the nineteenth century, use of the term became restricted to designation of infectious agents that could not be identified with a known kind of microbe.

In 1892, D. Iwanowsky found that the etiologic agent of tobacco mosaic disease could pass through filters that retained the smallest known bacteria. In 1899, M. W. Beijerinck found that this filterable agent could be precipitated by alcohol from an extract of an infected tobacco plant. Since alcohol was known to be generally suitable for inactivation (killing) of microorganisms, this observation implied that filterable agents were fundamentally different from microbes in other features as well as size.

As further evidence of differences between viruses and microorganisms, W. Schlesinger found in 1933 that a filterable agent that infected bacteria contained only protein and DNA; the smallest bacteria known contain also RNA, other polymeric substances, lipids, a variety of small organic molecules, and inorganic substances. In 1935, W. Stanley crystallized the agent of tobacco mosaic disease; crystallization, which depends on structural symmetry and complementary surfaces on the crystallized particles, had been reported for certain macromolecular constituents of living systems (e.g., enzymes), but not for any type of cell.

Viruses were finally visualized in the late 1930's, with the aid of the electron microscope. The virion form of tobacco mosaic virus was then seen to be a rod-shaped particle approximately 16 × 300 nm. Subsequent electron microscopic examinations of a variety of virions have revealed that the size, shape, and organization of the virion are constant characteristics of a virus. Fractionation and chemical analysis of virions have, however, revealed that the construction of the virion is basically the same in all types of viruses. Nucleic acid is contained as a core surrounded by a protein coat. Morphologic variation among viruses involves the shape of the protein-coated nucleic acid unit and, in a few instances, the presence of appendages or enveloping structures, the latter derived from cell components present in cells whether or not they contain any form of the virus.

Characteristics of Viruses

Virion Morphology. The virion is the infective form of a virus. The nucleic acid alone may be infective, but its infectivity is lost rapidly outside cells. The protein coating demonstrably increases the stability of infectivity; presumably, it is important to preservation of the infective unit during transit from one cell or organism to another. The protein coating also increases the specificity of the virion with regard to the types of cells it can infect and aids entry of the viral nucleic acid into the cell.

Two types of arrangements of nucleic acid and protein are illustrated diagrammatically in Figure 7-1. The virion which appears hexagonal in cross-section is icosahedral; the surface of the virion exhibits 20 triangular faces. The arrangement of the nucleic acid within the protein coat has not been determined and may vary among icosahedral virions. The other type of virion is cylindric and exhibits helical symmetry; the protein forms a hollow tube (with open or closed ends, depending on the virus) within which the nucleic acid is coiled.

The protein coat, or capsid, is composed of subunits, called capsomers. Some virions contain only one type of protein; in these types, each capsomer contains a few molecules of this protein and is of the same chemical composition as the others. Other virions are known to contain several proteins, whose distribution among the capsomers has not yet been determined. For any given virus, the number of capsomers is the same in each virion; since the size of a capsomer is a constant property of the virus, the size of a capsid and hence of a virion is constant (see Table 7-1).

The nucleocapsid may comprise the complete virion. In some animal and plant viruses, all or many of the virions released by an infected cell consist of a nucleocapsid surrounded by an envelope, which usually has short projections on its outer surface. The envelope, generally lipoprotein, is composed of a mixture of cell (lipid) and viral (protein) components in some viruses, and of cell (lipoprotein) components only in others. Tubular nucleocapsids of non-enveloped virions are generally straight rods, which may exhibit some

A   B

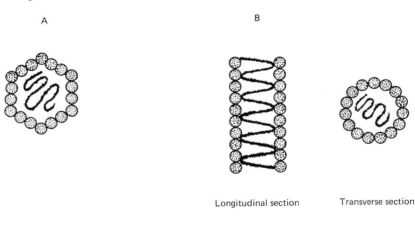

Longitudinal section   Transverse section

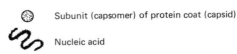   Subunit (capsomer) of protein coat (capsid)

Nucleic acid

Figure 7-1   Diagrams of two common types of virion construction. *A.* Icosahedral. *B.* Helical.

flexibility. Enveloped tubular nucleocapsids generally are convoluted within the envelopes.

The virions of many of the viruses that infect bacteria differ from these first two types in features peculiar to virions that infect procaryotic organisms.[2] The outstanding structural feature is an appendage that mediates attachment of the virion to a host cell and through which the nucleic acid moves from the nucleocapsid into the cell. This structure is commonly referred to as the "tail," the nucleocapsid as the "head." The head may be an icosahedron, octahedron, or elongated polyhedron. The tail usually exhibits helical symmetry.

The virions of some animal viruses (viz., the poxviruses) are structurally unique. They do not possess capsids composed of capsomers; rather, the nucleic acid is contained within at least two protein envelopes. The virions are ovoid or brick-shaped with rounded corners.

Virus Perpetuation/Virion Production. Cells infected with viruses may or may not produce virions. When a cell begins to produce virions shortly after infection by a virion, the infection is termed productive. When an infected cell does not produce virions, but gives rise to progeny cells some of which produce virions, the infection is termed latent or non-productive. Viruses are perpetuated in both ways, and the majority of viruses can establish either type of infection. Whether an infection becomes productive or latent depends on a variety of factors (not all yet identified), including principally the physiologic and immunologic state of the organism or the cell and characteristics of the virus. The first type of infection is described in this section; latent infection is discussed in the following section.

Certain features of productive infection seem typical of virus-cell systems. These are:

1. Attachment of the virion to the cell, called adsorption.
2. Penetration of the nucleic acid and in some cases other virion components into the protoplast.
3. Dissociation of viral nucleic acid from other virion components, called uncoating.
4. Modification of synthetic metabolic processes of the cell so that viral components are synthesized.
5. Assembly of newly synthesized viral components into virions.
6. Release of virions from the cell.

Once uncoating has occurred, infective virus cannot be detected on or within the cell. The uncoated nucleic acid is not infective except under specific conditions only recently devised for a few viruses. The disappearance of infectivity is characteristic of both productive and non-productive infections; infectivity

[2]The discovery that virions of the few viruses known to be produced by procaryotic algae exhibit the head-and-tail construction has been regarded as evidence of a close phylogenetic relationship between bacteria and blue-green algae. Viruses produced by procaryotic organisms are called phages—bacteriophages and cyanophages.

reappears when new virions are assembled. The time between uncoating and assembly of progeny virions is called the eclipse period.

These features have not yet been described in detail for all known productive infections, but they have been reported for a sufficient number of animal and bacterial virus infections to allow the inference that they are of general occurrence. Recent evidence for one plant virus (TMV) infection indicates that the same events occur in virus-infected plant cells. For most viral infections, at least the occurrence of an eclipse period has been demonstrated.

Details of each step vary with characteristics of the virus and of the cell. For example, virion release may be accompanied by disintegration of the cell, or the cell may remain intact and continue to release virions over a long period, possibly years. The length of time between adsorption and the onset of virion release varies from a few minutes (in some bacterial virus infections) to a day or longer (in some plant virus infections). It is affected by environmental factors, particularly temperature, as well as by virus and cell characteristics.

Electron micrographs of virus-producing cells of various organisms are presented at the end of this chapter. In eucaryotic cells, virion components may be synthesized and assembled in the nucleus and/or in the cytoplasm, depending mainly on the virus, but the site of synthesis may also vary among infected cells. The assembly of some virions is completed as they are released from the nucleus or the protoplast. Enveloped virions commonly acquire envelope components from the nuclear envelope or protoplast membrane as they pass through; less commonly, envelope components are derived from cytoplasmic membranes (probably endoplasmic reticulum). Among bacterial viruses, only the filamentous RNA-containing virions are known to be completed at the cell surface and released without rupture of the cell.

Virus Perpetuation/Non-productive and Inapparent Infections. Non-productive, or latent, virus infections occur widely among organisms that produce viruses, especially among animals and bacteria. The principal criterion by which a latent infection is recognized is the possibility of provoking the production of infective virions by at least some of the cells in the latently infected population. Latent infections may be provoked to productivity by a variety of physical and chemical factors. Generally, ultraviolet light is effective; it is used experimentally to provoke virion production by latently infected bacteria and cultured animal cells, and it is known to provoke latent animal viruses to initiate development of malignant tumors and leukemia.

The mechanism of latent infection has been elucidated only for some bacterial viruses. The best characterized is the relationship of bacteriophage lambda (λ) and *Escherichia coli*. This bacteriophage can cause productive infection and death of *E. coli* cells. However, a certain proportion of infected cells survive the period during which other cells produce virions and disintegrate. The progeny of the surviving cells can adsorb virions, but they cannot be productively infected by λ virions. They can be provoked by exposure to ultraviolet light to produce λ virions. This condition of immunity and potential productivity is designated the lysogenic state. The mechanism by which cells become lysogenized has been interpreted as indicated diagrammatically in Figure 7-2.

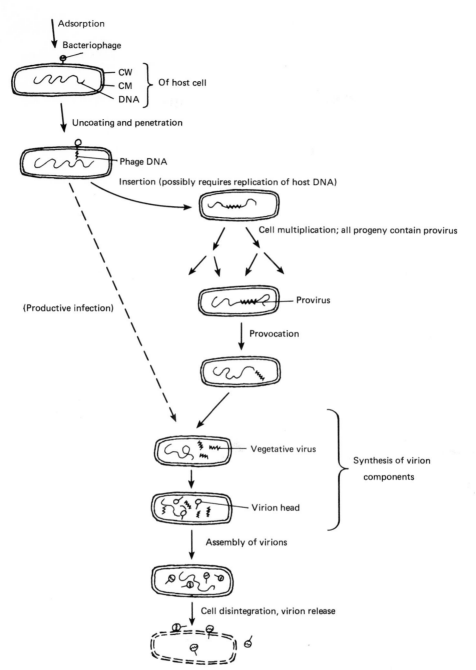

Adsorption

Bacteriophage

CW
CM } Of host cell
DNA

Uncoating and penetration

Phage DNA

Insertion (possibly requires replication of host DNA)

Cell multiplication; all progeny contain provirus

(Productive infection)

Provirus

Provocation

Vegetative virus

Virion head

} Synthesis of virion components

Assembly of virions

Cell disintegration, virion release

Interpretation of lysogeny. The virion adsorbs by its tail to the cell surface. Migration of the DNA from the virion head into the cell accomplishes penetration and uncoating in one step. Once inside the protoplast, the viral DNA becomes associated with the cell genome and is replicated with the cell DNA. In progeny of the lysogenized cell, the genome of the virus is contained within the single DNA molecule which is the cell's genome; this inserted genetic material is the provirus.

    Provirus represses the synthesis of enzymes that catalyze the synthesis of virion components. The repression apparently is mediated by a substance in the cytoplasm, since the genome of an infecting virion of the same virus is also repressed; the immunity of lysogenized cells is attributed to this repression.

    Exposure of lysogenic cells to provocative agents such as ultraviolet light results in dissociation of the provirus from the cell genome, elimination of the repression, and initiation of events that culminate in virion production and cell lysis.

Figure 7-2

Many latent animal virus infections have been recognized, and it is probably significant that they generally involve viruses whose virions contain DNA and whose DNA is synthesized in the nucleus of the virus-producing cell. Tumor-inducing viruses are exceptions; their virions may contain RNA or DNA. Latency may be similar in mechanism to lysogeny, but this has not yet been established for any animal virus.

In the case of both bacterial and animal viruses, it is not always simple to demonstrate that cells are latently infected. Since the criterion of such infection is the ability of the cells to be provoked to produce infective virions, an organism or cell line susceptible to infection by the virions must be available. The most suitable test systems (called indicators) are productively infected and show some readily detectable symptoms of infection (e.g., cell alteration or disintegration, or disease of the organism). When an indicator is not available, latency and inapparent infection are difficult to distinguish; an inapparent infection is productive, but the infection is not accompanied by detectable symptoms in the host.

Infection of humans by adenoviruses is an example of inapparent infection that, when first recognized, was thought to be a latent infection. Adenoviruses were first detected in cultured human cells derived from excised adenoid tissue. Upon prolonged cultivation of the cells, morphologic alterations appeared. Alterations could also be evoked in cultures of other types of human cells by agents produced in the adenoid cell cultures. The agents were identified as viruses. It is now estimated that 50 to 80 per cent of adult humans produce at least one type of adenovirus, but symptoms of disease (of the respiratory tract or eye) seem to occur only in infants and young children.

Origin of Viruses

Two phylogenetic origins have been proposed for viruses: (1) they arose and continue to arise as cell products; and (2) they have descended from microorganisms by loss of properties (called **reductive evolution**) not necessary for perpetuation of intracellular parasites. These proposals are discussed here as an illustration of the way in which the probability of untestable propositions can be evaluated by determining the agreement of their predictions with observations.

The first proposal implies that there is some advantage to an organism in producing viruses. Two possible advantages have been suggested. (1) Viruses are produced as carriers of cell components, particularly genetic transfer.[3] (2) Viruses are produced as agents that can suppress the development of populations of organisms that would compete for foods, space, mates, and so forth, by causing disease in the competitors. The second proposal implies that viruses are parasites (see Chap. 21), and that, initially, virus infection is an advantage to the parasite only. As the virus-host relationship evolves, the host population may adjust to the infection and even derive some benefit from it, including,

---

[3]Viruses can carry genetic material from cell to cell; see, for example, Chap. 19, "Transduction."

for example, using viruses for transferring genetic material or for suppressing development of populations of competitors.

Because of these implications, many of the predictions of the alternative proposals are the same. However, three major contrary predictions can be derived from the two alternatives. These contraries, which provide a basis for rejection of one of the proposals, are:

First Proposal. Viruses are cell products specialized for gene transfer and/or competitor suppression.

A. Variation in chemical composition and structural organization of viruses should not be greater than variation among other cell products that function analogously in different types of cells (e.g., photosynthetic organelles, flagella, ribosomes).

B. Viral nucleic acid should contain only information necessary for virus perpetuation within cells and transmission between organisms.

C. Virions could contain either DNA or RNA, since both are involved in the synthesis of cell products, and either could control a specific synthesis.

Second Proposal. Viruses are parasites descended by reduction from microorganisms.

A. Variation in chemical composition and structural organization of viruses should be as great as among microorganisms from which they can descend. Variation should reflect not only multiple ancestry, but also different stages of descent; some viruses should be primitive and similar to microorganisms; others should be highly evolved and more reduced.

B. Viral nucleic acid should contain information necessary for virus perpetuation within cells and transmission between organisms and other information of microbial origin that has not yet been eliminated by reduction.

C. Virions should contain DNA, with or without RNA, since DNA is a necessary constituent of genetic material of all microorganisms that have been examined in this regard.

The relevant observations are:

Prediction A. With the exception of a few animal viruses, virions are constructed of nucleic acid enclosed within the capsid, a shell composed of protein subunits. In the exceptions, one or more sheets of protein are present in lieu of a capsid. Envelopes present on some virions are derived from cell components that are synthesized by the cells whether or not they contain viral nucleic acid.

Prediction B. Viral nucleic acid contains information for polymerization of amino acids into proteins and of nucleotides into nucleic acids. The proteins may be enzymes that synthesize virion components and virion structural constituents; in certain viruses, some of the proteins are enzymes that degrade cell components such as cell wall material or nucleic acid. Viral nucleic acid is not known to contain information for the synthesis of lipids, carbohydrates, the precursors of proteins and nucleic acids, or for polymerization of amino acids into enzymes that catalyze energy-yielding reactions.

Prediction C. Some virions contain only RNA; they are otherwise similar in structure, composition, size, and behavior to virions in general. DNA-containing virions do not also contain RNA.

The reader may reach his own conclusion regarding the respective probability of the alternative proposed origins of viruses. The author's conclusion is expressed in the title of this chapter.

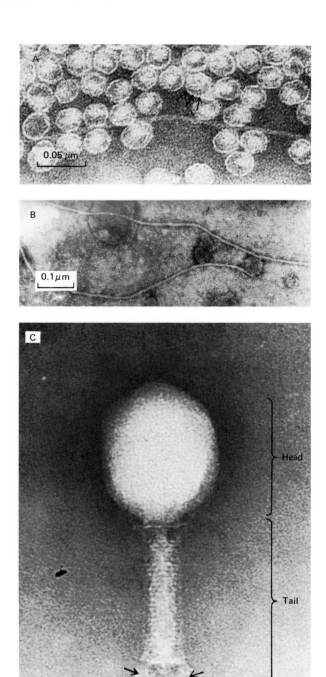

Three major morphologic types of bacteriophage virions. *A. Pseudomonas* phage 7s (icosahedral; RNA). The arrows indicate capsomers. (From Bradley, D. E., 1966. *J. Gen. Microbiol.,* **45:**83. By permission of Cambridge University Press.) *B. Escherichia coli* phage ZJ/2 (filamentous; DNA). (From Bradley, D. E., 1964. *J. Gen. Microbiol.,* **35:**471. By permission of Cambridge University Press.) *C. Escherichia coli* phage T4 (head-and-tail; DNA). The tail fibers that mediate attachment to the cell surface are contracted (arrows). (Courtesy of D. E. Bradley.)

Figure 7-3

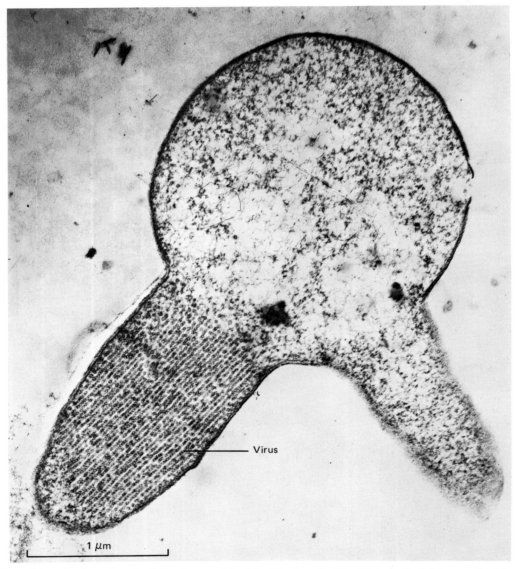

Virus

1 μm

Figure 7-4 Section of a cell of *Pseudomonas* infected with phage 7s (Fig. 7-3*A*). Part of the normally rod-shaped cell is swollen and rounded. A mass of regularly arranged virions occupies a large portion of the cell. (From Bradley, D. E., 1966. *J. Gen. Microbiol.*, **45**:83. By permission of Cambridge University Press.)

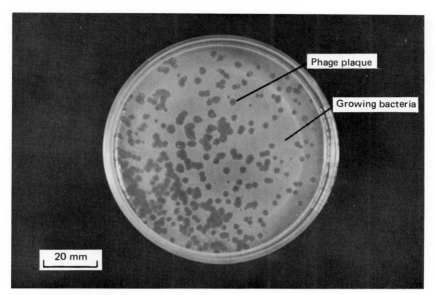

Bacteriophage PB2₁ plaques (dark, circular areas) on a lawn (light background) of *Agrobacterium tumefaciens* in a Petri plate. (From Stonier, T., J. McSharry, and T. Speitel, 1967. *J. Virol.*, **1**:268. By permission of the American Society for Microbiology.)

Figure 7-5

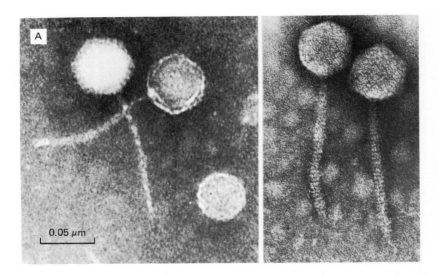

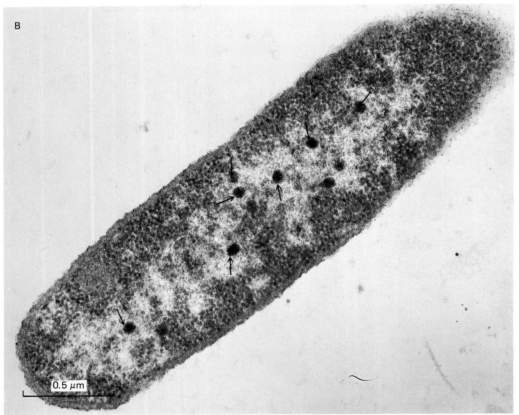

Figure 7-6 *Escherichia coli* phage lambda. *A.* Virions. *B.* Infected bacterium containing several dense masses of phage DNA (arrows). (From Kemp, C. L., A. F. Howatson, and L. Siminovitch, 1968. *Virol.,* **36**:490. By permission of Academic Press, Inc.)

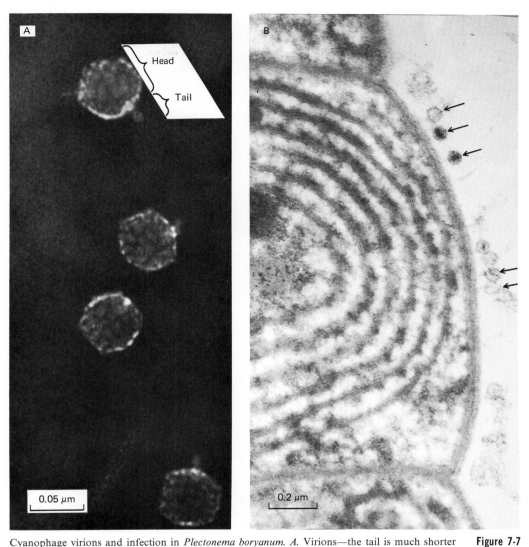

Cyanophage virions and infection in *Plectonema boryanum*. *A*. Virions—the tail is much shorter relative to the head than are the tails of bacteriophages T4 (Fig. 7-3*C*) and lambda (Fig. 7-6*A*). *B*. Virions (arrows) adsorbed by the tails to the wall of an algal cell. (Courtesy of K. M. Smith, R. M. Brown, Jr., and P. A. Walne.)

Figure 7-7

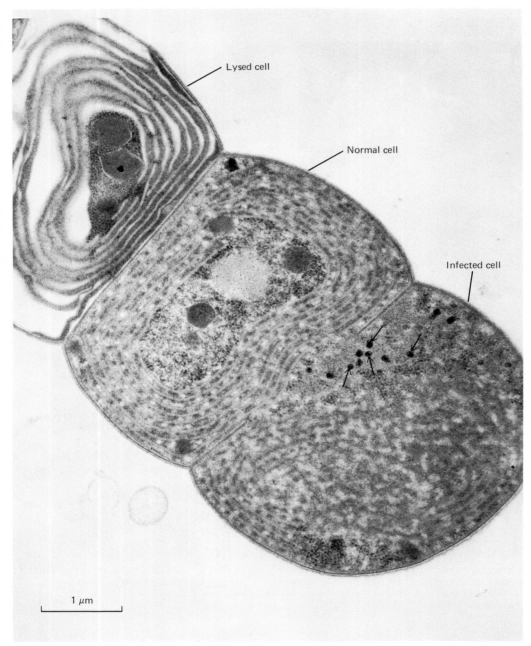

Lysed cell

Normal cell

Infected cell

1 μm

Figure 7-8 Cyanophage infection in a portion of a filament of *Plectonema boryanum*. One cell has been lysed. The middle cell appears uninfected. The photosynthetic membranes of the outer cell have been displaced from a region in which dense masses of viral DNA (arrows) appear. (Courtesy of K. M. Smith, R. M. Brown, Jr., and P. A. Walne.)

82

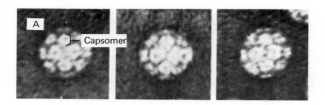

B

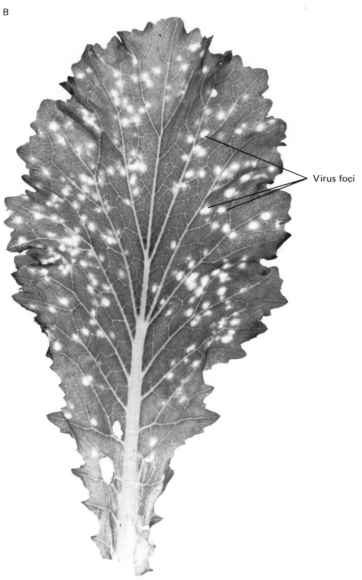

Virus foci

Turnip yellow mosaic virus (*TYMV*) virions and infection in Chinese cabbage. (By permission of Academic Press, Inc.) *A.* Virions. The capsomers are hollow angular prisms, rather than spheres, as in most virions. (From Hitchborn, J. H., and G. J. Hills, 1968. *Virol.,* **35:**50.) *B.* Cabbage leaf with foci of viral infection. The left side of the leaf was inoculated with virions, the right side with a purified preparation of viral RNA. (From Dunn, D. B., and J. H. Hitchborn, 1966. *Virol.,* **30:**598.)

Figure 7-9

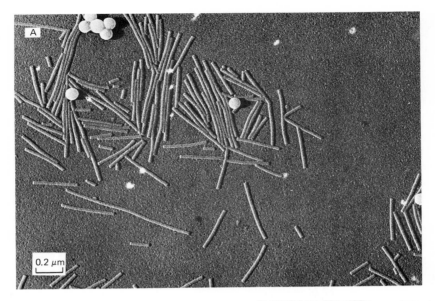

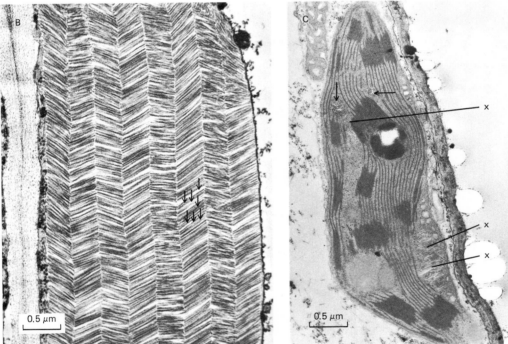

Figure 7-10 Tobacco mosaic virus (*TMV*) virions and infection in tobacco leaves. *A*. Virions, which typically vary in length, but are of constant diameter; the spheres are size indicators. (From Jensen, W. A., and R. B. Park, 1967. *Cell Ultrastructure*. By permission of Wadsworth Publishing Co., Inc., Belmont, Calif.) *B*. Virus crystal in cytoplasm, longitudinal sections of virions (arrows). *C*. Virus crystals in a chloroplast, transverse (arrows) and longitudinal (*x*'s) sections of virions. (*B* and *C* courtesy of T. A. Shalla and A. L. Granett.)

84

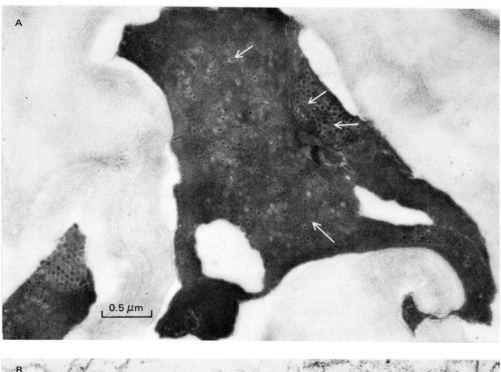

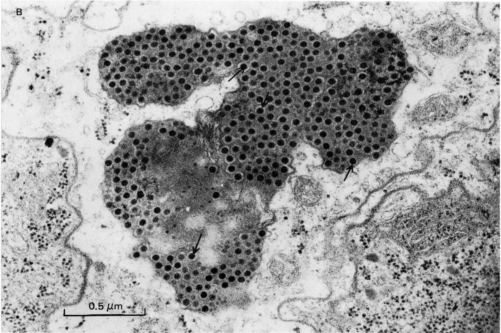

Wound tumor virus (*WTV*) infection. *A*. Virions (arrows) in necrotic areas of a stem tumor of the plant, a sweet clover (*Melilotus officinalis*). (Courtesy of E. Shikata and H. Hirumi.) *B*. Aggregated virions (arrows) in a glial cell of the central nervous system of the insect vector, a leafhopper (*Agallia constricta*). (From Hirumi, H., R. R. Granados, and K. Maramorosch, 1967. *J. Virol.,* **1**:430. By permission of the American Society for Microbiology.)

Figure 7-11

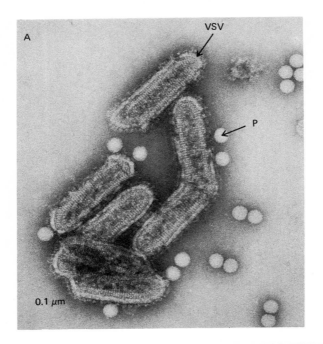

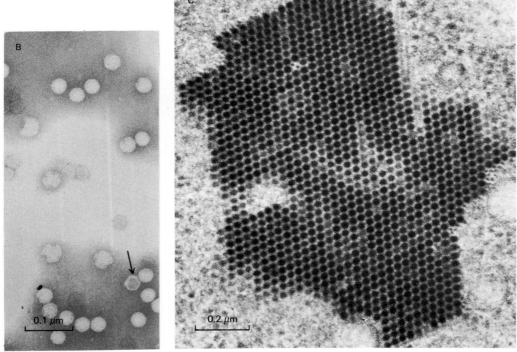

Figure 7-12   Animal viruses: vesicular stomatitis virus (*VSV*) of cattle and poliomyelitis virus of humans. *A.* A mixture of *VSV* and poliovirus (*P*) virions. The closed, bullet-shaped *VSV* virions are usually infective; open, thimble-shaped virions are not infective. (Courtesy of B. Mandel, R. W. Simpson, and R. E. Hauser.) *B.* Poliovirus virions. The arrow indicates a capsid that lacks RNA and in which the hexagonal outline of the icosahedral virion is apparent. (Courtesy of B. Mandel and R. E. Hauser.) *C.* Poliovirus crystal in cytoplasm of a cultured animal cell. (From Dales, S., H. J. Eggers, I. Tamm, and G. E. Palade, 1965. *Virol.,* **26**:379. By permission of Academic Press, Inc.)

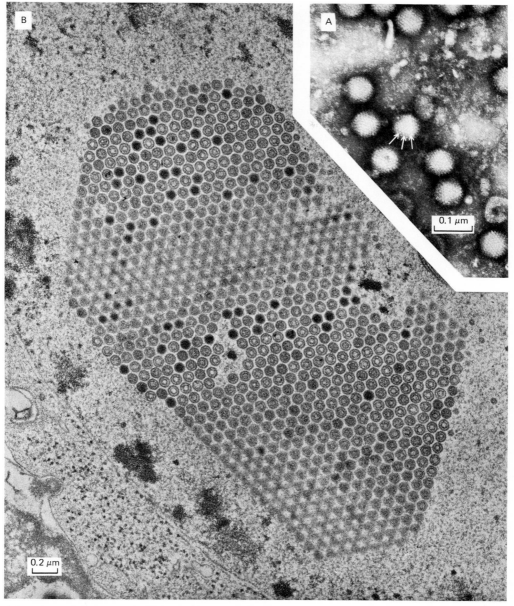

Adenovirus of humans. *A*. Virions (icosahedral). The arrows indicate capsomers. (From Dales, S., 1962. *J. Cell Biol.*, **13**:303. By permission of The Rockefeller University Press.) *B*. An intranuclear crystal of virus particles. (Courtesy of C. Morgan.)

Figure 7-13

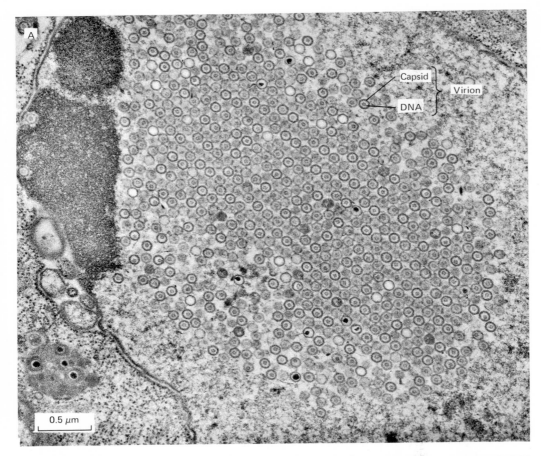

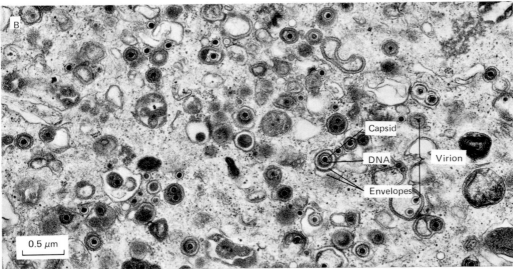

Figure 7-14   Herpes virus infection in cultivated animal cells. *A.* An intranuclear crystal of virus particles. Virion DNA and other components are synthesized in the nucleus. *B.* Virus in the cytoplasm. Most virions are enclosed within walled vacuoles, one or two particles per vacuole. The inner envelope is apparently derived from the nuclear envelope during passage of virions from nucleus to cytoplasm. (From Nii, S., C. Morgan, and H. M. Rose, 1968. *J. Virol.,* **2:**517. By permission of the American Society for Microbiology.)

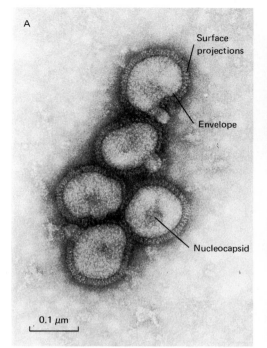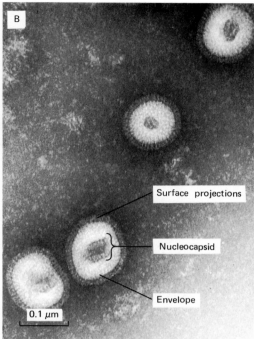

Influenza virus (a myxovirus) virions of humans. *A.* Normal appearance of the enveloped
virion. *B.* Virions after treatment with snake venom to aid visualization of the central, helical
nucleocapsid. (Courtesy of R. W. Simpson and R. E. Hauser.)

Figure 7-15

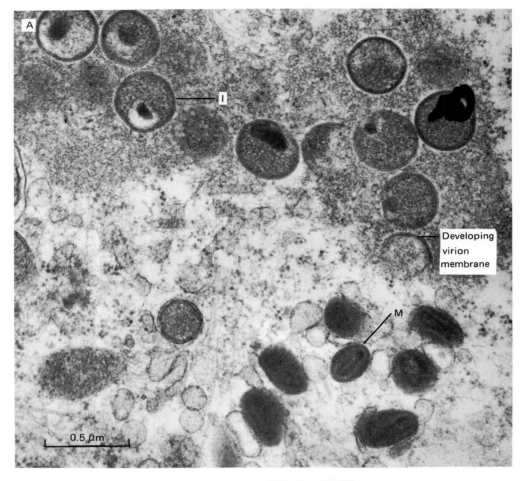

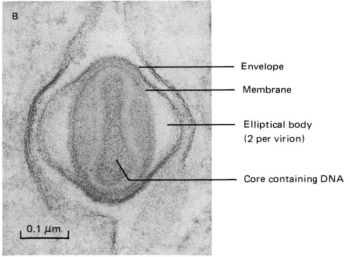

Figure 7-16   Vaccinia virus (a poxvirus). *A.* Intracytoplasmic virions at various stages of maturation (*I,* relatively immature; *M,* mature). Mature virions are more condensed and smaller than earlier stages. (Courtesy of S. Dales.) *B.* A mature virion lodged extracellularly between the cell membranes of two cells. (From Dales, S., 1963. *J. Cell Biol.,* **18**:51. By permission of The Rockefeller University Press.)

Chapter 8

Phylogeny of Structure

The recently obtained information concerning the fine structure of cells, the chemical composition of subcellular components, and the manner of functioning of certain macromolecular constituents implies the direct descent of certain components of cells. It can reasonably be proposed that the basic structures of all cells—the cell membranes and the nuclei—have descended from one ancestral type.

The membranes of all modern cells are similar in fine structure and chemical composition. It seems that the unit membrane, once evolved, did not undergo any significant modification. The principal difference between the cell membranes of procaryotic and eucaryotic cells is the tendency of the eucaryotic membrane to elaborate internally and thereby to provide membranous components that delimit portions of protoplasm and serve as barriers and surfaces.

The descent of nuclei has been accompanied by greater structural modifications, but these have not altered the role of DNA as the principal repository of genetic information. Also, the mechanism by which genetic information is expressed through the synthesis of RNA that moves into the cytoplasm and there directs the synthesis of proteins seems basically the same in primitive and advanced cells. The differences between the two general types of nuclei are the characteristics limited to eucaryotic nuclei. Presumably, these features (viz., nuclear membranes and basic proteins) have been added to the more primitive type of nucleus. As suggested in Chapter 9, these changes in nuclear organization have had very important consequences in allowing increased complexity of the organism.

A third cellular feature that has probably descended along one principal line, rather than having appeared in two or more separate lines, is the photosynthetic organelle. In bacteria, these organelles may be simple vesicles derived from the cell membrane or they may be stacks of membranes. In blue-green algae, the organelles are usually stacks of membranes that lie in the peripheral

91

region of the protoplast or, in some cases, are arranged irregularly within the protoplast. In procaryotic organisms, the membranes of the photosynthetic organelles are in direct contact with the cytoplasm and, as far as known, contain all the enzymes and pigments associated with photosynthesis.

In eucaryotic algae, the stacks of photosynthetic membranes are separated from the cytoplasm by a limiting membrane. In plants, the internal stacking pattern is relatively complex, with the chlorophylls localized in grana. Accordingly, it is possible that the structural evolution of photosynthetic organelles has involved principally an increase in the complexity of the organization of chlorophyll-containing membranes.

Some cell components serve analogous functions in different organisms, but vary considerably in fine structure and chemical composition. Such structures have probably arisen independently in different cell lines, rather than having descended directly from primeval through procaryotic to eucaryotic cells. Among these are cell walls, mitochondria, and flagella.

Whereas cell walls regularly function in conferring rigidity on cells and probably also influence permeability, particularly to water, the great variety of chemical compositions indicates that they are not phylogenetically related in all types of organisms. This is particularly the case for eucaryotic protists, where composition of cell walls often varies without correlation with other traits. For example, cellulosic walls are known to occur in all three major groups of eucaryotic protists and in slime protists, and other types of walls also occur in each group. Procaryotic walls, on the other hand, regularly contain mucopeptide as the principal structural material; this finding has furnished one of the most convincing biochemical bases for proposing that blue-green algae have descended from bacteria, or both groups from a common ancestor.

Mitochondria occur in eucaryotic, but not in procaryotic, algae. Since the respiratory enzymes of procaryotic algae are contained within the photosynthetic membranes, it is at least clear that procaryotic algae do not possess organelles specialized for respiration that could be regarded as functionally equivalent to or as precursors of mitochondria.

Similarly, the many differences in flagellar structure between bacteria and eucaryotic organisms and the absence of flagella from blue-green algae suggest that the two types of locomotor organelles originated independently. Among modern eucaryotic cells, there does not seem to be any recognizable precursor, or primitive form, of the flagellum. It seems probable that eucaryotic flagella arose independently more than once, but each time from a centriole, hence the same basic construction of all eucaryotic flagella.

This suggestion removes the question of origin from flagellum to centriole and implies that the origin of the centriole might have been unique. At present, evidence concerning a possible precursor of the centriole is not available. However, because the centriole exhibits more than one function in primitive eucaryotic cells and can give rise to self-perpetuating specialized organelles (flagellar basal bodies), it seems that, whatever its origin, the centriole appeared as an unspecialized cytoplasmic organelle that generated contractile fibers. The functions the fibers came to serve (locomotion, mitotic nuclear division) evolved according to the advantages obtained by the evolving cell line.

Chapter 9

Differentiation

Empirically, it must be concluded that the internal organization of cells has a profound influence on the potential for multicellular development and for differentiation of cell groups within the multicellular organism. In contrast to procaryotic cells, eucaryotic cells are capable of growing to much greater size (see Table 9-1); of maintaining a diploid genetic state, with the consequent increased potential for interactions among genes and for variation among individuals of a population; and, in multicellular organisms, of giving rise to lines of cells specialized for metabolic functions. Modern procaryotic organisms are predominantly unicellular. Even in multicellular procaryotic organisms, cells may be specialized for dissemination and/or for dormancy, but not for sexual processes or for metabolic processes, or even for support, attachment, or protection.

Eucaryotic organisms, on the other hand, range in complexity from colorless counterparts of algae that are unicellular, non-motile, lack cell walls, and subsist, like most bacteria, on organic substances absorbed from the environment; to organisms that can abstractly plan and remotely effect changes in their environment and could, if they chose, predetermine properties of their offspring.

An individual of every type of differentiated multicellular organism can develop from a single, uninucleate cell. The adult is formed by growth and cell division and by establishment of lines of cells specialized to perform particular functions. The initial cell contains the genetic information for direction of all the functions and for the course of cell specialization. The specialization of some cells for a given function requires that those cells lose other functions (or do not develop them), and that other cells lose (or do not develop) the function the specialized cells perform. In the establishment of lines of specialized cells, the loss of function must either be heritable or be constantly maintained by the environment of the cells.

TABLE 9-1.   Characteristic Size Ranges of Unicellular Protists

Type of Organism	Linear Dimensions (μm)	Approximate Volume (μm³)
Procaryotic		
Rickettsiae	0.3×0.3–0.5×2.0	0.01–0.25
Eubacteria	0.6×1.0–2×5	0.2–5
Algae	2×2–10×20	5–1,000
Eucaryotic		
Yeasts	2×5–10×30	10–1,500
Algae	5×5–50×100	70–125,000
Protozoa	10×10–100×300	5,000–1,500,000

There are probably several mechanisms by which heritable cell specialization occurs in differentiated organisms. There is increasing evidence that at least the following three mechanisms are operative in modern organisms. (1) Functions may be lost from a cell line by loss of genes; this is observed as a decrease in chromatin (the DNA-containing part of the nucleoplasm) and/or a reorganization of chromatin. This type of mechanism results in a cell line that has permanently lost potential as well as function. (2) Functions may be lost as the result of gene-gene interaction when one gene regulates, particularly when it suppresses, the activity of another gene. Such mechanisms, which seem to be much more common than chromatin loss, are often reversible, but are not usually reversed during normal development of the organism. (3) The intramolecular structure of nucleoprotein molecules may be altered so that the protein moieties interfere with the synthesis of RNA directed by the DNA, an initial step in the expression of a gene. This mechanism, still largely hypothetical, would be available only to eucaryotic, and not to procaryotic, organisms. Accordingly, it implies that the potential for differentiation is greater in eucaryotic organisms, whereas the other mechanisms would be available to both procaryotic and eucaryotic organisms.

In many instances now fairly thoroughly described, the expression of particular genes is dependent on the composition of the cytoplasm. For example, the presence of a substrate for an enzyme may induce the gene to direct synthesis of the enzyme; the presence of a high level of the product of an enzyme may repress the directive activities of the gene; the presence of other substances may allow or prevent the suppressive activities of regulatory genes; and (theoretically, at least) the presence of substances called hormones may stimulate or depress the expression of particular genes. Most such effects are quantitative, and the expression of the gene is related to the amount of the influential substance present at any given time. The cell line retains a greater potential than it exhibits. This type of mechanism seems to play a major role in early steps in multicellular development, when there may be little if any difference in nuclear composition and activity among cells; however, their cytoplasmic compositions begin to vary as the accumulation of contiguous cells alters the paths and rates of diffusion of metabolic products outward from the cells and of substrates inward from the environment. The environment of each specialized line of cells could be relatively constant if the cell lines became segregated into discrete masses, or tissues.

The development of tissues distinguishes plants and animals from protists, among which some metabolically specialized cells may arise in multicellular representatives, but these cells are not organized into tissues. Nevertheless, specialization of cells was a necessary evolutionary step preceding tissue differentiation, and the occurrence of metabolically specialized cells is evidence that protists (fungi and eucaryotic algae in particular) possess or have possessed the potential for producing descendants composed of differentiated tissues.

Most known mechanisms of differentiation do not imply that cell specialization should be limited to eucaryotic cells. Gene-gene and cytoplasm-gene interactions that are invoked to account for some differentiation also occur in bacteria; presumably they can occur in blue-green algae, as well.

Why, then, do multicellular procaryotic organisms not develop lines of metabolically specialized cells? Part of the answer may lie in the nuclear proteins of eucaryotic cells; the role of the proteins in differentiation may be underestimated at present. But part of the answer must lie in a difference between procaryotic and eucaryotic cells in their susceptibility to heritable loss of function. The initial advantage of subcellular compartmentalization was probably the greater independence of separate metabolic processes which allowed a more selective response by the cell to transient environmental changes favorable for one, but not another, process. A further, secondary, consequence of compartmentalization may have been increased difference in susceptibility of separate processes to inhibitory factors. Subsequently, specific functions could be lost independently—reversibly or permanently—and cells could thereby be specialized. Presumably, this also required genetic changes that directed orderly functional losses, and these changes could be expressed in the more highly organized eucaryotic protoplast, but not in a procaryotic cell.

Chapter 10

Fundamentals of Orderly Material Expansion

Definition and Description of Growth

Growth involves the removal of substances from the environment into the organism and their conversion into the specific substances of which the organism is composed. When these processes of uptake and conversion occur more rapidly than loss of substance to the environment, there is a net increase in mass of the organism. Increase in mass due solely to the uptake of water, which may be exchanged with the environment independently of other substances, is not considered growth. Water uptake does not result in an increase in the amount of substances peculiar to the organism. Accordingly, growth is defined as the aggregate of processes that results in an increase in the dry mass of an organism; it is an orderly material expansion of the living system.

The substances taken from the environment that are converted into cell components are designated **growth substrates.** The amount of growth is expressed as the net amount of dry mass synthesized; the rate of growth is expressed as the net amount of dry mass synthesized per unit time.

The synthesis of substances that contribute to the increase in dry mass occurs within cells. These substances may remain within the cell and become part of it; or they may be released by the cell and deposited on its surface; or, in multicellular organisms, they may be removed by a circulatory system to another site within the organism.

Quantitative studies of cellular processes are technically difficult because cells are so small that an individual growing cell cannot be weighed, nor can its constituents or individual processes be assayed. Quantitative chemical analyses and gravimetric measurements require much more material than is available in a single cell, and such determinations also involve destruction of the cells. Further, cells are responsive to environmental changes and dependent for their normal activities on the physical integrity of the cell membrane and the maintenance of internal organization. Any manipulation of cells could change their activities, permeability, or organization, thereby affecting the results of an assay. Consequently, the description of growth at the cellular level can be only as complete as techniques allow.

Of the various techniques available for quantitative study of growth within cells, synchronous cultivation (see Chap. 11) has proved especially valuable. This method provides a population of cells that reproduce more or less simultaneously, so that at any point in time, the majority of cells are at the same stage in the reproductive cycle. The population can be sufficiently large to allow the removal of a sample of a size suitable for assay without interrupting growth in the remaining cells. Assays of successive samples reveal changes in the population that can be interpreted relative to the average cell at successive points in its reproductive cycle.

Studies of synchronized populations have provided much of the information on which the following descriptions of cellular growth are based. Most such studies have employed cells that reproduce by binary fission. However, the generalizations seem relevant to growth of other types of cells, such as those that reproduce by budding and those that produce more than two progeny per reproductive event.

Growth of Eucaryotic Cells. The cell cycle of several types of eucaryotic cells is divisible into five periods, each characterized by the synthesis of particular cell constituents. The periods, which may overlap to some extent, are indicated in Table 10-1.

In synchronized eucaryotic cells, growth is discontinuous; most of the increase in dry mass occurs in the first half of the cell cycle (the G_1 period). Following this, most syntheses stop while DNA is synthesized during the S period. Since DNA accounts for only 2 to 5 per cent of the cell dry mass, only a small increase

TABLE 10-1.   Cell Cycle Periods Observed in a Variety of Eucaryotic Cells

Period	Approximate Duration as Proportion of the Entire Cell Cycle	Syntheses
G_1 (first growth period)	$<50\%$	Most of the RNA and protein
S (period of DNA synthesis)	ca. 20%	DNA (twofold increase)
G_2 (second growth period)	$<20\%$	Probably the precursors of structures for nuclear and cytoplasmic division
M (mitosis)	ca. 5%	None detectable; spindle (if formed) becomes visible
Fission	Variable	Cell wall, if formed

in mass occurs during the S period. Likewise, the amount of substance synthesized in the G_2 period is relatively small and apparently includes mainly those
cell components, such as precursors of the mitotic spindle, that function in
nuclear and in cytoplasmic division. Energy is produced and stored during this
period.

During the M period, synthetic activities are negligible. Apparently, the DNA
does not function in directing metabolic activities while undergoing either
replication or reorganization within the nucleus. During both the S and the
M periods, energy-yielding metabolic processes can continue, probably because
the catalysts and reactants are present and do not require continuous direction
from the nucleus. Since, in eucaryotic cells, these reactions occur in mitochondria, which contain some DNA, it is possible that mitochondria function largely
under their own direction, even when the nucleus is metabolically active.

The M period, during which nuclear division is completed, is followed in
most cells by subdivision of the protoplast into two units, each with one nucleus.
As cytoplasmic division proceeds, the nuclei become reorganized; in cells in
which the nuclear membrane disappears during mitosis, new nuclear membranes appear at this time.

The division of plant and many eucaryotic algal cells is completed by
construction of a cell plate across the equator of the cell perpendicular to the
axis along which the two daughter nuclei separate. The plate is synthesized
by endoplasmic reticulum that accumulates in the equatorial region; the new
cell wall is formed on the cell plate. Fission of naked (wall-less) cells results
from constriction of the cell at the equator, again, across the long axis of the
mitotic spindle. A peripheral furrow develops at the cell surface and deepens
until the cytoplasm has been separated into two uninucleate portions. As the
constriction is completed, the surface disjoins and the membrane of each new
protoplast closes over the area where separation occurred by apparently spontaneous fusion of the cell membrane.

The duration of a cell cycle under conditions optimal for cell reproduction
varies greatly among eucaryotic organisms. Plant and animal cells that can
be cultivated in the laboratory generally divide every 18 to 36 hours. The cell
cycles of uninucleate eucaryotic protistan cells that multiply by binary fission
vary in duration from about two hours to several days.

Growth of Bacterial Cells. Growth of procaryotic cells has been studied quantitatively in bacteria; relatively little information is available for blue-green
algae. Observations vary according to the method of study. Individual cells
whose growth and division were studied with the aid of an interference microscope, which allows calculation of the mass of a growing cell at intervals, were
observed to grow discontinuously. Most growth occurred within a fraction
of the time required for completion of the cell cycle; the position of the growth
period within the cycle and its duration varied with the incubation temperature.
Growth did not occur immediately around the time of cell division under any
conditions of incubation.

When populations of bacteria have been synchronized by any method other than mechanical selection of small cells by filtration, growth has been found to be discontinuous. Generally, RNA synthesis begins earlier in the cell cycle than other syntheses; protein synthesis begins soon after the amount of RNA has begun to increase; and DNA synthesis may occur in any part of the cycle or throughout the cycle.

In populations of one type of bacterium synchronized by selection of small cells by filtration, growth was continuous and autocatalytic. All syntheses occurred simultaneously and continuously, without a halt or detectable decrease in rate around the time of cell division, and the amount of cellular material synthesized in any short interval of time was proportional to the amount of material present at the beginning of the interval. The rates of all assayed syntheses continuously increased. Continuous growth has not been observed for other types of bacteria synchronized by the same method.

Generally, it seems that growth of procaryotic cells is discontinuous, as in eucaryotic cells. There is, however, one significant difference: RNA and protein synthesis can occur simultaneously with DNA synthesis in procaryotic cells, but not in eucaryotic cells. There is not a period within the procaryotic (bacterial) cell cycle equivalent to the S period of eucaryotic cycles. Presumably, because procaryotic DNA is not separated from the cytoplasm by a membrane, all areas of the DNA not actually undergoing replication can function in directing metabolism. Whether it is the eucaryotic nuclear membrane, intact during the S period whether or not it disintegrates during the M period, or the nucleoprotein itself that prevents DNA-cytoplasm interaction during the S period has not been determined.

The duration of cell cycles of synchronously dividing bacteria ranges from about 30 minutes to three or four hours. This is a second major difference between the cell cycles of bacterial and eucaryotic cells.

Relation to Reproduction

The amount of growth that is directly related to reproduction varies according to the morphology and life cycle of the organism. The life cycle comprises the events that occur between any point in the development of an individual and that same point in the development of its offspring. Maturity is the portion of the life cycle during which the organism is capable of reproduction.

Fission, cleavage, and budding are the basic mechanisms of reproduction in unicellular protists. They are summarized diagrammatically in Figure 10-1. The same basic mechanisms occur in multicellular protists within the cells specialized for reproduction or for gamete formation. A reproductive cell may release a succession of buds, may undergo binary or multiple fission before or shortly after release from the multicellular unit, or may undergo cleavage and release a large number of propagative units.

Reproduction by Fission of Unicellular Individuals. In unicellular organisms that reproduce by fission (binary or multiple), the entire mass of the protoplast is consumed in the formation of the next generation. This type of life cycle does not allow simultaneous existence of parent and offspring and is considered relatively primitive.

Most unicellular protists that reproduce by fission attain a maximum size, characteristic of the organism in a given environment, during each reproductive cycle. Growth halts and fission occurs in each individual when it attains that size. A constant number of progeny results from each reproductive event. In some unicellular protists, most of which are algae, reproduction apparently is initiated in response to environmental factors, rather than to size of the

Fission
------

1. Binary

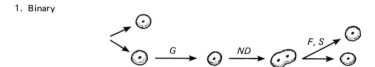

2. Multiple

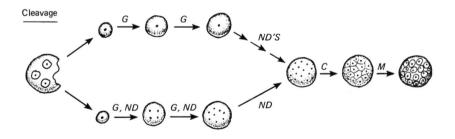

Cleavage

Budding

Basic reproductive mechanisms in protists. *G*, growth; *ND*, nuclear division; *F*, fission; *C*,   **Figure 10-1** cleavage; *M*, maturation; *S*, separation.

organism. The initial size of progeny is constant; consequently, the number of progeny produced per reproductive event is proportional to the size of the parent at the time of reproduction.

Reproduction via Specialized Propagative Units. Most multicellular and coenocytic protists reproduce by production of cells specialized for propagation. Only a fraction of the substance of the parent organism is consumed in the formation of progeny, and parent and offspring may exist as contemporaries.

The propagative units are typically produced in one portion of the organism, commonly by modification of individual vegetative cells. Modification may involve release of the protoplast of a growing cell from the multicellular organism, morphogenesis of the protoplast into a disseminative unit by formation of flagella or of a relatively thick wall, or subdivision of the protoplast into two or more units. Generally in these cases, growth is completed before reproduction is initiated. Reproduction is often accompanied by the accumulation, in the modified cells, of greater amounts of reserve foods than are found in growing cells.

Subdivision of the protoplast may occur by either of two mechanisms—successive fissions or progressive cleavage. These processes involve only the protoplast, not the cell wall (if present). Both generally result in uninucleate propagative units.

1. Successive fissions begin with fission of the protoplast into two units; then each of these undergoes binary fission. The number of protoplasts produced varies with the organism (usually uniform within a species), but the final number in all cases is a power of two (2, 4, 8, 16, 32 . . .). In some organisms, nuclear division occurs between each fission, and any one protoplast contains only one or two nuclei. In others, several nuclear divisions occur before cytoplasmic fission of the multinucleate protoplast begins.

2. Progressive cleavage of the protoplast may occur by elaboration of new cell membranes from the parent cell's membrane, by formation within the cytoplasm of unconnected membranes that develop into cell membranes, or, most commonly, by the appearance and elaboration of membrane systems that initially bound small vacuoles. This last process, called vacuolization, results in multiple subdivision of the cytoplasm by coalescence of the vacuoles, forming independent, membrane-bounded, uninucleate units. When cytoplasmic subdivision occurs by progressive cleavage, the protoplast is initially multinucleate, and further nuclear divisions do not occur during cleavage. In some protists, individual cells are multinucleate during growth; as a vegetative cell of this type of organism begins to develop into a reproductive cell, a wave of nuclear divisions often occurs as a first step in reproduction. In other protists, individual cells are uninucleate during growth; several generations of nuclei are produced shortly before cleavage begins.

When the propagative units are flagellated, the flagella appear only in the cells that result from the last fission or that appear when cleavage is completed. Similarly, when the propagative units possess cell walls, intermediate generations generally are naked, and walls are constructed only on the cells that will be released from the reproductive structure. From these observations, it can be inferred that certain synthetic activities occur late in the reproductive process.

Reproduction by Budding. A cell that will reproduce by budding first grows to the maximum size characteristic of the organism under a given set of conditions. Thereafter, practically all of its increase in mass reflects synthesis of constituents that will be inherited by daughter cells. On the surface of a parent cell, newly synthesized components are organized to form the incipient progeny (the bud). The bud increases in mass from nil to approximately that of the parent cell. It then separates from the parent. In budding yeasts, the parent cell and bud usually remain attached to each other until the bud is fully grown and both cells are about to repeat the budding process; at that time, they separate, resume growth, and release the next generation at about the same time. In most other budding protists, the bud is smaller than the parent cell at the time of separation. Because this bud grows for a while before reproducing, the subsequent generation is not produced synchronously from parent and bud.

Mechanism

Growth processes are chemical reactions catalyzed by enzymes and regulated by nucleic acids and by reactants, products, and cofactors of the reactions. All known enzymes are proteins. They are highly specific for the reactions they catalyze.

An enzyme functions by associating with its substrate, a reactant molecule. While associated with the enzyme, the substrate molecule loses or gains a subgroup (which may be an electron or pair of electrons, an atom, or a group of atoms); it is split into more than one molecule; or a bond or group of atoms within it undergoes rearrangement. The enzyme then dissociates from the altered molecule(s), which is the product. A different substrate or an enzyme cofactor may donate or receive a subgroup moved by the enzyme.

A law of thermodynamics states that the formation of an ordered system requires energy. Since living systems are more highly ordered than their environments, it follows that their expansion (growth), which occurs by conversion of environmental substances into systemic components, should require energy. Among growth processes, it is particularly those reactions whose products are or are built into cell components that require energy. Energy, like the substrates for growth, is obtained from the environment. Photosynthetic organisms utilize radiant energy (light); chemosynthetic organisms utilize chemical energy in matter. Energy from both sources is converted to a form that can be utilized in synthetic reactions. Generally, it is stored in high energy phosphate bonds within specific molecules; e.g., at least some of the energy in every type of living cell is stored in the nucleotide adenosine triphosphate (ATP), which is formed in an energy-consuming reaction between adenosine diphosphate (ADP) and inorganic phosphate.

The production and consumption of energy are controlled and balanced by regulatory processes. Some regulation involves interaction between an enzyme and its product. Other regulation involves substances produced within the cell specifically to interact with participants in the reactions, either to stimulate or to inhibit the occurrence of particular reactions.

The sum of all enzyme-catalyzed reactions and regulatory processes is called **metabolism.** Assimilatory metabolism comprises those reactions by which growth substrates are converted to cell components. Dissimilatory metabolism comprises those reactions by which energy is obtained from environmental substances. Regulatory metabolism includes a variety of mechanisms by which synthetic reactions are directed toward the synthesis of particular amounts of the specific cell components, and energy production is balanced with the needs of the cell (for motion as well as for assimilatory processes). All aspects of metabolism occur simultaneously within a growing cell.

Assimilatory Metabolism. The specific substances that can serve as growth substrates vary among organisms, but they are similar in composition to the extent that they must provide all the chemical elements of which the organism is composed. For living organisms generally, the following elements must be available in substrates, since they are present in protoplasm: C, H, O, N, S, P, K, Mg, Ca, Fe, Cl, and I (not bacteria); and trace metals such as Mo, Cu, Zn, and Co, which may vary among organisms. The substrates taken from the environment are converted to intermediate substances that serve as the reactants in synthetic reactions.

Dissimilatory Metabolism. Substrates of dissimilatory reactions are oxidized[1] and may thereby be converted to intermediates that can enter assimilatory processes. The more important products of the oxidation reactions, however, are the electrons released from the oxidized substrates. The transfer of these electrons among electron-transport molecules produced by the cell is accompanied by a change in the potential energy of the transport molecules as they are reduced and then reoxidized. Formation of substances such as ATP consumes and thereby stores for synthetic reactions some of the energy released during electron-transport reactions.

In all major groups of organisms (although not in every species of all groups), a series of iron-containing enzymes constitutes the electron-transport system. The iron atoms alternate between the ferric ($+3$; oxidized) and ferrous ($+2$; reduced) states as electrons are transported through the series of enzymes. Such a series is called a **respiratory chain.** The final electron acceptor is usually O_2, which is reduced to H_2O as the terminal step in respiration. This reaction is the basis for the requirement of the majority of living systems for O_2; when O_2 is not available, the transport molecules rapidly accumulate in the reduced state, and energy-yielding metabolism ceases.

---

[1]The term "oxidation" refers to the loss of one or more electrons by an atom or molecule. In biochemical oxidations, the electrons are usually accepted by an organic molecule or a metal atom complexed with an organic molecule; O_2 accepts electrons in only a few cases.

Substances other than O_2 can serve as terminal electron acceptors for some protists (notably certain yeasts and bacteria). Nitrate or sulfate may replace O_2 at the end of a respiratory chain; the reduced products, typically N_2 and sulfide, respectively, are excreted. This process is called anaerobic respiration. Fermentative metabolism does not involve a respiratory chain; electrons are shifted among organic molecules other than iron-containing enzymes. Although the fermentative type of energy metabolism allows some organisms to grow in the absence of O_2 (anaerobically), the energy yield is lower than that from respiratory metabolism. Fermentative organisms excrete reduced (energy-containing) organic molecules, e.g., alcohols and organic acids; the fermentation products are characteristic of the metabolism of the organism.

Photosynthesis is similar to respiration in that ATP is formed at the expense of energy released by transfer of electrons through a series of iron-containing enzymes. It differs from respiration by the use of light energy to excite (increase the potential energy of) the electrons while they are in chlorophyll molecules, before they are transported through the iron-enzyme system. The source of electrons for O_2-evolving photosynthesis is water; the O_2 arises as a by-product from the oxidation of H_2O. The source of electrons for non-O_2-evolving photosynthesis may be an organic compound, H_2, or a sulfur atom.

Regulatory Metabolism. This aspect of metabolism comprises a variety of processes that differ in mechanism. A certain minimum of regulation is inherent in the requirement of most synthetic reactions for a supply of energy. Similarly, any reaction in which metabolic intermediates (**metabolites**) are reactants depends on the occurrence of other reactions for a supply of reactants.

The synthesis of enzymatically active proteins is believed to be dependent on a continual supply of RNA molecules produced in the nucleoplasm. The linear order of the subunits of these molecules is believed to be determined by the linear order of the subunits of nuclear DNA. The RNA molecules are called messengers, because they supposedly carry information from genetic material to the cytoplasm, where the information is expressed in biochemical reactions. A messenger molecule associates with ribosomes in a polyribosome. At the polyribosome surface, amino acids are polymerized into a polypeptide in an order determined by the order of subunits in the messenger. The completed polypeptide is released from the ribosomes and assumes its function in the cell; in some instances, it may be assembled with other polypeptides to form catalytically active protein. This is a primary regulatory step that is directly influenced by the nucleoplasm and results in the synthesis of the catalysts.[2]

Enzyme synthesis is further regulated by the composition of the cytoplasm, which in turn may be modified by the environment. Certain synthetic enzymes

[2]This is a current theoretic interpretation of the mechanism of the expression of genes that direct the synthesis of enzymes. Predictions derived from it have not yet been found to disagree with observations, and some of its predictions seem to explain adequately various aspects of regulatory metabolism (including the synthesis of proteins that are not enzymes). See, for example, the following paragraph.

are not synthesized when their products are available from the environment; this phenomenon is called enzyme repression. Certain dissimilatory enzymes are synthesized only when their substrates are available from the environment; this phenomenon is called enzyme induction. A single hypothetic mechanism has been proposed to account for these two effects of the environment on enzyme synthesis, as follows. A repressor substance prevents expression of the gene carrying the information for synthesis of a given enzyme by preventing messenger RNA synthesis at that portion of the nuclear DNA. This repressor is identical with or derived from the environmental substance in enzyme repression; in enzyme induction, the repressor is produced by the cell (in the nucleus) and is inactivated by the environmental substance, the inducer.

Catalytic activity, as well as synthesis, of an enzyme is subject to regulation. When a product of the reaction catalyzed by an enzyme is not utilized or excreted, it may accumulate to a level that inhibits the activity of the enzyme. Also, when the final product of a chain of reactions accumulates, that product may inhibit activity of one or more of the enzymes in the sequence and thereby halt its own production. In some instances, enzymes are inhibited by substances quite different chemically from their substrates or products; apparently, these inhibitors react with the enzymes and alter their structure and hence their ability to associate with their substrates.

Another type of regulation is called coupling. The mechanism has not yet been elucidated; the phenomenon is observed as an otherwise unexplained requirement of either of two processes for the simultaneous occurrence of the other. There is also a constant quantitative relationship (for any given organism) between the two processes. For example, transfer of electrons through a respiratory chain is coupled to formation of ATP from ADP and phosphate. Electron transport ceases when phosphate is unavailable for formation of ATP. When both processes are operative, the ratio of moles of ATP formed to moles of O_2 consumed is constant.

Nutrition

The natural distribution of an organism and its ability to adapt to environmental changes are determined to a considerable extent by the types of substances it can utilize as food. Foods serve as the sources of elements and may also serve as energy sources. Any one organism can utilize only a limited number of substances as foods, and those particular substances must be available from the environment in order for the organism to grow and reproduce.

Nutrition is the sum of the processes by which an organism takes up foods from the environment and utilizes them for growth. Because carbon accounts for approximately 50 per cent of the dry mass of most organisms and is present in all the major constituents of cells, the type of substance an organism can utilize as a carbon source is an important nutritional characteristic. A second major nutritional characteristic is the manner in which an organism obtains energy for growth. These two characteristics, in combination, are used to distinguish four nutritional categories (Table 10-2).

Certain types of organisms exhibit different nutritional properties in different environments; such organisms are designated facultative. Thus, algae whose distribution implies that they grow in nature as photolithotrophs may grow in the laboratory as photolithotrophs and facultatively as chemoorganotrophs. Similarly, some bacteria that occur naturally in environments that support the growth of chemoorganotrophs may grow in the laboratory as chemoorganotrophs and facultatively as chemolithotrophs.

Fungi, protozoa, animals, and many bacteria can grow only as chemoorganotrophs. Generally, their nutrition is strictly organotrophic; only organic compounds can be oxidized as sources of energy or assimilated as sources of carbon. They are ultimately dependent on the metabolic activities of lithotrophs, which produce organic compounds from CO_2. Without biologic conversion of CO_2 to organic carbon, terrestrial carbon would accumulate as CO_2 and carbonates as a consequence of biologic and chemical oxidations. For this reason, organotrophs are sometimes referred to as heterotrophs, and the relatively independent lithotrophs as autotrophs.

Among lithotrophs, the photolithotrophs provide far larger quantities of organic material than do the chemolithotrophs. More importantly, they convert radiant energy from sunlight into chemical energy and thereby increase the amount of chemical energy on earth.

Among organotrophs, some can utilize only a few specific compounds or only one type of organic compound, whereas others can use any one of more than 20 different compounds. Two types of compounds are utilized by a wide variety of protists—carbohydrates and organic acids. Such compounds contain hydrogen and oxygen as well as carbon, and one compound can serve as a source of all three elements. Much of the H and O can also be obtained from water, which is a reactant in many metabolic reactions. Generally, a carbohydrate or acid that can be assimilated can also be oxidized as a source of energy; some of the carbon is eventually excreted as CO_2, the remainder being incorporated into cell constituents. A smaller number of organotrophs can utilize

TABLE 10-2. Nutritional Categories

Type of Nutrition	Principal Source of Energy for Growth	Principal Source of Carbon for Growth	Occurrence
Photolithotrophic	Light	CO_2	Plants, most algae, some bacteria
Photoorganotrophic	Light	Organic compounds	Some algae, some bacteria
Chemolithotrophic	Oxidation of inorganic compounds	CO_2	Some bacteria
Chemoorganotrophic*	Oxidation of organic compounds	Organic compounds	Animals, fungi, protozoa, most bacteria

*In saprophytic (or saprozoic) nutrition, inanimate materials are utilized; in parasitic and predatory nutrition, some or all of the materials utilized are animate.

compounds such as alcohols, aromatic compounds, hydrocarbons, or complex polymers such as pectin, chitin, cellulose, and lignin. Fungi and bacteria are particularly omnivorous and as a group can utilize for growth every known naturally occurring organic compound.

Elements other than carbon, hydrogen, and oxygen are obtained from the environment in a smaller number of sources. Nitrogen may be obtained from ammonia, nitrates (rarely nitrites), or atmospheric nitrogen (N_2) as inorganic sources; many organotrophs, particularly protozoa, can utilize only amino acids as nitrogen sources. Sulfur is assimilated either from sulfate or from organic compounds, particularly sulfur-containing amino acids, or, in a few instances, from sulfide. Phosphorus is generally obtained as inorganic phosphate; organic phosphates also can be utilized by many organisms. Most of the other elements present in protoplasm are assimilated in ionic form from inorganic salts.

Many organisms also require one or more specific organic compounds that they utilize unchanged in their metabolism. Such compounds are required in much smaller amounts than are sources of C, N, and S, and they are referred to as **micronutrients.** Micronutrients include amino acids, nucleic acid precursors, and vitamins the organism cannot synthesize, but that are essential for its synthesis of macromolecules or for specific metabolic reactions.

Micronutrient requirements among protists have been established for many microscopic organisms, but not as yet for a significant number of macroscopic types. Three vitamins—vitamin B_{12}, biotin, and thiamine—are commonly required by eucaryotic microprotists, which do not require other types of organic micronutrients. (Micronutrient requirements of bacteria that need only one or a few such substances are more diverse.) A requirement for B_{12} is particularly common among algae, especially marine representatives; B_{12} is often the only organic micronutrient required by such organisms. Among unicellular flagellates, particularly algae that have colorless counterparts and their colorless relatives, thiamine is often the only vitamin required; some of these organisms also require B_{12}. Among protozoa,[3] only certain small amebae are known to require vitamin B_{12}. Most protozoa with relatively simple micronutrient requirements need thiamine, and some also require biotin. Vitamin-requiring lower fungi usually need thiamine and/or biotin. The widespread occurrence of requirements for these three vitamins implies that they are available in many natural habitats, and that ability to synthesize them is less important to survival than is the ability to synthesize other cofactors.

Organisms that require numerous micronutrients are referred to as nutritionally dependent (on specific cofactor syntheses by other organisms), exacting, or fastidious. Most fastidious protists are bacteria, fungi, or protozoa that occur naturally only as parasites (especially of animals), as saprophytes in rich organic environments such as milk, or as predators. Because their hosts, substrates, or prey contain a variety of micronutrients, these protists have been able to survive without the ability to synthesize many of each of the types of organic micronutrients essential for their development.

[3]The nutritional requirements of most protozoa are satisfied only by foods of complicated, largely undetermined composition.

Chapter 11

Laboratory Cultivation

Isolation of Pure Populations

For most microbiologic investigations, whether of the physiology and growth, life cycle, genetics, specific metabolic properties, or role in disease of a given protist, it is necessary that a genetically homogeneous population of the organism be available. Genetic homogeneity, or purity, is presumed when the entire population has descended by asexual reproduction from a single individual. Such **pure cultures** of protists are usually established by isolation of an individual in an otherwise protist-free environment where it grows and reproduces.

Isolation by Manipulation of Individuals. Individual cells of algae and protozoa, pieces of algal and fungal filaments, or spores of fungi can be removed from natural materials, such as water, mud, rotting vegetation, and soil suspensions, with the aid of small instruments and a low power microscope. The material is placed in a shallow glass dish (a watch glass or a Petri plate) and observed through the microscope. Filaments can be removed from the material with forceps, and single cells or spores with capillary pipettes. At the moment the observer removes the organism from the natural material, he will (if dextrous) have isolated the organism from other large protists. However, smaller organisms, especially bacteria that are not visible under a low power microscope, may still be present. To eliminate these, the filament or cell is placed in sterile water or a salt solution, moved about, and then picked up again. This is repeated several times before the cell or filament is placed in or on a growth medium.

This technique has been used for decades to obtain isolates of algae, fungi, and protozoa. It has been improved lately by the addition of antibiotics and sometimes detergents to washing fluids and growth medium. These agents

111

kill or prevent the growth of bacteria that often adhere to other protists too tightly for removal by rinsing.

Enrichment Cultivation. The isolation of bacteria usually involves a preliminary step, called enrichment cultivation. This step increases the proportion of the desired bacteria in the population present in the natural material. The technique, which is an application of the theory of natural selection, was devised around the turn of the twentieth century by Winogradsky and by Beijerinck. It has also been used to some extent in the isolation of other protists, especially algae and yeasts.

Three ingredients make a successful enrichment culture:

1. A sample of natural material that contains the organism sought. The higher the proportion of the organism in the natural population, the better the chance of enrichment to a level that allows isolation.

2. A chemical environment (the enrichment medium) especially suitable for multiplication of the desired organism. The medium should not favor or, if possible, should inhibit the multiplication of other types of protists present.

3. Physical conditions of incubation that also selectively favor multiplication of the desired organism.

A minimum knowledge of the physiologic properties of the organism is necessary for preparation of an enrichment culture. Some properties can be inferred from the distribution of the organism in nature, since its various habitats will usually be alike with respect to types of nutrients, illumination, pH, O_2 tension, and temperature. Each of these factors should be simulated in the enrichment culture. The technique is also suitable for the isolation of bacteria of particular physiologic properties—whether or not the investigator knows in advance that such organisms exist.

Examples of enrichment cultivation of bacteria and algae are presented in Table 11-1. In each case, the natural material is placed in the liquid enrichment medium; the mixture is incubated under the specified conditions and observed microscopically (if the organism can be recognized by morphologic traits) for the appearance of significant numbers of the desired organism. When a level suitable for isolation (preferably, predominance) has been attained, a sample of the culture is removed to an isolation medium. If an increase in proportion of the desired organism has occurred, but the proportion is still too low to allow isolation, a sample may first be removed to a second enrichment culture, where the environment is the same as in the first culture.

A few enrichment procedures depend on selective attachment of organisms to non-living substrates, rather than on general physiologic properties. Such a technique is used, for example, in the isolation of water molds (Phycomycetes; see Chap. 14). A sample of water serves as the natural material and as enrichment medium; to the water are added boiled hemp seeds or dead houseflies. The water molds grow attached to such substrates and appear as fine filaments on the seeds or flies. The filaments are removed with forceps as in direct manipulation isolation procedures, or their spores may be collected in a capillary pipette.

TABLE 11-1. Conditions for Enrichment Cultivation of Some Bacteria and Algae

Inoculum	Medium	Atmosphere	Temperature	pH	Organisms Enriched
A. Phototrophs (cultures illuminated)					
1. Pond water	ss1,* NaCl	Air, 5% CO_2	25° C	6-8	N_2-utilizing blue-green algae
2. Pond water	ss1, NaCl and NaNO$_3$	Air, 5% CO_2	25° C	6-8	Green algae
3. Pond water or mud	ss1, NaCl, NH$_4$Cl, Na-malate,† and y.e.	Anaerobic	25° C	7-7.5	Photoorganotrophic bacteria
B. Chemolithotrophs					
1. Soil or mud	ss1, NH$_4$Cl, and Na$_2$S$_2$O$_3$	Air	25° C	4-7	Sulfate-forming bacteria
2. Soil or water	ss1, NH$_4$ Cl, and CaCO$_3$	Air	25° C	8.5	Ammonia-oxidizing bacteria
C. Chemoorganotrophs					
1. Steamed soil or ensilage	y.e.ss*	Air	55°-60° C	7	Thermophilic spore-forming bacteria
2. Plant materials or milk	y.e.ss and glucose	Anaerobic	30° C	4-6	Lactic acid-forming bacteria
3. Sewage	y.e.ss, CaCO$_3$, and glucose	Air or anaerobic	30° C	7	Coliform bacteria
4. Fruits, unpasteurized beer	y.e.ss and ethanol	Air	30° C	6	Acetic acid-forming bacteria
5. Marine mud	ss2, NH$_4$Cl, and Na-lactate,† in sea water	Anaerobic	30°-50° C	7	Marine sulfate-reducing bacteria
6. Crushed legume nodules	y.e.ss, NaCl, CaCO$_3$ and mannitol	Air	25° C	6.5	Symbiotic N_2-utilizing bacteria

*The salts solutions ("ss") contain:
ss1—MgSO$_4$, K$_2$HPO$_4$, FeSO$_4$, CaCl$_2$, MnCl$_2$, NaMoO$_4$; similar concentrations can be used for the organisms indicated.
ss2—MgSO$_4$, K$_2$HPO$_4$, Fe(NH$_4$)$_2$(SO$_4$)$_2$; CaCl$_2$, Na$_2$SO$_4$.
y.e.ss—yeast extract, MgSO$_4$, K$_2$HPO$_4$.
†Malate and lactate are salts of non-nitrogenous organic acids (malic and lactic, respectively).

Final Steps. The final steps in the isolation of microscopic protists usually employ a nutrient medium solidified as a gel. The gelling substance most commonly used is agar,[1] a substance that is extracted from certain red algae and is neither inhibitory for nor digestible by most protists.[2] A few protists can digest agar, and a few others are inhibited by it. The latter types are cultivated on media solidified with silica. The advantage of solidified media is that they allow physical separation of individual cells, which then multiply in a small area free of other organisms.

Aerobic organisms are usually inoculated onto the surface of the solidified medium by a procedure called streaking;[3] this technique, illustrated in Figure 11-1A, results in dilution of the cells over the surface of the medium so that only the predominant organisms are deposited and isolated toward the end of the streak. Anaerobes, whose development is enhanced by or dependent on the exclusion of air (O_2) from the culture, may be suspended in agar-containing medium that has been melted and cooled to ca. 50°C. The suspension is diluted by transfer of a portion of the mixture to another tube of molten, sterile medium; this is repeated through several successive dilution steps. Toward the end of the dilution series, the cells are suspended in isolation from each other and remain in position when the medium solidifies upon cooling to less than 42°C (see "shake" cultures, Fig. 11-1B).

The composition of the solidified medium is usually the same as that of the enrichment medium, since it has already proved suitable for growth of the desired organism. The composition of the medium used in a direct isolation procedure is based, like that of enrichment media, on the expected or desired physiologic properties of the organism sought.

The solidified medium that has been inoculated either directly from natural material or from an enrichment culture is then incubated. During incubation, the organisms grow and multiply in their isolated positions and eventually accumulate as macroscopic masses of distinctive form and color. Such masses are called **colonies** (see Fig. 11-2); if accumulation ceases when the mass is visible only in a microscope, the mass is called a microcolony. The majority of isolated colonies will arise from individual cells and so constitute clones, the genetically homogeneous populations that have been the goal of the procedure. A population derived from a clone and carried through subsequent cultures is referred to as a strain or isolate.

A mixture of colony types usually appears in the first culture on solidified medium. Pure cultures are obtained by removing some cells from an isolated colony and repeating the streaking or "shake" dilution steps. This is repeated

---

[1]Agar is routinely used at 1 to 2 per cent (w/v). An aqueous suspension of agar becomes liquid at 100°C and gels as the medium is cooled to ca. 42°C. Once gelled, the medium becomes liquid again only when rewarmed to 100°C.

[2]Agar itself is usually inert to protists, but most commercial preparations are not pure. A 2 per cent (w/v) suspension of a typical commercial preparation of agar in distilled water also contains, per liter: 120 mg Ca, 24 mg Mg, 20 mg Na, 8 mg P, 3.8 mg Al, 2.6 mg B, 2 mg Fe, and 0.08 mg Cu, but not any detectable amounts of K or Mn.

[3]This is the procedure devised by R. Koch in the 1870's; see Chap. 3.

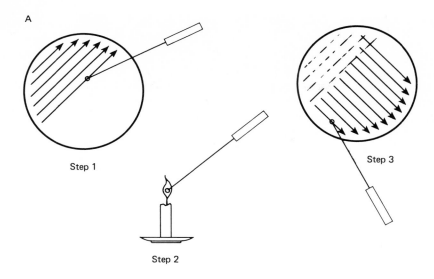

A

Step 1

Step 2

Step 3

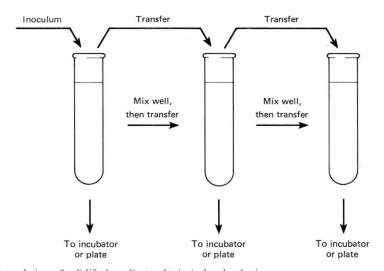

B

Inoculum   Transfer   Transfer

Mix well,   Mix well,
then transfer   then transfer

To incubator   To incubator   To incubator
or plate   or plate   or plate

Inoculation of solidified media to obtain isolated colonies.

Figure 11-1

  A. Streaking (see Fig. 11-2*A*).

  Step 1. A sample of microbes (the **inoculum**) is picked up with a sterile inoculating loop (a wire of platinum or nickel-chromium alloy, mounted in a heat-resistant handle) and spread over a small area of the medium in the Petri plate.

  Step 2. The loop is sterilized by being heated red hot in a flame.

  Step 3. The inoculum is spread over the remainder of the plate by drawing the cooled, sterilized loop across part of the inoculated area, then streaking in a single direction in each parallel line.

  B. Shake cultures and poured plates (see Fig. 11-2*B*). The medium contains a solidifying agent, but is molten during inoculation. Inoculation and transfer may be made with an inoculating loop or a pipette. The instrument must be sterile for each transfer. The tubes may be incubated, or the contents of each may be poured into a Petri plate to solidify.

115

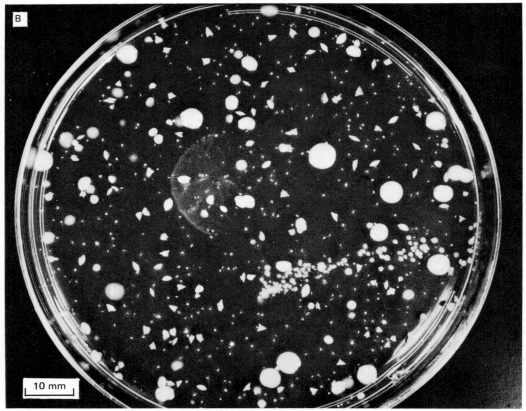

Figure 11-2 Appearance of isolated bacterial colonies. *A.* A streaked plate. (From Canale-Parola, E., S. L. Rosenthal, and D. G. Kupfer, 1966. *Antonie van Leeuwenhoek J. Microbiol. Serol.,* **32**:113. By permission of the Nederlander Vereniging von Microbiologie.) *B.* A poured plate. (From Stedham, M. A., D. C. Kelley, and E. H. Coles, 1966. *Appl. Microbiol.,* **14**:525. By permission of the American Society for Microbiology.)

as many times as necessary to obtain a culture containing only one type of colony, and usually at least two more times to ensure purity.

Predators and Parasites. The techniques outlined above are suitable for isolation of protists that can exist as free-living organisms and are capable of growing at the expense of dissolved nutrients. They are used successfully for the majority of microscopic algae (including colorless counterparts), fungi, and bacteria, but are of only limited use for protozoa. Certain modifications are necessary for the cultivation of protozoa that require particulate foods. In some cases, this requirement can be met by providing killed yeast or bacterial cells or finely chopped meats as the principal foods and other nutrients in soluble form. Most protozoa, however, have not yet been cultivated in axenic (without foreigners) cultures; a few can be grown in monoxenic (one foreigner, which is eaten) cultures. Preparation of the latter type requires determination of a suitable food organism, which is then added to a population of the protozoa as the sole organic nutrient or in addition to soluble nutrients. Certain algae, yeasts, and bacteria are commonly used; a few protozoa thrive only on other protozoa.

The isolation of parasitic microorganisms is usually more readily accomplished by inoculating natural material into a healthy host, which may be an individual of the natural host group or an organism sufficiently closely related to the natural host that the parasite can multiply in it. Natural hosts can often be used for cultivation of parasites of plants and protists, but the maintenance of a variety of healthy animal hosts is often too expensive (in feed, space, and time required to care for them and their quarters). For this reason, a standard group of animal hosts may be maintained in a laboratory for the purpose of isolating or maintaining populations of parasites. Hosts that may be used include pure cultures of animal cells maintained by methods similar to those used for maintenance of free-living microbes (malignant cells are particularly suitable for artificial cultivation), embryonated chicken eggs, mice, rats, chickens, hamsters, guinea pigs, rabbits, and human volunteers. The use of living hosts is particularly important in the cultivation of disease-producing (pathogenic) parasites, because their ability to cause disease may be altered (usually diminished or lost) by cultivation in artificial media.

Pure Cultures

Maintenance. The maintenance of pure cultures of protists requires exclusion of all other viable protists from the culture media and vessels and from equipment used to manipulate the pure populations. Bacteria and fungi (molds) are particularly difficult to exclude, because they or their spores are universally present in air and on all surfaces exposed to air and can be expected in all waters and almost all chemicals used in the preparation of media.

Accordingly, the autoclave is standard equipment in microbiology laboratories. An autoclave is a pressure chamber to which steam is admitted; as the pressure in the autoclave increases due to admission of steam to a chamber of constant volume, the temperature of the steam rises. Materials to be **sterilized** (rid of viable protists) are placed in the autoclave and heated to 121° C for 15 minutes. This is sufficient to kill the most heat-resistant protists, bacterial endospores. Dry heat can also be used; however, it is less efficient than moist heat, and 180° C for three hours is the minimum dry heating sufficient to sterilize. Heat-labile materials must be sterilized by other methods such as microfiltration for liquids and gases, ultraviolet irradiation for surfaces, or exposure to noxious gases such as ethylene oxide for surfaces or open vessels.

Aseptic techniques comprise all manipulations of sterile materials or pure populations of protists that prevent microbial contamination—the entry into the materials or cultures of extraneous microorganisms. The most common source of contaminants is air, which cannot be excluded from cultures opened for inoculation, sampling, or other manipulations. However, the microbial content of air is proportional to the amount of dust it carries; its role as a source of contamination is reduced by antidust house(lab)keeping practices. Any other non-sterile material with which a culture or a sterilized preparation comes in contact can also be expected to provide contaminants. Asepsis, as a laboratory (or surgical or industrial) practice, requires constant avoidance of physical contact between sources of contaminants and contaminable preparations; this practice is better demonstrated with regard to specific manipulations than described further in general. The reader is referred to a laboratory manual in microbiology or to a demonstrator, if available.

Media. A **nutrient medium** is a preparation of chemicals that contains all the substances other than gases that are necessary for growth and multiplication of the organism to be cultivated. The medium may contain exclusively chemically identified substances in known amounts ("defined" medium), or it may contain substances of unknown composition ("complex" medium). In either case, the concentrations of nutrients, the osmotic strength, and the pH must be suitable for development of the organism.

Complex media usually contain extracts or digests of natural materials such as soil, plants, meats, yeast cells, or proteins from milk or plants. Some of these preparations are available commercially in dehydrated form (as peptones, tryptones, casein hydrolysates, casamino acids, meat extract, yeast extract, and others). Although their chemical composition is not fully known, they are usually of consistent quality and composition, and media prepared with them are reproducible. Complex media are particularly useful for cultivation of organisms with multiple or unknown nutritional requirements, as general media for maintenance of culture collections that include organisms with different nutritional requirements, and, for reasons of economy, for large-scale cultivation of protists in industrial processes.

Defined media are used in studies of nutrition, metabolism, morphogenesis, and genetics. A defined medium usually contains known amounts of the sources of carbon, nitrogen, sulfur, and phosphorus, of a few inorganic salts, and of micronutrients; some elements, particularly metals, that are required in trace amounts may be present in determinable (though usually undetermined) amounts as contaminants of known constituents.

Seven examples of defined media and the microorganisms that can be cultivated in them are listed in Table 11-2. The preparation of such media is more complicated than the preparation of complex media, and the design of a suitable defined medium for a particular isolate may require months of trials with a variety of empirically designed nutrient mixtures. One difficulty often encountered is that relative amounts of certain nutrients, e.g., amino acids for protozoa and cations for algae, influence the availability of other nutrients for the organism's growth. In such cases, defined mixtures (called "cocktails" by microbiologists) may be added, rather than individual nutrients, to determine whether growth is enhanced.

A simple test of the suitability of a medium that supports measurable growth is afforded by microscopic examination of the culture. If development is normal, the morphology of the cells will be as uniform as can be expected according to their life cycle; this implies that the medium contains all necessary nutrients in suitable proportions. If the cells are growing, but conditions are not optimal, irregular forms (e.g., unusually long or flexible cells, swollen cells, lysed cells, cells in clumps or chains not seen in natural populations, algal cells with little if any chlorophyll, amebae without pseudopodia) will be present in unusually high proportion.

Incubation. The general conditions of incubation are as important to the cultivation of microorganisms as is the composition of the medium. Three factors affect the growth of most microbial cultures: wavelength and intensity of light; tensions of specific gases in the atmosphere; and temperature.

For photosynthetic development generally, either daylight or, more commonly, light from artificial lamps is used to illuminate the cultures; that is, the entire visible spectrum and some ultraviolet and infrared light are provided. However, not all the light provided can be used by a given type of phototroph. The organism must be able to absorb the light and use it to excite electrons within the chlorophyll molecules. The wavelengths that are utilizable depend on the type of chlorophyll synthesized by the organism. One chlorophyll (chlorophyll a) is common to algae and plants; it absorbs red light of 650 to 700 nm wavelength. Bacteriochlorophylls c and d, present as the principal photosynthetic pigments in green photosynthetic bacteria, absorb red light of 750 to 800 nm. Bacteriochlorophylls a and b, the principal photosynthetic pigments of all photosynthetic bacteria other than the green types, absorb infrared light of 875 to 925 nm and ca. 1030 nm, respectively. Light absorbed by some of the other pigments (carotenoids and minor chlorophylls) present in photosynthetic organelles can also be used in photosynthesis.

The intensity of light also affects the rate of photosynthesis. The rate of bacterial photosynthesis generally increases with light intensity to levels at which the heat produced by the light source begins to inhibit growth. For any given alga, there is typically an optimal intensity, above and below which photosynthesis is slower or less efficient in terms of ATP formed per unit of light energy available.

The growth of non-photosynthetic organisms may also be affected by light. Pigmented organisms generally are indifferent or relatively insensitive to light,

(Medium Constituents Given in Amount per Liter)

Brevibacterium*

20 g	glucose
40 g	alanine
7 g	K_2HPO_4
3 g	KH_2PO_4
0.2 g	$MgSO_4 \cdot 7H_2O$

Tetrahymena†

2.5 g	glucose
1.0 g	Na-acetate
0.7 g	Tween 85 (a mixture of fatty acids)
1 unit	Protogen
0.1 g	$MgSO_4 \cdot 7H_2O$
25 mg	$Fe(NH_4)_2(SO_4)_2 \cdot 6H_2O$
0.5 mg	$MnCl_2 \cdot 4H_2O$
0.05 mg	$ZnCl_2$
50 mg	$CaCl_2 \cdot 2H_2O$
5 mg	$CuCl_2 \cdot 2H_2O$
1.25 g	$FeCl_3 \cdot 6H_2O$
1 g	K_2HPO_4
1 g	KH_2PO_4
110 mg	alanine
206 mg	arginine
122 mg	aspartic acid
10 mg	glycine
233 mg	glutamic acid
87 mg	histidine
276 mg	isoleucine
344 mg	leucine
272 mg	lysine
248 mg	methionine
250 mg	proline
394 mg	serine
326 mg	threonine
72 mg	tryptophan
162 mg	valine
160 mg	phenylalanine
0.1 mg	Ca-pantothenate
0.1 mg	nicotinamide
1 mg	pyridoxine · HCl
0.1 mg	pyridoxal · HCl
0.1 mg	pyridoxamine · HCl
0.1 mg	riboflavin
0.01 mg	pteroylglutamic acid
1 mg	thiamine · HCl
0.5 μg	biotin
1 mg	choline · HCl
30 mg	guanylic acid
20 mg	adenylic acid
25 mg	cytidylic acid
10 mg	uracil

Nostoc‡

0.15 g	K_2HPO_4
0.2 g	$MgSO_4 \cdot 7H_2O$
0.025 g	$CaCl_2 \cdot 2H_2O$
0.025 g	Na_2SiO_3
2 mg	$FeCl_3 \cdot 6H_2O$
0.4 mg	$MnCl_2 \cdot 4H_2O$
0.4 mg	$Na_2MoO_4 \cdot 2H_2O$
0.6 mg	H_3BO_3
0.04 mg	$CuSO_4 \cdot H_2O$
0.04 mg	$ZnSO_4 \cdot 7H_2O$

Rhizopus§

25 g	glucose
3.0 g	NH_4NO_3
2.5 g	$MgSO_4 \cdot 7H_2O$
2.7 g	KH_2PO_4
2.1 g	K_2HPO_4
5 mg	Zn^{+2} (as sulfate)
2 mg	Ca^{+2} (as chloride)
2 mg	Mn^{+2} (as sulfate)
0.6 mg	Mo^{+6} (as molybdate)
0.4 mg	Cu^{+2} (as sulfate)
0.4 mg	Co^{+2} (as sulfate)
100 μmoles	K-versenate (chelating agent)

Soil Algae‖

0.25 g	$NaNO_3$
0.175 g	KH_2PO_4
0.075 g	K_2HPO_4
0.075 g	$MgSO_4 \cdot 7H_2O$
25 mg	NaCl
25 mg	$CaCl_2$
4.98 mg	$FeSO_4 \cdot 7H_2O$
8.82 mg	$ZnSO_4 \cdot 7H_2O$
1.57 mg	$CuSO_4 \cdot 5H_2O$
1.44 mg	$MnCl_2 \cdot 4H_2O$
11.42 mg	H_3BO_3
0.71 mg	MoO_3
0.49 mg	$Co(NO_3)_2 \cdot 6H_2O$
50 mg	EDTA (chelating agent)
31 mg	NaOH (to neutralize the EDTA)

TABLE 11-2. Examples of Defined Media for Cultivation of Microorganisms (*cont.*)

Ashbya #		Ochromonas**	
20 g	sucrose	1.5 g	lactic acid (as Na-salt; contains Ca)
5 g	asparagine		
0.5 g	KH_2PO_4	3 g	glutamic acid
0.5 g	$MgSO_4 \cdot 7H_2O$	1.5 g	arginine-glutamate
1 g	NH_4NO_3	0.8 g	asparagine
0.2 g	myo-inositol	1 g	glycine
0.2 mg	thiamine	2.8 g	histidine $\cdot$ HCl $\cdot$ H_2O
1 μg	biotin	0.5 g	lysine $\cdot$ HCl
0.01 mg	B ⎫	0.1 g	methionine
0.02 mg	Mo ⎪	0.2 g	serine
0.2 mg	Fe ⎬ as salts	0.5 g	Na-acetate $\cdot$ $3H_2O$
0.18 mg	Zn ⎪	0.5 g	Na-butyrate
0.04 mg	Cu ⎪	5 g	propylene glycol
0.02 mg	Mn ⎭	1 g	pentane-1,5-diol
		8 g	Na_2-glycerophosphate $\cdot$ $5H_2O$
		5 g	"Quadrol"
		0.2 g	nitrilotriacetic acid (chelating agent)
		0.05 g	$MgCO_3$
		0.05 g	$MgSO_4 \cdot 7H_2O$
		0.08 g	$Fe(NH_4)_2(SO_4)_2 \cdot 6H_2O$
		0.025 g	K_2SO_4
		5μg	biotin
		0.6 mg	thiamine $\cdot$ HCl
		6.6 mg	Fe ⎫
		5.3 mg	Mn ⎪
		3.3 mg	Zn ⎪
		3.3 mg	Mo ⎬ as salts
		0.33 mg	Cu ⎪
		0.33 mg	Co ⎪
		66 μg	B ⎪
		66 μg	V ⎪
		26 μg	I ⎪
		13 μg	Se ⎭

* *Brevibacterium liquefaciens,* a non-exacting chemoorganotrophic bacterium that requires an organic nitrogen source. (From Ide, M., A. Yoshimoto, and T. Okabayashi, 1967. *J. Bact.,* **94**:317.)

† *Tetrahymena pyriformis,* a ciliate protozoon. This medium is "semidefined"—the exact chemical composition of Protogen, a growth-stimulating preparation sometimes added to culture media for protozoa, is not known. (From Kidder, G. W., V. C. Dewey, and R. E. Parks, Jr., 1951. *Physiol. Zool.,* **24**:69.)

‡ *Nostoc muscorum,* a N_2-utilizing blue-green alga. (From Lazaroff, N., and W. Vishniac, 1962. *J. Gen. Microbiol.,* **28**:203.)

§ *Rhizopus,* strain MX. This type of glucose-ammonium-salts medium is generally suitable for non-exacting chemoorganotrophic fungi and bacteria; it may be supplemented with micronutrients for cultivation of exacting chemoorganotrophs. (From Margulies, M., and W. Vishniac, 1961. *J. Bact.,* **81**:1.)

‖ Soil algae. This medium is generally suitable for fresh-water and soil algae. (From Deason, T. R., and H. C. Bold, 1960. *Phycological Studies. I. Exploratory Studies of Texas Soil Algae.* University of Texas Press, Austin.)

Ashbya gossypii, a plant pathogenic fungus. (From Robbins, W. J., and M. B. Schmidt, 1939. *Bull. Torrey Bot. Club,* **66**:139.)

** *Ochromonas danica,* an unusually exacting photoorganotrophic alga. (From Packer, E. L., S. H. Hutner, D. Cox, M. A. Mendelow, H. Baker, O. Frank, and D. Amsterdam, 1961. *Ann. N.Y. Acad. Sci.,* **92**:486.)

121

but some colorless forms cannot grow, grow more slowly, or may even be killed if the cultures are illuminated. Certain pigments, especially carotenoids, seem to protect cells from damage that results from light-catalyzed reactions between cell constituents and O_2.

The atmosphere in which a culture is incubated may serve as a source of nutrients or it may inhibit growth. The latter is particularly the case for anaerobes whose growth is prevented by O_2 and for microaerophiles, organisms that require O_2, but whose growth is inhibited at an O_2 tension equivalent to that of air at sea level. Air must be excluded from cultures of anaerobes; it may be replaced by N_2, a mixture of N_2 and CO_2, by H_2 or He, or by illuminating gas that is ignited within the incubation chamber so that traces of O_2 are removed by combustion of the gas. Microaerophiles may be cultivated in chambers containing an atmosphere with a low proportion (e.g., 5 per cent) of O_2. Liquid cultures of both types of organisms can be grown exposed to air in media containing substances (e.g., thioglycollate) that react spontaneously with O_2 and thereby prevent it from diffusing into the culture. A relatively simple method of cultivating anaerobes in liquid medium is to fill a tube with inoculated medium and close the tube with a tightly fitting screw cap.

O_2, N_2, CO_2, H_2, and CH_4 are nutrients that are supplied in gaseous form. O_2, which is essential for aerobic respiration, is required for growth by most bacteria, most fungi other than yeasts, and most free-living protozoa. Although algae produce O_2 as a by-product of photosynthesis, the endogenous supply may not be adequate for growth, and cultures of many types must be incubated aerobically.

N_2 can serve as a nitrogen source for several types of bacteria and for some, possibly all, heterocyst-forming blue-green algae. All N_2-utilizing protists can also use nitrogenous compounds as nitrogen sources and often grow more rapidly with combined nitrogen than with N_2.

Obligate lithotrophs require CO_2 as a carbon source for growth. Some photolithotrophic algae can assimilate organic substances, but they generally store such carbon as reserve food; only the carbon of CO_2 assimilated in photosynthesis is used directly in synthesis of cell constituents. Obligate chemo-lithotrophs, all of which are bacteria, seem restricted to CO_2 as the principal carbon source. Although a few can assimilate one or more organic compounds, they nevertheless depend on CO_2 as the major source of carbon for growth.

H_2 can serve as an oxidizable substrate for some photosynthetic bacteria, a few strains of algae, and some chemolithotrophic bacteria. None of these organisms is restricted to H_2 as a source of electrons.

Methane (CH_4) is utilized, as far as known, only by a few types of bacteria. Energy is obtained by respiration of the electrons derived by oxidation of CH_4 to CO_2, and the carbon of the CO_2 or of an intermediate oxidation stage is assimilated.

Protists, like many higher organisms, cannot regulate their internal temperature. Consequently, their metabolic processes occur at the temperature of their environment. There is a range of temperature within which any given protist can grow in a given environment.[4] At the lower end of the range, growth is very slow; the rate increases to a maximum at an optimal temperature, and decreases above the optimal. Depending on the optimal temperature, the organism is designated a psychrophile, mesophile, or thermophile, approximately as indicated in Figure 11-3.

The effects of temperature on growth reflect the chemical nature of growth processes and the thermal lability of enzymes. At low temperatures, the rate of metabolic reactions is low, and net synthesis of cell constituents may not occur. At higher temperatures, sufficient energy and precursors can be produced and accumulated to allow net synthesis, which is growth, at a rate that increases with temperature up to the optimal temperature. At temperatures above the optimal, heat-catalyzed degradation of essential cell constituents opposes their synthesis and activities, and the growth rate is lower. These degradations are more influential than lack of thermal energy (at temperatures below optimal), and the maximum growth temperature is usually closer to the optimal than is the minimum.

The maximum growth temperature may be influenced by the composition of the medium. At incubation temperatures in the upper portion of the range where growth is possible, many microprotists require a greater variety of nutrients than at lower temperatures. Apparently, specific synthetic activities of an organism vary in their sensitivity to heat inhibition; at higher temperatures, some activities must be compensated for by environmental supplies of nutrients.

[4]Growth rate is affected by factors other than temperature; therefore, growth rates at different temperatures are comparable only if all other conditions of incubation are identical.

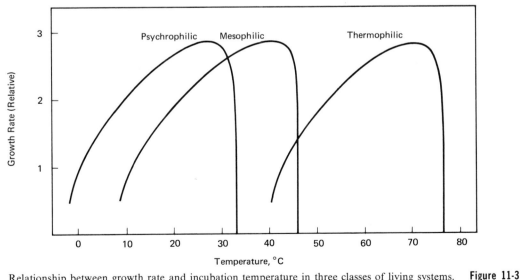

Relationship between growth rate and incubation temperature in three classes of living systems.   **Figure 11-3**

Measurements of Growth

Direct Methods. Growth is measured directly by determination of the dry weight of cell-associated substance at intervals during incubation.

In liquid cultures in which the cells grow evenly suspended or can be suspended by agitation that does not affect growth rate, the measurement is performed by removing a known volume of the culture to a centrifuge tube. The sample is then subjected to centrifugal forces that cause the cells to settle rapidly to the bottom of the tube. The liquid is then decanted, the cells resuspended in a wash solution of the lowest osmotic strength that does not cause osmotic lysis of the cells (preferably distilled water), and the centrifugation is repeated. This washing is repeated at least two or three times to remove unassimilated medium constituents and excreted metabolic products. The final resuspension is transferred to preweighed vessels, placed in an oven (usually at 90° C), and dried to constant weight. The weights of the empty cup and of constituents of the washing solution are subtracted from the final weight; the difference is the dry weight of the cells. Alternatively, the suspension may be passed through a preweighed filter that retains the cells; then the filter plus cells (and not solution constituents) is dried and weighed.

When cells cannot be evenly dispersed in a liquid medium, an alternative, less suitable method must be used. One such method is to inoculate and incubate several cultures in identical fashion (parallel cultures) and remove all cells from one of the cultures at each interval. The principal difficulty of this method is that measurements on parallel cultures deviate more from theoretic values than do successive samples from one culture.

Many filamentous fungi grow as cohesive mats on a liquid surface. A floating mat can sometimes be removed from the medium in one piece, blotted on successive pieces of absorbent paper or washed on a filter, and then dried and weighed.

For measurements of growth on solid media, parallel cultures must be used. For each measurement, all the cells from one culture are washed off the surface of the medium, then prepared for weighing as described above for cells from liquid medium. Cultures on solidified medium are less suitable for growth measurements than are liquid cultures because the efficiency of removal of cells from solid medium is lower. Also, the cells usually heap up in more than one layer on the surface of the medium, and while the nether cells grow in the presence of higher concentrations of nutrients from the medium, the upper cells have freer access to the atmosphere. Thus, the environment of the cells varies through the culture, and the rate of growth may not be uniform within the population.

Indirect Methods. Indirect measurements of growth can often be made more conveniently than direct weighings of dried cells. Such methods can be used routinely once they have been standardized by correlation with direct measurements. A few of these methods are described below.

1. Light Scattering. When cells grow evenly dispersed in liquid medium, the density of the population can be estimated by the amount of light scattered by the suspended cells. Scattering is measured by passing a beam of light through the culture in an instrument containing a photocell that registers the amount of light scattered at a 90-degree angle (the turbidimeter) or the amount of light that passes through without being scattered (the photometer). In the latter instrument, the amount of light lost from the beam is proportional to the density of the cells. This method is suitable for small (at most ca. 5 μm diameter), unicellular organisms that do not accumulate in large masses during growth. Large cells, clumps, and filaments do not scatter light in proportion to their mass.

2. Metabolic Products. During growth of many microorganisms, particular metabolic products are excreted in constant proportion to growth and throughout incubation. Some of these products are easily measured. For example, acid production can be measured as a decrease in pH, and O_2 evolution by algae can be followed by cultivating the organisms in a closed vessel to which a manometer, a device that registers changes in gas pressure, or an O_2 analyzer is attached. Instruments are now available for continuous measurement and automatic recording of the appearance of metabolic products, including acid, O_2, and CO_2.

3. Selected Cell Constituents. Protein accounts for a fairly constant proportion of the dry weight of growing cells, and nitrogen accounts for a constant proportion of protein. Accordingly, quantitative chemical assay of either of these constituents allows estimation of dry weight.

4. Linear Measurements. Many filamentous fungi are routinely cultivated on solidified rather than in liquid media; in liquid media, they often do not complete development, particularly sporulation, and typically they do not grow evenly dispersed through the liquid. Growth of a fungal mycelium can be followed in a single culture on solid medium by periodic measurement of the diameter of the colony or of the distance between growing edge and point of inoculation in an elongated vessel. The diameter or length increases linearly with time, and the rate is constant for a given combination of fungus and cultural conditions. However, these linear growth rates do not correlate well with rate of dry weight increase, since the degree and rate of branching within the perimeter are influenced by factors different from those that cause variation in rate of elongation of the leading filaments. Nevertheless, linear extension is one dimension of growth, and its measurement is suitable for some physiologic studies.

5. Viable Counts. Viable counts are used to determine the rate of multiplication of organisms in a growing population. When multiplication occurs at regular intervals during growth so that the viable units are of nearly uniform size, and all progeny are viable, the multiplication rate equals the growth rate. Estimation of growth rate by determination of multiplication rate is generally suitable for liquid cultures of unicellular organisms that multiply by fission, if each fission results in the same number of progeny, and these separate from each other at a regular interval after fission.

The most commonly used procedure for determination of viable counts is outlined below and diagrammed in Figure 11-4.

a. A measured volume of the culture is removed to a known volume of a diluent liquid. The diluent should not support multiplication or cause any loss of viability. Generally, a solution of inorganic salts of appropriate pH and osmotic strength is used.

b. The diluted sample may be further diluted by transfer of a measured volume of the first dilution through a succession of measured portions of diluent fluid (dilution blanks). At each step, the culture is diluted by a factor expressed as the ratio:

$$\text{Dilution factor} = \frac{\text{Volume of sample (or of preceding dilution)}}{\text{Volume transferred plus volume of dilution blank}}.$$

The overall dilution factor from culture to last dilution in the series is the product of all intervening dilution factors.

c. A measured volume of the final dilution is transferred to solidified medium by one of three methods: by spreading the sample over the surface of solidified medium contained in a Petri plate; by mixing the sample with molten medium which is then allowed to cool and gel (in a Petri plate if aerobes, in a culture tube if anaerobes); or by collecting the cells in the sample on a membrane filter which is then placed on the surface of solidified medium in a Petri plate. Several such cultures may be prepared using samples of different volumes of more than one dilution in the series. These cultures are incubated until the viable units have given rise to visible colonies.

d. The colonies are counted and the viable units are calculated as in the following example.

Average count: 156 colonies per culture inoculated with the equivalent of
                 0.5 ml of 10^{-4} dilution.
Calculations: $156 \times 1/0.5 = 312$ viable units/ml of 10^{-4} dilution.

$$312 \times 1/10^{-4} = 312 \times 10^4 = 3.12 \times 10^6 \text{ viable units/ml of}$$
undiluted culture at the time of sampling.

6. *Total Particle Counts.* The multiplication rate may also be determined by counting the number of cells, viable and non-viable. In a healthy growing culture of unicellular microbes, the proportion of non-viable cells is negligible and constant, so that the rate of increase in number of particles is the same as the rate of increase in number of viable units. The direct count is performed on a dilution of the culture, and the calculations are the same as for viable counts. Two types of microscopic methods are used. One is enumeration of cells contained in a chamber of known volume which is examined through a microscope. The second, which is especially useful for opaque fluids such

as milk and blood, is enumeration of cells in a dried film on a microscope slide. The film is prepared by drying a measured volume of the sample on a calibrated area of the slide, so that a unit of area is equivalent to a given volume of the liquid sample. A third method for particle counting involves passing a known volume of the diluted sample through an aperture that allows passage of only one particle at a time. The cells (particles) that pass through the aperture are enumerated electronically.

7. *Weighing of Wet Cells.* This method is similar to dry weight determination with the exception that cells or mycelial mats prepared for weighing are not dried. Usually, the cells or mats are washed in preweighed centrifuge tubes or on preweighed filters. The tube or filter containing the cells is weighed; the weight of packed cells is the calculated difference between the weight of container plus cells and the weight of the empty container. This method is

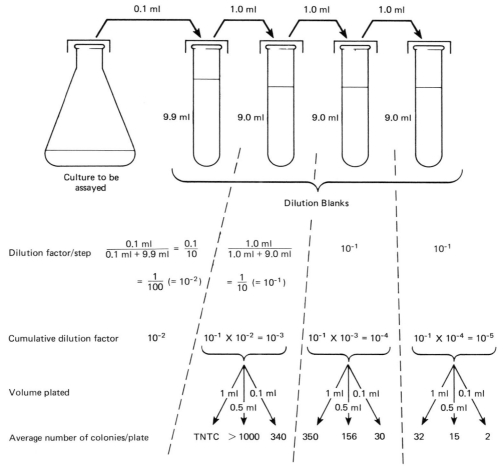

Technique for enumeration of viable units ("viable count").   Figure 11-4

only approximate, for two reasons. First, during the manipulations incidental to the preparation of microbes for weighing, the water content of the cells may be altered. Second, a tightly packed mass of wet microbial cells contains water in intercellular spaces; the mass of the included water may be as much as 25 per cent of the mass of the organisms, but varies with the shape and rigidity of the cells.

Closed-System Cultivation

Most laboratory cultures are closed systems: the supply of nutrients and the volume of culture liquid are finite and are fixed at the time the culture is inoculated. Most physiologic studies are performed with such cultures. Because the systems are finite, growth and all associated processes will begin, proceed, and cease. It is important to interpretations of observations on such cultures that the time course of this series of growth phases be known, because the physiologic condition of the cells varies in the different phases.

Growth Curves. Cultures of most microbes whose growth can occur and be accurately measured in liquid media pass through the same series of growth phases. These phases, first described in quantitative terms for bacterial cultures, are indicated in the generalized growth curve of Figure 11-5A. Such growth curves are observed for unicellular protists that multiply by fission or by autospore formation (see "Algae," Chap. 17). The phases of growth, factors that influence them, and corresponding physiologic states of the cells are described below.

1. Lag Phase. For some time after inoculation of the nutrient medium, the amount of cellular material remains unchanged. This is a period of physiologic adjustment during which the cells may need to synthesize new enzymes and re-establish minimal intracellular concentrations of substrates, enzymes, and inorganic ions. As the several metabolic systems necessary for growth in the environment of the culture become functional, growth begins.

2. Phase of Increasing Growth Rate. This is a transition phase during which growth rate increases from zero to the maximum. It reflects the randomness of adjustment by individuals in the population, and the increase in rate of growth of each individual as the rates of its separate metabolic processes become maximum.

3. Phase of Exponential Growth. Growth of populations[5] of unicellular, undifferentiated organisms under optimal conditions is balanced and autocatalytic. Within each cell cycle, each cell constituent is produced in constant (balanced) proportion to all other constituents. Some of these constituents are

---

[5]This discussion relates to growth of populations, for which the dynamics of growth may be different from the dynamics of growth for individuals (discussed in Chap. 10).

catalysts, so that as the amount of catalysts increases, the rates of the reactions they catalyze increase. Consequently, the rate of growth is proportional to the amount of growing substance. This is expressed by the equation:

$$dC/dt = kC$$ *Eqn. 11-1*

where C is the amount of cellular substance, t is time, and k is the instantaneous growth rate constant for the culture; dC/dt is, then, the rate of change in C. The

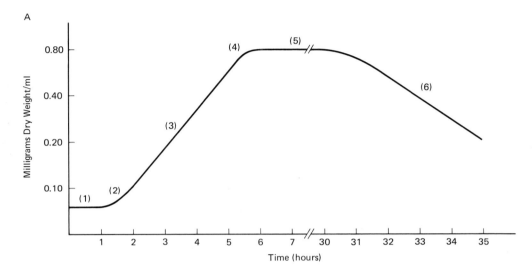

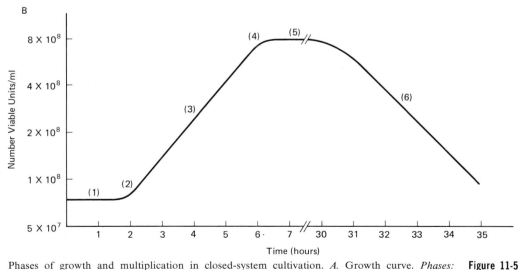

Phases of growth and multiplication in closed-system cultivation. *A*. Growth curve. *Phases:* **Figure 11-5** (1) lag phase; (2) phase of increasing growth rate; (3) phase of exponential growth; (4) phase of decreasing growth rate; (5) maximum stationary phase; (6) decline phase. *B*. Multiplication curve.

growth rate constant, k, is relative increase per unit time; it is expressed as reciprocal time (usually hr^{-1}). Integrating Eqn. 11-1 yields:

$$C_t = C_{t=0}\ e^{kt} \quad \text{or} \quad ln\ C_t = ln\ C_{t=0} + kt \qquad \textit{Eqn. 11-2}$$

where e is the base of natural logarithms. These equations reveal that the logarithm of C is directly proportional to time. Since the logarithm of C is the exponent of the base of the logarithm, it can equivalently be stated that this exponent is directly proportional to time; hence the designation "phase of exponential (or logarithmic) growth."

The "growth rate" of a culture is usually expressed as the time required for a cell mass doubling, or as the proportional increase in cell mass per hour. For example, the growth rate of the culture whose growth curve is presented in Figure 11-4A is 1.2 hours per doubling, or 0.8 per hour (cell mass increases by 80 per cent per hour). This rate is influenced by the temperature, the nature of the carbon source, the concentration of an essential nutrient if very low, the variety of nutrients available, the intensity of utilizable light for photosynthetic organisms, and—for facultative anaerobes, both photosynthetic and non-photosynthetic—the tension of O_2. The effects of specific carbon sources vary with the organism. Within a range characteristic of the organism, growth rate generally increases in proportion to each of the other factors.

4. *Phase of Decreasing Growth Rate.* When growth ceases as a consequence of the exhaustion of a single essential nutrient, while all others are still available, the phase of transition from exponential growth to the stationary phase is brief; in a liquid medium, the nutrient becomes inadequate for all the cells simultaneously. When conditions other than exhaustion of a single nutrient are responsible for a cessation of growth, the transition phase is prolonged. For example, in a complex medium, an organism may be provided with metabolic intermediates and micronutrients that it is able to synthesize in environments lacking them; these are non-essential nutrients. As the exogenous supply is depleted, the organism begins to synthesize these substances, and growth slows as it becomes necessary for the cells to synthesize an increasing number of metabolites. The transition phase is also prolonged when the population becomes so dense that O_2 is consumed more rapidly than it can diffuse into and throughout the culture. Similarly, a high density of cells growing photosynthetically results in mutual shading of the cells; as the light received by individual cells decreases in intensity, the growth rate decreases.

5. *Maximum Stationary Phase.* Growth eventually ceases when essential nutrients are exhausted or, less commonly, when metabolic products accumulate in the medium to concentrations inimical to growth. In the former case, cells in early stationary phase are potentially metabolically active and, if transferred to fresh medium, may resume exponential growth without a significant lag period. As the stationary phase continues, the cells begin to degenerate and lose intracellular constituents by leakage, by consumption of precursors in continuing metabolic processes, or as the result of disintegrations or

chemical alterations of cell constituents; such disintegrations may also occur during growth, but the altered substances are excreted and replaced by synthesis, or repaired. Eventually, the permeability barrier may disintegrate and the cells begin to lyse.

The population density in maximum stationary phase is usually determined by the initial concentration of the first essential nutrient to be exhausted. This is usually the carbon source, but may be any other element source, a micronutrient, or the energy source if different from the carbon source. The growth yield of a culture is defined as the difference between maximum density and initial density; the latter is often negligible, and the yield is approximately the final density. The yield is directly proportional to the initial concentration of the limiting nutrient, as illustrated in Figure 11-6.

6. Decline Phase. During the decline phase, there is a net decrease in weight of sedimentable cellular material in the culture. This is a consequence of loss of selective permeability and of lysis—disintegration of the cells. The disintegration of some organisms is hastened by the activity of hydrolytic enzymes which in the growing cell may be contained within lysosomes or may function to break bonds in cell components in order to allow insertion of additional subunits. In other cases, disintegration is very slow, and the maximum weight may be maintained for months.

Multiplication Curves. Multiplication curves include the same phases as growth curves (see Fig. 11-5*B*).

Multiplication, like population growth, is exponential, since the number of cells produced during an interval of time is determined by the number of

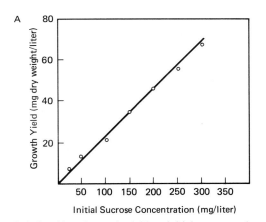 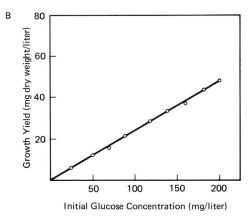

Relationship of growth yield to initial concentration of the growth-limiting nutrient in closed-system cultivation. *A. Bacillus subtilis* in a defined medium with sucrose the limiting nutrient. *B. Escherichia coli* in a defined medium with glucose the limiting nutrient. [Replotted from data in table IX (A.) and table VII (B.) in Monod, J., 1942. *Recherches sur la croissance des cultures bactériennes,* Hermann (pub.), Paris.]   **Figure 11-6**

potential parent cells present at the beginning of the interval. This is expressed
by the equation

$$dN/dt = k'N$$ Eqn. 11-3

where N is the number of cells, t is time, and k' is the instantaneous multiplication rate constant (relative increase in number of cells per unit time,
expressed as reciprocal time). As the rate of multiplication becomes constant
and exponential, k' equals k, and the average cell size is constant. This relationship between growth and multiplication is maintained through most of the
phase of exponential growth. During this time, the cells are physiologically
homogeneous and vary only with respect to the processes specifically necessary
for or halted during cell fission.

For organisms that multiply by binary fission, the multiplication rate is
usually expressed in terms of the cell doubling time, which is the time required
for the number of cells to double. For such organisms, cell doubling time is
equated with generation time, a more general term that may also refer to the
time required for a quadrupling of a population of organisms (e.g., certain
algae) that produce four progeny per generation. The generation time is
routinely determined from a plot of the number of cells against time on
semilogarithmic coordinates, as illustrated in Figure 11-5B. It can also be
calculated by using the cell counts from two points within the phase of exponential multiplication and the following equations.

$$N_{t_2} = N_{t_1} \times P^n$$ Eqn. 11-4

where N_{t_1} is the number of cells present at the earlier time, N_{t_2} is the number
of cells present at the later time, n the number of generations that occurred
during the interval $(t_2 - t_1)$, and P the number of progeny produced per
generation. Then

$$\log N_{t_2} = \log N_{t_1} + n \log P$$ Eqn. 11-5

and

$$n = \frac{\log N_{t_2} - \log N_{t_1}}{\log P} = \frac{\log(N_{t_2}/N_{t_1})}{\log P}$$ Eqn. 11-6

P is known for the organism; N_{t_2} and N_{t_1} are determined by cell counts; n
can be calculated. Since generation time (G) is time per generation,

$$G = \frac{t_2 - t_1}{n}$$ Eqn. 11-7

In organisms that develop dormant stages, differentiation of vegetative cells
into resting cells may begin as growth slows or in early stationary phase; later
in stationary phase, a major proportion of cells may be in the dormant form.

When dormant stages are not produced, a phase of decline in viability may
begin within only a few hours after growth ceases. Loss of viability may be
accompanied by cell lysis, in which case direct cell counts decline with viable

counts. More often, viability is lost before the cells lyse, and a decline phase is observed by viable counts long before it is detected by direct cell counts or weighings. Apparently, the cells may lose essential metabolites before becoming structurally disorganized and are unable to restore these substances even if transferred to an environment usually favorable for growth. This is inferred in part from studies of viability decline in which more than one type of counting medium was used. Generally, the greater the variety of nutrients available in the counting medium, the later the onset of the decline in viable counts.

Continuous Cultivation

Populations of some types of microorganisms can be maintained in continuous growth by providing them with a continuous supply of nutrients and allowing (theoretically) an infinite expansion of volume of the culture. In practice, this is achieved by continuous displacement of a portion of the culture by an equal volume of fresh, sterile medium; the displaced portion is discarded or used for assays or for extraction of metabolic products. Continuous growth may be exponential or linear, depending on the manner in which fresh medium is added.

In the turbidostat, fresh medium is added and some of the culture is displaced whenever the cell density reaches a predetermined level that is less than the maximum it would reach if the culture were not diluted. Growth is exponential, and the rate is characteristic of the organism in that medium and the same as during the phase of exponential growth under the same conditions in a closed-system culture.

In the chemostat, the cells are allowed to grow to incipient stationary phase; growth ceases as the result of exhaustion of a single essential nutrient. Just as growth ceases, a portion of fresh medium displaces some of the culture, and for a short time the cells resume growth by utilizing the nutrient provided in the fresh medium. Growth is linear, and the rate is determined by the rate of addition of nutrient, since the amount of cell material produced per unit time is directly proportional to the amount of limiting nutrient provided per unit time.

Continuous cultures have been used experimentally in studies of physiologic properties (e.g., enzyme synthesis and effect of environment on cell composition) and in genetics, especially in determining rates of mutation. They have been adapted industrially on larger scales for obtaining a continuous supply of a commercially important metabolic product, e.g., an organic acid or an antibiotic, that is excreted by the microorganism either during growth or as growth ceases.

Cultivation of Synchronously Reproducing Populations

In closed-system and continuous cultivation, the populations of growing cells are randomized with respect to the reproductive cycle. At any point in time,

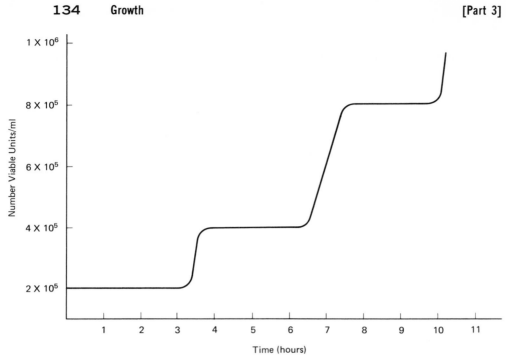

Figure 11-7   Relationship between viable count and time in a synchronously reproducing population (idealized).

some organisms have just reproduced, others are preparing to reproduce, and others are at intermediate stages of the cycle. For purposes of determining whether and how metabolic activities vary during the cycle, it is necessary that all individuals in a population initiate and complete their cycles at the same time. Synchronously reproducing populations have been obtained with a variety of protistan cells and with cultured cells of higher organisms. Idealized synchronous reproduction is illustrated in Figure 11-7.

Three general types of methods are used to obtain synchronously reproducing populations. These methods provide populations in which reproduction occurs periodically throughout the population, and each wave of reproduction occurs within a period that is only a fraction of the time required for completion of the reproductive cycle by an individual. The choice of method is determined in part by the purpose for which the population is synchronized, and in larger part by empiric determination of which method is successful with a particular organism or cell population. The three general methods are described briefly below.

1. Synchronization by Physical Factors.   Visible light, ultraviolet light, and heat may affect metabolic processes differentially so that the majority of cells in a growing population accumulate at one stage in the reproductive cycle. Progress beyond that stage is very slow or may not occur until the inhibiting factor (e.g., ultraviolet light or excess heat) is removed, or the required factor (light or sufficient heat) becomes available once again. In instances where light or a minimal amount of heat is necessary for completion of the reproductive cycle within a given period of time, synchronization can be accomplished by a routine of light/dark or optimal temperature/suboptimal temperature alternations. Once a population has been synchronized, it may continue to reproduce periodically for one or more cycles without continued alternation of the stimulus. However, when environmental conditions are constant, reproduction eventually returns to randomness in the population.

2. Synchronization by Nutrient Availability. When cells are starved for a particular nutrient or for several nutrients, their metabolism may reach a point where sudden availability of the nutrient(s) permits completion of cell division after an interval that is practically the same for all cells in the population. Thus, alternation of unavailability and availability of nutrients can be used to synchronize some populations, particularly of bacteria and of yeasts.

3. Synchronization by Segregation of Cells in One Stage of the Cycle. These methods depend on differences in physical properties or behavior of cells in different stages of the reproductive cycle; such properties must allow physical separation of one type of cell from all others by mechanical means. Mechanical segregation is preferred for certain types of physiologic studies because it involves a minimum of physiologic change (stress).

a. Synchronized Populations Derived from Cultures Containing Only Vegetative Cells. Synchronized populations of bacteria have been obtained by filtering a growing population through stacks of filter paper that allow passage only of the smallest cells. These cells are at the earliest point in the division cycle. Synchronized populations of budding yeasts have been obtained by low-speed centrifugation of growing cultures. The large cells that sediment first are at the earliest stage of releasing buds. Some ciliate protozoa cease motility during cell fission; synchronized populations of such organisms have been obtained by cultivation of the cells in an inverted conical vessel with a stopcock at the apex of the cone. Dividing cells fall into the area just above the stopcock, and a population of cells in the fission period of the reproductive cycle can be collected through the stopcock.

b. Synchronized Populations Derived from Cultures Containing Cells Specialized for Dormancy. (These methods usually provide only one cycle of synchronized development.) Spores of molds can be washed free of vegetative filaments. Most of the spores begin to germinate shortly after being transferred to fresh nutrient medium; the proportion of germinating spores may be increased by brief heating of the spore suspension. Bacterial endospores can be prepared free of viable vegetative cells by heating a mixed population of cells and spores to 100° C for two to three minutes. The heating kills the vegetative cells and stimulates the spores to germinate. When the population is then transferred to a nutrient medium, germination occurs in a synchronized fashion; one or more subsequent cycles of vegetative cell division may also occur synchronously.

Part 4

Major Groups of Protists

Chapter 12

Taxonomy and Nomenclature

Taxonomic Criteria

"The basis of classification depends on the discovery of some significant traits, significant in the sense that on the basis of the traits the subject matter can be organized into a system. Such traits, however, are only slowly discovered, and cannot be determined on formal grounds alone" (Cohen and Nagel, p. 243).

According to the theory of biologic evolution, the variety among living forms existing today is the result of descent with modification. It follows from the theory that it should be possible to classify modern organisms in a system whose hierarchy reflects the order in which modifications have accumulated along respective lines of descent.

In such a natural system of classification, a significant trait is one that, having appeared in one or more individuals in a generation, was retained throughout all subsequent generations to the present. The other individuals of that generation perpetuated the line of descent from which the new trait was absent. Accordingly, the appearance of a significant trait marks a point of divergence of descent, and organisms are more or less closely related according to the generation at which their respective histories converge in a common ancestor.

In addition to serving as a test of predictions of the theory of evolution, classification of living organisms is valuable in more immediately practical ways.

1. A classification scheme condenses and orders a large quantity of information.

2. A classification scheme serves as a guide to the extent of observation sufficient to support a generalization. In an empiric science, when a generalization is formulated, it must be verified in more than one instance. If the instances

139

are very similar, the verification is limited, not general. Greater probability of the generalization is attained if it is verified in instances that are dissimilar, but related by the generalization. The phenomenon with which the generalization is concerned must be observed in many different types of organisms, and the generalizer must know how to select the appropriate organisms. This he can infer from a suitable classification scheme.

3. Finally, the process of arranging organisms requires that a considerable amount of information be available about all the organisms, reveals the sort of information useful in such arranging, and thereby implies significance of the traits that must be determined for all the organisms to be arranged. In this way, classifying stimulates further examination of poorly described organisms, re-examination of organisms once thought to be adequately described, and search for organisms that might exist.

The basis of biologic classification is intended to be evolutionary history **(phylogeny)**; therefore, it is essential that evidence of evolutionary relationships be available. In the cases of plants and animals, especially the latter, a fossil record of ancestral forms is available. This aids the taxonomist in discerning the order in which modifications have appeared in some lines.

It is also important that the limits of the smallest grouping be defined. Again, in the plants and animals, this smallest group, the species, is recognized as a category represented by "a population of similar individuals, alike in their structural and functional characteristics, which in nature breed only with each other, and which have a common ancestry" (Villee, glossary).

In classifying the protists, however, the taxonomist is faced with the problem of inferring relationships without the aid of a fossil record of ancestral forms, and of recognizing species among organisms that do not breed. The oldest fossils known, which are more than 3 billion years old, contain alga-like and filamentous forms that seem basically similar in structure to certain modern organisms. The discovery of these fossils, of which there are very few, was reported in 1968. Prior to their discovery, the oldest available fossils were about 1.9 billion years old; these contain algae, fungi, and protozoa very similar to today's forms. Protistan forms distinctly more primitive than certain modern organisms have not been discovered; the fossil record does not yield clues to protistan phylogeny such as whether algae gave rise to fungi, or vice versa, or whether their origins were independent.

Probable phylogenetic relationships are deducible from principles of evolution formulated in the light of relationships that have been established among higher organisms. These principles deal with the entire organism—its organization and developmental processes, physiology, heredity, and habitat—since each aspect of its existence has evolved within the context of the others. These principles can be used as a basis for designating the most primitive representative of a given type of organism; other representatives display ever greater modification of the basic form. The principles are summarized below.

Organization. The general trend is toward greater complexity. Within the cell, this involves compartmentalization of metabolic functions and development of organelles specialized for such functions as locomotion or attachment. In multicellular organisms, some of the cells may serve specific functions, e.g., as reproductive structures or protection of such structures. Occasionally, forms that are relatively advanced in several aspects are simple in organization; these are usually regarded by taxonomists as forms derived from structurally more complex ancestors by reduction, i.e., by loss of structural complexity.

Physiology. The general trend is toward greater dependence on metabolic activities of other organisms; nutritional independence within a group of otherwise similar organisms is considered more primitive than dependence. Among lithotrophs, this involves development of specific nutritional requirements for organic substances such as vitamins. Among organotrophs, specific compounds may be required as sources of carbon and energy, and amino acids as sources of nitrogen. Parasitic organisms tend to become dependent on the entire physicochemical environment found only in the host body.

Heredity. The general trend is toward making greater use of the potential for variation available by mixing and recombination of genes. This is accomplished in three ways: (1) by increasing the frequency of sexual phenomena until every generation is sexually produced; (2) by ensuring genetic differences between sexual partners through development of secondary sex characteristics; and (3) by prolonging the diploid phase so that temporarily adverse genes can be perpetuated until the environment is suitable for development of individuals in which those genes are expressed, to the point of eliminating any development of haploid individuals.

Habitat. The general trend is from an aquatic habitat toward existence independent of a watery environment. Intermediate forms usually require an aqueous environment for at least one phase of the life cycle, e.g., for germination of a dormant stage.

Classification Schemes

The classification of protists used here is based on more complete schemes that can be found in the reference materials cited in the bibliography for Part 4. In the following five chapters, the major groups of protists are described with regard to general characteristics, and particular microbes are described in some detail as illustrations of the distinctive characteristics of the major group as well as the extent of variation within the group.

The protists are treated here as four groups of equivalent taxonomic rank, subkingdoms. These are bacteria, fungi, protozoa, and algae. Slime protists are presented as a separate group without a specified taxonomic rank; the types of organisms assigned to this group exhibit properties intermediate between those typical of fungi and those typical of protozoa.

In some recent classification schemes, the bacteria have been grouped with the procaryotic algae, and the latter have been separated from eucaryotic algae.

However, the characteristics that blue-green algae share with other algae seem to be more influential in their distribution in nature than are the characteristics they share with bacteria. If the environment is the source of selective pressures, then the algal traits of blue-green algae have been more significant in the evolution of these organisms. Accordingly, with the acknowledgment that their characteristics are clearly intermediate between those of bacteria and those of eucaryotic algae, and that the group probably reflects the descent of algae from procaryotic bacteria-like ancestors, the blue-green algae are grouped here with the other algae.

The principal disagreements among protistologic taxonomists arise from the lack of taxonomic distinction between protozoa and algae, and between protozoa and fungi. Several groups of flagellated unicellular or colonial photosynthetic organisms are classified in widely used systems both as photosynthetic protozoa and as flagellated algae. Since photosynthetic capacity is a trait typical of algae, and flagellation occurs in all three groups of eucaryotic protists, it seems more reasonable to classify such organisms as algae. The slime protists are usually classified both as protozoa and as fungi. The groupings used in this text generally follow systems of phycology and mycology in preference to those of protozoology.

The terms used to designate the subkingdoms are defined in Table 12-1, which summarizes the properties of the types of organisms referred to by these designations. The traits of each subkingdom, as of each taxonomic group discussed in this chapter, are those typical of the group. In every category at every taxonomic level, there may be one or more types of organisms that are not typical; these types are classified on the basis of their similarity to typical organisms or their probable similarity to or descent from ancestors of typical representatives.

Presumably because of their long evolutionary history in a wide variety of changing habitats, modern protists exhibit very few characteristics that have appeared only recently or only in one line of descent. Consequently, protists, even more so than plants and animals, must be classified on the basis of combinations of characteristics. Taxons cannot be defined on the basis of single characteristics unique to particular groups.

TABLE 12-1.   Subkingdoms of Kingdom Protista

Name	Refers to Protists That Are
Bacteria	Procaryotic and non-photosynthetic or whose photosynthesis is not accompanied by the evolution of molecular oxygen
Algae	Procaryotic or eucaryotic, photosynthetic, contain chlorophyll a as a photosynthetic pigment, and can evolve O_2 as a by-product of photosynthesis
Fungi	Eucaryotic, chemoorganotrophic, and in which the characteristic unit of vegetative structure is a multinucleated branching filament or a primitive version of such a structure
Protozoa	Eucaryotic, chemoorganotrophic, and that exhibit a tendency toward elaborate subcellular differentiation and do not exhibit a tendency toward filamentous organization

Nomenclature

Few living organisms (viz., humans and their pets) have names; other living organisms do not. The categories in which humans classify types of organisms have names, and the categories are defined by the characteristics of the organisms assigned to them. It is a common practice among biologists to simplify their discussions of organisms by referring to an organism or a type of organism by the name of the category in which it is classified. This shorter usage is often employed in this text; in each instance, however, the name refers to a category, and the organism that is illustrated or discussed exemplifies the characteristics of the sort of organism placed in that category.

The categories, called **taxons,** are arranged in a hierarchy such that each species is included in a genus, each genus in a family, each family in an order, each order in a class, each class in a phylum or division, and each phylum or division in a kingdom. Subcategories are admitted to the hierarchy where they are useful because the next lower taxons are numerous or heterogeneous. In this text, generally, the smallest category mentioned is the genus, although species names usually appear in the figure legends. Common, or informal, names are also used in many instances to eliminate the need for listing several genera.

The name of a species is italicized; that of a genus is italicized and capitalized; and the names of higher taxons are capitalized, but not italicized. The major taxons above genus can often be recognized by their endings. The classification systems for bacteria, fungi, and algae employ the following endings: class—(variable), order—"-ales," family—"-aceae." The system followed here for classification of protozoa employs: class—"-ea," order—"-ida," family—"-idae." The name of a taxon above genus is usually derived from the name of a genus that the higher taxon includes. Only species names may be used more than once throughout biologic classification; accordingly, a species name must be preceded by an indicator (name or initial) of the genus in which it is included.

The names used for biologic taxons are usually derived from Greek or Latin, although the coining of names from other languages is also permitted. The name of a category at any level is intended to be descriptive; names of persons and places (e.g., *B. bassiana* after Bassi, and *P. Hawaiiensis*) are occasionally used. The majority of names reflect certain characteristics of the organisms in the category. They can serve as mnemonics for the student who can translate the names into English descriptions. A list of translations of some common Greek and Latin lexical items used in biologic nomenclature is presented in the following section.

Some Greek and Latin Lexical Items Used in Biology

This list does not include items that occur commonly in the general vocabulary of English and whose translations are not peculiar in biology.

G. *a-, an-*/not, without
G. *acantha*/thistle, prickle
G. *acanthos*/flower
L. *aceti-*/vinegar

L. *acinus*/grape seed
G. *acro-*/apex
G. *actino-*/ray
L. *acus*/needle
G, L. *aero-*/air
L. *albo-*/white
L. *ambi-*/both
G. *amoebo-*/change
G. *amphi-*/around
G. *amylo-*/starch
G. *andro-*, *-androus*/male
G. *angio-*, *-angium*/vessel
G. *aniso-*/unequal
L. *anser*/goose
G. *anthero-*/flowery
G. *arch-*, *-arch*/primitive, beginning
G. *asco-*/sac, bag
L. *aureo-*/golden
G. *auxo-*/growth
L. *avis*/bird
L. *bacillo-* (dim.) /stick, rod
G. *bacteri-*, *-bacter*/stick, rod
L. *basid-*/pedestal
G. *batracho-*/frog
G. *bio-*, *-be*/life
G. *blasto-*, *-blast*/bud, rudiment
G. *blepharo-*/eyelash
L. *bos, bovi-*/cattle
G. *bysso-*/flax, linen
G. *butyro-*/butter
L. *calci-*/lime
L. *canis*/dog
L. *capilli-*/hair
G. *carpo-*, *-carp*/fruit
L. *caseo-*/cheese
G. *caryo-*/nut, nucleus
L. *cauda-*/tail
G, L. *caul-*/stem
G. *cereo-*/tail
L. *ceri-*/wax
L. *ceruleo-*/sky blue
G. *chaeto-*, *-chete*/bristle
G. *chitino-*/covering
G. *chlamydo-*/cloak
G. *chloro-*/green
G. *chrom(at)o-*, *-chrome*/color

G. *chroo-*/colored
G. *chryso-*/golden
L. *cili-*/eyelash
G. *citro-*/lemon
G. *clado-*/branch
G. *cleisto-*/enclosed
G. *coccino-*/scarlet red
G. *cocco-*/berry
G. *coelo-, celo-, -cele*/hollow
G. *coeno-*/in common
G. *coleo-*/sheath
G. *collo-*/glue
L. *-colous, -cola*/inhabit
G. *conidio-*/dust
L. *corneo-*/horn
L. *cortici-*/bark
L. *cuti-*/skin
G. *cyano-*/blue
G. *cyatho-*/cup
G. *-cyst*/cavity
G. *cyto-*, *-cyte*/cell
G. *dendro-*, *-dendron*/tree
G. *derm(at)o-*/skin
G. *desm-*/bond
G. *dictyo-*/net
G. *didymo-*/twin
G. *dino-*/terrible
G. *diplo-*/double
L. *e-*/without
G. *-enchyma*/infusion
G. *entero-*/intestine
G. *entomo-*/insect
G. *eremo-*/solitary
G. *erythro-*/red
G. *eu-*/well, proper
L. *falci-*/sickle
L. *faveo-*/honeycomb
L. *-fer, -ferous*/bear, carry
L. *ferri-*/iron
L. *fil-*/thread
L. *fissi-*, *-fid*/split, cleft
L. *flagellum*/whip, scourge
L. *flavo-*/yellow golden
L. *flos*/flower
L. *fructi-*, *frut-*/shrub
L. *fucus*/seaweed

L. *-fuge*/avoiding
L. *fulvi-*/reddish yellow
L. *fungus*/mushroom
L. *fusi-*/spindle
G. *galacto-*/milk
L. *gall-*/cock
G. *gamet-*, *-gam*/spouse
G. *gamo-*/marriage
G. *gast(e)ro-*/stomach
L. *gela-*/freeze
L. *gemma(to)-*/gem
G. *geno-*, *-gen*/racial, producing
L. *germin-*/seed
L. *glaber*/smooth
G. *glauco-*/gray-green
G. *glio-*/glue
L. *glomer-*/ball
L. *glutini-*/glue
G. *gono-*, *-gony*/offspring, seed
L. *gregi-*/crowd
L. *griseo-*/gray
G. *gymno-*/naked
G. *gyn-*, *-gynous*/female
G. *halo-*/salt (sea)
G. *haplo-*/single
G. *hapto-*/touch
L. *haustus*/drunk up
G. *helico-*/spiral
G. *helio-*/sun
G. *h(a)em(at)o-*/blood
G. *hetero-*/different
G. *holo-*/entire
G. *homo-*, *homeo-*/alike
L. *humus*/soil
G. *hyalo-*/glass, crystal
G. *hymeno-*/membrane
G. *hyph-*/web
G. *hypno-*/sleep
G. *icthyo-*/fish
G. *-idion, -idium*/ (dim. suffix)
G. *iodo-*/blue
G. *iso-*/equal
G. *kerato-*/horn
G. *kineto-*, *-kinesis*/motion, movement
L. *lacti-*/milk
L. *lamin-*/plate

L. *legumen*/vegetable
G. *lemma*/bark
G. *leuko-* (*leuco-*)/white
L. *ligni-*/wood
G. *limno-*/lake, marsh
G. *litho-*, *-lith*/stone
G. *lobo-*/lobe
G. *lopho-*/crest
L. *lor-*, *loric-*/thong
L. *luci-*, *-lux*/light
L. *luteo-*/yellow mud
G. *lyso-*, *-lytic, -lysis, -lyte*/loosen, dissolve
G. *mastigo-*/whip
G. *meio-*/less
G. *melano-*/black
G. *mero-*, *-mere, -merous*/part
G. *meso-*/middle
G. *metro-*, *-meter*/measure
G. *micro-*/small
G. *mito-*/thread
G. *morpho-*/form
L. *mus, muri-*/mouse
L. *mut-*/change
G. *myco-*, *myceto-*, *-myces*/fungus
G. *nan-*, *nann-*/dwarf
L. *-nate*/born
L. *navi-*/ship
G. *necro-*/dead
G. *nema(to)-*, *-neme*/thread
G. *nephro-*/kidney
L. *nigri-*/black
L. *nocti-*/night
L. *nutri-*/nourish
G. *nympho-*/maiden
G. *ochreo-*/pale yellow
G. *-oecium*/dwelling
G. *-oid*/like
G. *oligo-*/few
G. *-ont*/being
G. *oo-*/egg
G. *ortho-*/straight
L. *ovo-*/egg
L. *pallido-*/pale
G. *para-*/beside
L. *pari-*/equal
L. *pariet-*/wall

G. *partheno-*/maiden
G. *pecti-*/congealed
G. *pelago-*/sea
L. *pelli-*/skin
L. *peni-*/tail
L. *penna-*, *pinna-*/feather
L. *-petal*/seeking
G. *phaeo-*/brown, dusky
G. *phago-*, *-phage*/eat, devour
G. *pheno-*/visible, appearing
G. *philo-*, *-phile*, *-philous*/love
G. *phoro-*, *-phore*/bear, carry
G. *photo-*, *phos-*/light
G. *phyco-*/seaweed
G. *phyllo-*, *-phyll*/leaf
G. *phylo-*/tribe
G. *phyto-*, *-phyte*/plant
L. *pileo-*/cap
G. *plano-*, *plankto-*/wandering, roaming
G. *plasmo-*, *-plasm*, *-plast*/molded
G. *podo-*, *pedo-*, *-pede*, *-pod*, *-podium*/foot
L. *pom-*/apple
G. *porphyro-*/violet
G. *protero-*/before
G. *proto-*/first
G. *psittakos*/parrot
G. *psychro-*/cold
L. *pull-*/chick
L. *purpureo-*/violet red, purple
G. *pygo-*, *-pyge*/rump
L. *rami-*/branch
G. *raphe*/seam
L. *reni-*/kidney
G. *rhabdo-*/staff
G. *rhino-*/nose
G. *rhizo-*, *-rhiza*/root
G. *rhodo-*/red
G. *rhyncho-*/snout
L. *roseo-*/rose red
L. *rubri-*/red
L. *rumin-*/throat
G. *saccharo-*/sugar
G. *sapro-*/putrid
G. *sarco-*/flesh
G. *schizo-*, *schisto-*/split
G. *scler-*/hard

G. *scolex*, *scoleco-*/worm
G. *-scopic*/look
G. *septico-*/decaying
L. *septo-*/enclosure
L. *serra-*/saw
L. *seta-*/bristle
G. *sidero-*/iron
G. *siphon-*/tube
G. *sito-*, *-site*/food
G. *soma(to)-*, *-some*/body
G. *soro-*/receptacle
L. *speci-*/type
G. *sperma-*/seed
L. *spici-*/spike
L. *spini-*/spine
L. *spirali-*/twisted
G. *spiro-*/coil
G. *sporo-*, *-spore*/germ, seed
L. *spumi-*/foam
G. *-stasis*, *-stat*/stop
G. *-stele*/pillar
G. *steno-*/narrow
G. *stereo-*/solid
G. *sticho-*/row
G. *stigma(to)-*/mark
L. *stolo*/shoot, branch
G. *stoma(to)-*, *stomo-*, *-stome*/mouth
G. *strepto-*/twisted
G. *stylo-*/pen, column
L. *sulci-*/furrow
L. *sus*, *sui-*/pig
L. *taxi-*, *tacti-*/touch
G. *taxo-*/arrangement
G. *tele(o)-*, *telo-*, *teleuto-*/far, end
L. *testa*/brick, tile, shell
G. *thalasso-*/marine
G. *thallo-*/branch, shoot, sprout
G. *thamno-*/shrub
G. *thece-*, *-theca*/case, sheath
G. *thigmo-*/touch
G. *thio-*/sulfur
G. *toko-*/child
G. *-tome*, *-tomy*/cut
G. *toxi-*, *toxo-*/poison
G. *-troph-*/nourish

G. *-trop-*/turn
L. *tuber-*/swelling
L. *-ula, -ule, -ella, -illus, -illium*/ (dim. suffix)
L. *uredo*/itch, blight
L. *vacca, vacci-*/cow
L. *vacuo-*/empty
L. *verti-*/turn, whorl
L. *vesico-*/bladder
L. *violaceo-*/blue

L. *viridi-*/green
L. *-vorous*/eat, consume
G. *xantho-*/yellow
G. *xeno-*/strange
G. *xero-*/dry
G. *xylo-*/wood
G. *zoo-, -zoon*/animal
G. *zygo-, -zygy*/joined
G. *zym(at)o-, -zyme*/leaven

13

Bacteria

General Characteristics

The bacteria are procaryotic organisms that are non-photosynthetic or whose photosynthesis is not accompanied by the evolution of molecular oxygen. The groups recognized in this discussion as bacteria are listed in Table 13-1.

Morphology (Fig. 13-1). The bacteria include the smallest living organisms known, and only a few photosynthetic types of bacteria exceed the size of the smallest unicellular eucaryotic organisms. The relatively small size of bacterial cells is typical even of those types whose growth habit is multicellular and similar to the habit of algae or of molds. Accordingly, it is usually possible to recognize the bacteria in a mixed microbial population solely on the basis of cell size.

Most unicellular bacteria are rod-shaped (cylindric, with more or less rounded ends), and in almost all bacteria that develop as multicellular units, the component cells are approximately cylindric. Unicellular bacteria may also be spindle-shaped (fusiform), helical (spirilliform), comma-shaped (vibrioid), spheroid (coccoid), or ovoid; a few types are irregular, the cell shape varying from one individual to another in an otherwise homogeneous population. In one morphologically unique group, the spirochetes, the cell is a slender, flexible cylinder wound into a helix around a fibrillar axial filament.

Cells of certain unicellular bacteria tend to adhere to each other following cell division. The cells accumulate in characteristic arrays that reflect the plane(s) in which cell divisions occur. Thus, more or less regular clumps, sheets, or chains of cells are formed. These accumulations are not regarded as multi-cellular states because (1) they are transient and occasional, not a regular feature of the life history of individuals or populations, (2) their occurrence

149

TABLE 13-1. The Major Groups of Bacteria

Group	Order(s)*	Distinctive Feature(s) of the Order	Mechanism of Motility	Gram Reaction
Eubacteria	Eubacteriales	None; heterogeneous group of unicellular bacteria that lack the distinguishing features of any of the other orders	Flagella, peritrichous	+, −, variable
	Pseudomonadales	Unicellular in which flagella arise only from cell poles; includes physiologically similar non-motile bacteria	Flagella, polar or lophotrichous	−
Budding bacteria	Hyphomicrobiales	Reproduction by budding	Flagella, polar or peritrichous	−
Mycoplasmas	Mycoplasmatales	Definite cell wall absent, cell shape irregular	—	−
Rickettsiae (and Chlamydia)	Rickettsiales	Obligate intracellular parasites of animals	—	−
Filamentous bacteria	Chlamydobacteriales	Cells in sheathed trichomes	Flagella, lophotrichous	−
	Caryophanales	Cells in trichomes without sheaths	Flagella, peritrichous	−
Spirochetes	Spirochaetales	Helical cell with axial filament	Cellular undulations	−
Myxobacteria	Myxobacterales	Gliding motility	Gliding	−
Actinomycetes	Actinomycetales	Mycelial habit	Flagella, polar or lophotrichous. (Rare.)	+

*Orders as recognized in Bergey's *Manual of Determinative Bacteriology* (7th ed., 1957). Bergey's order Beggiatoales is regarded in this text as a category of non-photosynthetic counterparts of blue-green algae (Chap. 17).

A. Unicellular Forms

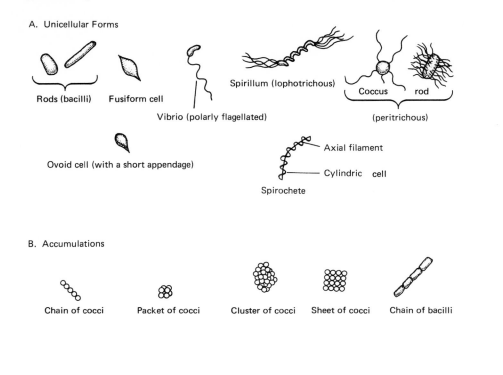

B. Accumulations

Chain of cocci   Packet of cocci   Cluster of cocci   Sheet of cocci   Chain of bacilli

C. Multicellular Forms

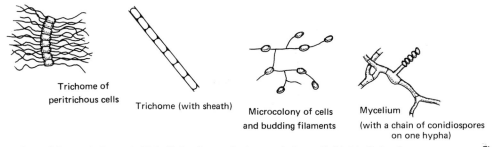

Trichome of
peritrichous cells   Trichome (with sheath)   Microcolony of cells   Mycelium
                                                and budding filaments   (with a chain of conidiospores
                                                                          on one hypha)

Bacterial morphology. *A.* Unicellular forms. *B.* Accumulations. *C.* Multicellular forms.   **Figure 13-1**

and dimensions are influenced by environmental factors that do not otherwise affect growth or cell division, and (3) the metabolic activities and developmental potential of individual cells are not detectably affected by inclusion within such accumulations.

Three types of multicellular vegetative states are known that are characteristic of certain bacteria in most environments. These are trichomes, microcolonies containing budding filaments, and mycelia. A trichome is a chain of cells that remain linked to each other indefinitely. The trichome grows in length, and the number of cells increases as the result of cell divisions throughout the chain. Reproduction of a bacterial trichome occurs by subdivision of the unit into two (sometimes more) multicellular units, or by release of unicellular units from the end of the chain. In some genera, a tubular sheath surrounds the cells; one or more trichomes may be enclosed within the sheath.

Microcolonies are formed by the photosynthetic bacteria that produce buds from the ends of filamentous outgrowths of the cell. As the buds mature, they produce further filaments and buds; the filaments may also branch and give rise to buds. The resulting microcolony comprises cells united by the filaments. It is reproduced by fragmentation into smaller multicellular units or, presumably, by release of an occasional bud from its parent filament.

The most elaborate multicellular state occurs among the actinomycetes. Following germination, a unicellular reproductive unit develops into a chain of cells that branches extensively and becomes a mass of chains of cells. This mass is a bacterial mycelium. Specialized branches may be formed that subdivide into unicellular units that serve as the reproductive and disseminative stage.

Reproduction and Dormancy. Reproduction in bacteria typically occurs by binary fission. Multiple fission is rare among bacteria. Reproduction by budding occurs in only a few types. Release of unicellular propagative units occurs in some multicellular bacteria, as mentioned above. Multicellular bacteria can also reproduce from fragments of one or more cells released from the multicellular unit by external mechanical forces.

Reproduction in bacteria is universally independent of sexual events; i.e., it is asexual. Sexual events can occur in bacteria, but reproduction is not associated with them. As far as known, bacteria are haploid throughout their life cycles. Diploid states resulting from sexual events are typically transient and partial (see Chap. 19).

Specialization for dormancy is not typical of bacteria; however, three types of dormant stages occur, each type characteristic of only one or a few groups of bacteria. (1) **Endospores** are formed, usually one per cell, by differentiation of a portion of the protoplast into a typically thick-walled, relatively dehydrated unit that is released from the remainder of the cell when the cell lyses. (2) **Cysts** and **microcysts** are derived from entire individual cells; the vegetative cell becomes shortened or spheric and develops a thickened wall. (3) The unicellular disseminative units called **conidia** that are produced by some mycelial bacteria are dormant; they can survive at least for several days without nutrients or water. Each of these types of dormant stages is resistant to desiccation. Their resistance to other environmental factors such as heat, sunlight, and chemicals that inactivate growing cells is variable; endospores are generally much more stable under a variety of adverse conditions than are cysts and conidia.

Locomotion. Locomotion in eubacteria and filamentous bacteria is due to the activity of flagella, of which there may be one to several hundred per cell.

The distribution of flagella on the cell is used as a primary taxonomic criterion among eubacteria. Three general patterns occur: polar (one polar flagellum), lophotrichous (several polar flagella), and peritrichous (lateral flagella) distribution. These are illustrated in Figure 13-1.

The motility of spirochetes is generally attributed to contraction of the fibrils of the axial filament; such contraction apparently causes the helix to elongate and shorten and to move by a serpentine mechanism. Locomotion of spirochetes appears to depend on some environmental resistance to their movement; cells suspended in a medium of low viscosity rotate about their long axes, whereas in viscous media or when in contact with a solid surface the cells rotate and also move rapidly and often jerkily in a direction parallel to their long axes.

Gliding locomotion is typical of myxobacteria. It occurs only when the cell is in contact with a solid surface; the motion of the cells is smooth, not jerky as in the spirochetes. The mechanical basis of this type of locomotion is not yet understood.

Distribution and Physiologic Diversity. Bacteria occur in every type of habitat that can support living organisms. Bacteria grow in all types of soils and bodies of water and survive prolonged suspension in air. They parasitize or are otherwise associated with every type of organism.[1] Bacteria are present, often with fungi, in every type of inanimate organic material undergoing chemical transformation ("decomposition"); every naturally occurring organic compound can be altered chemically by some type of bacterium.

This exceptionally wide natural distribution is a reflection of the physiologic diversity of this group, which exceeds that of all other groups of organisms together. In contrast to all other organisms, the bacteria include representatives that can grow in inorganic environments without illumination; i.e., all known chemolithotrophs are bacteria. Every form of nitrogen and of sulfur, whether organic or inorganic, is suitable as a source of that element for the development of one or more kinds of bacteria. As a group, bacteria can grow photosynthetically and in the dark, aerobically and anaerobically, and over a wider range of pH values and of temperatures than any other group.

Many of the habitats in which bacteria can grow are also suitable for the development of other protists, with which the bacteria must compete for growth substrates. However, any habitat that supports the growth of a variety of microbes usually includes several niches, which can be defined in terms of their chemical composition. Particularly in soil, where substances may absorb selectively to the surfaces of particles of certain composition, these niches may be physically separate. Each such niche supports the growth of a narrower range of physiologic types than can grow in the larger habitat, and the narrower this range, the greater the probability that some type of bacterium will occupy the niche.

---

[1]Bacteria and other protists that inhabit humans are discussed in Chap. 22. The relationship of protists to human diseases is not treated extensively in this part of the text.

For certain physiologic types of bacteria, there are counterparts among other groups of protists. However, the details of the common physiologic properties are sufficiently different to allow the bacteria to occupy niches distinct from those occupied by the higher forms. For example, photolithotrophic bacteria utilize for their photosynthetic activities electron sources and light wavelengths that are not utilized by algae (or by photoorganotrophic bacteria). The photo-organotrophic bacteria, in turn, occur in anaerobic environments and can utilize organic compounds that are rarely suitable as substrates for fermentative metabolism, and the few types of algae that can grow photoorganotrophically are aerobes.

Chemoorganotrophic bacteria usually share their chemical environment with protozoa and fungi. Three physiologic traits contribute to the survival of bacteria in habitats where these other protists occur: (1) free-living bacteria are generally more independent nutritionally than are protozoa, and their activity does not depend on the availability of specific micronutrients in the environment; (2) bacteria can utilize a greater variety of organic compounds as sources of energy and carbon than can fungi and protozoa; and (3) whereas the majority of fungi and protozoa require ammonia or organic nitrogen and reduced sulfur (inorganic or organic) as sources of nitrogen and sulfur, most free-living bacteria can also use nitrates and sulfates, and some can use N_2, a capability not known to occur among protozoa or filamentous fungi. Chemo-organotrophic bacteria that can be cultivated in the laboratory typically exhibit much higher metabolic rates than those exhibited by protozoa and fungi. Although high rates of metabolism (and growth) are not likely to be sustained for long periods in a natural environment, the capacity for rapid growth probably allows bacteria to respond more quickly to transient favorable conditions than is possible for other protists.

Because bacteria are far more diverse physiologically than morphologically, their classification is based largely on physiologic traits. Consequently, many higher taxons (e.g., families) are fairly homogeneous with respect to physiologic traits, but include rods and cocci, and in some cases spirilla as well.

The Gram Reaction. A brief description of the distinctive features of the orders of bacteria was presented in Table 13-1, as well as an indication of the **gram reaction.** This property is not used as a taxonomic criterion, above the rank of family, but it is so well correlated with combinations of other traits that all but one of the orders is homogeneous with regard to this property.

The gram stain was developed in 1884 by a Danish physician, Christian Gram, as a procedure for detecting disease-producing bacteria in animal tissue. The gram stain reaction is determined by microscopic examination of cells that have been successively stained with a basic dye (usually crystal violet), treated with an iodine solution, and rinsed with an organic solvent such as acetone or alcohol. Gram-positive cells retain the violet stain. Gram-negative cells are decolorized by the solvent; the fourth step in the procedure is application of a red stain (usually safranin) so that gram-negative cells can be visualized.

Gram was studying gram-positive bacteria; animal tissue is gram negative.

Of the ten orders listed in Table 13-1, all but two contain only gram-negative bacteria. Some representatives of Eubacteriales are gram positive or gram variable; in the latter type, the gram reaction varies among individual cells and even within a cell. All the actinomycetes that can be stained (see Mycobacteriaceae section) are gram positive.

Although gram positiveness is exhibited by a minority of types of bacteria, many of the bacteria that directly affect the welfare of man, particularly his health, are gram positive. These include such organisms as the causative agents of diphtheria, pneumococcal pneumonia and scarlet fever, most of the bacteria that sour milk and spoil foods, and most of the bacteria whose natural habitat is the skin and mucous membranes of the human body. Accordingly, the gram reaction is of considerable practical value in identifying and ultimately controlling the bacteria that influence the public health.

Order Eubacteriales

The order Eubacteriales includes a wide variety of bacteria that are placed in a single order on the basis of their lack of the morphologic traits used to distinguish the bacteria of the other orders. Generally, they are unicellular (or transiently multicellular), but gram reaction and cell shape vary among the families.

Families Bacteroidaceae and Enterobacteriaceae. The contents of the intestines of healthy warm-blooded animals are composed mainly of bacteria. Seventy per cent of the nitrogen in human feces is accounted for by the nitrogen in bacterial cells. The predominant enteric organisms in the human are anaerobic, gram-negative, rod-shaped bacteria of the genus *Bacteroides* and of other genera of family Bacteroidaceae. This family comprises irregular and rod-shaped bacteria, most of which are somewhat difficult to cultivate in the laboratory. They usually require anaerobic conditions and many organic micronutrients. Artificial media are usually supplemented with body fluids, e.g., blood serum or ascitic fluid, for cultivation of these organisms.

About 10 per cent of the bacterial population of the intestine of man and other mammals is accounted for by facultative anaerobes. These are the coliform bacteria, mainly members of the genus *Escherichia,* and closely related types such as *Proteus.* They are representatives of a large group of similar organisms that occur in a variety of habitats; all are placed in the family Enterobacteriaceae on the bases of both morphologic and physiologic properties. All are gram-negative rods that, if motile, bear peritrichous flagella. They can grow aerobically by respiratory metabolism and anaerobically by the fermentation of sugars. Most isolates can grow in chemically defined media that contain one sugar, ammonium ion as a source of nitrogen, inorganic salts, and (for some isolates) one organic micronutrient.

The coliform bacteria are classified informally as two groups: the coli group and the aerogenes group. The former group includes principally parasitic (intestinal) types which produce a mixture of organic acids (formic, acetic, lactic, and succinic) and some ethanol as products of their fermentation of glucose; this is called a "mixed-acid fermentation." It is characteristic of *Escherichia coli,* the species that occurs normally in human intestines. The aerogenes group includes organisms that, during fermentation, typically convert a larger proportion of glucose to neutral products, particularly 2, 3-butylene glycol. A mixture of acids is also produced. This "butylene glycol fermentation" is characteristic of *Aerobacter aerogenes,* a free-living species that occurs in water and may also be found in soil. The aerogenes type of fermentation is accompanied by the production of gases (CO_2 and H_2); the production of gas is variable in the coli type of fermentation.

   For purposes of water sanitation, three groups of coliform bacteria are recognized: (1) free-living aquatic forms of the aerogenes group, likely to be present in any water supply; (2) normally parasitic forms of the coli group, which do not survive more than about a week in lakes, rivers, or reservoirs; their presence indicates recent pollution of the water by animal feces; and (3) parasitic forms that cause enteric diseases; they are usually not present in the feces of healthy humans; when present in water supplies in only small numbers, they can cause disease in humans who consume the water. The diseases that are communicated among humans through water supplies polluted with human feces include typhoid fever (caused by *Salmonella typhosa*), bacillary dysentery (caused by *Shigella* spp., principally *Sh. dysenteriae,* see Fig. 13-11), and enteric and paratyphoid fevers of varying severity (usually caused by *Salmonella* species).

   Enterobacteriaceae also include a diverse group of plant parasites. These are classified in the genus *Erwinia,* which includes both mixed acid and butylene glycol fermentative types. These organisms invade stems, roots, leaves, flowers, fruits, or tubers of living plants and cause dry necroses, wilts, soft rots, or galls; their hosts include woody plants, grasses, succulents, and tuberaceous plants.

Family Bacillaceae. The family Bacillaceae contains gram-positive or variable rod-shaped bacteria that are typically motile and peritrichously flagellated; the distinctive feature of this group is the development of endospores. Two genera, *Clostridium* and *Bacillus,* accommodate the anaerobic and aerobic spore-formers, respectively. Representatives of both genera occur commonly in soil. Clostridia are usually present in decaying plant and animal remains, and also occur in animal intestines as normal inhabitants. Bacilli are often found in dairy products as well as plant material and soil, and rarely in animals.

   Clostridium isolates are strict anaerobes, and the vegetative cells of some types die when exposed to O_2 only briefly—a matter of seconds. During growth, they obtain energy by the fermentation of carbohydrates and proteins. Their fermentative activities typically result in a mixture of products including acids, gases, and neutral substances such as various alcohols and acetone; and putrid odors. They have been employed in the industrial production of organic solvents from carbohydrates.

   For technical reasons, the aerobic spore-formers are easier to handle in the laboratory, and most of the information concerning the structure and development of endospores has been obtained from studies of sporulation in *Bacillus* representatives. The relatively limited amount of information about *Clostridium* spores indicates, however, that the process and the product are similar in both genera.

Distinguishable steps in the development of endospores are indicated in Figure 13-2. The details of sporulation are discussed in Chapter 18. Sporulating cells and germinating spores are illustrated in Figures 18-2 and 18-3.

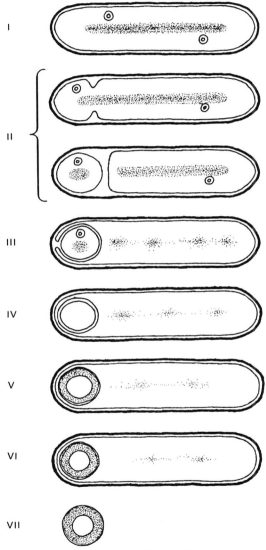

Stages in sporulation in Bacillaceae. *I*, Preseptation—axial chromatin; *II*, septation; *III*, en-   **Figure 13-2**
gulfment of spore protoplast (shown nearly completed); *IV*, cortex formation; *V*, coat formation
(spore becomes refractile); *VI*, maturation; *VII*, free spore—sporangium has disintegrated.

Spore components (Fig. 13-3) are, in order from the exterior: a loosely-fitting covering, the exosporium (not present in all species); a spore coat, which may have two distinct layers; a cortex, which is a concentric mass of fibrils; a spore wall, which is very thin in some cells, particularly of clostridia; a spore membrane often difficult to distinguish in electron micrographs from the spore wall; and a central core, which contains nucleoplasm and certain types of ribosomes. The water content of the spore is less than 50 per cent of its mass, in contrast to about 75 per cent for vegetative cells, and it seems that particularly the core is dehydrated.

Endospores are typically resistant to inactivation by heat and may survive more than 30 minutes of boiling. However, the heat resistance of endospores varies among isolates and with the conditions under which sporulation occurred. Maximum heat resistance is observed for spores formed in a medium in which the carbon source is exhausted while calcium ion is still available. Such spores contain large amounts (up to 8 per cent of the dry weight) of dipicolinic acid, an organic substance known to occur naturally only in bacterial endospores. It is associated with calcium and localized within the core, where it possibly plays a role in the stabilization of dehydrated proteins.

The heat resistance of endospores has been of great concern to food processors and physicians, especially surgeons. Human diseases caused by members of Bacillaceae can be traced to the presence of spores in preserved foods and in wounds resulting from violence (automobiles, assaults, wars), surgery, or mechanically assisted childbirth. The Bacillaceae species that cause diseases in humans normally occur in soil, in animal intestines and feces, and on vegetation. The diseases they cause are botulism (*Clostridium botulinum*), tetanus (*C. tetani*), and gas gangrene (*C.* spp., commonly *C. perfringens*). Anthrax (*Bacillus anthracis*) is primarily a disease of animals such as livestock, but can occur in humans who handle livestock and animal products such as wool and hides. Another *Bacillus* species (*B. thuringensis*) causes a toxic disease of insects; the toxin accumulates as a crystal within the bacilli during sporulation. The crystalline toxin is released when the cell disintegrates and liberates the endospore.

Family Micrococcaceae. The bacteria of this family are gram-positive, -negative, or -variable spheric organisms that divide in more than one plane so that long chains of cocci do not accumulate when cells do not separate after division. The family includes chemoorganotrophic bacteria, which may be aerobes, anaerobes, or facultative anaerobes. Representatives are found in soil, decomposing organic materials, and water; the aerobic and facultative anaerobic types are commonly found in agricultural products, particularly dairy products. Many types survive drying and exposure to sunlight, the latter particularly if the cells are pigmented, and are commonly found in the air.

One group of micrococci, placed in the genus *Staphylococcus*, exists in nature only on the skin, in skin glands, and on the mucous membranes of warm-blooded vertebrates. They become established in the nose and on the skin of newborn humans within ten days after birth. When introduced into certain

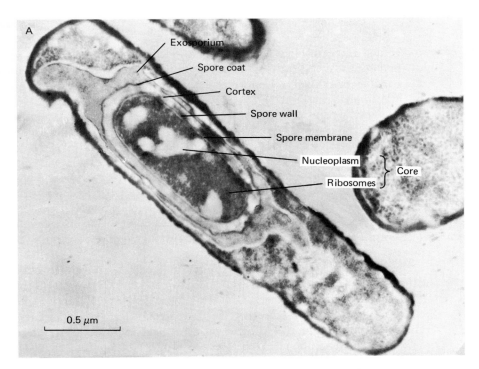

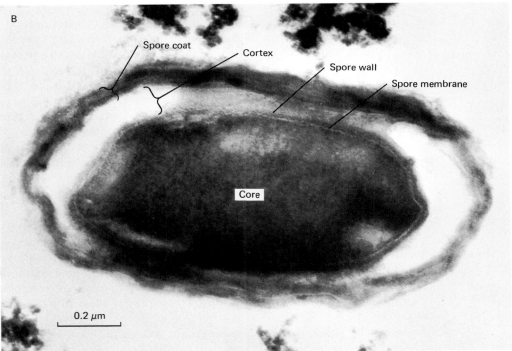

Bacillus spores (see also Figs. 18-2 and 18-3). *A.* A sporulating cell ("sporangium") of *B. cereus*. (From Remsen, C. C., D. G. Lundgren, and R. A. Slepecky, 1966. *J. Bact.,* **91**:324. By permission of the American Society for Microbiology.) *B.* A free spore of *B. megaterium*. (Courtesy of D. G. Lundgren and N. Slepecky.)

Figure 13-3

foods such as cream-filled pastries or meat salads containing mayonnaise, cocci of the species *S. aureus* grow and elaborate a toxin. Persons who consume the food contract food poisoning which is severe in its short-lived symptoms, but not fatal.

The other genera of this family comprise cocci that are differentiated on the basis of grouping of cells that occurs particularly on solidified media and in natural materials. Species are differentiated according to physiologic traits.

Two genera (*Micrococcus* and *Sarcina*) of micrococci are widespread in nature. *Micrococcus* species occur in association with various animals and animal products (milk, urine, skin secretions), soil, mud and sea water, and natural and artificial brines. The cells occur singly or in irregular clusters; most isolates are non-motile, but motile forms occur that bear one or several flagella. The gram reaction varies among isolates, although some species are regularly positive or negative.

Micrococci isolated from brines are halophilic and can grow in salt (NaCl) concentrations of up to 30 per cent. Although the upper limit of salt tolerance varies somewhat from species to species, most isolates can survive and some can grow in salt-free media; that is, they are not obligate halophiles. Their ability to remain intact in salt-free media is probably due to the presence of a definite mucopeptide cell wall, which is thin or absent from the rod-shaped salt-dependent halophiles (*Halobacterium;* see Pseudomonadales, below).

Sarcina species (Fig. 13-4) are usually present in air, mud, and sewage sludge. The cells of some species are relatively large for Micrococcaceae (up to 4 or 5 μm in diameter; others are usually not more than 2 μm in diameter). Typically, at least under certain conditions, the cells divide successively in three perpendicular planes and accumulate in regular three-dimensional packets of 8, 16, or 32 cells. Young *Sarcina* cells of all species are gram positive, but many become gram negative under conditions that retard growth. Like the genus *Micrococcus, Sarcina* includes a variety of physiologic types and is subdivided into species on bases of pigmentation and physiologic properties.

One species, *Sporosarcina* (*Sarcina*) *ureae,* forms endospores that are structurally similar to Bacillaceae spores and share their remarkable heat resistance. These cocci are gram positive and in some environments are motile by means of a single flagellum per cell.

Family Lactobacillaceae. All representatives of this family are gram positive and grow well only on carbohydrates, from which they produce lactic acid by fermentation. Some species can grow in the presence of air, but they are not able to utilize O_2 by respiration; whether or not O_2 is present, these organisms obtain energy for growth by fermentative processes. Other species comprise organisms that can grow anaerobically only; a few of these are killed by exposure to O_2.

Rods as well as cocci are placed in this family. Among the cocci, cell division occurs in only one plane (or at most two), so that cells occur as individuals, in pairs, tetrads, or chains, but not in packets or clusters. The rods, like the

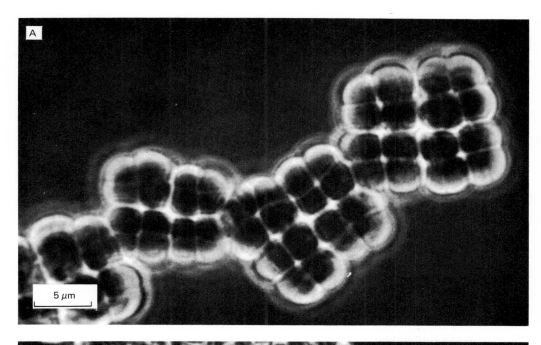

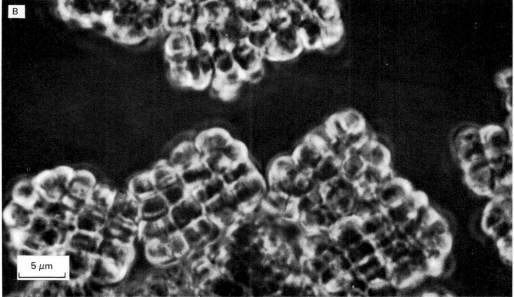

Sarcina spp. *A. S. maxima,* living cells. *B. S. ventriculi,* living cells. (From Holt, S. C., and E. Canale-Parola, 1967. *J. Bact.,* **93**:399. By permission of the American Society for Microbiology.)   **Figure 13-4**

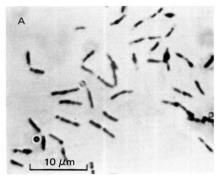 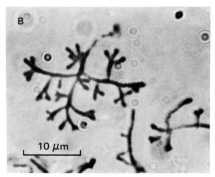

Figure 13-5   *Lactobacillus bifidus,* stained cells. *A.* Unbranched cells, cultivated in a complex organic medium. *B.* Dichotomously branched cells, cultivated in the same medium as the cells in *A,* but supplemented with NaCl (0.35 *M*). (From Kojima, M., S. Suda, S. Hotta, and K. Hamada, 1968. *J. Bact.,* **95**:710. By permission of the American Society for Microbiology.)

cocci, commonly accumulate in chains. The cells of some species tend to branch in certain environments (Fig. 13-5).

These lactic acid bacteria are represented by two ecologic groups—those types that occur primarily as animal inhabitants, and those types that occur in dairy products and on plants; representatives of the latter group become especially numerous in plant materials undergoing anaerobic decomposition.

The animal hosts of lactic acid bacteria are usually warm-blooded vertebrates; man and his domesticated animals have their respective lactic acid bacterial inhabitants of the mouth and upper respiratory tract, the intestines, and the vagina. Two groups of cocci account for most of the diseases of humans that are caused by lactic acid bacteria: the pneumococci (*Diplococcus pneumoniae*), which are commonly present in the upper respiratory tract, but whose development in the lungs causes pneumococcal pneumonia; and the beta-hemolytic[2] streptococci (*Streptococcus pyogenes*). These streptococci occasionally inhabit humans without causing disease, but their presence usually results in acute pharyngitis, called "strep throat." A variety of diseases accompany or follow streptococcal throat infections (see Table 22-2).

The alpha-hemolytic streptococci (*Streptococcus salivarius* and others) are normal human inhabitants and rarely cause human disease. Because of the green zone around their colonies on blood-containing agar medium, these organisms are commonly referred to as the viridans group of streptococci. Because they reside in the mouth and rapidly convert sugars to lactic acid, they are currently regarded as a major cause of the first step in tooth decay—dissolution of the enamel.

Saprophytic lactic acid bacteria occur in a variety of organic materials, particularly those that accumulate on farms. Some of the lactic acid bacteria

[2]When these streptococci are cultivated on artificial medium containing red blood cells, the blood cells in the immediate vicinity of the bacterial colonies lyse. The clear, colorless zone around the colonies is the phenomenon designated **beta-hemolysis.** Alpha-hemolytic streptococci cause blood cells around their colonies to disintegrate, but not dissolve; the zone of **alpha-hemolysis** is cloudy and greenish.

found in dairy products and harvested plants originate in animal feces that contaminate such products, but others are perpetuated solely in storage places and on utensils. Their fermentative activities alter the materials in which they occur, in some cases rendering the materials more suitable as foodstuffs, in some cases spoiling the materials for human or livestock consumption. Their fermentations have been exploited by man in the conversion of milk to products such as butter, cheeses, yogurt, and milk drinks (e.g., kefir and buttermilk); and in the pickling of vegetables (cucumbers become pickles, cabbage becomes sauerkraut) and vegetation (green fodder becomes ensilage).

Families Propionibacteriaceae and Corynebacteriaceae. The family Propioni-bacteriaceae is represented predominantly by rod-shaped, non-spore-forming, gram-positive, typically non-motile bacteria. They are commonly found in dairy products. They can continue to grow in such materials after development of lactic acid bacteria by virtue of their ability to ferment lactic acid, an ability uncommon among living systems. They convert lactic to a mixture of propionic and acetic acids and CO_2. In cheeses, their presence results in the development of large gas bubbles; they can be isolated from any natural "Swiss" cheese.

The corynebacteria are found free-living in soil, in decomposing organic matter, and in dairy products, and as inhabitants of plants and animals. They are distinguished from other gram-positive, non-spore-forming, basically rod-shaped eubacteria by their inability to ferment sugars, with the exception of certain pathogenic types that ferment carbohydrates to lactic or propionic acids. They are also distinguished by a combination of morphologic traits: the cells are typically swollen toward one or both poles; cells stained with methylene blue appear beaded; and cell division may be completed by a snapping motion, which results in the cells becoming aligned at acute angles or in rows with their long axes parallel. Motility occurs in some of the parasitic forms; flagella may be sparse (one to four per cell in plant parasitic *Corynebacterium* spp.) or numerous (in animal parasitic *Listeria*), but in all cases the flagella are peritrichous.

The free-living corynebacteria are active in the aerobic oxidation of organic material; typically, an individual isolate can utilize a fairly wide variety of organic compounds for its growth and is independent of organic micronutrients. Many can utilize inorganic nitrogen sources such as nitrate and ammonium salts. Certain species are, for non-spore-forming bacteria, unusually heat-resistant; they can be isolated from pasteurized milk and from heat-disinfected dairy utensils.

Corynebacteria that normally inhabit humans can usually be cultivated on peptone or other routinely used complex media. These media must be supple-mented with animal materials such as blood, serum, or poultry eggs for the cultivation of pathogenic corynebacteria, e.g., *Corynebacterium diphtheriae*, the causative agent of diphtheria (see Chap. 22, "Diphtheria").

Families Azotobacteraceae and Rhizobiaceae. Two families of Eubacteriales are best known for their ability to utilize N_2 as a source of nitrogen for growth.

Although this capacity is now known to occur in many other types of bacteria (e.g., anaerobic spore-formers and photosynthetic and chemoorganotrophic pseudomonads), N_2 fixation seems to play a greater role in the survival of azotobacters and rhizobia than of the other types.

The bacteria classified in the family Azotobacteraceae are gram-negative spheroid, rod- or oval-shaped forms that, when motile, possess peritrichous flagella (Fig. 13-6). Only one genus, *Azotobacter*, is recognized by Bergey's *Manual*, but the genus *Beijerinckia* is also used by many bacteriologists. These bacteria occur in soil and, less commonly, in fresh water. They are aerobic, utilize carbohydrates as sources of carbon and energy, and can utilize inorganic nitrogenous compounds such as nitrate or ammonia as well as N_2 as sources of nitrogen for growth. Atmospheric nitrogen is reduced to ammonia for use in biosynthetic processes. It is characteristic of these organisms that they excrete

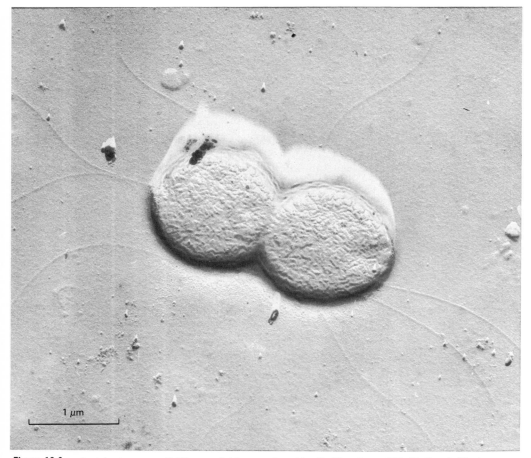

1 μm

Figure 13-6   *Azotobacter* sp., a dividing peritrichous, spheroid cell. (Courtesy of M. D. Socolofsky.)

a considerable amount of the ammonia and thereby increase the content of combined nitrogen of the soil in which they grow.

The azotobacters are unusual among representatives of Eubacteriales in the ability of some strains to produce dormant cysts (Figs. 13-7 and 13-8). The cysts are not so resistant to heat and desiccation as are endospores, but they can survive for long periods without nutrients.

The family Rhizobiaceae includes the genus *Rhizobium,* represented by gram-negative rod-shaped bacteria. They can live independently in soils, but are found only in areas where leguminous plants are also growing. They enter the root hairs of such plants and multiply within the cells (Fig. 13-9). Division of root cells is stimulated by the infection, and white or pink nodules develop to macroscopic size on the roots. If the rhizobia and plant constitute an "effective" pair, N_2 fixation occurs in the nodules. Some of the fixed nitrogen is used by the rhizobia and the plant for their growth; some is released into the soil. Additional fixed nitrogen is added to the soil when the plants die and decay in the field.

Family Neisseriaceae. The family Neisseriaceae comprises two genera of parasitic cocci which are aerobic or facultatively anaerobic (*Neisseria*) or anaerobic (*Veillonella*). Although representatives of *Veillonella* and rarely *Neisseria* can be found in warm-blooded animals other than man, these bacteria are most commonly reported from human sources. In man, certain species of *Neisseria* occur normally in the upper respiratory tract, whereas *Veillonella* species occur mainly in the mouth and digestive tract.

The most serious diseases caused by representatives of Neisseriaceae are epidemic meningitis (*N. meningitidis*) and gonorrhea (*N. gonorrhoeae*). Both organisms have become highly adapted to the human body, particularly with regard to the narrow temperature range maintained by the host. They die rapidly when dried, or when cooled below about 25° C for several hours. This adaptation is reflected in the epidemiology of the diseases they cause. Meningococcal meningitis is not common in the general population, but may spread rapidly among armed forces personnel crowded in barracks; the organism is acquired through the respiratory tract. Gonorrhea is a venereal disease, the gonococcus being transmitted by direct contact between infected tissues and an uninfected person.

Diseases directly attributed to *Veillonella* species are few. However, these bacteria are commonly encountered, apparently as secondary invaders, in patients with measles, dental abscesses, tonsillitis, or scarlet fever.

Family Brucellaceae. The bacteria classified in the family Brucellaceae are rod-shaped or elongated spheroids. Many are motile by means of peritrichous flagella. Brucellaceae representatives are typically smaller than most other types of eubacteria; the short dimension may be only about 0.2 μm, and the long dimension of rods up to 1 μm. Some tend to elongate beyond 1 μm, but the

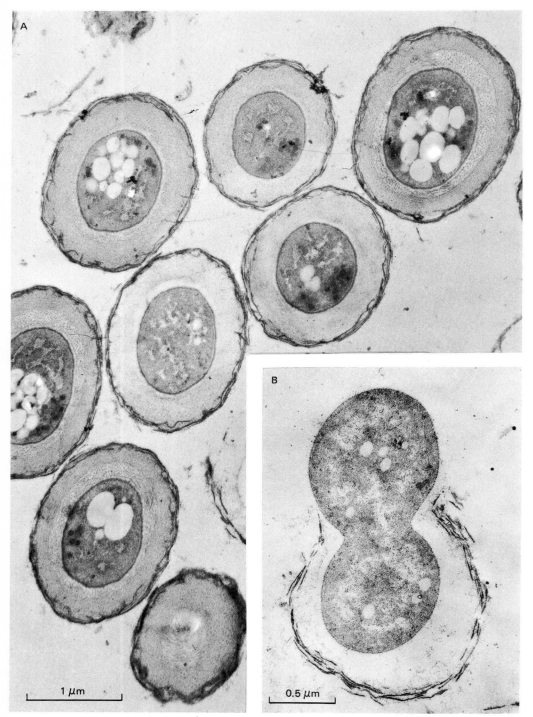

Figure 13-7   *Azotobacter* cysts. *A.* Dormant cysts. *B.* A germinating cyst, subsequent to rupture of the cyst wall and prior to the first fission of the growing cell. (From Wyss, O., M. G. Neumann, and M. D. Socolofsky, 1961. *J. Biophys. Biochem. Cytol.,* **10**:555. By permission of The Rockefeller University Press.)

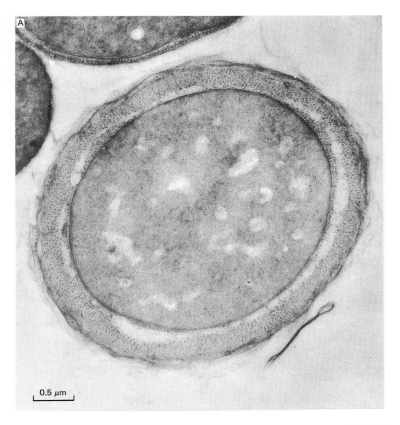

0.5 μm

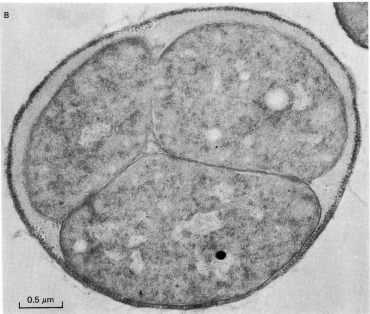

0.5 μm

Giant cysts of *Azotobacter*, formed by certain strains. *A.* A dormant cyst. *B.* A cyst at an early stage in germination. Fission may occur within a giant cyst prior to emergence of the protoplast(s) from the cyst wall; one to four cells may emerge. (From Beaman, B. L., L. E. Jackson, and D. M. Shankel, 1968. *J. Bact.*, **96**:266. By permission of the American Society for Microbiology.)   **Figure 13-8**

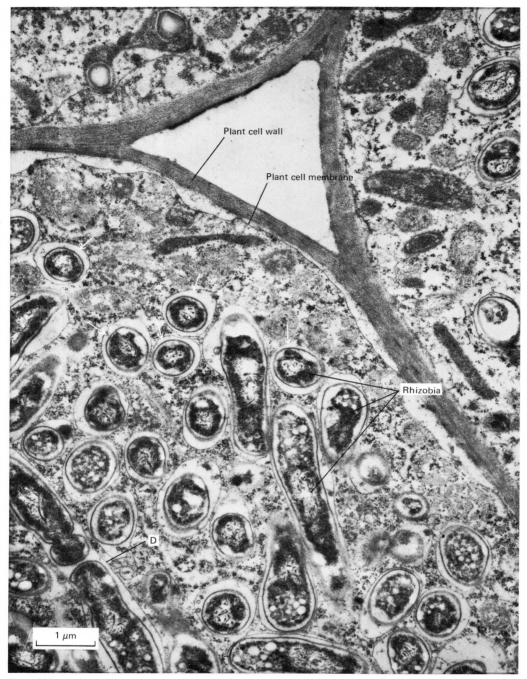

Plant cell wall

Plant cell membrane

Rhizobia

D

1 μm

Figure 13-9 Rhizobia (*Rhizobium japonicum*) within cells of five-day-old soybean nodules. The vesicle (arrows) within which each bacterium is enclosed was derived from the plant cell membrane as the bacterium entered the plant protoplast. The bacteria multiply within their vesicles (as at *D*), and in older nodules most of the vesicles contain several bacterial cells. (From Goodchild, D. J., and F. J. Bergersen, 1966. *J. Bact.*, **92**:204. By permission of the American Society for Microbiology.)

long cells are still less than 0.5 μm in diameter. All representatives are animal parasites; their hosts include a few cold- and a wide variety of warm-blooded vertebrates. Pathogenic strains may enter the host body through intact mucous membrane or skin and invade the bloodstream and internal organs; many types grow intracellularly in specific types of cells of the host.

Species of the genera *Pasteurella* (plague, tularemia), *Bordetella* (whooping cough), *Haemophilus* (upper respiratory infections, meningitis, chancroid), *Brucella* (undulant fever), and others (conjunctivitis) cause the human diseases indicated in parentheses. Many diseases of livestock and poultry and other domesticated animals are also caused by Brucellaceae representatives.

Order Mycoplasmatales

The order Mycoplasmatales comprises bacteria that lack a cell wall and whose cell form, consequently, is irregular. They occur as free-living organisms in soil and sewage and as parasites of animals. Only one genus, *Mycoplasma,* has been established within this order; species are differentiated on bases of colonial morphology and physiologic properties.

Mycoplasmas can be cultivated in the laboratory only in media containing high concentrations of organic materials and blood serum or other body fluid. The cells are osmotically fragile, and the media must also contain solutes (NaCl is usually used) at concentrations that afford an osmotic pressure approximately that of blood plasma. Most isolates also require vitamins, nucleic acid precursors, and O_2; a few types are anaerobes or facultative anaerobes. Parasitic mycoplasmas require steroids such as cholesterol; steroids are utilized, at least in part, as components of the cell membrane. So far as known, steroids are not required for the growth of any other type of bacterium. On solidified media, mycoplasmas form colonies (Fig. 13-10*A*) that do not exceed 0.5 mm in diameter when fully developed; the maximum diameter varies among isolates and may be as little as 20 μm.

Apparently as a consequence of the absence of a cell wall, any of three mechanisms of reproduction is available to an individual mycoplasmal cell: (1) fission, with two or more progeny of approximately equal size; (2) budding of small units formed at the cell surface; (3) internal reorganization by which most of the protoplast is converted into several small units that, when completed, are released through the parent cell surface. The reproductive units formed by the second and third processes are called elementary bodies; they are the smallest known viable bacteria. In electron micrographs (Fig. 13-10 *B–D*), apparently mature elementary bodies measure as little as 150 nm in diameter.

Mycoplasmas seem to inhabit many animals without causing disease, even though they multiply in regions of the body that are normally sterile, including blood, joint and pleural fluids, and the spinal column. In man, they are a part of the normal microbiota of the mucous membranes of the mouth and the genitourinary tract. Disease-producing types of mycoplasmas grow intracellularly in their hosts. In diseased hosts, the parasites are usually found in cells

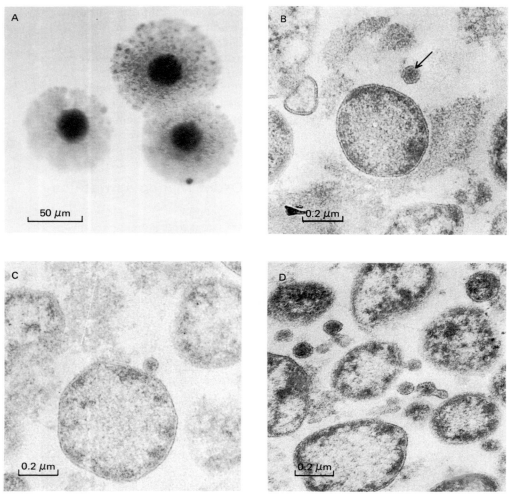

Figure 13-10 *Mycoplasma. A.* Three colonies of approximately maximum size, with the dense central area and diffuse outer region typical of *Mycoplasma* colonies on solidified media. (Courtesy of K. Hummeler.) *B.* A cell and an elementary body (arrow) with an angular outline typical of this strain (strain G). *C.* A cell with an elementary body arising, apparently as a bud. *D.* A mixture of cells of various sizes and elementary bodies. (*B, C,* and *D* from Hummeler, K., N. Tomassini, and L. Hayflick, 1965. *J. Bact.,* **90:**517. By permission of the American Society for Microbiology.)

of the central nervous system and of the linings of fluid-containing cavities, e.g., around the lungs, joints, and viscera. Several diseases of livestock and rodents are known to be due to mycoplasmal infections, including bovine pleuropneumonia, sheep and goat lactating disease (agalactia), and nervous diseases of rats and mice. Only one human disease, primary atypical pneumonia, has been demonstrated to result from a mycoplasmal infection.

Order Rickettsiales and Chlamydia

The order Rickettsiales accommodates small (see Fig. 13-11) rod-shaped (0.3 × 1 μm) or spheroid (0.3 μm diameter) bacteria that occur in nature in the gut lining of arthropods, typically as intracellular parasites. Although the natural hosts apparently are not diseased by rickettsial infections, diseases are produced in mammals that acquire rickettsiae from the saliva of blood-sucking arthropods, from arthropod feces deposited on broken skin, or, in one case (Q fever), from dried infected material that is inhaled.

Rickettsiae have not yet been cultivated in inanimate environments. They seem able to grow and multiply only within living animal cells. Because of this obligate intracellular habitat and their small size, rickettsiae have been regarded as possibly the type of protist from which viruses could descend. However, several kinds of evidence indicate that they are not structurally or biochemically different from other unicellular bacteria. (1) Electron micrographs of sectioned rickettsiae reveal a cellular organization typical of bacteria; none of the characteristic subcellular structures is absent. (2) Mucopeptide has been identified by chemical analysis as a constituent of the cell wall of one type of rickettsia (*Coxiella burnetii*). (3) Most types of rickettsiae are rod-shaped, which implies that they possess walls more rigid than protoplasm.

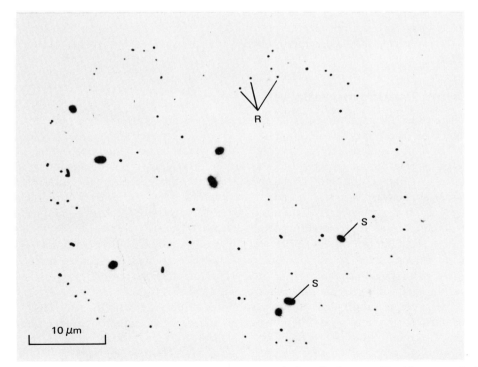

A stained preparation of *Shigella dysenteriae* (*S*) and *Coxiella burnetii* (*R*). (Courtesy of **Figure 13-11** R. Silberman.)

(4) The growth of some types in chick embryos (though not in humans) is inhibited by penicillin; the effectiveness of this antibiotic, which specifically inhibits mucopeptide synthesis, implies that such rickettsiae possess mucopeptide as an important constituent of their cell walls. (5) Finally, rickettsiae reproduce by binary fission; this distinguishes them from the wall-less mycoplasmas, as well as from viruses.

In most respects other than host range, the rickettsiae are similar to vertebrate parasites informally designated chlamydia, which are not classified in any order of bacteria. Chlamydia occur naturally in birds and mammals; they cause psittacosis in birds and granulomatous diseases and pneumonia in humans.

Bacteria of both groups are unusually permeable to solutes. Substances such as large, electrostatically charged ions can enter these cells, and nucleic acids leak out into the suspending medium during procedures used for the separation of the parasites from their host cells. The few physiologic studies that have been accomplished with these organisms have revealed that they lack many biosynthetic systems and possess only portions of respiratory systems.

The information available at present suggests that rickettsiae and chlamydia are capable of intracellular parasitism by virtue of their high permeability to metabolic intermediates that do not pass in or out through the permeability barrier of most cells; they have, accordingly, been able to dispense with certain metabolic processes that occur in the host cells. However, because of the decrease in the selectivity of their permeability barrier, they can survive only in environments that constantly replenish the substances the microbes cannot retain.

Order Pseudomonadales

The order Pseudomonadales is represented predominantly by one morphologic type; the typical pseudomonad is a gram-negative, rod-shaped cell (Fig. 13-12) approximately 0.5 μm by 1 to 2 μm, which occurs singly, reproduces by transverse binary fission, and is motile by means of a polar flagellum or tuft of flagella. As presently constituted, the order also includes vibrioid (Fig. 13-13), spirilliform (Fig. 13-14), and a few coccoid types, and some non-motile types. All are gram negative, do not form endospores or cysts, and reproduce by fission or, rarely, by budding from the cell surface.

Also placed in this order are bacteria whose physiologic properties otherwise occur, among eubacteria, only among typical pseudomonads. As a consequence, all but one type (*Rhodomicrobium;* order Hyphomicrobiales) of photosynthetic and all chemolithotrophic bacteria are placed in this order.

The order is subdivided into two suborders. Suborder Rhodobacteriineae accommodates the photosynthetic types, and suborder Pseudomonadineae the non-photosynthetic types.

Suborder Rhodobacteriineae. Three families (Table 13-2) of photosynthetic bacteria can be distinguished by the chemical nature of their photosynthetic pigments and the substances that serve as external sources of electrons for photosynthesis.

The green and purple sulfur bacteria occur in natural habitats that are anaerobic and illuminated and contain reduced inorganic sulfur, usually H_2S. These conditions are found in the black mud in shallow areas of ponds in which organic matter is undergoing decomposition by sulfate-reducing anaerobic bacteria, and at the source of sulfur springs. Such environmental conditions may also occur in deeper portions of stratified lakes or ponds. Since these habitats are not generally suitable for other microbial growth, the photosynthetic forms may multiply until macroscopically visible masses of green or reddish growth accumulate.

Most of the information available regarding the physiologic traits of green bacteria is based on observations of *Chlorobium* isolates. *Chlorobium* types

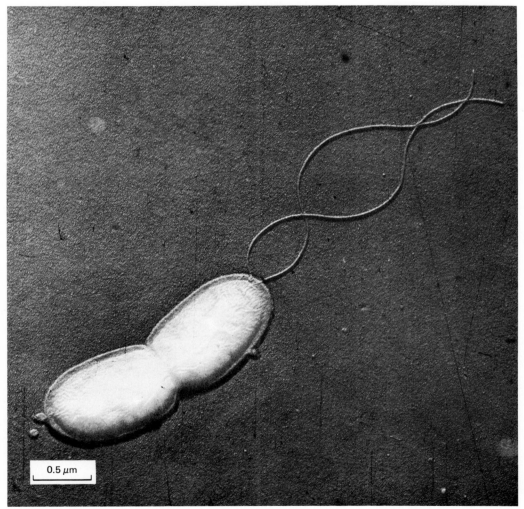

0.5 μm

Pseudomonas fluorescens, a dividing cell with two flagella at one pole. (From Houwink, A. L.,   **Figure 13-12** and W. van Iterson, 1950. *Biochim. et Biophys. Acta,* **5**:10. By permission of Elsevier Publishing Company.)

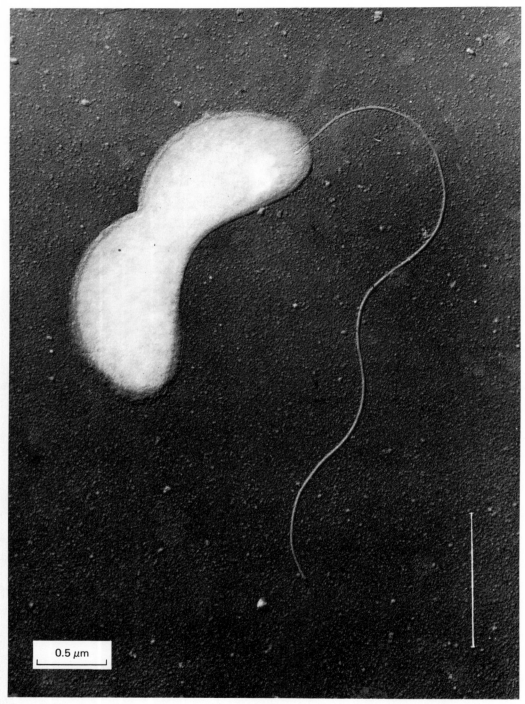

0.5 µm

Figure 13-13 *Desulfovibrio* sp., a dividing cell with a single polar flagellum (see also Fig. 13-18). (Courtesy of A. L. Houwink.)

174

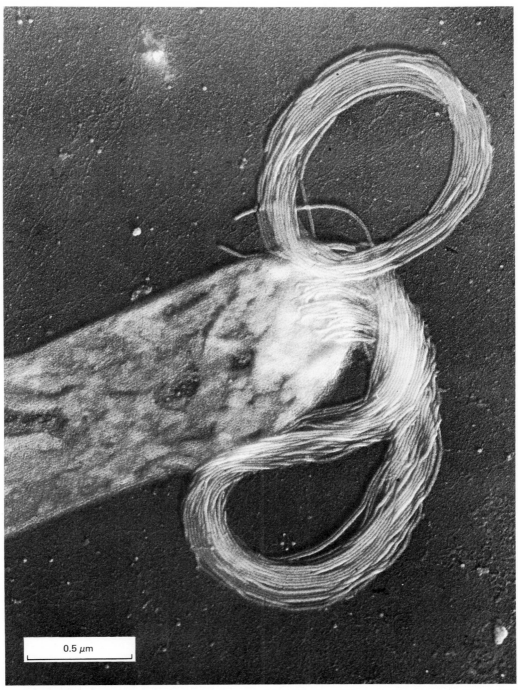

0.5 μm

Spirillum sp., pole of a spontaneously lysed cell; a small hook is discernible as the base of each **Figure 13-14**
flagellum in the dense polar tuft. (From Houwink, A. L., 1953. *Biochim. et Biophys. Acta,* **10**:360.
By permission of Elsevier Publishing Company.)

TABLE 13-2.   Distinguishing Features of the Families of Suborder Rhodobacteriineae

Family	Principal Photosynthetic Pigment	Source of Electrons for Photosynthesis
Chlorobacteriaceae (green sulfur bacteria)	Bacteriochlorophylls* c and d	Reduced inorganic sulfur compounds
Thiorhodaceae (purple sulfur bacteria)	Bacteriochlorophyll a and/or b	Reduced inorganic sulfur compounds
Athiorhodaceae (non-sulfur purple bacteria)	Bacteriochlorophyll a and/or b	Organic compounds

*Bacteriochlorophyll a as a minor component.

are rod-shaped or ovoid organisms that frequently accumulate in chains (Fig. 13-15); they are non-motile. The cell diameter in healthy cultures is slightly less than 1 μm. Sulfide, sulfur, H_2, and, for some isolates, thiosulfate can serve as sources of electrons for energy production by photosynthesis and for reduction of CO_2, the principal carbon source for growth. All isolates are strict anaerobes and are incapable of development without illumination. During growth in the presence of sulfides, the bacteria may cause the accumulation of sulfur granules in the medium (see Fig. 13-15*A*).

The purple sulfur bacteria are physiologically similar to the green types in their requirement for illumination, reduced sulfur compounds, and anaerobic conditions for growth. However, in contrast to the *Chlorobium* group, the purple sulfur bacteria can assimilate a major proportion of carbon for growth from organic compounds rather than CO_2. Whether electrons from sources other than reduced sulfur could support their growth cannot rigorously be tested, because they also seem to require reduced sulfur compounds as sources of sulfur atoms for biosynthesis.

The description of the physiologic properties summarized in the preceding paragraph is based on studies of those purple sulfur bacteria that have been cultivated in the laboratory, particularly members of the genera *Thiospirillum* (spirilliform) and *Chromatium* (rod-shaped), and to a lesser extent *Thiopedia* (coccoid).

The largest bacteria are classified in Thiorhodaceae. The cells of some species of *Thiospirillum* are several micrometers in diameter and up to 100 μm in length. Sulfur granules may be stored internally by purple sulfur bacteria during growth in the presence of sulfide, and the granules are particularly obvious within cells of the larger types (Fig. 13-16). Such cells are also sufficiently large that their red or purple color can be seen in individual living cells with the aid of a light microscope.

The pigments responsible for the red or purple appearance of Thiorhodaceae representatives are similar to those in non-sulfur purple bacteria. Red, purple, brown, and yellow carotenoid pigments are present in representatives of both groups; these pigments obscure the blue-green color of the bacteriochlorophyll. The green sulfur bacteria contain only yellow carotenoids, and masses of the cells appear green or yellow-green.

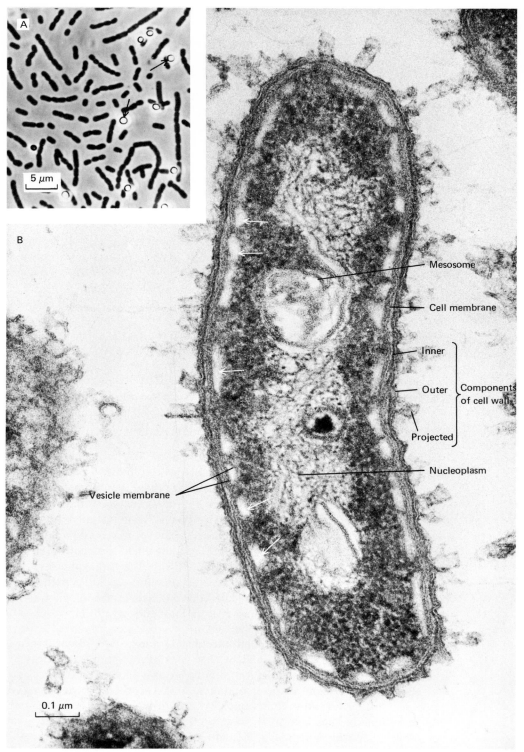

Chlorobium thiosulfatophilum. A. Living cells, many in chains. The arrows indicate sulfur granules. (Courtesy of N. Pfennig.) *B.* Longitudinal section showing peripheral arrangement of the membrane-bounded photosynthetic vesicles (arrows). (From Cohen-Bazire, G., N. Pfennig, and R. Kunisawa, 1964. *J. Cell Biol.,* **22:**207. By permission of The Rockefeller University Press.)

Figure 13-15

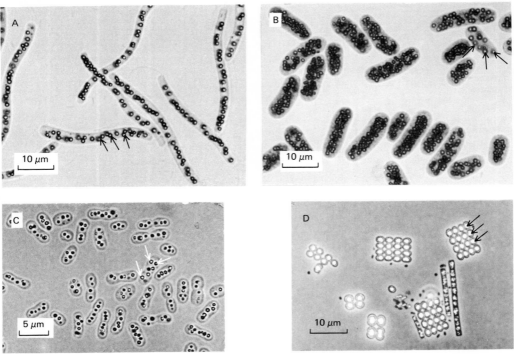

Figure 13-16   Thiorhodaceae. The arrows indicate sulfur granules. *A. Thiospirillum jenense. B. Chromatium okenii. C. C. vinosum.* (A, B, and C courtesy of N. Pfennig.) *D. Thiopedia sp.* (the large cocci) in a mixed population in an enrichment culture from lake water. (Courtesy of P. Hirsch.)

Like the sulfur bacteria, the non-sulfur purple bacteria develop photosynthetically under anaerobic conditions. However, many isolates are also capable of growing aerobically in the dark, using organic compounds as sources of carbon and respiratory metabolism for obtaining energy from oxidation of organic compounds. This alternation is particularly significant in Athiorhodaceae representatives as an implication of the phylogenetic relationship between the photosynthetic sulfur bacteria and the chemoorganotrophic pseudomonads; the non-sulfur purple bacteria possess the same photosynthetic pigments as the purple sulfur bacteria and the same oxidative pathways as non-photosynthetic pseudomonads. The athiorhodacean physiologic traits occur in cells of typical pseudomonad morphology and in spirilla.

Suborder Pseudomonadineae / Lithotrophic Groups. Two major types of chemolithotrophs are distinguished by the types of inorganic substances that can be utilized as electron sources for lithotrophic growth. Bacteria of the family Nitrobacteraceae use nitrogen compounds, and Thiobacteriaceae representatives use sulfur and sulfur compounds. A third group, classified in the family Methanomonadaceae, comprises bacteria that use methane, which is not commonly oxidized biologically, H_2, and CO.

Nitrobacteraceae representatives, the "nitrifying bacteria," are soil-inhabiting aerobes that carry out the oxidation of inorganic nitrogen, an essential step in the natural cycling of nitrogen (Chap. 20). There are two groups of genera in the family. One group, typified by *Nitrosomonas,* accommodates bacteria that oxidize ammonia to nitrite. The other group accommodates bacteria that oxidize nitrite to nitrate; this group is typified by *Nitrobacter.* The family is heterogeneous morphologically; rods, cocci, and spirilla are included within it. *Nitrosomonas* is a typical pseudomonad; *Nitrobacter* comprises non-motile rods that multiply by budding.

Representatives of only one Thiobacteriaceae genus, *Thiobacillus,* have been obtained and studied in pure cultures. Except for a few non-motile isolates, the thiobacilli are typical pseudomonads. They occur widely in soils, in fresh and sea water, and often in sewage. In most habitats, they utilize sulfide that is released during decomposition of organic material; they oxidize the sulfide aerobically to sulfur and finally to sulfate. The production of sulfate lowers the pH of the environment, since this is the anion of a strong acid. Two species are remarkably tolerant to high concentrations of acid. *Thiobacillus thiooxidans* grows optimally in a medium of pH 2 to 3.5 and can grow until the H_2SO_4 is slightly more concentrated than 0.1 *N. T. ferrooxidans* occurs naturally in acid soils, such as in peat bogs, and in acid mine wastes and water shed from acidic, iron-containing soils. It can obtain energy by the oxidation of ferrous iron as well as from oxidation of sulfur compounds.

In 1934, *T. novellus* was isolated and described as a bacterium that exhibited typical thiobacillus lithotrophy, but could also grow as a chemoorganotroph. Since then, other facultatively lithotrophic thiobacilli have been isolated. Their discovery stimulated re-examination of the "strictly lithotrophic" types. At present, most of the experimental evidence indicates that strictness is related to energy metabolism; many lithotrophs, while utilizing inorganic compounds as electron sources, can simultaneously assimilate some organic carbon.

Suborder Pseudomonadineae / Organotrophic and Facultative Lithotrophic Groups. The remaining three families of Pseudomonadales described here accommodate chemoorganotrophic bacteria. A few of these can grow facultatively as lithotrophs. Representatives of most of the genera of these families occur widely in nature and are usually encountered in any sample of fresh water. They also occur in marine environments, in soils, and in associations with other organisms (particularly algae and plants); some are parasites of plants, and a few representatives can parasitize animals.

This large group is subdivided into three families on the basis of morphologic properties. Family Caulobacteraceae is distinguished by the presence on each cell of an elongated appendage called a stalk. Family Spirillaceae is represented by non-stalked vibrios and spirilla. All others are placed in family Pseudomonadaceae.

The most commonly encountered representatives of Caulobacteraceae, the "stalked bacteria," are classified in *Caulobacter.* Each typical cell bears a slender (ca. 0.15 μm diameter) outgrowth of the cell wall and membrane; at the outer

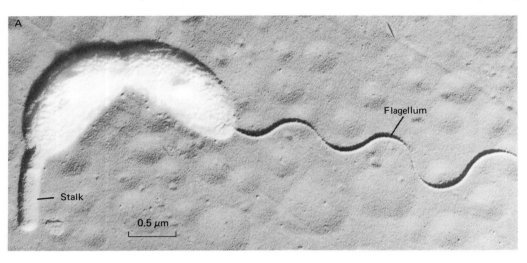

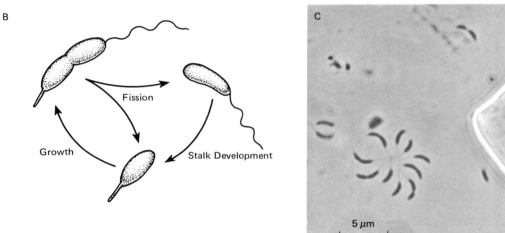

Figure 13-17 *Caulobacter. A.* A dividing vibrioid cell with a stalk at one pole and a single flagellum at the other pole. *B.* Diagram of the life history. *C.* Living cells, one group in a rosette. (*A* and *C* from Poindexter, J. S., 1964. *Bact. Rev.,* **28:**231. By permission of the American Society for Microbiology.)

end of these stalks is an adhesive material by means of which the cells can attach to inanimate surfaces and to the surfaces of other protists. In natural materials (fresh or sea water or soil), they are commonly found attached in this way to other bacteria.

Cell division in caulobacters is asymmetric: one progeny cell possesses the distinctive stalk and is non-motile; the other possesses a single polar flagellum, is motile, and does not possess a stalk (Fig. 13-17). The latter cell is the swarmer stage. Before a swarmer proceeds to cell division, it loses its motility and develops a stalk. The swarmer stage probably serves to ensure dissemination of these bacteria, which are or can be sessile.

Representatives of Spirillaceae are classified partly on the basis of morphology, and most of the generic names reflect the distinction made between a cell that is curved (e.g., *Vibrio, Cellvibrio, Desulfovibrio*) and one in which the curvature is reversed periodically so that the cell is helical (e.g., *Spirillum, Paraspirillum*). However, this distinction cannot be made in all cultures, because rapidly dividing spirilla may have only one turn, and slowly dividing vibrios may elongate and appear as spirilla or helical chains of vibrios; and different isolates may vary in this trait (see Fig. 13-18).

The genus *Vibrio* includes free-living aquatic and marine vibrios and almost all of the few pseudomonads that occur naturally as animal parasites. This small group of parasites includes the cholera vibrios, which are facultative anaerobes. They grow anaerobically by fermenting sugars.

The genus *Bdellovibrio* was established to accommodate a type of unusually small (diameter less than 0.3 μm) vibrio that has been found in soil, water, and sewage. These organisms are cultivated in the laboratory as parasites of other bacteria, and since most fresh isolates cannot grow in the absence of host cells, *Bdellovibrio* representatives are presumed to exist in nature as parasites of bacteria.

Two different mechanisms of this parasitism have been reported; both may occur in nature. In one type, the *Bdellovibrio* cell attaches to the surface of the host cell, releases enzymes that disrupt the host cell, and then assimilates as nutrients the substances released from the disintegrated host. In the second type, the *Bdellovibrio* attaches to the host cell and then burrows through the

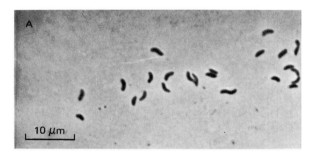

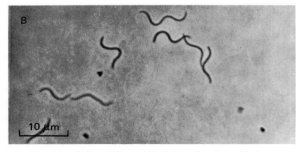

Desulfovibrio, living cells. *A.* Vibrioid cells of the Hildenborough strain. *B.* Spirilloid cells of the   **Figure 13-18**
Walvis Bay strain. (From Campbell, L. L., M. A. Kasprzycki, and J. R. Postgate, 1966. *J. Bact.,*
92:1122. By permission of the American Society for Microbiology.)

cell wall and establishes itself between cell membrane and cell wall; from this position, it digests and assimilates the host protoplasm. Reproduction has been observed to occur by elongation of the parasite, followed by multiple fission resulting in about six progeny.

The genus *Cellvibrio* contains free-living soil inhabitants that are capable of digesting cellulose. They are widely distributed in soils and participate in the biologic decomposition of plant and algal remains. The ability to hydrolyze cellulose is not widespread among microorganisms; the only other widely distributed bacteria that can degrade cellulose to assimilable products are myxobacteria, actinomycetes, and one group of corynebacteria. Marine vibrios that can digest insoluble algal components such as agar and alginic acids play a corresponding role in the decomposition of brown and red algae.

Desulfovibrio (Figs. 13-13 and 13-18) representatives are notorious for their presumed role in the "fouling" of submerged surfaces such as ship bottoms, wharf pilings, and the linings of pipes and canals. The "fouling" is attributed in part to the production of large amounts of sulfide by these bacteria. They are anaerobes that respire by reducing sulfate (and less oxidized forms of inorganic sulfur) to sulfide. Due to their production of sulfide, which combines with iron to form the black FeS, they blacken the anaerobic mud in which sulfur-oxidizing photosynthetic bacteria occur.

Spirillum is a genus of bacteria that typically occur in stagnant water; one species (*S. minus*) has been reported as an animal (rat) parasite, and some representatives can be found in decomposing organic matter and in soil containing putrefying materials. The free-living types are usually microaerophilic. This can be observed in wet mounts of natural materials containing spirilla and of pure cultures; the cells are motile and accumulate in a wet mount in a ring some distance from the aerobic edge of the cover slip and away from the center, which becomes anaerobic as the bacteria in the mount consume the O_2.

Although the chemoorganotrophic spirilla share the morphology of some of the photosynthetic bacteria, they are not represented by large forms. The largest of the colorless spirilla is only about 1.5 μm in diameter.

Family Pseudomonadaceae includes strictly respiratory types that are widely distributed in soil and water. Many of these can grow aerobically by reducing O_2 and anaerobically by reducing nitrate to N_2. They are active in the oxidation of organic materials to CO_2 and H_2O; an individual isolate may be capable of utilizing as its sole source of carbon and energy any one of nearly 100 different organic compounds. This remarkable versatility in carbon utilization is unparalleled in any other microbial group. These pseudomonads also account for much of the reduction of nitrate to N_2 and other gases, an important step in the natural cycling of nitrogen. Most of these bacteria are placed in *Pseudomonas*. Some representatives of this genus are facultative lithotrophs that can develop in an inorganic environment containing H_2, CO_2, and inorganic salts. Some types display a metabolism intermediate between litho- and organotrophy; they oxidize organic compounds to CO_2 for energy and fix the CO_2 as their carbon source.

Family Pseudomonadaceae also includes the acetic acid bacteria (*Aceto-bacter*, Fig. 13-19, *Gluconobacter*), which oxidize ethanol to acetic acid. They are capable of continuing growth in the acidic environment resulting from this partial oxidation of ethanol and can accumulate up to 11 per cent acetic acid; the pH finally reaches less than 4. They occur naturally in souring plant products, including fruits, vegetables, grains, wine, and beer. They are employed commercially in the production of wine vinegar. One representative has the unusual property, among bacteria, of producing cellulose; cellulose strands accumulate extracellularly, and in undisturbed liquid media they form a tangled, floating mat in which the cells are suspended at the surface of the liquid.

One genus of this family, *Halobacterium,* is represented by obligate halophiles. They occur naturally in marine brines and salt lakes. Isolates typically require at least 12 per cent NaCl in the medium in order to grow and grow optimally at NaCl concentrations up to saturation (ca. 30 per cent, depending on the temperature). The basis of their requirement for high concentrations

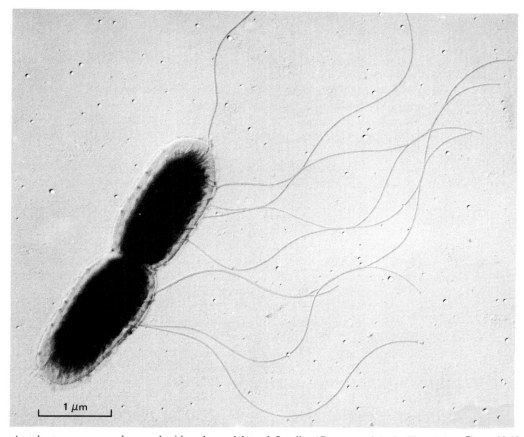

Acetobacter sp., a pseudomonad with polar and lateral flagella. (Courtesy of A. L. Houwink.) **Figure 13-19**

of NaCl apparently is structural, rather than physiologic. Whereas enzymes extracted from cells of these halophiles generally retain their catalytic activities at very low salt concentrations, cells and cell envelopes derived from halophile cells disintegrate when suspended in low-salt solutions.

Chemical analyses of the cell envelopes have revealed that the components typical of the rigid layer of procaryotic cell walls are present in relatively small amounts or are undetectable. The evidence available at present implies that the rigidity of the obligate halophile envelope is due to electrostatic binding of particular cations (Na^{+1}, Mg^{+2}), rather than to a specific structural material.

The family Pseudomonadaceae also includes plant parasites (*Xanthomonas*) which cause necrotic diseases in their hosts; free-living, soil-dwelling forms (*Azotomonas*) which are active, like *Azotobacter,* in N_2 fixation; anaerobic, fermentative organisms (*Zymomonas*) which ferment carbohydrates to ethanol and CO_2 as do yeasts; and marine forms (*Photobacterium*) which are capable of luminescence.

Orders Hyphomicrobiales and Chlamydobacteriales

The two orders Hyphomicrobiales and Chlamydobacteriales accommodate bacteria that seem related to pseudomonads and may have been derived from pseudomonad ancestors by structural modification.

In hyphomicrobia, reproduction occurs by the formation of buds, typically from slender outgrowths of the cell. These "budding filaments," which are about 0.2 μm in diameter, occur in chemoorganotrophic soil bacteria (*Hypho-microbium*) and in photosynthetic bacteria (*Rhodomicrobium*) whose physiologic properties are similar to those of Athiorhodaceae. The developmental cycles of these two types of budding bacteria are illustrated in Figure 13-20; see also Figure 13-21.

The order Chlamydobacteriales contains bacteria that occur as trichomes which typically are ensheathed; a given type is either non-motile throughout the life cycle or produces swarmer cells that bear polar flagella, singly or in tufts.

Representatives of *Sphaerotilus* (Fig. 13-22) are commonly found in standing or running water of high organic content. The trichomes may be free-floating, but are usually attached to the surfaces of rocks, pipes, or cement linings as in ditches or canals, where they may accumulate in macroscopically visible masses. The trichomes often reach 1 cm in length.

Sphaerotilus swarmers are produced near the end of the trichome; they swim out of the sheath and eventually settle onto a substrate and develop into typical sheathed trichomes. The chemical composition of the sheath has not yet been determined; the sheath and cells are usually colorless in *Sphaerotilus*. In the related genera *Leptothrix* and *Toxothrix,* oxides of iron and/or manganese are typically deposited in the sheath, coloring it brown; the cells are colorless.

Order Caryophanales

Bacteria of the order Caryophanales occur in trichomes that typically are not ensheathed. They are further distinguished from Chlamydobacteriales types by peritrichous rather than polar flagellation of swarmer cells. The cells of a mature trichome may also be flagellated and the trichome motile. The possession of flagella is a major distinction between Caryophanales representatives and colorless counterparts of blue-green algae, which lack flagella.

Caryophanales representatives are seen in scrapings from the human mouth, in the intestinal contents of animals, especially herbivores, and in decomposing organic materials. Isolates of *Caryophanon* grow in pure cultures as chemoorganotrophs. The cells are discoid, measuring 2 to 3 μm in diameter and less than 2 μm in length; their trichomes often reach 200 μm in length. The trichome reproduces by separation into at least two trichomes; in cultures approaching the maximum stationary phase, the trichome may dissociate into unicellular units.

Order Spirochaetales

The spirochetes are unicellular bacteria whose cells are elongated, flexible, and wound into a helical form around an axial fibrillar filament (Fig. 13-23). The cylinder and filament are enclosed within an outer, flexible, close-fitting envelope. Species are differentiated on bases of dimensions of the cells and

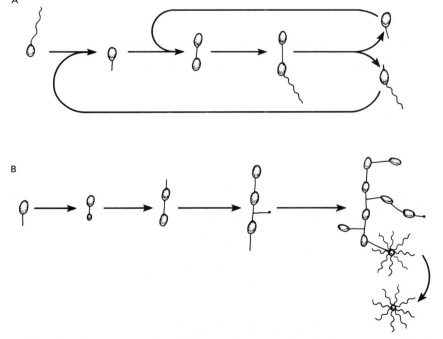

Life histories of two types of budding bacteria. The cycles differ in the tendency of the bud to separate from the filament on which it arises. A. *Hyphomicrobium.* The bud usually separates from the filament and is motile by means of a single subpolar flagellum for some time before it develops a filament and begins to reproduce. B. *Rhodomicrobium.* The bud usually remains attached and is not flagellated; the occasional bud that separates possesses peritrichous flagella. The development of *Rhodomicrobium* motile cells has not been observed, but presumably they eventually lose their flagella and establish new microcolonies.   **Figure 13-20**

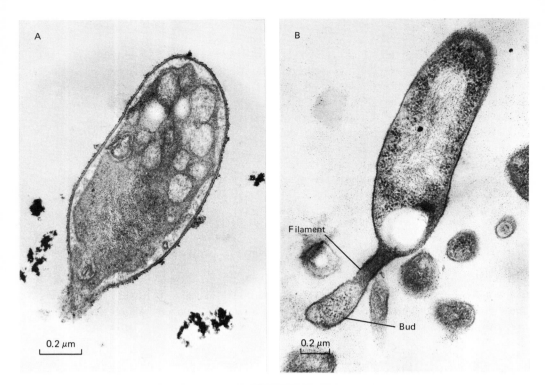

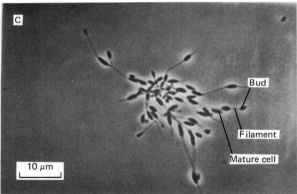

Figure 13-21 Budding bacteria. *A.* Longitudinal section of a cell of *Hyphomicrobium* sp.; the function of the membrane-bounded vesicles is not known. *B. Hyphomicrobium vulgare* cell with filament and small bud. (*A* and *B* from Conti, S. F., and P. Hirsch, 1965. *J. Bact.,* **89**:503. By permission of the American Society for Microbiology.) *C.* Photomicrograph of a microcolony of *Rhodomicrobium* sp. (see also Fig. 5-8). (Courtesy of P. Hirsch.)

186

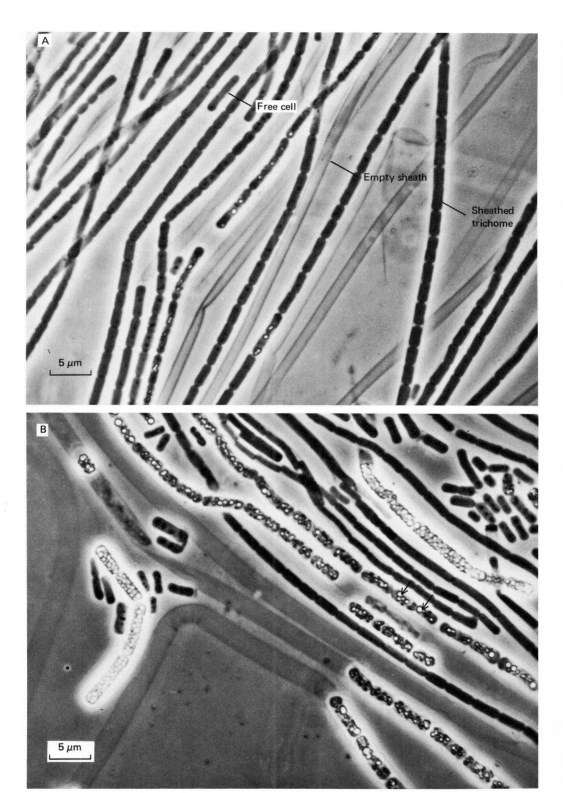

Labels within image A: Free cell, Empty sheath, Sheathed trichome, 5 μm

Labels within image B: 5 μm

Sphaerotilus natans cells, trichomes, and empty sheaths. *A.* Cultivated with 1 g glucose (the carbon source) per liter of medium. *B.* Cultivated with 2.5 g glucose per liter of medium, which increases the amount of carbon-reserve granules (arrows) within the cells. (Courtesy of W. L. van Veen and E. G. Mulder.)

Figure 13-22

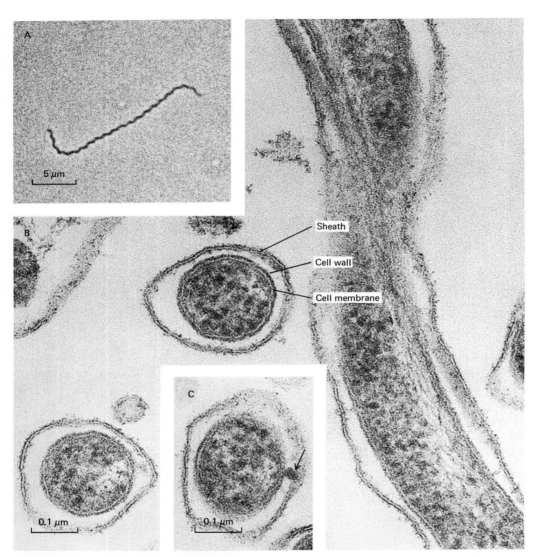

Sheath

Cell wall

Cell membrane

Figure 13-23 *Spirochaeta stenostrepta.* A. Living cell. (From Canale-Parola, E., S. C. Holt, and Z. Udris, 1967. Isolation of Free-living, Anaerobic Spirochetes, in *Arch. f. Mikrobiol.,* **59:**41–48. By permission of Springer-Verlag, Berlin, Heidelberg, New York.) B. Longitudinal and transverse sections. C. Transverse section showing the axial filament (arrow) within the sheath. (*B* and *C* from Holt, S. C., and E. Canale-Parola, 1968. *J. Bact.,* **96:**822. By permission of the American Society for Microbiology.)

the axial filaments, the frequency and amplitude of the turns of the helix, and, for parasitic representatives, the hosts they inhabit.

The fibrils of which the axial filament is composed are structurally similar to eubacterial flagella. Each fibril is attached subterminally to only one—not to both—of the poles of the cell (Fig. 13-24). Following transverse fission of

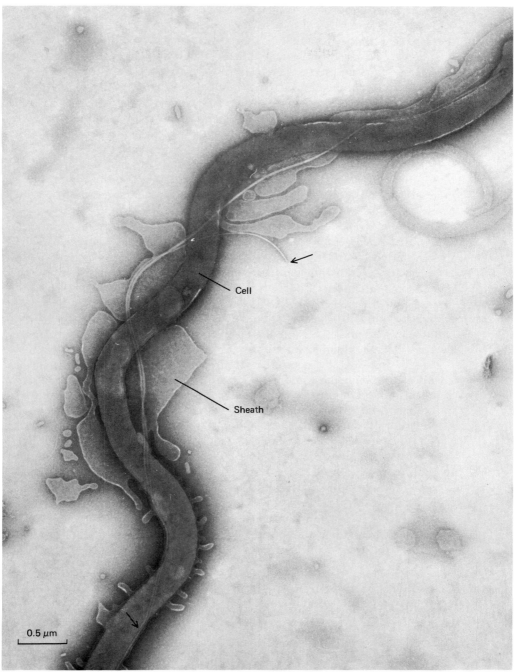

Spirochaeta aurantia, showing the region of overlapping of the axial filaments from opposite **Figure 13-24** poles of the cell. The arrows indicate the distal ends of the axial filaments. The site of the emergence of one filament from a subpolar position is circled. The sheath appears in this type of preparation as a flattened, irregular layer. (From Breznak, J. A., and E. Canale-Parola, 1969. *J. Bact.,* **97**:386. By permission of the American Society for Microbiology.)

the cell, new fibrils presumably arise from the newly formed pole of each progeny cell. As each fibril increased in length, it would become oriented within the filament among the full-length fibrils already present.

The order is subdivided into two families: Spirochaetaceae for the larger (ca. 0.5 μm by more than 30 μm) spirochetes, which are free-living or parasitic in shellfish; and Treponemataceae for spirochetes that are only about 0.2 to 0.3 μm in diameter and do not exceed 16 μm in length. Most of the smaller spirochetes are parasites of warm-blooded vertebrates.

Free-living spirochetes occur widely in fresh and sea water and are particularly abundant in areas containing H_2S, sewage, or high concentrations of organic matter as in stagnant water. They are microaerophilic chemoorganotrophs and thus physiologically similar to *Spirillum* species.

The family Treponemataceae is subdivided into three genera: *Leptospira*, *Borrelia*, and *Treponema*. A few *Leptospira* types are free-living and occur in fresh water ponds and in tap water; these can be cultivated as microaerophiles in media such as hay infusion. Others are parasites of rodents, especially rats, and of some intentionally domesticated animals, in which they may not cause disease. Humans become infected by contact with spirochete-containing urine of infected animals. Isolates of these parasitic types can be grown in pure cultures in media supplemented with blood serum; like the free-living forms, they are microaerophilic.

Borrelia representatives occur commonly as innocuous inhabitants of various vertebrates. In man, they inhabit the mouth and genitalia; one type is regularly found in oropharyngeal lesions in cases of Vincent's angina (trench mouth) in company with a *Bacteroides* species. The role of the spirochete in production of the lesions has not been elucidated. *Borrelia recurrentis* is the only species known to cause a distinct disease, relapsing fever, in humans.

Treponema species are known to occur naturally only in humans and rabbits. In rabbits, they cause a disease similar to syphilis. In humans, they cause syphilis (*T. pallidum*), yaws (*T. pertenue*), and various skin diseases and also occur as non-pathogenic parasites in the oral cavity and on the genitalia. They do not survive away from the body and are transmitted among humans by direct contact. In the host, treponemes multiply more slowly than most pathogenic bacteria; they divide not more than once every 24 hours.

Order Myxobacterales

Myxobacteria grow as individual cells that are typically embedded in a mass of slime they produce during growth. The cells may be cylindric or fusiform. They are typically flexible, and the cells are contorted as they move by gliding on solid surfaces (see Fig. 13-25). The myxobacteria are widespread in soil and common as inhabitants of the dung (intestines?) of herbivorous animals. A few types parasitize fish, causing diseases that may be fatal.

In soil and in dung, myxobacteria are active in the degradation of complex organic materials including cellulose, chitin, and bacterial cell walls. In the laboratory, pure cultures can grow on mineral media to which paper or living or heat-killed bacteria have been added as the sole source of carbon for myxobacterial growth. They digest these insoluble carbon sources by releasing into the environment enzymes that degrade the large molecules to smaller compounds that can be absorbed. All types of myxobacteria that have been isolated are aerobes. Some are marine types that require at least 0.5 per cent NaCl for growth; these are found on living and on dead, decaying marine algae.

Four general types of myxobacteria are distinguished on the basis of the life cycle. The *Cytophaga* cycle is the simplest; the cells exist only as vegetative cells (Fig. 13-25). *Sporocytophaga* types can form microcysts; a vegetative cell ceases growth, becomes approximately spheric, and builds a thick outer wall. These microcysts are resistant to desiccation, but not especially resistant to heat. Upon germination, one rod-shaped vegetative cell emerges from the cyst wall.

The other two types are referred to as fruiting myxobacteria. Representatives of the *Myxococcus* group behave in a fashion that requires response of vegetative cells to the presence and behavior of other vegetative cells of the same type. At some point during growth and multiplication, vegetative cells embedded in a common mass of slime aggregate in groups containing thousands of cells. The aggregated cells convert to cylindric microcysts. Slime is exuded within and around the aggregate, forming a fruiting body that may reach 2 mm in diameter. The fruiting bodies are often brightly colored yellow, orange, or red; they are detectable macroscopically on the surface of dung pellets, and sometimes on soil.

Polyangium types (Fig. 13-26) develop fruiting bodies from aggregated populations; the individual cells are somewhat shortened from the vegetative

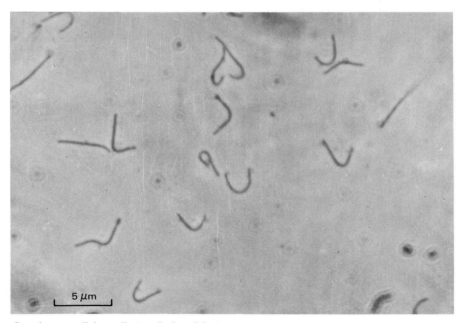

Cytophaga sp., living cells (motile by gliding).   Figure 13-25

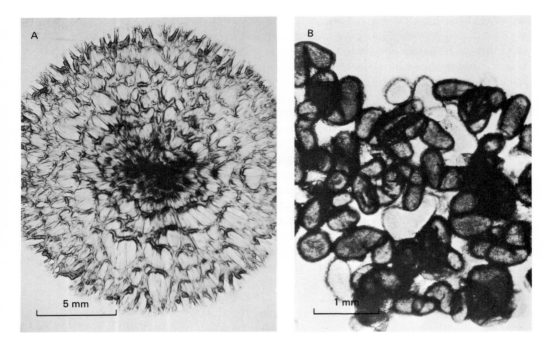

Figure 13-26 Fruiting myxobacteria. *A.* A mass of cells of *Polyangium fuscum* aggregating toward a central area. *B.* Cysts of *P. fuscum,* each containing hundreds of dormant cells. *C.* Fruiting body of *Chondromyces apiculatus.* Each of the pointed bodies in the cluster is a cyst. (Courtesy of H. Kühlwein.)

192

state, but do not possess thick walls. The slime exuded around the aggregate hardens and serves as a common cyst wall. Some of the slime may contract as it hardens and form a pedestal on which one or more cysts rest (Fig. 13-26C). Upon germination, the cyst wall breaks, and the dormant cells emerge and resume vegetative development.

Order Actinomycetales

The order Actinomycetales accommodates bacteria in which there is a distinct tendency toward mycelial development. It embraces a range of organisms from those in which this tendency is observed as rudimentary branching of individual cells, to those that develop as extensive mycelia differentiated into vegetative and fruiting (sporulating) portions. The majority are non-motile, aerobic, free-living organisms that occur abundantly in soil and can also be isolated from dust and from fresh water.

In their natural habitats, the free-living actinomycetes are active in the oxidation of organic materials. Some are capable of oxidizing hydrocarbons, which are not widely utilized by other microbes, as sources of carbon and energy. As a group, they are active in degradation of insoluble, high molecular weight organic substances including cellulose, chitin, proteins, waxes and paraffins, and rubber.

A few types are plant pathogens; they can be isolated from diseased plants and the soil in which such plants are growing. Some actinomycetes are animal parasites, and several diseases of humans and livestock are due to these types.

The order is subdivided into four families on the basis of the extent of mycelial development and the occurrence and structure of mycelial portions specialized for production of reproductive units.

Mycobacteriaceae. Mycelium rudimentary, amounting only to more or less frequent branching of rod-shaped cells or of short chains of rounded cells. Reproduction is by fission, typically binary, and often unequal. Non-motile.

Actinomycetaceae. Definite, aseptate mycelium. Reproduction is by formation of septa and fragmentation of mycelium into unicellular units or, rarely, by production of specialized branches that fragment. Non-motile or motile as single cells by means of one to four peritrichous flagella. Example genera: *Nocardia* (aerobic), *Actinomyces* (anaerobic or microaerophilic).

Streptomycetaceae. Definite, septate mycelium. Specialized branches produce unicellular spores (conidia) borne singly, in clusters, or in straight or spiral chains. Non-motile.

Actinoplanaceae. Definite, septate mycelium. Unicellular spores contained within sporangia (sporangiospores) are borne on specialized branches. Conidia may be formed on a mycelium that also produces sporangiospores. Motility by means of a single flagellum is typical of the sporangiospores of one genus (*Actinoplanes,* Fig. 13-27).

The non-motile unicellular reproductive units of the last three groups are dormant; they germinate by producing one to three outgrowths (germ tubes) that develop into mycelia.

Family Mycobacteriaceae. Family Mycobacteriaceae includes bacteria that grow predominantly as unicellular, unbranched rods on most artificial media. The gram reaction of mycobacteria cannot be determined, since their retention of the stain when rinsed with organic solvents does not require prior treatment with an iodine solution. Their relationship to mycelial actinomycetes is reflected in their physiologic properties, in the tendency of some isolates to grow as branched cells, and in a high lipid (wax) content of the cells. The lipids are especially prominent in *Mycobacterium* cells and may account for 20 to 40 per cent of the dry weight.

The staining procedure called the acid-fast stain was developed for the detection of mycobacteria in clinical specimens. In this procedure, the cells are stained with a hot (ca. 100° C) solution of phenol and the dye basic fuchsin, then rinsed with an acidified organic solvent. Acid-fast cells are stained only if heated to steaming and are not decolorized by the rinsing. Acid fastness of vegetative cells occurs only in mycobacteria and a few types of corynebacteria and is probably due to the high lipid content of the cells. A mild acid fastness (staining that resists decolorization does not require steaming) is observed in some *Nocardia* (Actinomycetaceae) representatives.

Many types of mycobacteria occur as free-living organisms in soil, water, and dairy products, where they are active in the aerobic oxidation of lipids and hydrocarbons. Some mycobacteria are parasites of animals in which they may cause disease, including tuberculosis (*M. tuberculosis*) and leprosy (*M. leprae*). The parasitic mycobacteria generally grow more slowly in artificial media than do the free-living types; they also grow more slowly in their hosts than do many other bacterial parasites of animals. This is characteristic of parasitic actinomycetes, as of many parasitic spirochetes, and is reflected in the production of prolonged, slowly progressive diseases by both types of pathogens.

Family Streptomycetaceae. The free-living soil bacteria of the family Streptomycetaceae are so numerous in fertile soils that they are responsible for the characteristic odor of fresh, moist garden soil. They are aerobic and active in the decomposition of complex organic materials. On solidified artificial

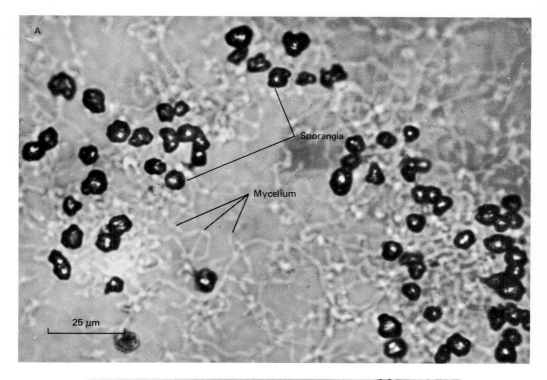

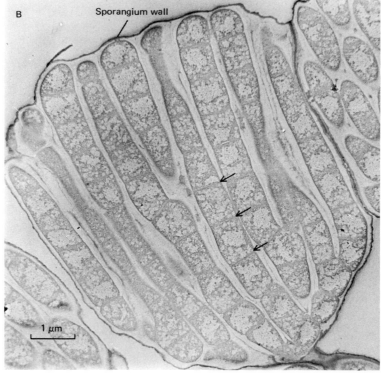

Actinoplanes sp. *A.* Surface of a colony with sporangia on the vegetative mycelium. (Courtesy **Figure 13-27** of H. A. Lechevalier.) *B.* Longitudinal section through an immature sporangium. Transverse walls (arrows) are formed within parallel hyphae within the sporangium, subdividing each hypha into units that develop into spores. (Courtesy of P. E. Holbert and H. A. Lechevalier.)

medium, a densely packed mycelium develops on the agar surface; colonies reach a maximum diameter characteristic of the isolate, the composition of the medium, and the conditions of cultivation. On the aerial surface of the mycelium arise erect, usually unentangled filaments that differentiate into conidia. In the genus *Streptomyces* (Fig. 13-28), conidia are borne in straight or spiral chains. In *Micromonospora,* conidia are borne singly or in clusters on straight or branched filaments.

The development of *Streptomyces* conidia is illustrated in Figure 13-29. Initially aseptate, the aerial filament develops septa that subdivide its protoplasm into several units of approximately equal size. Each developing spore constructs a wall within the wall of the parent filament. When the outer wall disintegrates in the region of each septum, the spores become separated and are carried away on air currents.

Streptomyces isolates produce a variety of antibiotics useful in the treatment of bacterial and fungal diseases of man and domesticated animals (see Table 23-2). Among these are streptomycin and tetracyclines (Aureomycin, Terramycin); the tetracyclines are "broad-spectrum" antibiotics, so called because they are effective in the treatment of diseases caused by gram-negative as well as gram-positive bacteria and a few protozoa. Except for penicillin and griseofulvin, which are produced by molds of the genus *Penicillium,* practically all the useful antibiotics available at present are obtained from cultures of *Streptomyces* representatives.

The mycelial development of the higher actinomycetes is the most complicated morphologic pattern observed among bacteria. However, even among these organisms, there is not any indication of a trend toward the development of sterile tissue. Such trends are observed only in higher, eucaryotic protists.

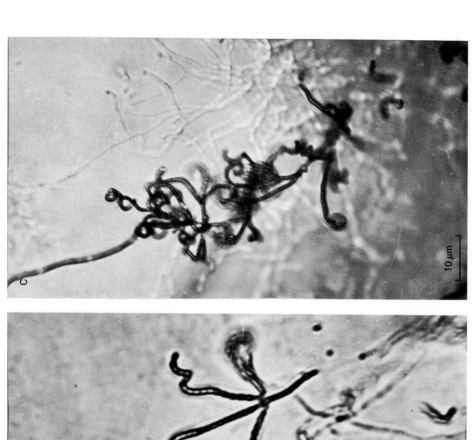

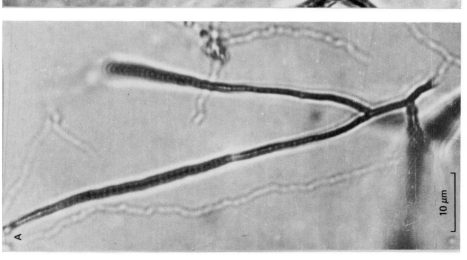

Conidia on conidiophores in *Streptomyces* spp. Vegetative mycelium is visible in the background, below the plane of focus. *A. S. roseochromogenus.*   **Figure 13-28**
B. S. coelicolor. C. S. fradiae. (Courtesy of M. P. Lechevalier and H. A. Lechevalier.)

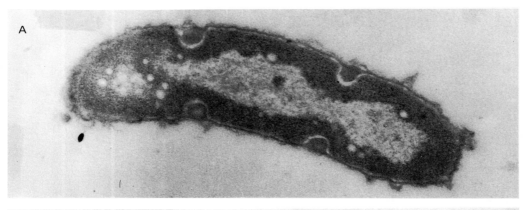

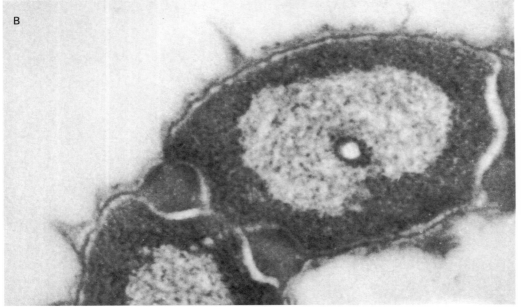

198

C

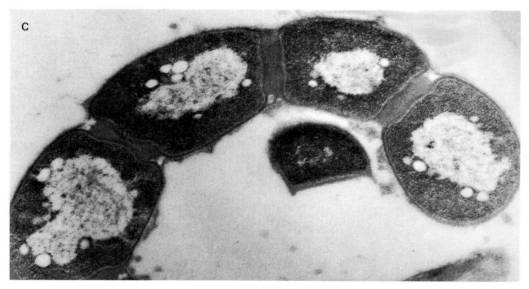

Successive stages in sporulation in *Streptomyces*. *A*. Oblique-longitudinal section of a young **Figure 13-29** conidiophore; the nucleoplasm is still a continuous mass, and the transverse walls have just begun to form. *B*. At a later stage the nucleoplasm is discontinuous and the transverse wall nearly completed. *C*. At a late stage each wall is complete between each pair of conidia. (From Rancourt, M. W., and H. A. Lechevalier, 1964. *Can. J. Microbiol.*, **10**:311. By permission of the National Research Council of Canada.)

Chapter 14

Fungi

General Characteristics

Fungi are eucaryotic, chemoorganotrophic protists. Practically all fungi are non-motile in the vegetative phase of development, and most types develop vegetatively as mycelia (see below). The entire fungus individual that develops from a single cell or fragment of another individual is called a **thallus.**[1] The thallus includes the vegetative portion and all specialized structures.

With few exceptions, fungi produce unicellular propagative units called **spores** (Fig. 14-1).[2] Spores of some fungi are flagellated and thereby motile; other fungi produce only non-motile spores, which may be dormant. Spores are produced in two ways by almost all classes of fungi: asexually and sexually. Asexual spores are produced by differentiation of the growing thallus as a regular feature of the life cycle of each individual. Nuclear fusions are not involved in their formation. Sexually produced spores possess nuclei derived from the nuclei of two parents. With a few exceptions, the parents and the spores are haploid; two parental nuclei fuse to form a diploid, zygote nucleus, from which haploid spore nuclei are derived by reductive nuclear division. In the majority of fungi that produce sexual spores, these spores and/or the structures within which they are borne (the "fruits") are morphologically distinguishable from asexual spores and fruiting structures. Generally, the sexual spores or fruits of a given fungus are more resistant to adverse conditions

---

[1]"Thallus" is a botanic term designating a plant body that is not differentiated into stems, roots, and leaves; its use in the description of algae and fungi is a consequence of their traditional classification as plants.

[2]A spore is functionally related to the fungus as a seed is to the plant. Spores differ from seeds in that they do not contain preformed embryos.

201

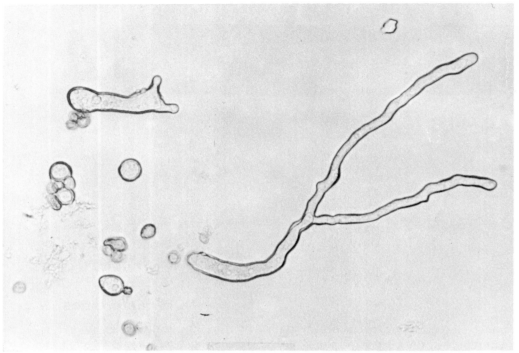

Figure 14-1   Germinating sporangiospores of *Rhizopus,* a terrestrial mold. Each of the two germinating spores in this photomicrograph is growing from left to right. (Courtesy Carolina Biological Supply Company.)

than are the corresponding asexual products and more likely to be capable of prolonged dormancy.

The group is subdivided into classes that are distinguished primarily by morphologic traits of the sexual stages and spores, and secondarily by morphologic features of the thallus and of the asexually produced spores. The distinguishing features of the classes are listed in Table 14-1.

Thallus Morphology. The characteristic unit of vegetative structure in fungi is a non-motile, multinucleate, branching tube, the **hypha** (Fig. 14-2); a mass of hyphae constitutes a **mycelium.** The wall of the hypha is semirigid, and the protoplasm within the wall is mobile. In lower fungi, the vegetative protoplasm is uninterrupted; such an organism, in which most or all of the nuclei exist in a common cytoplasm, is referred to as a **coenocyte.**[3] Through most of the mycelium, the hyphae do not possess cross-walls derived from the hyphal walls. Such cross-walls, called **septa,** are formed only at the base of reproductive structures, where they separate the vegetative protoplasm from that which is to be used in the formation of propagative units. The hyphae of a few lower fungi are constricted at intervals, and a granular material

[3]The term plasmodium is usually used when the organism does not possess a cell wall; see, for example, p. 311.

TABLE 14-1. Distinguishing Features of Classes of Fungi

Class	Thallus	Asexual Spores	Products of Sexual Fusion: Fruit or Spore	Germination Product
Lower Fungi (The Phycomycetes)				
Chytridiomycetes	From unicellular, holocarpic to rhizomycelial and mycelial, both eucarpic	Zoospores with single posterior whiplash flagellum	Resting sporangium	Zoospore or germ tube
Hyphochytridiomycetes	As Chytridiomycetes	Zoospores with single anterior tinsel flagellum	—	—
Oomycetes	Aseptate hyphae	Zoospores with two flagella—one whiplash, one tinsel	Oospore	Germ sporangium, which releases zoospores; or germ tube
Zygomycetes	Typically aseptate hyphae; rarely septate hyphae	Aplanospores, as sporangiospores, sporangiola, or conidia	Zygospore	Germ sporangium, which releases aplanospores
Higher Fungi				
Ascomycetes	Unicellular, or septate hyphae	Conidia	Ascus, ascocarp containing ascospores	Germ tube
Basidiomycetes	Septate hyphae	Conidia or none; also a few unique types	Basidiocarp containing basidiospores	Germ tube
Deuteromycetes (Fungi Imperfecti)	Septate hyphae	Conidia	—	—

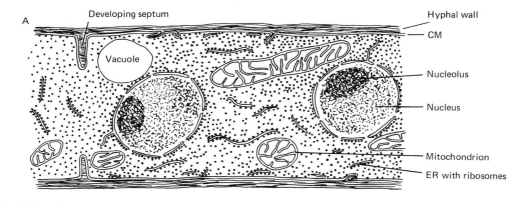

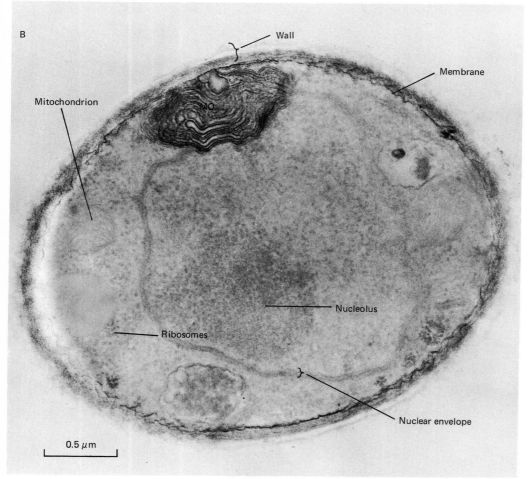

Figure 14-2   Fungal hyphae. *A.* Diagram of longitudinal section of a generalized hypha with a developing septum.

   B. Transverse section of a hypha of the basidiomycete *Lenzites saepiaria.* The function of the membranous organelle (*MO*) is not known. (From Hyde, J. M., and C. H. Walkinshaw, 1966. *J. Bact.,* **92:**1218. By permission of the American Society for Microbiology.)

(cellulin) different in chemical composition from the hyphal wall may plug the area within the constriction. These interior walls are called pseudosepta, because they are not derived from the hyphal wall. Pseudosepta also occur in some unconstricted hyphae.

The hyphae of the higher fungi are typically septate throughout, but the septa within the vegetative portions of the organism are incomplete. These septa result from ingrowth of the hyphal wall to form a peripheral ring within the hypha, leaving a central pore through which cytoplasm and nuclei can migrate from one compartment to the next. The inner rim of the typical Ascomycete septum is structurally simple; it may be somewhat thicker than areas of the septum closer to the hyphal wall, but it is not associated with additional structures (Fig. 14-3). In contrast, in Basidiomycetes,[4] the pore in the septum is partly enclosed on either side by a hemispheric structure associated with the inner region of the septum. This partial enclosure of the pore is believed to provide an impediment to protoplasmic streaming within the hypha and thereby a means of controlling the rate and amount of protoplasmic flow. The diameter of the pore and the orientation of the structures associated with it are altered when protoplasm streams through the pore (Fig. 14-4). Presumably, these changes are a function of the septal region itself that allow protoplasmic streaming, and are not results of the streaming.

The incomplete septa of the higher fungi allow many nuclei to exist in a common cytoplasm, but afford the additional structural strength of cross-walls. The septa subdivide the protoplasm into compartments that are uninucleate, binucleate, or multinucleate, depending on the species. Although the hyphae are not composed of protoplasts separated by membranes, the compartments are traditionally referred to as cells.

The thallus of several lower fungi and of yeasts is characteristically a single cell. These organisms are nevertheless recognizable as fungi by their cell wall structure and composition and their mode of reproduction, and, in the yeasts, by characteristics of their sexual stages. Also, unicellular stages similar to some of these unicellular fungi occur in life cycles of filamentous fungi or as alternative developmental forms that develop in certain environments (see Chap. 18, "Dimorphism").

Sporulation. In some lower fungi, the entire thallus is converted into the reproductive structure(s). Such forms are called **holocarpic.** The other lower fungi and the higher fungi that convert only a part of the thallus into reproductive structures are called **eucarpic.** In holocarpic types, successive generations cannot exist as contemporaries; in eucarpic types, several successive generations may exist contemporaneously.

Generally, the lower fungi bear their asexual spores within a sac-like structure called a **sporangium;** the **sporangiospores** may be motile by means of flagella **(zoospores)** or non-motile **(aplanospores).** The higher fungi bear non-motile spores at the tips of specialized hyphae, the conidiophores. Such spores,

---

[4]Secondary mycelium; see p. 248.

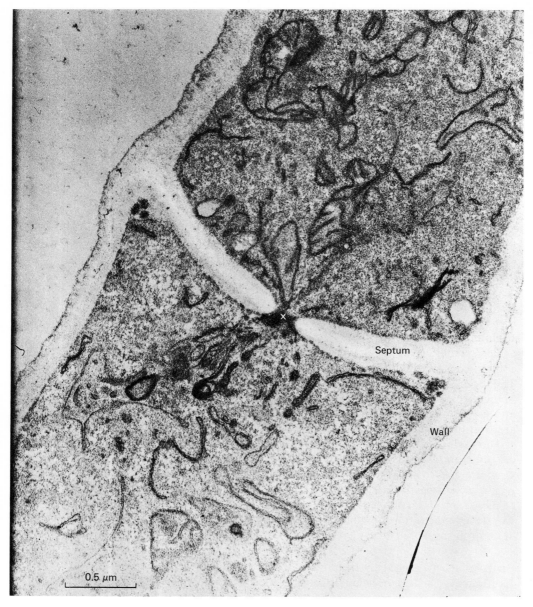

Septum

Wall

0.5 μm

Figure 14-3 Ascomycete type of incomplete septum in a vertical section of a septum of *Gliocladium deliquescens.* Movement of cytoplasmic components through the septal pore is implied by the orientation of cytoplasmic membranes and mitochondria toward the pore (*x*). (Courtesy of R. T. Moore.)

Figure 14-4 (*at right*) Basidiomycete type of incomplete septum. *A.* Vertical section of a septum in *Exidia glandulosa.* The pore (*x*) lies within the swollen inner rim of the septum and is partly covered above and below by the pore caps. (Courtesy of R. T. Moore.)

Vertical sections through the septa of *Rhizoctonia solani* with (*B*) the cytoplasm at rest and (*C*) during protoplasmic streaming through the pore. (From Bracker, C. E., and E. E. Butler, 1964. *J. Cell Biol.,* **21:**152. By permission of The Rockefeller University Press.)

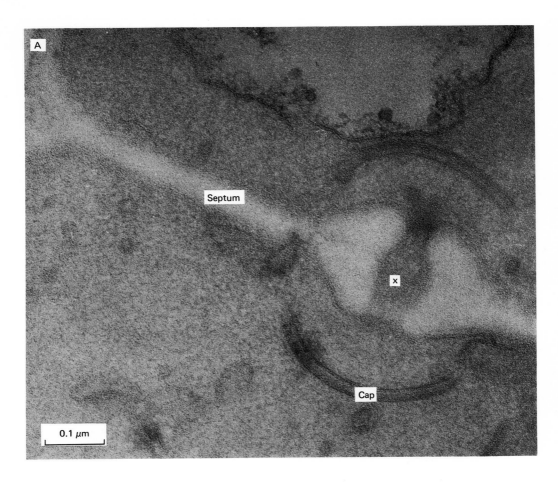

Septum

x

Cap

0.1 μm

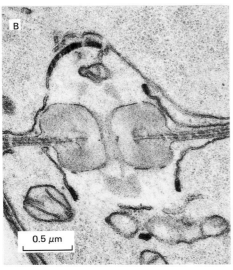

0.5 μm

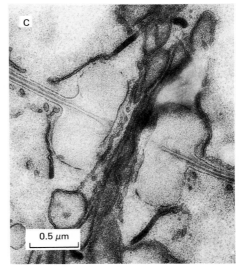

0.5 μm

207

called conidiospores or **conidia,** are typical of Ascomycetes, but uncommon among Basidiomycetes. Many Basidiomycetes form sexual spores only.

The mating cells (gametes) of some fungi are not distinguishable as male and female. Most fungi, however, produce gametes that differ morphologically and/or behaviorally. Generally, the larger gamete of a pair is regarded as female, the smaller as male; a gamete that leaves the structure in which it was formed and later fuses with a relatively stationary mate is regarded as male. The majority of fungi that form distinguishably male and female gametes are hermaphroditic; i.e., each thallus produces both types of gametes.

Some thalli are self-fertile; in these types, gametes produced by an individual thallus can fuse sexually. These types are called **homothallic.** A thallus that produces gametes that cannot fuse with each other, even if differentiated as male and female, is called **heterothallic;** its gametes can fuse only with gametes produced on another thallus. In several such types that have been investigated, sexual compatibility has been attributed to genetic traits that can be detected only by mating uncharacterized isolates with standardized strains of known fertility patterns, called mating types. Sexual compatibility has not been correlated with other traits of these fungi, although there are presumably differences in physiology or chemical composition between compatible gametes. Inherited mating type characteristics not correlated with other traits occur in some representatives of each of the three major groups of eucaryotic protists.

Classification

For many fungi, sexual fruits are produced only under certain environmental conditions. Consequently, the complete, or "perfect," life cycles of many individual types of fungi are not yet known. Since the classification of fungi is based primarily on the characteristics of the sexual spores and fruits, the imperfectly described fungi must be classified on other bases. Among lower fungi, such types are classified according to characteristics of asexual spores and hyphal morphology, on the presumption that their sexual traits, if ever observed, will justify their taxonomic placement. Imperfect higher fungi are provisionally placed in the class Deuteromycetes. Most of the sexual stages that have been found for members of this group are ascomycetous. When sexual stages are found, the organisms are reclassified in Ascomycetes or Basidiomycetes.

The classification used here is based on the revised scheme of Alexopoulos (1962).

Representatives of each of several classes are described in the following sections to illustrate common features of fungal development as well as some of the distinguishing peculiarities among modern fungi. Both parasitic and free-living forms are introduced to illustrate the modifications that have contributed to the survival of fungi in diverse habitats.

Class Chytridiomycetes

The chytrids are typically aquatic fungi; they occur as free-living organisms and as parasites of algae, small animals, and other aquatic fungi. Chytrids also inhabit moist soils and occasionally are found as parasites of vascular plants. The distinguishing characteristic of this group is the production at one or more stages of the life cycle of a motile cell possessing a single posterior whiplash flagellum.

Three orders are distinguished as follows.

Chytridiales. Mycelium absent; rhizoidal system in some species.

Blastocladiales. Mycelium present; sexual fusion involves two motile gametes.

Monoblepharidales. Mycelium present; sexual fusion involves one motile gamete and one non-motile gamete.

Order Chytridiales. The Chytridiales that are considered most primitive are holocarpic and complete their life cycle entirely within a host organism. In more advanced parasitic forms, the nucleated portion of the thallus and the sporangium are attached to the surface of the host. Nutrients are absorbed through rhizoids; these are anucleate filamentous structures that grow into the host tissue. The rhizoids of free-living forms similarly serve to anchor the organism to its non-living substrate and absorb nutrients.

Olpidium viciae is an example of a holocarpic chytrid that does not have a rhizoidal system. The infective unit is a unicellular, presumably uninucleate non-motile cyst. When in contact with the wall of a cell of its host, *Vicia unijuga* (vetch), the cyst dissolves a small pore in its own wall and that of the host. The fungal protoplast then moves out of the cyst wall and into the host cell, where it becomes attached to the host nucleus and begins to grow. Growth is accompanied by the formation of a thick envelope around the fungal protoplasm. The nucleus divides repeatedly, and eventually the cytoplasm cleaves. The naked, flagellated spores resulting from the cleavage are contained within the envelope, which serves as the sporangium wall.

The host cell wall disintegrates, and the spores are released through a small opening in the sporangium. The spores may either encyst and then initiate a new asexual cycle, or fuse in pairs. The respective members of a copulating pair usually arise from different sporangia, but sister spores can copulate. The immediate product of fusion is a motile, biflagellate, binucleate cell that encysts, then infects a host cell by the same mechanism used by single zoospore cysts. The sporangium resulting from this infection, however, is a resting sporangium that can survive the winter. Before or during germination, the nuclei fuse, divide reductively, and then give rise to many reduced nuclei. Ultimately, the resting sporangium liberates zoospores that encyst and begin the asexual cycle.

Rhizophidium couchii (Fig. 14-5) is a parasite of the green alga *Spirogyra;* it is a eucarpic chytrid. The zoospore attaches to the surface of a *Spirogyra* filament and develops rhizoids. Simultaneously, the portion of the zoospore

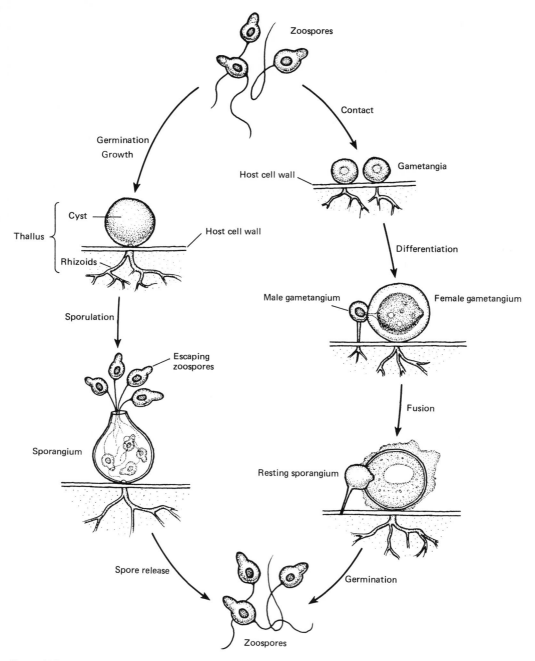

Figure 14-5 Life history of *Rhizophidium couchii*.

that has remained outside the host grows into an approximately spheric multi-nucleate thallus. Eventually, the cytoplasm is cleaved around the nuclei, flagella appear, and the thallus is thereby converted to a zoosporangium. The zoospores are released through weakened areas in the sporangial wall. They may infect another *Spirogyra* cell, or they may develop into gametangia.

Gametangia seem to be initiated only after two zoospores come in contact with each other while attached to a host cell wall. One zoospore grows until it is several times larger than the other. A pore or fertilization tube develops between the gametangia, and the protoplast of the smaller migrates into the larger; they thus behave as male and female. A thick wall develops around the fertilized female, which is converted into the resting stage. Nuclear fusion and meiosis have not been observed, but are presumably completed within the resting sporangium. Numerous zoospores are released upon germination of the resting sporangium; the spores either initiate infection and the asexual cycle or develop into gametangia.

A rhizomycelium is a branching, filamentous thallus of irregular diameter; it is coenocytic, but the nucleated portions of protoplasm are united by anucleate portions. This primitive type of mycelium occurs in *Nowakowskiella* (Fig. 14-6), a free-living eucarpic chytrid. The encysted zoospore begins to grow at one point on its surface; this localized growth results in development of a tubular projection called a germ tube. As the germ tube elongates and branches, the spore nucleus divides; one or both of the daughter nuclei migrate into the developing rhizomycelium. Eventually, all the nuclei of the thallus are found only in swellings within the filaments; the slenderer portions of the filaments do not contain nuclei.

Order Blastocladiales. Blastocladiales comprises chytrids with a definite mycelium composed of coenocytic hyphae that branch. In lower forms, the entire mycelium, which is naked during growth, is converted into zoospores. In higher forms, the mycelium bears specialized reproductive structures and may also bear rhizoids. In one family, Blastocladiaceae, the life cycle involves an alternation between a thallus that produces spores and a thallus that produces gametes. This alternation is known to occur among filamentous fungi only in this family.

It is characteristic of the zoospores, gametes, and zygotes of this group that the nucleus is surrounded by a large structure called a nuclear cap (Fig. 14-7). This cap is composed of densely packed ribosomes that disperse through the cytoplasm during germination. Presumably, the condensation of ribosomes conserves the amount of ribosome resynthesis that would otherwise be necessary during germination. Electron micrographs of two zoospores are presented in Figure 14-8*A* and *B*; see also Figure 14-9. A nuclear cap is rare among fungal cells, and has been seen only in Blastocladiales and in *Nowakowskiella;* a ribosomal region (Fig. 14-8*C*) occurs in zoospores of hyphochytrids (see Hyphochytridiomycetes, below).

A second distinctive morphologic feature of this order is the resting sporangium. Its thickened wall is typically brown, and its outer surface is covered with minute indentations. Development of resting sporangia occurs mainly when the organisms become crowded, or when the CO_2 content of the environment is elevated artificially in a laboratory culture. This morphogenetic response would, in nature, relieve a pressing competition for space and food by shunting some of the population into dormancy.

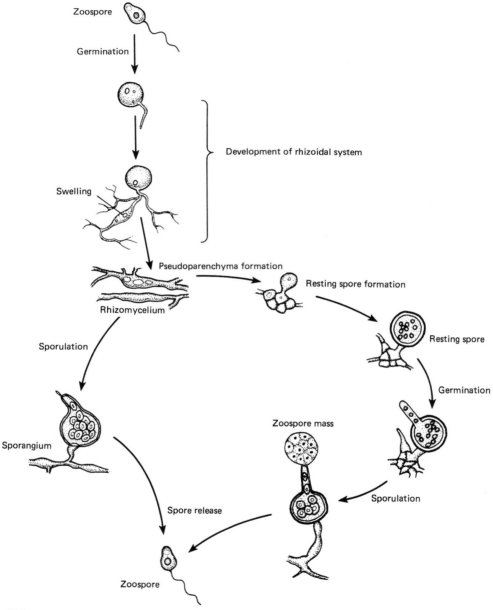

Figure 14-6   Life history of *Nowakowskiella ramosa*.

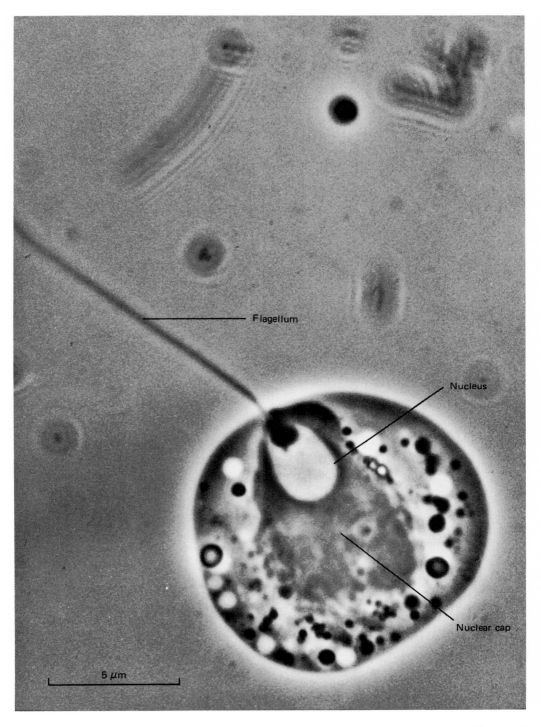

A living zoospore of *Blastocladiella emersonii*, slightly flattened by pressure of the cover slip. **Figure 14-7** (Courtesy of M. S. Fuller.)

213

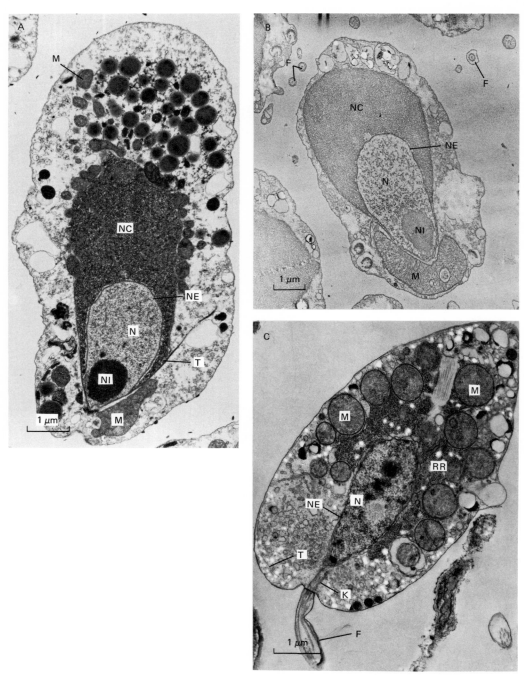

Figure 14-8 Longitudinal sections of chytrid (*A* and *B*) and hypochytrid (*C*) zoospores. *N*, nucleus; *Nl*, nucleolus; *NE*, nuclear envelope; *NC*, nuclear cap; *RR*, ribosomal region; *M*, mitochondrion; *T*, microtubules; *F*, flagellum; *K*, kinetosome. *A*. *Allomyces macrogynus.* (Courtesy of M. S. Fuller.) *B*. *Blastocladiella emersonii.* The zoospore typically has a single mitochondrion. Several transverse sections of flagella are visible in the background. (Courtesy of J. S. Lovett.) *C*. *Rhizidiomyces apophysatus.* The nucleus is partly surrounded by a dense ribosomal region that is less discrete than the nuclear cap of the chytrids. (From Fuller, M. S., 1966. *Proc. XVIII Symp. Colston Res. Soc.*, p. 67. By permission of the Colston Research Society and Butterworths, publishers.)

214

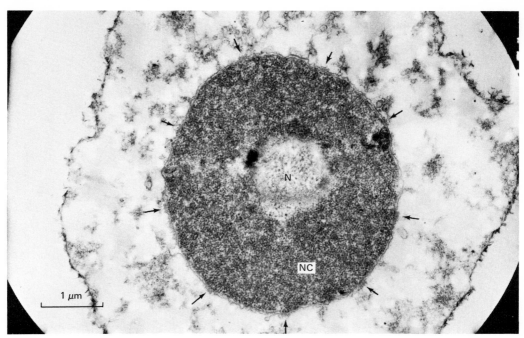

Blastocladia ramosa zoospore—transverse section through the nuclear cap showing regular spacing   **Figure 14-9**
of nine triplets of microtubules (arrows) around the cap (see Fig. 14-8*A*). (From Fuller, M. S., and
S. A. Calhoun, 1968. "Microtubule-kinetosome Relationship in the Motile Cells of the Blastocladiales," in *Zeit. f. Zellforsch. und mikroskop. Anat.*, **87**:526–33. By permission of Springer-Verlag,
Berlin, Heidelberg, New York.)

    The life cycle of one representative of this order, *Allomyces,* is illustrated
in Figure 14-10. The thallus of *Allomyces* consists of a thick-walled, branching
hyphal system that bears rhizoids at the base and sporangia or gametangia
on the branches. The stage designated the sporothallus is diploid; it gives rise
to two types of sporangia. In the thin-walled mitosporangia, diploid zoospores
are formed that develop into sporothalli; their nuclei are derived by mitosis
from a diploid parental nucleus. The mitospores of the Blastocladiales are
released through a pore at the outer pole of the sporangium. The meiosporangia
are the resting sporangia. While the resting sporangium is dormant, the nucleus
is suspended in early meiosis. A few weeks or many years later, the meiotic
process is completed during germination of the sporangium. Upon germination,
a crack develops along a defined line in the thick outer wall of the sporangium.
Numerous weak spots develop in the thin inner wall; as these are ruptured
by the pressure of the spore mass within the wall, the spores escape through
the resulting pores. The zoospores that are released are haploid and develop
into gametothalli.

    Gametangia (Fig. 14-11*A* and *B*) which are male (orange) and female
(colorless) develop on the gametothallus. Two gametangia arise as delimited,
adjacent cells on each side branch of the coenocytic thallus. Although the nuclei
of both cells have been derived from the single haploid nucleus of the zoospore,

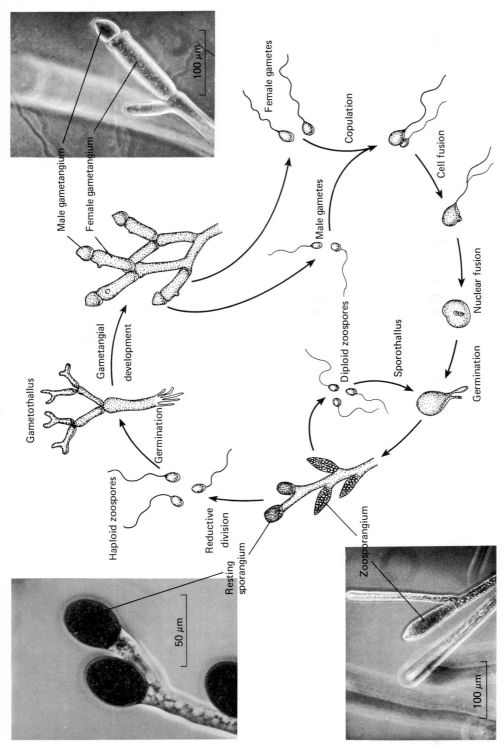

Male gametangium

Female gametangium

100 μm

Female gametes

Male gametes

Copulation

Cell fusion

Nuclear fusion

Gametothallus

Gametangial
development

Germination

Haploid zoospores

Diploid zoospores

Sporothallus

Germination

Reductive
division

Resting
sporangium

Zoosporangium

50 μm

100 μm

Figure 14-10 Life history of *Allomyces macrogynus*. (Photomicrograph of resting sporangia from Emerson, R., 1958. *Mycologia,* **50:**589. By permission of *Mycologia* and The New York Botanical Garden. Other photomicrographs courtesy of R. Emerson, from Brice, A. T., 1953. "Syngamy and the Alternation of Generations in *Allomyces*—A Watermold," a film. By permission of A. T. Brice, Phase Films.)

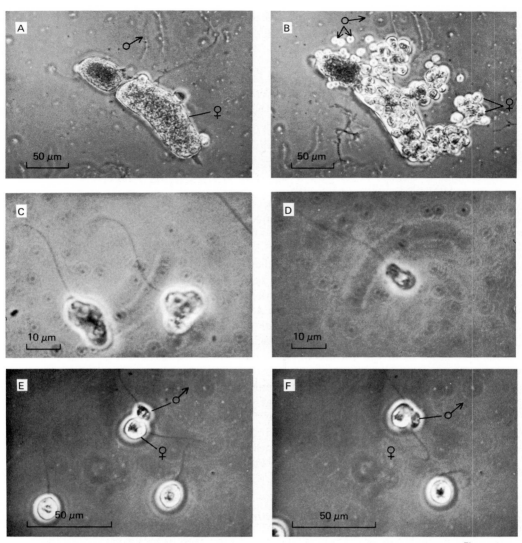

Gametangia, gametes, and copulation in *Allomyces macrogynus. A.* Gametangia. *B.* Same game-   **Figure 14-11**
tangia, releasing gametes. *C.* Two female gametes. *D.* A male gamete. *E* and *F.* Two successive
stages in copulation and fusion of a pair of gametes. (Courtesy of R. Emerson, from Brice,
A. T., 1953. "Syngamy and the Alternation of Generations in *Allomyces*—A Watermold," a film.
By permission of A. T. Brice, Phase Films.)

and therefore carry the same genetic complement, the two protoplasts behave
differently following their separation by a septum. The male synthesizes DNA
preferentially among cell components; eventually, its protoplast contains an unusually high proportion of DNA. Orange pigment (mainly gamma-carotene)
is synthesized, and the motile cells released from the mature gametangium are
small (Fig. 14-11*D*) and orange. The female gametangium usually matures
more slowly than the male. Its ultimate size is greater than that of the male,

but the number of nuclei and of gametes released is approximately the same. The female gametes (Fig. 14-11C) contain about the same proportion of DNA as does vegetative protoplasm; they are motile, colorless, and contain the nuclear cap that will be present in the zygote. They produce a hormone called sirenin, which attracts the male gametes.

The zygote is formed by fusion of a pair of motile male and female gametes. (Fig. 14-11E and F). In contrast to zygotes of other chytrids, the Blastocladiales zygote develops into a growing thallus (the sporothallus), which is diploid, rather than into a dormant stage.

Order Monoblepharidales. The highest point in structural complexity of the chytrids is found in the order Monoblepharidales. These organisms, still typically aquatic, develop as extensive, freely branching aseptate hyphae. The zoosporangia are borne at the tips of otherwise undifferentiated hyphae. The zoospores encyst and germinate into mycelia by means of germ tube production.

Sexual events in these organisms are unique to this order, but could be primitive versions of the sexual behavior of the Oomycetes. Two gametangia are differentiated at a hyphal tip of the same thallus that produces zoosporangia. The number of gametangia is markedly increased in laboratory cultures when the incubation temperature is elevated. One gametangium, the oogonium, is large and adjacent to the hypha. The smaller gametangium, the antheridium, arises from the surface of the larger one. The antheridium releases several motile male cells, which swim about and eventually approach the oogonium. Within the oogonium is the female gamete, the oosphere. Depending on the genus, the oosphere may emerge from the oogonium before or after fertilization. The zygote secretes a thick wall around itself as the gamete nuclei fuse. The resulting oospore is dormant. Eventually, it germinates by germ tube formation and develops into a haploid vegetative mycelium. Meiosis presumably occurs during germination. The life cycle of *Monoblepharis* is illustrated in Figure 14-12.

Class Hyphochytridiomycetes

The Hyphochytridiomycetes are distinguished from the chytrids by the mode of flagellation of motile cells. In members of this class, the flagellum is borne at the anterior end of the cell and is of the tinsel type. All known forms are aquatic, occurring, like the aquatic chytrids, as free-living forms or as parasites of algae or of other fungi.

The thalli and life cycles are generally similar to those of the lower chytrids. One principal difference is in the behavior of the sporangial protoplasm, which emerges from the sporangium through an exit tube before cleavage delimits the zoospores (Fig. 14-13).

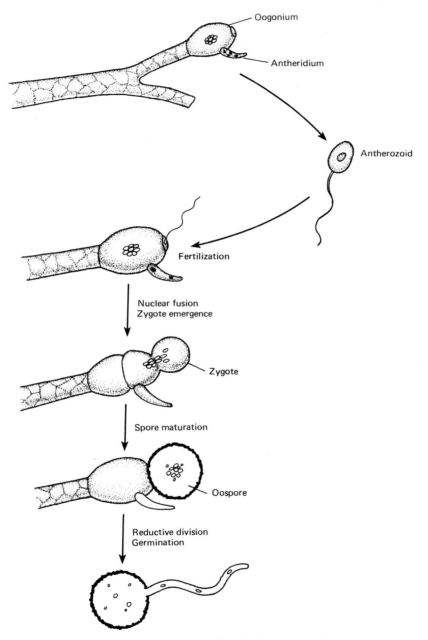

Diagram of sexual structures and events in *Monoblepharis polymorpha*.

Figure 14-12

219

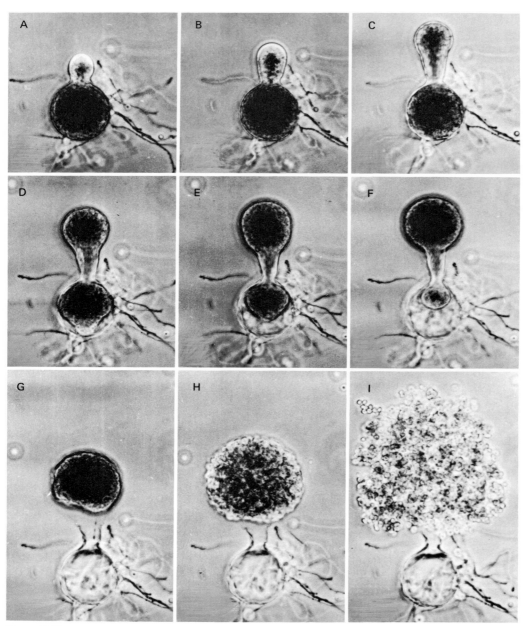

Figure 14-13 Successive stages (*A-I*) in the formation and release of zoospores in *Rhizidiomyces* sp. (From Fuller, M. S., 1962. *Amer. J. Botany*, **49**:64. By permission of the Botanical Society of America and the *American Journal of Botany.*)

Class Oomycetes

The third class of flagellated fungi discussed here, the Oomycetes, is generally more advanced toward the higher fungi than either of the other two groups. This is reflected in several ways. (1) The majority are filamentous and eucarpic, although some are unicellular and holocarpic. (2) Flagellation is restricted to asexually produced spores; gametes are not flagellated. (3) Sexual fusion characteristically involves two morphologically different gametangia; the product of fusion, the oospore, germinates by means of a germ tube. (4) A few higher forms do not produce flagellated cells at any stage; their propagative units are disseminated by air currents. (5) In some forms, the hyphae that will bear the sporangia are morphologically distinguishable from vegetative hyphae. The fertile hyphae are sporangiophores.

The structural material of the oomycete wall is cellulose, whereas in the chytrids it is usually chitin. This implies that these two groups descended independently of each other, even though the Oomycetes seem to represent advanced forms of chytrids like those in Monoblepharidales.

The oomycete zoospores bear two flagella—one of the whiplash type, as in chytrids, and the other of tinsel type, as in hyphochytrids. Two types of zoospores, "primary" and "secondary," are formed by many Oomycetes. Primary zoospores issue from a zoosporangium, carry two anterior flagella, and eventually encyst. The cyst germinates as a secondary zoospore, which carries two lateral flagella and encysts after a period of motility. The second cyst germinates either as another secondary zoospore or, more commonly, as a germ tube that develops into the vegetative stage.

A generalized oomycetous life cycle is presented in Figure 14-14. Question marks are inserted after the indications of meiosis because mycologists currently disagree about the stage at which it occurs. If it occurs in the zygote, as in most fungi, the thallus is haploid, and only the zygote is diploid. If it occurs in the gametangia, for which there is increasing evidence, the thallus is diploid, and only the gametes are haploid.

The Oomycetes have played a much more pronounced role in human history than have the other flagellated fungi. Among the hosts of parasitic Oomycetes are economically important organisms including fish and crop plants. Fish and their eggs are attacked by species of *Saprolegnia*. Sugar beets, potatoes, grains, and fruits are destroyed during their cultivation and in storage by Oomycetes such as *Phytophthora* (agent of potato blight) and *Plasmopara* (grape downy mildew). The story of man's reckoning with these adversaries, especially during the nineteenth century, is recounted at some length in the very enjoyable work *Advance of the Fungi* by E. C. Large. The Oomycetes of the potato famine in Ireland and of the loss of wine grapes in France were among the first protists to be recognized as disease germs, and the study of these diseases in the mid-nineteenth century contributed to the argument that some diseases are due to microbial infections.

Four orders of Oomycetes are distinguished, primarily on the basis of zoospore morphology, and secondarily on thallus morphology.

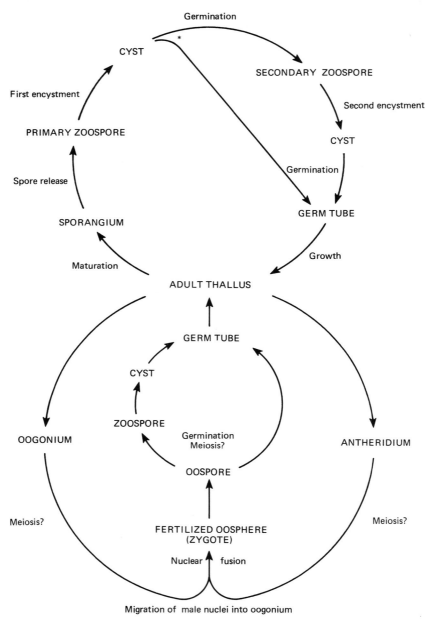

Figure 14-14 Generalized oomycete life history.

*The number of sequential zoospore encystments varies among genera. There may be one, two, or more than two. In the last case all zoospores after the first one are of the secondary type.

222

Saprolegniales. Primary zoospores are usually formed; secondary spores may also be produced. Holocarpic or eucarpic; hyphae, when present, are not constricted.

Leptomitales. Primary zoospores are formed; secondary spores may also be produced. Eucarpic; hyphae constricted.

Lagenidiales. All zoospores produced are of the secondary type. Holocarpic.

Peronosporales. All zoospores produced are of the secondary type. Eucarpic.

Order Saprolegniales. Saprolegniales representatives are of widespread occurrence. Almost any sample of fresh water will contain representatives of *Saprolegnia* or *Achlya*. These are usually the organisms referred to as water molds. They also occur in soil, and some species are parasites of aquatic animals and others of vascular plants.

The unicellular forms are similar to chytrids, existing as epiparasites of marine algae and obtaining nutrients from the host cells by means of rhizoids. Their zoospores and sexual cycles, however, are typically oomycetous.

The thallus of higher Saprolegniales types is a mycelium consisting of thick-walled, aseptate, freely branching hyphae. The zoosporangia are typically borne at the hyphal tips and are of about the same diameter as the hyphae. In one genus, *Saprolegnia*, sporangia may be formed successively on one hyphal tip, each new sporangium arising within the empty wall of its predecessor. In some other genera, the entire sporangium is shed when mature, and its spores are released at some distance from the parent mycelium.

Primary zoospores may represent the only motile stage in the life cycle, or they may account for one of two or more motile stages, each of the others accounted for by secondary spores. In some species, the primary spores are not released; rather, they encyst within the sporangium and germinate in situ. Especially in those species in which the sporangium is deciduous, the secondary zoospores may emerge from the sporangium and swarm for a period, or they may encyst and germinate by germ tube while still within the sporangium. These alternative behaviors seem to be influenced by the presence of water, which increases the proportion of spores that swarm. Both types of behavior can be observed among the spores of one sporangium.

The production of chlamydospores is another means of asexual propagation in the filamentous Saprolegniales. These are thick-walled apical portions of hyphae that are separated from the parent hypha as single units or as chains of spores. Chlamydospores are not motile; they germinate by germ tubes.

In *Saprolegnia* (Fig. 14-15), the sexual structures may arise at the tip of a hypha or within the hypha. In either case, the protoplasm of the gametangium is separated from the vegetative protoplasm by a septum early in gametangial development. *Saprolegnia* and most of the other genera of this order are hermaphroditic and homothallic.

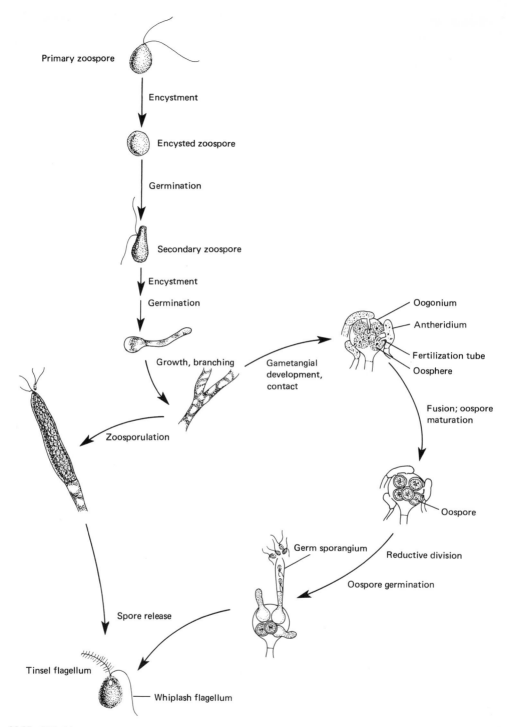

Primary zoospore

Encystment

Encysted zoospore

Germination

Secondary zoospore

Encystment

Germination

Growth, branching

Gametangial development, contact

Oogonium

Antheridium

Fertilization tube

Oosphere

Fusion; oospore maturation

Zoosporulation

Oospore

Germ sporangium

Reductive division

Oospore germination

Spore release

Tinsel flagellum

Whiplash flagellum

Figure 14-15 Life history of *Saprolegnia*.

224

In two species of the genus *Achlya,* the thalli are not hermaphroditic. Some thalli produce only antheridia and are, accordingly, male, while other individuals are female and produce only oogonia. The gametangia are formed only in the presence of a thallus of opposite sex (see Chap. 18).

Order Peronosporales. The order Peronosporales includes parasites of higher plants that are used as foods in Europe and the Western Hemisphere. Since these fungi can cause extensive damage to crops, they can be and have been responsible for famine and for economic disasters. The agents of downy mildews, white rusts, and damping-off disease are members of Peronosporales.

From a biologic point of view, these fungi are of special interest because they seem to be the most advanced fungi that produce flagellated stages. All members of the order are filamentous, and some have become highly adapted to terrestrial existence.

The mycelium of the Peronosporales consists of coenocytic, freely branching hyphae. In the family (Peronosporaceae) which is represented by the most advanced forms, the sporangiophores arise as branches that reach a characteristic length. Only when this length is attained does the differentiation of the sporangium begin. The morphology of these sporangiophores is characteristic of the genus. Four types are illustrated in Figure 14-16. Each of the organisms illustrated is a parasite of vascular plants and causes downy mildew of its host.

The germ tubes of germinating spores of some of these fungi infect the host by growing into the tissue through a stoma of the leaf. When a stoma is not encountered, the germ tube may produce a flattened hypha, the appressorium, which lies close against the host surface. A protrusion arises from the inner surface of the appressorium and penetrates a host epidermal cell. Inside the host, the fungus begins to grow from the extension of the appressorium.

Generally, the mycelium of the parasite grows intercellularly within the host; mycelial growth is not restricted to the confines of a single host cell. Nutrients are obtained from the host cells through special hyphal branches, haustoria, which penetrate the wall and membrane of the host cell. The form of the haustorium varies with the fungus species; it may be simple, elongated, branched, or knobbed.

As the mycelium grows, it may give rise to branches toward the stomata of the leaves. These branches extend out of the stomata and develop sporangia. In species that sporulate in this manner, the sporangia usually break off from the sporangiophores and are carried by the wind to new hosts. Many asexual generations are produced during the growing season of the host, and the parasite spreads rapidly through a population of host plants.

The sexual cycle of these parasites is in many cases restricted to the end of the growing season. The oospores that result are dormant and sufficiently resistant to cold and drying to survive the winter. Early in the following season, the oospore germinates and releases zoospores that infect young host plants. In some species, the oospore produces a germ tube that soon forms a spo-

Figure 14-16   Four types of Peronosporales conidia and conidiophores. *A. Bremia. B. Phytophthora. C. Peronospora. D. Plasmopara.*

rangium (called a germ sporangium), from which infective zoospores are released.

The oogonium of most Peronosporales types usually contains only one oosphere. The oosphere is often uninucleate, but is multinucleate in some species. Similarly, the antheridia may contain one or several nuclei. The fertilization tube through which the male nuclei migrate to the oosphere must grow through the periplasm, a thick layer of protoplasm that apparently nourishes the oosphere and produces the oospore wall.

Germination of the sporangia of Peronosporales generally results in the release of zoospores, invariably of the secondary type. In the species (all in the family Pythiaceae) that cause damping-off disease of plant seedlings, the zoospores are formed in a vesicle protruding from the sporangium. The thin wall of this vesicle disintegrates suddenly after the spores have become motile, and the spores swim away. In many species of higher Peronosporales, sporangial germination may alternatively occur by germ tube production. In this case, the entire sporangium acts as a spore, producing only one germ tube and one thallus. In all instances that have been investigated, it has been found that low temperature and high humidity favor zoospore formation; under such conditions, a film of water may be present on the host plant surface or on soil particles, and the zoospores swim about in this film. As the temperature rises above about 15° C, the swarming period decreases, and at temperatures around 25° C, germination is predominantly by germ tube. At higher temperatures, the sporangia die within a few hours if they have not germinated. Thus, hot, dry summers are unfavorable to the spread of Peronosporales, whereas in cool, moist years an entire crop may become diseased as the result of infection by these fungi. In the Irish potato famine of the 1840's, the potato blight fungus (*Phytophthora infestans*) was carried throughout much of Ireland within two rainy growing seasons.

Class Zygomycetes

The class Zygomycetes comprises fungi that are predominantly terrestrial. They are similar to the flagellated fungi in that the hyphae are usually aseptate; complete septa are present only at the bases of sporangia and gametangia. Also, their spores are typically borne in sporangia; however, in some forms the sporangia regularly behave as spores and do not release smaller units. A series of modifications of sporangia in the Zygomycetes culminates in a monosporous, deciduous unit that germinates by germ tube; the wall of the spore is fused with that of the sporangium. It is, structurally, a conidium. More than one step in this series can be observed on an individual thallus of some Zygomycetes; other Zygomycetes form only sporangiospores or only conidia.

The sporangiospores of Zygomycetes are not flagellated and not motile; they germinate by germ tube production without any change equivalent to encystment. Sexual fusion involves two indistinguishable gametangia that fuse completely; the zygote is converted to a thick-walled, dormant zygospore. The class name indicates this type of zygote development.

A means of vegetative propagation that occurs in Zygomycetes and in Ascomycetes is the production of arthrospores. These are small, nucleated portions of hyphal tips that separate from the parent hypha. In both groups, they can germinate and grow into a new thallus. In Zygomycetes (order Entomophthorales) and yeasts (unicellular Ascomycetes), they can behave as gametes and copulate with each other. In filamentous Ascomycetes, they can behave as male gametes and fertilize the female (ascogonium).

The three orders recognized within the class Zygomycetes are distinguished by characteristics correlated to a large extent with the respective habitats of the groups.

> **Mucorales.** Asexual propagation by sporangiospores; only a few species produce conidia.

Entomophthorales. Asexual propagation by modified sporangia or by conidia; conidia forcibly discharged. Most representatives are parasites of insects (see Chap. 21).

Zoopagales. Asexual propagation by modified sporangia or by conidia; conidia not forcibly discharged. All representatives are parasites of protozoa or small animals such as nematodes.

Order Mucorales. Most of the Mucorales are free-living. They sometimes develop on foodstuffs such as stored fruits and bread. One group of Mucorales comprises parasites of other fungi; the majority of hosts for these parasites are other Mucorales types (see Chap. 21).

The thallus is a mycelium composed of branching, aseptate hyphae. A few members of Mucorales form septa at regular intervals throughout the hyphae; these septa are perforate, and the protoplasm is continuous within the hyphae. Some species produce specialized hyphae called stolons, by analogy to the runners of plants. At points along the stolon where it contacts a solid surface, rhizoids are produced that anchor the thallus to the substrate. The sporangiophores are often produced opposite the rhizoids, as illustrated in Figure 14-17B.

The structure of the sporangium and the sporangiophore varies greatly among the Mucorales, and more than one type can be found on a single thallus. The most primitive manner of sporulation is the delimitation of a peripheral protoplasmic mass within the swollen tip of a hyphal branch. This mass is subdivided into minute spores; several thousand spores may be released when the sporangial wall disintegrates. The sporangiophore may be simple or branched, or the sporangia may arise in whorls along the main portion of the sporangiophore; arrangement is characteristic of the genus. A more advanced form of the sporangium contains only a few spores or only one. Such a structure is called a sporangiolum. In species that produce sporangiola predominantly or exclusively, large masses of sporangiola are formed; thus, the total number of propagative units per sporangiophore is not markedly reduced relative to the sporangium-bearing thalli, but the mode of formation of the individual unit is different. The difference between a one-celled sporangiolum and a conidium is structural; the walls of the sporangium and spore are fused in the conidium, but are separate in the sporangiolum. Mucorales can also produce chlamydospores and arthrospores.

Sexual fusion in Mucorales is essentially the same as in all Zygomycetes in which it has been observed. Two growing hyphae produce short side branches that grow toward each other until they are in contact. As the tip of each branch begins to enlarge, it becomes subdivided internally by a septum. The outer delimited portion is the gametangium. Its wall dissolves at the point of contact with the other gametangium, the protoplasts fuse, and a thick warty wall develops around the fusion cell. In most genera, the gametangia are multinucleate; many pairs of nuclei fuse as the zygospore wall is built, and it is

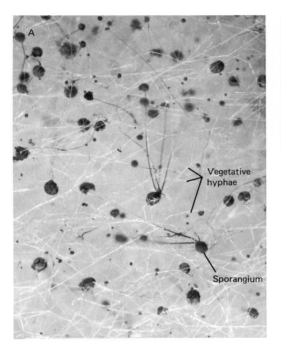

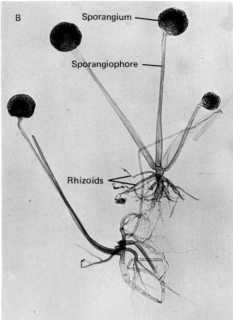

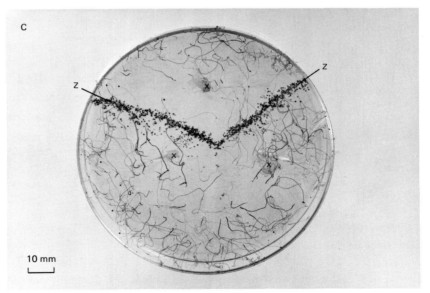

10 mm

Rhizopus sp. *A.* Surface of a colony. *B.* Detail of sporangiophores and rhizoids. *C.* A Petri plate **Figure 14-17** inoculated at separate sites (*x*'s) with three different strains. The lower two strains are of the same mating type, the upper strain is of the opposite (compatible) mating type. Where hyphae of the upper strain meet hyphae of either of the lower strains, zygospores (*Z*) are formed. (Courtesy Carolina Biological Supply Company.)

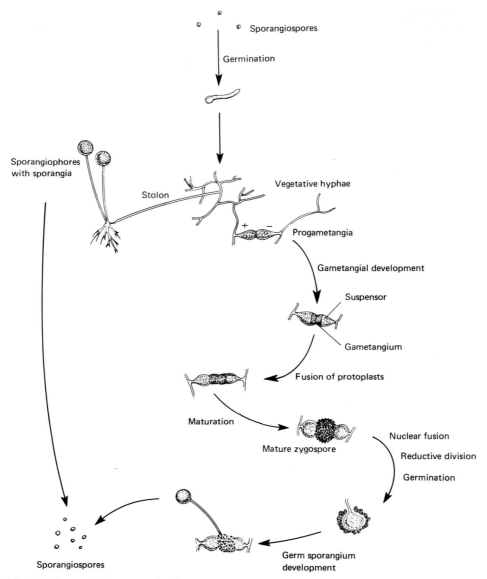

Figure 14-18 Life history of *Rhizopus stolonifer*.

presumed that nuclei that have not fused before the dormant period begins do not survive. The zygospore usually must rest for several weeks to several months. Only after this period can it germinate.

Meiosis occurs early in germination of the zygospore. As illustrated in Figure 14-18 for *Rhizopus,* the germ tube from the zygospore produces a germ sporangium that, except for its origin, is indistinguishable from an asexually produced sporangium. The spores are typically uninucleate and haploid.

Many Zygomycetes are heterothallic (see Fig. 14-17*C*). In these types, game-tangial formation usually is initiated only in the proximity of a compatible thallus. In studies of heterothallism in *Mucor* and *Phycomyces,* low molecular weight organic substances have feen found that are released into the environ-ment by certain thalli; these substances stimulate gametangial development specifically in thalli of compatible mating types.

Class Ascomycetes

Ascomycetes are distinguished from all other fungi by the production of ascospores. An ascospore is formed within a sac, the **ascus,** derived from a single cell. The spores are formed by a process called free cell formation; in this process, a complete cell cortex is formed around a nucleated portion of protoplasm. Some cytoplasm of the maturing ascus characteristically is not included within spores; the mature spores are entirely separate from each other and from the ascus wall, lying free in the excluded cytoplasm (Fig. 14-19). The young ascus contains a single diploid nucleus, from which the spore nuclei are derived by meiosis so that ascospores are invariably haploid. Depending on the number of mitotic divisions that follow meiosis, and on the number of nuclei included in each spore, there may be one to hundreds of spores formed per ascus. In the majority of Ascomycetes, four binucleate or eight uninucleate ascospores are formed. The asci and ascospores vary in size, shape, and fine structure, and in the type of structures in which the asci are borne.

The class Ascomycetes accommodates organisms whose thalli are unicellular and others that develop as extensive mycelia. Several means of vegetative propagation occur among the Ascomycetes, including production of arthro-spores, chlamydospores, conidia, and blastospores (spores that arise as buds on hyphae), and binary fission and vegetative budding. New individuals can also arise from nucleated hyphal fragments.

Three subclasses are distinguished.

Hemiascomycetidae (Lower Ascomycetes). Asci are single-walled and not contained in an ascocarp.[5] Ascogenous hyphae[5] are not formed.

Euascomycetidae (Higher Ascomycetes). Asci are single-walled or, if double-walled, are borne in an apothecium.[5] Asci are usually borne in ascocarps and are formed from ascogenous hyphae.

Loculoascomycetidae (Higher Ascomycetes). Asci are double-walled, are borne in cavities within hyphal masses, and are formed from ascogenous hyphae. Generally similar to Euascomycetidae types.

[5]Structures described in section on Euascomycetidae.

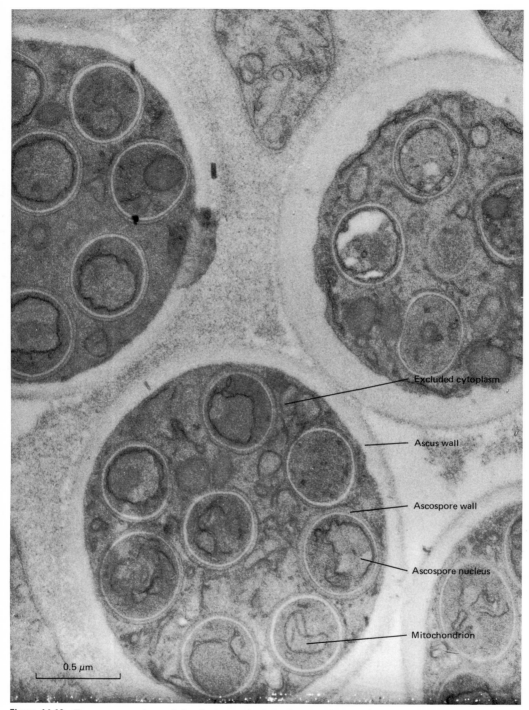

Excluded cytoplasm

Ascus wall

Ascospore wall

Ascospore nucleus

Mitochondrion

0.5 μm

Figure 14-19 Transverse sections of developing asci of *Cordyceps militaris*. (Courtesy of R. T. Moore.)

Class Ascomycetes / Subclass Hemiascomycetidae

This subclass accommodates the simplest Ascomycetes, in terms of structure and development. The manner in which ascospore formation is related to the life cycle is more variable than in the higher groups, where it regularly follows a fusion of nuclei. For these reasons, the members of this subclass are regarded as primitive.

Order Endomycetales. The order Endomycetales comprises four families, each of which exhibits one or more primitive features, as follows. In Ascoidaceae, numerous ascospores are formed from each zygote. In all other Ascomycetes, with the exception of a single Saccharomycetaceae species (*Kluyveromyces polysporous*), each ascus contains only one to eight ascospores. The hyphae of Spermophthoraceae are coenocytic; asexual spores are formed in a sac (sporangium); and these spores can behave as gametes. Copulation of unicellular gametes is unique to this family among filamentous Ascomycetes. The thalli of Saccharomycetaceae are unicellular. The Endomycetaceae are primitive only in the sense that the asci are not formed in a fruiting structure, as they are in higher Ascomycetes.

The family Saccharomycetaceae comprises unicellular Ascomycetes which reproduce asexually by budding (Fig. 14-20) or by binary fission. These are the ascomycetous yeasts. Many yeasts are known that do not form asci; they are accommodated in the class Deuteromycetes, but are presumably closely related to the ascomycetous yeasts.

For agriculture and the food-processing industry, the yeasts are the most important members of Hemiascomycetidae. *Saccharomyces cereviseae,* also known as "baker's yeast" and "brewer's yeast," has been used by man for centuries in the production of bread and of beer and wine. Various yeasts are used to produce particular kinds of foods and beverages (see Table 23-8). Yeasts occur in a variety of natural habitats in which organic content, especially of sugars, is fairly high. They can be found in and on animals, including humans, in soil, and on plants—particularly in the nectar of flowers and on fruits. They are known to cause diseases of plants and animals and spoilage of refrigerated foods.

In the life cycle of the genus *Saccharomyces* (Fig. 14-21), there are two vegetative phases—one haploid and one diploid. Reproduction in both phases occurs by budding; the cells of the two phases are not easily distinguished from each other except by the slightly greater size of diploid cells. Meiosis in the diploid cells is probably initiated in response to some environmental factor(s), since the frequency of sporulation within a population can be increased by incubating diploid cells in certain media. The haploid cells that arise from germinating ascospores can copulate immediately or grow and reproduce indefinitely as a haploid population. The species illustrated is heterothallic. Mating types are indicated in the diagram as + and −. In other genera of yeasts, the life cycle may include only a haploid or only a diploid vegetative phase.

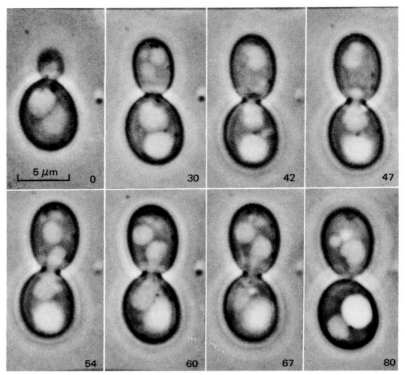

Figure 14-20 Successive stages in budding in *Saccharomyces cerevisiae*. The numbers indicate the time in minutes. Between 47 and 67 minutes, the nucleus is elongated and extends through the opening between the parent cell and the bud. (From Robinow, C. F., and J. Marak, 1966. *J. Cell Biol.,* **29**:129. By permission of The Rockefeller University Press.)

The thallus of Endomycetaceae representatives is a well-developed, septate mycelium. Asexual reproduction is accomplished by the production of arthrospores and blastospores. In some species, the cells are multinucleate, in others uninucleate. The gametangia of all species are uninucleate. They arise as side branches of vegetative hyphae. When contact is established between two gametangia, each is delimited by the formation of a septum at its base. The gametangia and then their nuclei fuse. The resulting ascus contains one to eight ascospores, depending on the species.

Class Ascomycetes / Higher Ascomycetes

The fungi of subclass Euascomycetidae are mycelial and bear their asci in fruiting structures derived from vegetative hyphae. They reproduce asexually by formation of conidia, chlamydospores, and arthrospores. Which type of asexual spore is produced by a thallus depends on its genetic traits, but is also strongly influenced by environmental factors.

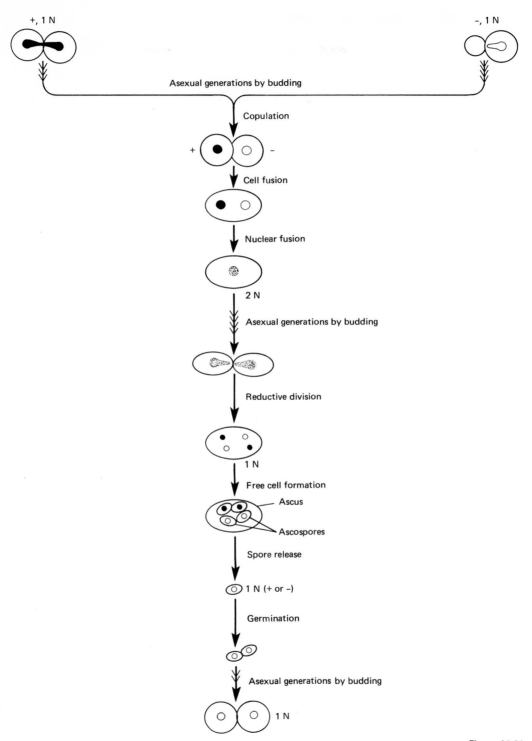

+, 1 N

−, 1 N

Asexual generations by budding

Copulation

+ −

Cell fusion

Nuclear fusion

2 N

Asexual generations by budding

Reductive division

1 N

Free cell formation

Ascus

Ascospores

Spore release

1 N (+ or −)

Germination

Asexual generations by budding

1 N

Life history of *Saccharomyces*.

Figure 14-21

235

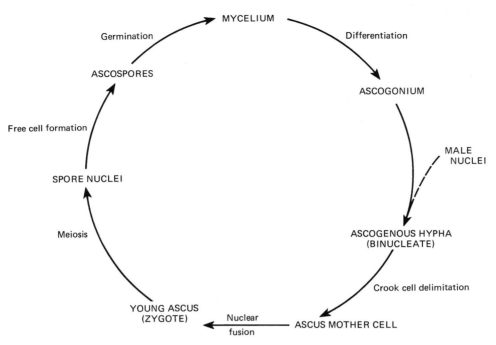

Figure 14-22 Generalized life history of higher Ascomycetes.

Ascosporulation. The sequence of events common to ascospore production in higher Ascomycetes is diagrammed in Figure 14-22. Note that ascospore production is typically a means of sexual propagation. The diploid nucleus of the young ascus is formed within the ascus mother cell by the fusion of two haploid nuclei. Both nuclear fusion and meiosis occur within the cell whose cortex becomes the ascus.

Depending on the species, the female gametangium, the ascogonium, may arise spontaneously on a vegetative hypha, in response to the proximity of a sexually compatible hypha or spore, or after the surrounding vegetative hyphae have begun to develop into the fruiting structure. The ascogonium of most types is multinucleate and either flask-shaped or coiled. A long, neck-like projection called the trichogyne develops on the flask-shaped ascogonium; the trichogyne is the receptive organ. Male nuclei enter the trichogyne, if present, and migrate to the base of the ascogonium. The ascogenous hyphae (see Fig. 14-33) then develop as outgrowths from the ascogonium. The cells of these hyphae are binucleate, and presumably each pair consists of one nucleus from each parent. Mitoses are simultaneous throughout the ascogenous hyphae and in the ascogonium. After some proliferation of the binucleate hyphae, the apical cell of each hypha bends into a crook shape. Within this crook cell, the nuclei divide mitotically, and then two septa are formed so that two of the resulting cells are uninucleate, and the center cell is binucleate. The binucleate cell is the ascus mother cell.

The nuclei in the ascus mother cell fuse, and the cell thereby becomes the young ascus. Meiosis follows fusion; the zygote nucleus, the only diploid stage in the life cycle, does not divide mitotically. Usually, one mitotic division follows meiosis. The eight haploid nuclei are then included with some cytoplasm into the ascospores. Variations among higher ascomycetes related to ascospore production include (1) the source of male nuclei, which may vary even among the fruits of a single thallus; (2) the length of the resting period between spore formation and germination; (3) the structure within which the asci are borne; and (4) the structure of the ascus and the means by which it releases the spores.

1. In many species, multinucleate male gametangia (antheridia) develop as differentiated branches of the thallus; the antheridium fuses with the ascogonium at one point, and the male nuclei migrate into the female structure. In some Ascomycetes, uninucleate units called spermatia are produced on special hyphae in a manner similar to the formation of conidia; the spermatia differ from conidia in that they cannot be induced to germinate and develop into thalli. They are assumed to be specialized for the fertilization of ascogonia. The conidia of most Ascomycetes can serve the same function as spermatia. Certain types of Ascomycetes produce two types of conidia: macroconidia, which typically contain more than one nucleus, and microconidia, which are uninucleate. In such organisms, the microconidia are the usual source of male nuclei, but in contrast to spermatia, they are viable as individuals. Fusion of vegetative hyphae can result in fertilization when nuclei from one hypha migrate into the ascogonia of the other, and the nuclei of the two hyphae are compatible. In relatively rare cases, ascogonia may develop without fertilization by exogenous nuclei; the nuclei that fuse in the ascus mother cell in such instances are identical.

2. Some ascospores are mature and can germinate as soon as their formation is complete. Others require several months of dormancy before they can germinate. The bases of ascospore dormancy and its termination have not yet been elucidated, although empirically devised methods such as heating and treatment with acids have been found that induce germination of some kinds of dormant ascospores.

3. The fruiting structures are derived from vegetative hyphae that grow around the developing asci and assume a characteristic form. In most cases, they serve as protective structures that release or expose the asci only under conditions suitable for spore release and germination. They usually represent sterile tissue, and the hyphae that compose the fruiting body do not resume vegetative growth after the spores have been released. They are not, however, equivalent to specialized tissues of higher organisms, since they serve only a reproductive and protective function, rather than a structural or metabolic function in a growing organism.

Four types of fruiting bodies are recognized; the cleistothecium, perithecium, and apothecium are illustrated in Figure 14-23. These types are called ascocarps; each ascus or, much more commonly, each group of asci is contained within a structure with a distinct wall derived from hyphae that proliferate

A

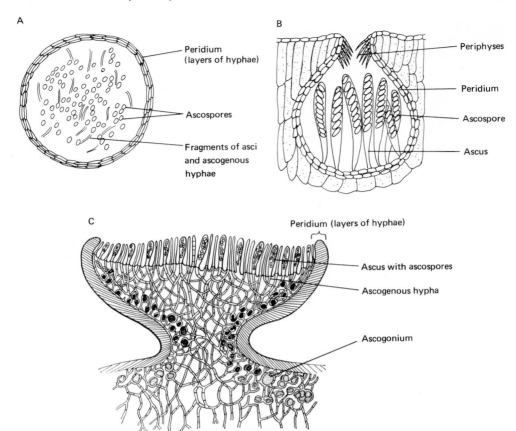

Peridium
(layers of hyphae)

Ascospores

Fragments of asci
and ascogenous
hyphae

B

Periphyses

Peridium

Ascospore

Ascus

C

Peridium (layers of hyphae)

Ascus with ascospores

Ascogenous hypha

Ascogonium

Figure 14-23 Three types of ascocarps. *A.* Cleistothecium. *B.* Perithecium. *C.* Apothecium.

around the asci and become closely interwoven. In some cases, the hyphae may fragment into cells of approximately equal diameter that are closely pressed together to compose the wall structure.

Depending on the species, the ascocarp may be of such size that it can be detected readily on such substrates as dead leaves, fallen wood, or soil (see Fig. 14-24). Many are colored bright red, orange, or yellow. Any one type may be formed as an independent structure or may be embedded within a larger, usually very tough mass of hyphae called a stroma. A stroma may contain one to several ascocarps.

The fourth type of fruiting body, the ascostroma, is a stroma that contains asci or groups of asci within cavities (locules) in the stroma tissue. Some ascostromata can be distinguished from stroma-borne perithecia only by microscopic examination of the fruits to determine whether there is a distinct ascocarp wall within the stroma tissue.

4. There are four principal means of ascospore release, and they are correlated to some extent with the type of fruiting body. Asci borne in cleistothecia typically release their spores when the ascus wall dissolves in air-borne mois-

Macroscopic ascocarps. *A. Morchella angusticeps. B. Urnula* sp. *C. Peziza* sp. (Courtesy Carolina Biological Supply Company.)

Figure 14-24

ture. The asci of most perithecia persist, and the spores are released by bursting of the asci. In apothecial fungi, the asci generally have a pore at the apex through which the ascospores are (often forcibly) released; the ascal pore in some groups is covered by a cap until the spores are ready to be discharged. The fourth mechanism occurs in the double-walled asci. The outer, thick wall wears away over a period of months until the inner wall is exposed. Water is taken up by the exposed inner wall, which swells, bursts, and thereby frees the ascospores.

Conidiosporulation. Asexual reproduction in the filamentous Ascomycetes is typically by production of conidia. These spores are usually produced on aerial hyphae and are disseminated by air currents. Almost any sample of air will contain such conidia, as well as sporangiospores of Zygomycetes. They typically germinate readily in environments suitable for vegetative growth. In temperate climates, they are produced in great numbers during the warmer months, and ascospores are produced only in the autumn. In tropical climates, conidia are produced throughout the year, and ascospores may be produced rarely or not at all in the native environment.

Conidia and the hyphae on which they are formed, the conidiophores, vary in form. These variations are not correlated with the type of ascospore fruiting body. The morphology of conidiospores and conidia is the basis of classification of the Fungi Imperfecti, and many Ascomycetes are known by two names—that given the fungus according to its classification as an ascomycete, and that given according to the morphology of its asexual spores and sporophores.

Examples. The *Talaromyces* representative of Figure 14-25 is a cleistothecium-forming ascomycete. Although this species seems to be homothallic, mating gametangia usually arise on separate hyphae. The ascocarp wall is a mat of loosely woven hyphae that extends into the interior of the cleistothecium. Large numbers of conidia of the *Penicillium* type are formed as the principal means of asexual propagation. This organism and its close relatives (perfect and imperfect) are most commonly found on citrus fruits, where their blue, green, or yellow conidia accumulate in patches on the surface of the rotting fruits.

The *Neurospora* representative of Figure 14-26 bears its asci in perithecia. It is commonly encountered on bread and is a nuisance in bakeries; known as the red bread mold, this rapidly growing fungus spreads by producing large numbers of air-disseminated, pink, *Monilia*-type conidia, which germinate readily. The mature ascocarp contains only asci; internal sterile hyphae are not present.

Venturia inaequalis (Fig. 14-27) is represented by parasites of a variety of ornamental and fruit plants; economically, the most important of these hosts is the apple tree. The ascospores mature in the ascostroma during the winter months. In the spring, the stroma cracks open, and the ascospores are forcibly released at the time the flower buds are forming. The buds are penetrated by the germ tubes of the ascospores, and the conidia (*Spilocaea pomi*) are soon produced and washed by rain onto leaves, buds, or fruits. Each of these can

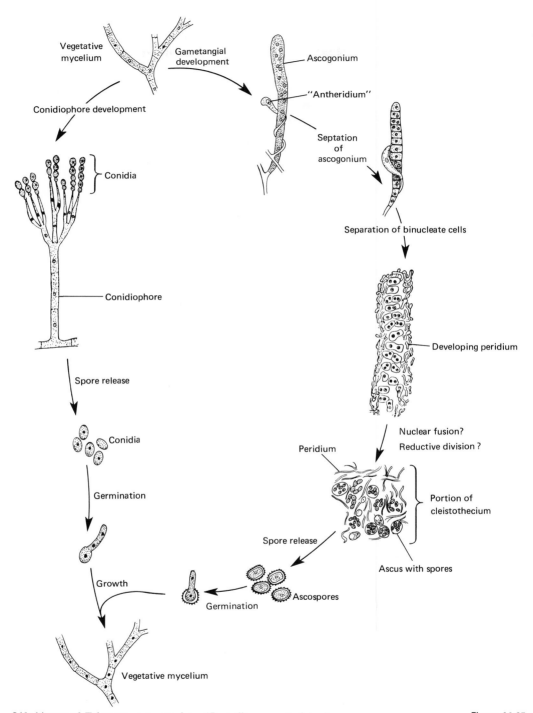

Life history of *Talaromyces vermiculatus* (*Penicillium vermiculatum*).

Figure 14-25

241

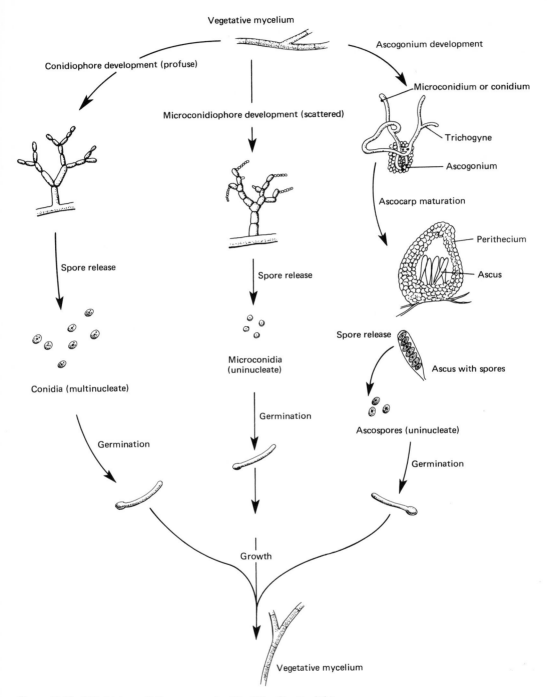

Vegetative mycelium

Conidiophore development (profuse)

Ascogonium development

Microconidium or conidium

Trichogyne

Ascogonium

Microconidiophore development (scattered)

Ascocarp maturation

Perithecium

Ascus

Spore release

Spore release

Spore release

Ascus with spores

Conidia (multinucleate)

Microconidia (uninucleate)

Ascospores (uninucleate)

Germination

Germination

Germination

Germination

Growth

Vegetative mycelium

Figure 14-26 Life history of *Neurospora sitophila* (*Monilia sitophila*).

242

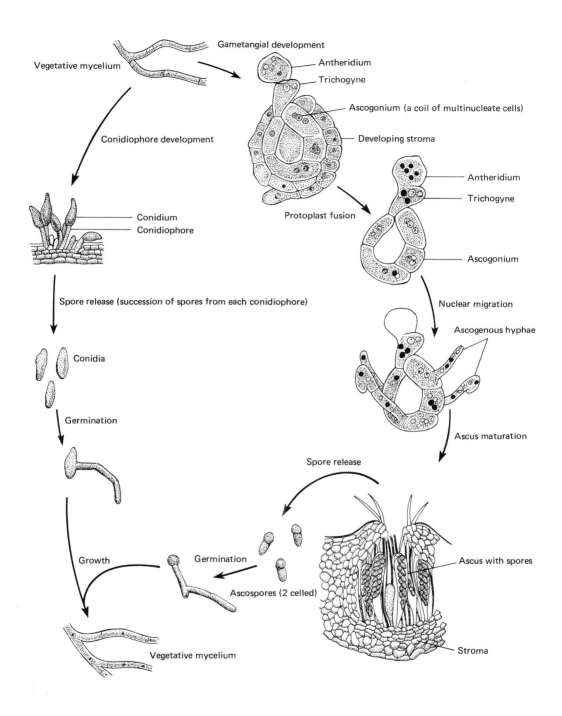

Life history of *Venturia inaequalis* (*Spilocaea pomi*).

Figure 14-27

243

be infected by the germinating conidia. The vegetative hyphae grow intracellularly, and those hyphae that eventually invade the epidermis develop into the fruiting structures. The stromata and ascogonia arise late in the summer as the leaves begin to die. The leaves fall to the ground, and the fruiting bodies they contain complete their maturation in the dead leaves.

Fungi Imperfecti (Class Deuteromycetes)

All the varieties of asexual fruits of Ascomycetes are found among the Fungi Imperfecti, and these varieties include all types known among the imperfect fungi. The conidia of Ascomycetes and Fungi Imperfecti vary in shape, color, number and position of septa, form of the conidiophores, and organization of conidiophores into fruits. Several types of conidia and conidiophores are illustrated in Figures 14-28 and 14-29. The conidiophores usually arise individually as aerial side branches from the vegetative hyphae or grow out in tight clusters. Plant parasites often form their conidiophores on mats of vegetative or stromal tissue; the conidiophores are typically short and unbranched and give rise to a succession of conidia. The pressure of the accumulating spores causes the cuticle or epidermis of the host to rupture, and the spores are released into the air or in a droplet of sticky, often colored fluid. Insects attracted to the droplet may carry the conidia to new plant hosts.

One group of Fungi Imperfecti do not produce spores of any type; they are perpetuated, it seems, solely by mycelial growth. The few representatives of this group that have been induced to fruit under experimental conditions have been found to be Basidiomycetes.

Many destructive plant parasites, as well as some of the most pernicious fungal pathogens of humans, are classified as Fungi Imperfecti. Human illnesses caused by these fungi include blastomycoses (which may develop into tuberculosis-like conditions), histoplasmosis, and lesser troubles such as ringworm, athlete's foot, thrush, and possibly dandruff. Many of these pathogens are imperfect yeasts that also grow as extensive mycelia under certain conditions. The group also includes fungi that are predaceous; these capture protozoa and small worms, sometimes with highly specialized trapping structures (Fig. 14-30). They absorb nutrients from the protoplasm of their prey by means of haustoria.

Class Basidiomycetes

A generalized basidiomycete life cycle is diagrammed in Figure 14-31. Basidiospores are haploid and usually either uninucleate or binucleate (Fig. 14-32). Although the majority are unicellular, several types become two- or four-celled early in germination. The spore germinates by producing one or more germ tubes that grow into septate mycelium. The cells are typically uninucleate. This primary mycelium usually does not fruit, and only in the more primitive Basidiomycetes does it grow extensively.

Common terrestrial molds, as Fungi Imperfecti. *A.* Surface growth of *Aspergillus. B.* Conidia and conidiophores of *Penicillium.* (Courtesy Carolina Biological Supply Company.)   **Figure 14-28**

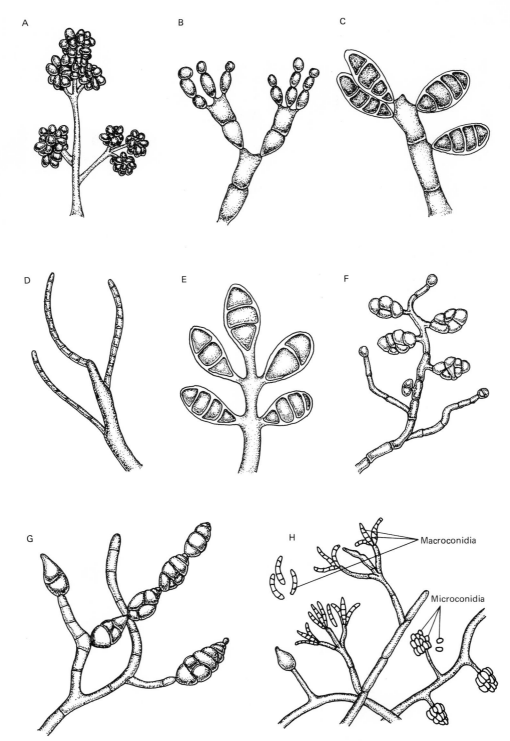

Figure 14-29 Eight types of conidia and conidiophores in Fungi Imperfecti. *A. Botrytis. B. Hormodendrum. C. Helminthosporium. D. Cercospora. E. Epidermophyton. F. Stemphylium. G. Alternaria. H. Fusarium.*

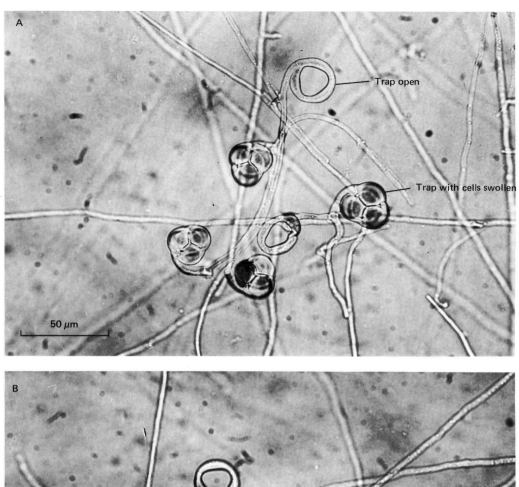

A

Trap open

Trap with cells swollen

50 μm

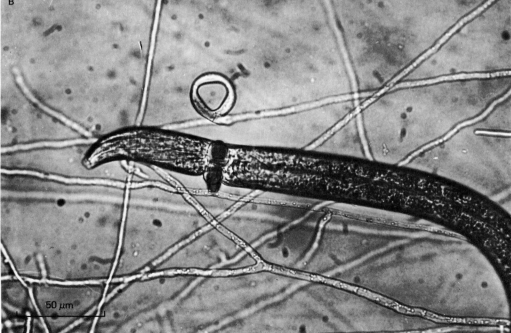

B

50 μm

Arthrobotrys dactyloides, a predaceous imperfect fungus that traps and digests nematodes. **Figure 14-30**
A. Vegetative hyphae bearing the three-celled rings by means of which nematodes are held.
B. A nematode caught in the grip of one of the ring traps. (Courtesy of D. Pramer.)

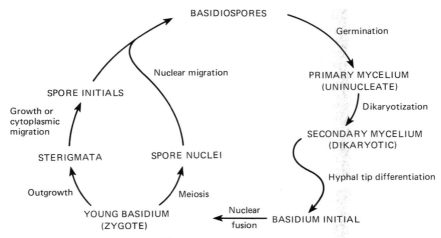

Figure 14-31   Generalized life history of Homobasidiomycetes.

The Dikaryon. The life cycle is completed only if the primary mycelium gives rise to a secondary mycelium. The secondary mycelium is dikaryotic—each cell contains two nuclei that are genetically different or, less commonly, several nuclei of two kinds. The characteristics of the dikaryon are determined by both sets of genes, as in diploid organisms, but the nuclei are not fused.

Establishment of the dikaryon may be accomplished in any of several ways, depending mainly on the species. Fusion of two primary mycelia is a common means. The dikaryotic cell formed as the result of fusion may give rise to new hyphae that soon outgrow the smaller primary mycelia, or it may serve as a source of rapidly multiplying nuclei that migrate into primary mycelium until most of the cells are dikaryotic. In many Basidiomycetes, the dikaryon can also be established following fusion of two germinating spores, or a spore and a primary hypha.

Once established, the dikaryotic condition is apparently maintained in all or most of the cells of the mycelium. A morphologic feature peculiar to, but not universal among, Basidiomycetes is regarded by some mycologists as a structural mechanism for maintenance of dikaryosis. The feature is called a clamp connection. Its development is illustrated in Figure 14-33, in which the development of an ascogenous hypha is also illustrated. The similarities of these two structures are regarded as evidence of the descent of Basidiomycetes from Ascomycetes; the clamp-connected dikaryotic mycelium could represent a vegetative form descended from the fruiting hyphae of an ascomycetous ancestral type.

In basidiomycete hyphae, as the two septa are formed, the wall between the hook and the inner cell dissolves, and the nucleus in the hook moves back into the main hypha. This process is repeated after each nuclear division; both cells resulting from septum formation and dissolution following nuclear division are dikaryotic, and both septa are incomplete (Fig. 14-34).

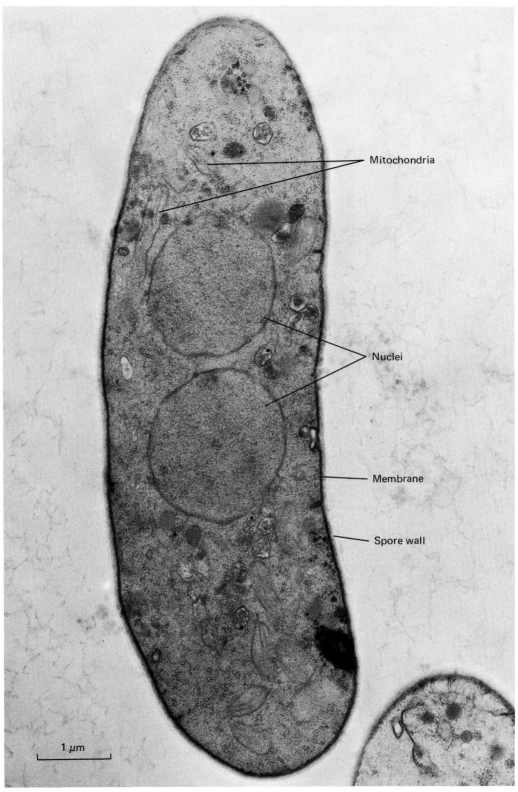

Mitochondria

Nuclei

Membrane

Spore wall

1 μm

Longitudinal section of a binucleate basidiospore of *Lenzites saepiaria.* (From Hyde, J. M., and **Figure 14-32**
C. H. Walkinshaw, 1966. *J. Bact.,* **92**:1218. By permission of the American Society for Microbiology.)

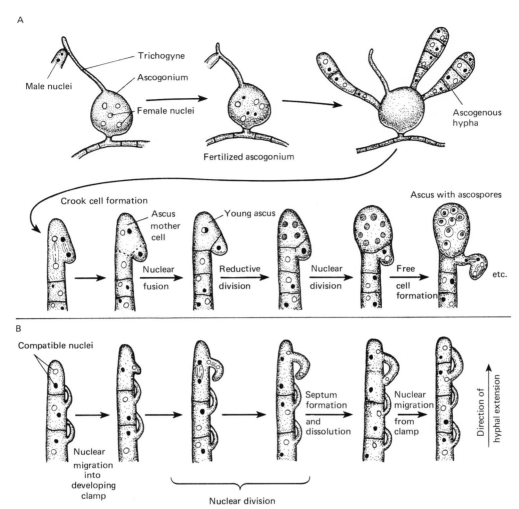

Figure 14-33 Diagrammatic comparison of (*A*) development of ascogenous hyphae and asci with (*B*) clamp connection formation. In some Ascomycetes, only one ascus develops on each ascogenous hypha; in others, more than one ascus develops, as indicated here.

The dikaryotic, septate, extensively branched mycelium of a typical basidiomycete is the principal portion of the thallus. It penetrates the substrate and absorbs nutrients. Parasitic Basidiomycetes usually grow intercellularly within their hosts and obtain nutrients from the host cells by means of haustoria. The most familiar Basidiomycetes grow in the soil or in wood; only their fruiting bodies are visible on the substrate surface. The fruits, called basidiocarps, contain the basidiospores.

Basidiosporulation. Basidiospores are produced as follows. The apical compartment of a growing hypha begins to enlarge. As the process is initiated, one mitotic division usually occurs, usually accompanied by formation of a clamp connection, whether or not clamps occur elsewhere along the hypha. The two nuclei that remain in the outer cell, the basidium initial, fuse. The diploid zygote nucleus then undergoes meiosis. The four haploid meiotic products are the spore nuclei. Meiosis is accompanied by the appearance of slender processes called sterigmata that grow out from the young basidium;

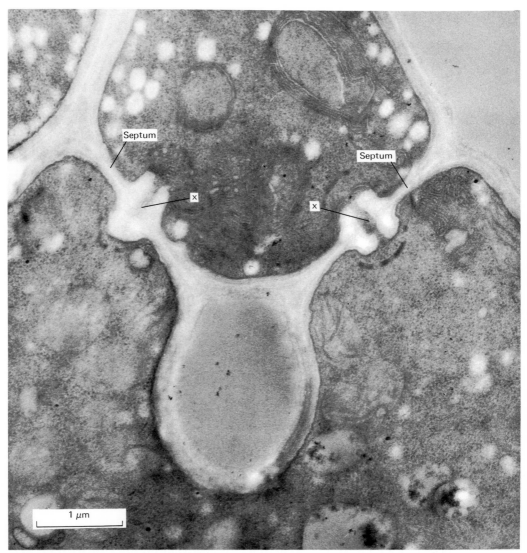

Vertical section through a clamp connection in *Lenzites saepiaria;* both septa are incomplete and their pores (*x*'s) are associated with apparatus apparently typical of basidiomycete (dikaryotic) hyphae. (From Hyde, J. M., and C. H. Walkinshaw, 1966. *J. Bact.,* **92:**1218. By permission of the American Society for Microbiology.)   **Figure 14-34**

there are usually four in the higher Basidiomycetes, but often only two in more primitive forms. A bud forms on each sterigma, and one spore nucleus squeezes through the narrow sterigma and enters each bud. The nucleated buds are the basidiospores. The basal cell within which nuclear fusion and meiosis occur and from which the sterigmata arise is the **basidium.** It degenerates after releasing one pair or tetrad of basidiospores. Germination of the spores completes the life cycle.

Because the basidiospores are formed as the result of nuclear fusion (and meiosis), they are considered sexual propagative units. Most Basidiomycetes, however, do not develop any sex organs or produce any cells specialized as gametes (the rust fungi, Uredinales, are exceptional in this regard). Compatible nuclei are brought together by fusion of unspecialized cells. Nevertheless, genetic mixing is ensured in most by heterothallism; at least 90 per cent of the basidiomycete species that have been studied have proved to be heterothallic.

Basidiocarps vary considerably in their morphology (and edibility). They are commonly known as mushrooms and toadstools, bracket fungi, stinkhorns, earthstars, puffballs, and others. Most of the fruits of higher Basidiomycetes are macroscopic, these ranging in size from about 1 mm to more than 1 m. Other notable variations are in color and texture.

Classification.   The structure of the basidium is used as the principal basis for subdivision of the class, and characteristics of the fruiting bodies as secondary criteria. The class Basidiomycetes is subdivided into two subclasses.

> **Heterobasidiomycetidae**
> **(Lower Basidiomycetes).** Basidium is septate or otherwise subdivided, or consists of a promycelium (see Fig. 14-35).
> **Homobasidiomycetidae**
> **(Higher Basidiomycetes).** Basidium is globose or club-shaped and is not subdivided.

Class Basidiomycetes / Subclass Heterobasidiomycetidae

Order Uredinales. This order is represented by fungi with complicated life cycles (see, for example, Fig. 14-35). The Uredinales, or rust fungi, are plant parasites many of which require two unrelated plant hosts in order to complete the life cycle. In these forms, the primary mycelium develops on the "alternate" host, produces the only differentiated sex organs that occur among Basidiomycetes, and forms dikaryotic spores (aeciospores). These spores germinate into secondary mycelium on the "primary" host, and there produce one or two kinds of binucleate spores. One kind (uredospores) reinfects the primary host; these spores are not produced by all rust fungi. During germination of the second kind of spore (teleutospores), nuclear fusion, meiosis and basidiospore production occur. The basidiospores infect the alternate host and develop into primary mycelium to complete the life cycle. A few rust fungi carry out all the stages on a single host.

The life cycle of wheat rust fungus, *Puccinia graminis,* is diagrammed in Figure 14-35. It is representative of the complexity of life cycles among these fungi. This organism produces all four types of spores that occur among rust fungi and requires two hosts.

Order Ustilaginales. This order comprises another group of plant parasites—the smut fungi. They are more similar to the higher Basidiomycetes than are the rusts, particularly in their lack of sex organs and in a limited development of the primary mycelium.

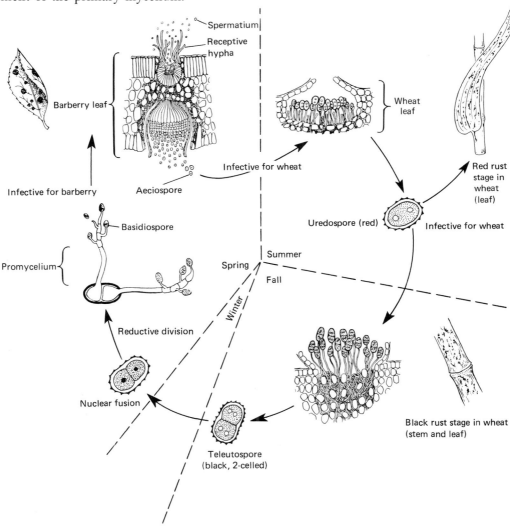

Life history of the wheat rust fungus, *Puccinia graminis.*   Figure 14-35

The basidiospores of the smut fungi behave in various ways, depending in part on the species and in part on environmental factors such as availability of a suitable plant host or proximity of a sexually compatible thallus. The spores may bud, fuse with other buds or with hyphae, or produce germ tubes that become primary mycelia. This mycelium, which grows within the host inter- or intracellularly, depending on the fungus species, may produce uni-nucleate, haploid conidia. Generally, however, it is converted early in its development to a secondary mycelium by fusion with a compatible spore or hypha. Hyphae of the secondary mycelium that reach the surface of the host produce dikaryotic conidia that germinate readily and spread the infection through a population of hosts. As these events occur, the host often continues to grow without displaying any disease symptoms.

As the fruit of the host (e.g., grain kernels) begins to mature, the disease is manifested by the appearance of masses of smut fungus spores, which may entirely replace the fruit of the plant. These spores arise throughout the plant in some infections. Regardless of where in the host they appear, they are all formed in the same manner. Masses of dikaryotic hyphae accumulate at certain sites within the infected plant. The hyphae fragment into dikaryotic cells that develop thick walls. These are the smut spores, which usually remain dormant until spring. In some species, nuclear fusion occurs within the spores before the dormant period begins; such spores are uninucleate and diploid during the winter. In most species, nuclear fusion occurs as one of the first steps in germination.

Class Basidiomycetes /
Subclass Homobasidiomycetidae

The basidium of higher Basidiomycetes is a single, club-shaped cell that produces basidiospores as buds on sterigmata. Typically, four spores are pro-duced by each basidium (Fig. 14-36), although one to eight may occur in a few species. The basidium is an apical cell of a vegetative dikaryotic hypha; nuclear fusion and meiosis occur within the basidium.

The Homobasidiomycetidae are classified on the bases of morphology of the basidiocarp and its component parts. These fruiting bodies are often very complex in structure, and most are macroscopic.

Series Hymenomycetes. The Hymenomycetes form basidiocarps that open before the basidiospores are mature. The spores are typically discharged forcibly by the basidium. Within the basidiocarp, the basidia are arranged in a layer of hyphae called the hymenium; non-fruiting hyphae may also be present in this layer.

The fruiting bodies of practically all Hymenomycetes are found on the surface of the growth substrate—soil, trees, fallen wood or cut lumber, and other complex organic materials. The larger basidiocarps usually extend some distance away from the substrate and discharge the spores into moving air currents between the hymenium and the substrate.

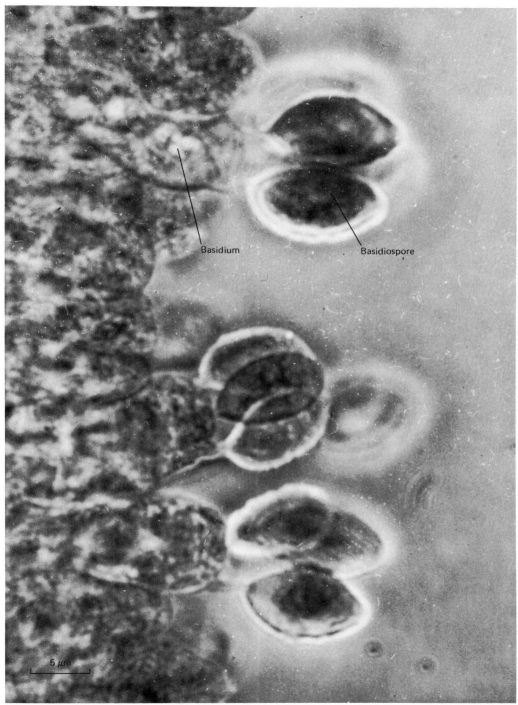

Basidium

Basidiospore

5 μm

Basidia and basidiospores of *Coprinus* sp. The central basidium has three attached basidiospores; **Figure 14-36** one has been detached (below the plane of focus). (Courtesy of R. T. Moore.)

255

Two types of hymenomycete basidiocarp construction are illustrated in Figures 14-37 and 14-38.

The basidiocarp usually begins as a knot of proliferating hyphae within the submerged vegetative mycelium; the hyphae become organized into tissues as they emerge from the substrate. Some of the hyphae become the external covering, others becomes the base that supports the fruiting tissue, others constitute the fleshy interior, and the tips of still others develop into the hymenium. In many Hymenomycetes, most of the tissues are developed while the basidiocarp is young; increase in volume of the basidiocarp results from enlargement of cells, rather than from any further cell multiplication. Although the mature basidiocarp is composed of tissues that vary in structure and in function, most portions can, if broken from the fruiting body, regenerate normal dikaryotic mycelium.

The composition and thickness of the hyphal wall are responsible for the texture of each tissue of the basidiocarp. In mushrooms, the hyphae of the supporting structure, the stipe, are thin-walled; the stipe is soft and usually decays readily. In certain other Hymenomycetes, e.g., bracket fungi, the hyphae of the supporting structure are thick-walled; the structure is tough or even woody in texture. This is particularly common in perennial basidiocarps, which persist for years and produce basidiospores at intervals.

The internal tissues of the fruiting body are also variable in texture. The soft interior of mushrooms is composed of chains of elongated, thin-walled cells derived by completion of hyphal septa. Some cells within the chains may be approximately spheric; their occurrence varies among genera. The interior tissue is covered on the upper surface by a layer of hyphae with short, tightly interwoven side branches, which presumably protects the interior against loss of water.

The lower surface of the interior tissue is folded along lines that radiate from the stipe. These folds, called gills, bear the hymenium. The hyphal tips that constitute the hymenium arise perpendicular to the gill surface. The basidiospores are discharged into the space between gills and are carried away by air currents. Movement of air over the gills stimulates spore discharge.

Low humidity inhibits fruiting body formation in many Hymenomycetes. Relatively high temperatures, especially above 25° C, are also unfavorable. Although responses to light are influenced by other factors, when these others are optimal, any one fungus will respond consistently to light. There is one broad correlation between response to light and natural habitat. In soil- and dung-dwelling Hymenomycetes, the early stages of fruiting body formation are inhibited by light, but once the basidiocarp is formed, the expansion of the cap occurs only in the presence of light.[6] In contrast, the basidiocarps of bracket fungi that grow on trees are indifferent to light until nearly mature; the hymenium is then exposed only in the presence of light.

---

[6]One notable exception to the second response is observed in *Agaricus campestris*, the commercial mushroom used as food in the United States; cap expansion occurs only in darkness.

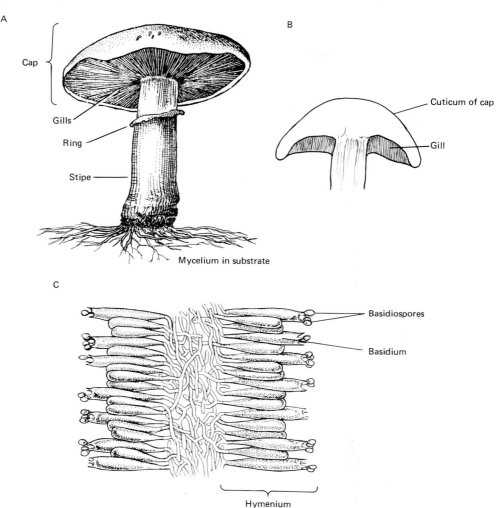

Diagram of mushroom (Hymenomycetes) basidiocarp construction. *A*. Mature basidiocarp. **Figure 14-37**
B. Vertical section through cap. *C*. Vertical section through a gill.

Series Gasteromycetes. The mature basidiocarp of the Gasteromycetes is surrounded by a thick, usually tough wall derived from hyphae. This wall, called the peridium, may have one to several layers. Within the peridium is a mass of hyphae called the gleba; the basidia arise on these hyphae. When the spores mature, the basidia and often also the entire gleba disintegrate, leaving the spores free within the peridium. Gasteromycete basidiocarps remain closed (Fig. 14-39) at least until the spores are mature. Even then, rupture of the fruiting body wall by external forces may be the only way in which the spores are exposed and subsequently dispersed.

The consistency of the contents of the mature gasteromycete basidiocarp is used as a major taxonomic criterion. It may be dry and powdery as in the puffballs, slimy as in the stinkhorns, cartilaginous, or waxy. The last of these is characteristic of the bird's-nest fungi, which bear groups of about two to six fruiting bodies within a cup-shaped structure. The mature fruiting bodies are splashed out of the cups by raindrops and may land as far as 4 ft from the cup. One of these fungi is illustrated in Figure 14-40; it is apparent in the drawing that further structures are specialized, again from hyphae, in the development of these Basidiomycetes.

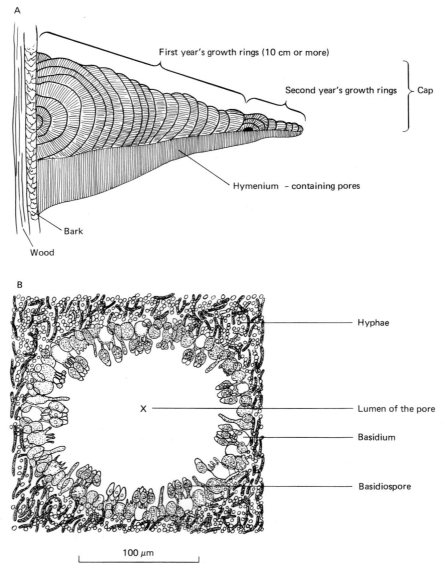

Figure 14-38 Diagram of bracket fungus (Hymenomycetes) basidiocarp construction. *A*. Vertical section of fruiting body. *B*. Cross-section of a pore.

Fruiting bodies of earthstars (*Geastrum* sp., Gasteromycetes). (Courtesy Carolina Biological Supply **Figure 14-39** Company.)

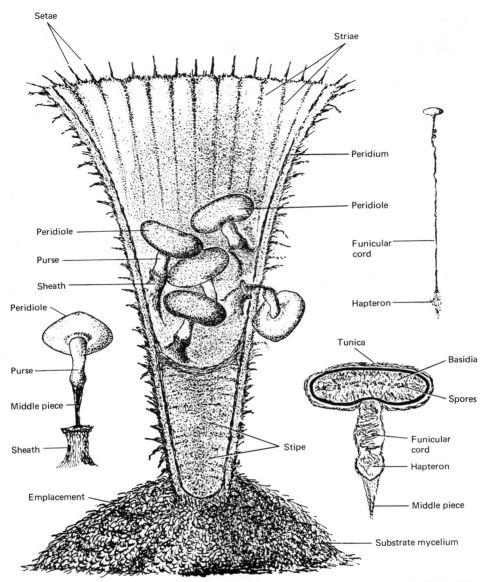

Figure 14-40 Diagram of a fruiting body of the bird's nest fungus *Cyathus striatus*. (From Brodie, H. J., 1951. *Can. J. Botany,* **29**:224. By permission of the National Research Council of Canada.)

Chapter 15

Protozoa

The protozoa are eucaryotic, chemoorganotrophic protists that occur as solitary unicellular individuals or as colonies. They are distinguished from fungi by their marked tendency toward subcellular differentiation and their lack of tendency toward filamentous organization. Further, most major types of protozoa can ingest particulate foods, for which some have acquired elaborate organellar systems.

There are two evolutionary consequences of the acquisition of the capacity for ingestion. One is that such organisms must be able to trap or pick up particles that are too large to diffuse to them through the environment. Since the foods of protozoa often include other microbial cells, which may be motile, many protozoa are hunters and are typically motile in the principal vegetative stage of the life cycle. Motility may be achieved through the action of flagella or cilia, by protoplasmic flow (especially within pseudopodia), or by a gliding movement of unexplained mechanism. Most non-motile protozoa have retained flagella, cilia, or pseudopodia for use in gathering particulate food.

Second, this type of food acquisition has allowed the free-living protozoa to accumulate complex nutritional requirements, particularly for vitamins and amino acids that are not widely available in solution in nature. They are present in the living organisms that protozoa consume. Many protozoa have been cultivated only in the presence of other cells (living or killed); consequently, there is as yet little information available about the chemical, physiologic, and genetic properties of many types of protozoa.

Classification

The classification of protozoa used here is a modification of the system of Hall (1953) and Jahn and Jahn (1949). The group is subdivided into four phyla, each of which represents a major trend in the evolution of protozoa and may represent an independent natural group. The four phyla, listed below, are distinguished mainly by the mechanism of locomotion in the principal vegetative phase. Each group includes both free-living and parasitic forms, except Sporozoa, all of whose members are parasitic.

Mastigophora (Flagellates). Locomotion by means of one to hundreds of flagella per individual.

Sarcodina (Amebae). Locomotion by means of protoplasmic flow, usually through pseudopodia.

Sporozoa (Sporozoa). Locomotion by gliding movement; external organelles of locomotion absent.

Ciliophora (Ciliates and Suctoreans). Locomotion by means of cilia; also, non-motile organisms that use cilia for feeding or possess locomotor cilia in young stages.

General Characteristics

Morphologic Specializations. The subcellular specializations of protozoa include appendages, internal organelles, surface structures, shells, and skeletons. Several of these are described briefly in the list in Table 15-1.

A minimum number of each required organelle must somehow be provided to new individuals as they arise. Three mechanisms are possible: (1) replication of each organelle before reproduction; (2) resorption of the old organelle and production of a new one for each product of reproduction; and (3) retention of an organelle by one member of the next generation and construction of a new organelle of the same kind by each of the other progeny. Each of these means occurs among protozoa; the particular mechanism varies with the species.

Reproduction, Sex, and Dormancy. Asexual reproduction occurs in all protozoa. The mechanism varies with the type of protozoon. Flagellates, simple amebae, and ciliates commonly reproduce by fission, one organism subdividing into two (or a few) organisms that are essentially identical with each other and with the parent when young. Suctoreans usually bud, one individual giving rise to a succession of smaller individuals. Multinucleate organisms, particularly ameboid forms, can undergo a process called **plasmotomy,** in which one organism divides into two or more individuals among which the parental nuclei are distributed randomly. A process called **schizogony** occurs among some organisms of this form. In schizogony, the multinucleate organism gives rise, within a short time, to many (in some instances more than 100,000) uninucleate buds; a mass of anucleate protoplasm is usually left unused (Fig. 15-4).

TABLE 15-1. Structural Specializations That Occur in Protozoa

Structure	Description	Distribution Among Protozoa
Internal Structures		
Ectoplasm and endoplasm	Respectively, the outer and inner zones of cytoplasm; the zones are not separated by any structure, but they contain different cellular components and are of different consistencies (Fig. 15-1)	Typical of protozoa
Food vacuole	Transient, membrane-bounded vesicle formed at the cell surface, inner surface of the cytostome, or inner end of the cytopharynx to envelop food; the vacuole migrates (apparently passively) through the cytoplasm as the food is digested	Occurs in all protozoa that ingest particulate food
Cytopharynx	A passageway through which ingested particles pass from cytostome into a food vacuole; in some protozoa, detectable only during ingestion; in others, well defined structurally and associated with permanent structures such as rods (Fig. 15-2)	Occurs in most protozoa with cytostomes
Contractile vacuole	Membrane-bounded vesicle usually fixed at a site within the cytoplasm; fluid from the cytoplasm accumulates within the vacuole and is expelled from it to the exterior	Occurs generally among freshwater protozoa and is of variable occurrence among marine and parasitic protozoa
Kinetosome	Also called a blepharoplast, or a basal granule, body, or structure; it is the intracytoplasmic basal portion of a flagellum or cilium; described in Chap. 6	Occurs with flagella and cilia
Fibrillar bundle	Myoneme, rod, and microtubule are names that designate slightly different structures composed of groups of parallel fibrils; some axostyles are also fibrillar bundles; myonemes, axostyles, and axial rods are known to be contractile; by contraction or by shearing movements, some of these structures possibly generate or sustain intracellular motion, aid in locomotion or in maintenance and alteration of cell shape	Occurrence is widespread among protozoa
Surface Structures		
Muciferous body	Membrane-bounded organelle that lies just within the cell surface; it discharges its contents to the exterior; the contents may be used to construct cyst walls	Occurs in certain flagellates and ciliates

TABLE 15-1. Structural Specializations That Occur in Protozoa (*cont.*)

Structure	Description	Distribution Among Protozoa
Trichites, trichocysts, and haptocysts	Structures similar to and presumably evolved from muciferous bodies; during discharge, the contents form a proteinaceous thread that aids in predation and possibly in defense against predators	Occur in certain flagellates and ciliates
Cytostome	A distinct, usually permanent area that can be opened for ingestion of foods; generally circular when open, but sometimes slitlike; fibrils or fibrillar bundles associated with the cytostome function to widen it for feeding and to guide the food vacuole into the endoplasm	Occurs in most ciliates; rudimentary or temporary cytostomes occur in some flagellates and amebae
Oral groove and peristome	An indentation of the cell surface leading to the cytostome; it aids in concentrating particulate foods, thereby reducing the amount of fluid ingested, and in trapping food near the cytostome; a peristome is an elaborate oral groove.	Occur in a few flagellates; particularly common in ciliates
Undulating membrane	In certain flagellates, a flap of the cell cortex with which a flagellum is associated; the flagellum functions in locomotion in some undulating membranes, but not in others (See Fig. 15-3). In certain ciliates, fused cilia that function as a unit, usually to aid feeding	
Tentacle	Slender cytoplasmic appendage with prehensile capacity; it is used for capturing prey and ingesting its protoplasm	Typical of suctoreans, and occurs in one group of ciliates
Cytopyge	A site on the cell surface that opens for elimination of undigested contents of food vacuoles; located within the oral groove or near the posterior end of the cell	Occurs in ciliates
Uroid	Transient, short, slender protrusion at the posterior end of the cell; it seems to result from eversion of a food vacuole during egestion or from retraction of pseudopodia	Occurs in amebae and ameboflagellates
Skeletal Structures and Shells		
Pellicle	Outer surface of the protozoon, closely apposed to the cell membrane and possibly derived from it; thickness, number of layers, and flexibility are variable	Occurs generally among protozoa

TABLE 15-1.   Structural Specializations That Occur in Protozoa (*cont.*)

Structure	Description	Distribution Among Protozoa
Shell, test, lorica, envelope	Loosely fitting coverings usually external to the pellicle; in Foraminifera (shelled amebae), the shell is covered with protoplasm; the shape, rigidity, and composition are variable; apparently afford protection against mechanical damage	Occur in all major groups of protozoa except the sporozoa
Skeletal plates	Flattened, usually rigid units embedded in the ectoplasm, pellicle, or a flexible test; their composition is variable; they provide a hard, protective surface	Occur in some ciliates and amebae
Spicules, spines	Elongated, rigid units that arise within the cytoplasm and often extend through the cell surface to the exterior; their shape and composition are variable; they provide a rigid internal skeleton; spicules are usually not fixed in position; spines are usually in constant spatial relationship to other cell components	Occur in certain amebae, particularly those that exist as free-floating individuals

Several kinds of sexual phenomena have been observed among protozoa. In many forms, fusion of a pair of gametes, followed by fusion of their nuclei, initiates a stage in the life cycle; this is commonly—but not universally—a resting stage. The gametes may be morphologically indistinguishable, as in many flagellates and in certain amebae and sporozoa; in many species, however, the gametes are different, at least in size, and often also in form. Morphologically distinguishable gametes are common among sporozoa. Among Ciliophora, nuclear fusions occur within cells that have exchanged nuclei during a temporary, conjugal association. Following the nuclear exchange, the conjugants dissociate, and each exconjugant gives rise to its respective progeny by binary fission or budding. Conjugation does not result in a change in cell form or initiate a stage of the life cycle.

The typical resting stage of most protozoa is a cyst; the resting stage of sporozoa is called a spore. Two functional types of cysts are formed: **protective** cysts, which serve as dormant stages that may be disseminated, and **reproductive** cysts, within which the number of individuals increases before germination. In some species, sexual fusion occurs within reproductive cysts, in which case this stage is also called a **fertilization** cyst. Protective cysts generally seem to be formed in response to adverse environmental conditions, particularly scarcity of water or of suitable foods. They are usually uninucleate and more resistant to desiccation and extreme temperatures than the vegetative stage. Although

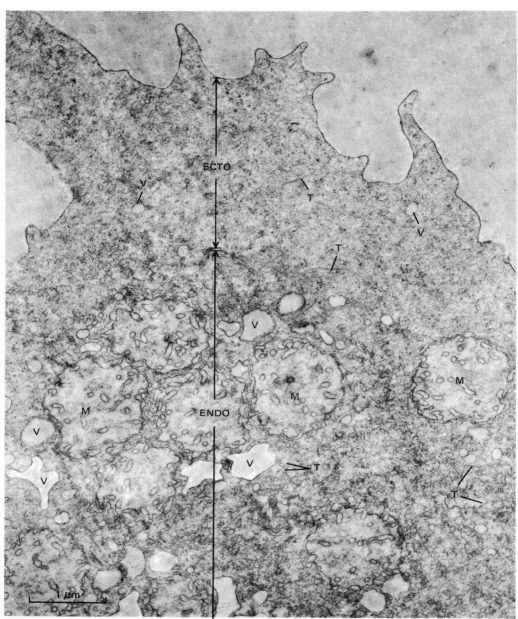

Figure 15-1 Section of a portion of an *Amoeba proteus* cell. The ectoplasm (*ECTO*) contains microtubules (*T*), an occasional small vacuole (*V*), but not any other distinctive subcellular components. The endoplasm (*ENDO*), in contrast, is rich in mitochondria (*M*) and contains numerous vacuoles, some microtubules, and the nucleus (not visible in this section). (From Schäfer-Danneel, S., 1967. "Strukturelle und funktionelle Voraussetzungen für die Bewegung von *Amoeba proteus*," in *Zeit. f. Zellforsch. und mikroskop. Anat.*, **78**:441–62. By permission of Springer-Verlag, Berlin, Heidelberg, New York.)

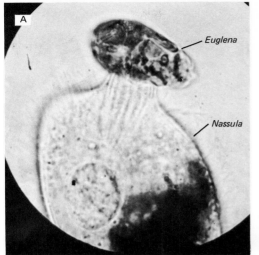
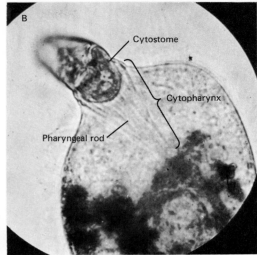
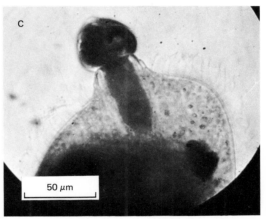

Three successive stages in ingestion of a euglenid by the ciliate *Nassula lateritia*. *A*. The oral region   **Figure 15-2**
of the ciliate is attached to the euglenid. *B*. The cytostome is open and part of the euglenid has
entered the ciliate. *C*. Most of the euglenid is within the cytopharynx, which in this ciliate is
associated with structures called pharyngeal rods. (Courtesy of E. Fauré-Fremiet.)

reproductive cysts represent a regular stage in the life cycle, their appearance
in a population can also be influenced by environmental factors; this is particularly well documented for parasitic protozoa.

The cyst walls that have been analyzed chemically are predominantly protein; in addition, they may contain lipids and carbohydrates. In at least two
genera of amebae (*Acanthamoeba* and *Naegleria*), cellulose is present, but in
much smaller proportions than in cell walls of algae and some fungi.

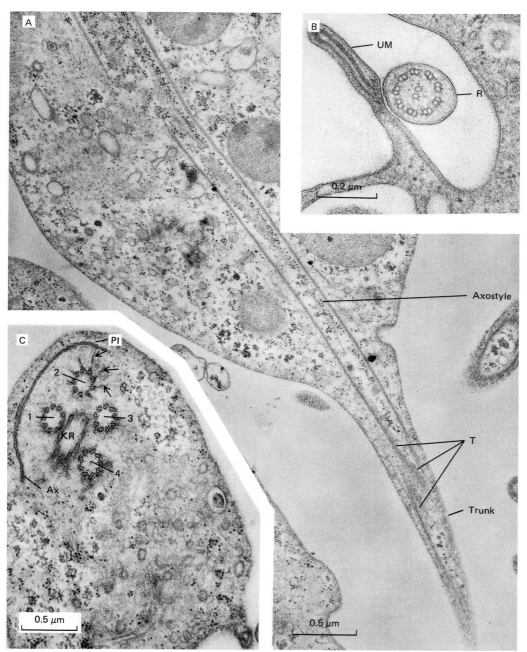

Figure 15-3 Sections of *Trichomonas gallinae* showing several of the subcellular specializations of protozoa (see also Fig. 15-10). *A.* Longitudinal section of the posterior end of an individual; the microtubules (*T*) of the axostyle extend from the anterior pole (not shown) through the tail-like "trunk" of the cell. *B.* Transverse sections of the undulating membrane (*UM*) and the flagellum (*R*) associated with it. This "recurrent" flagellum trails along the surface of the flagellate. *C.* Section near the anterior pole showing, in transverse section, the four kinetosomes (1, 2, 3, and 4) of the flagella that extend anteriorly and, in oblique section, the kinetosome (*KR*) of the recurrent flagellum. The fine extensions (arrows) adjacent to the uppermost kinetosome are regarded as rootlets and are presumed to anchor the kinetosome. The structure labeled *Pl* (pelta) is an organelle that overlaps the anterior extension of the axostyle (*Ax*). (From Mattern, C. F. T., B. M. Honigberg, and W. A. Daniel, 1967. *J. Protozool.,* **14:**320. By permission of The Society of Protozoologists and *The Journal of Protozoology.*)

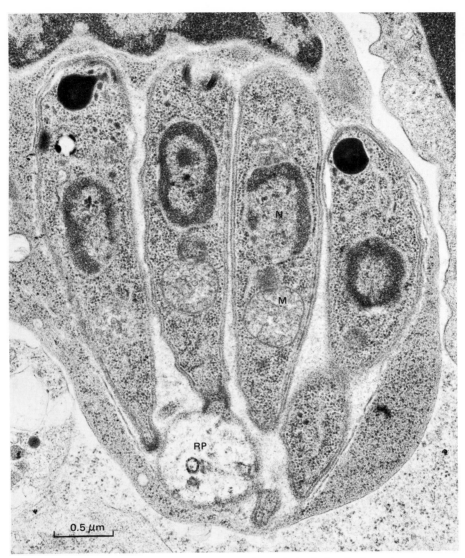

Figure 15-4

Schizogony in *Plasmodium elongatum,* an agent of avian malaria, during the formation of merozoites (see Fig. 15-21) within a canary erythrocyte. Each merozoite contains one nucleus (*N*) and
one mitochondrion (*M,* not shown in one of the cells). One merozoite has not yet separated from
the residual body of protoplasm (*RP*). (From Aikawa, M., C. G. Huff, and H. Sprinz, 1967.
J. Cell Biol., **34:**229. By permission of The Rockefeller University Press.)

Phylum Mastigophora

The phylum Mastigophora is the most heterogeneous and probably the oldest
group of protozoa. The basic locomotor organelle is the flagellum. It is usually
associated with a nucleus and internal organelles that vary among the orders.

Like all protozoa, the flagellates are classified almost exclusively according to morphology; many parasitic flagellates are assigned to species according to the hosts with which they are associated. Only the class Zoomastigophorea is treated here in this phylum.[1] There are five orders.

Rhizomastigida. One to fifty flagella per individual; pseudopodia are formed by flagellated stages, or ameboid and flagellate stages are interconvertible. Most are free-living. Reproduction by binary fission. Encystment common. Cells are uninucleate or, less commonly, multinucleate.

Protomastigida. One to two flagella per individual; some forms with pellicle; others, although with a delicate pellicle, are not motile by pseudopodia. Most are parasitic. In some forms, a flagellum borders an undulating membrane. Reproduction by longitudinal binary fission, less commonly by multiple fission or budding. Encystment common. Typically uninucleate; a few species multinucleate.

Polymastigida. Three to eight flagella per individual; rarely more. A cytostome or oral groove is present in some genera. At least one genus is dimorphic, with an ameboid stage. Inhabit digestive tract of animals. Reproduction by binary fission, typically longitudinal. Encystment known for some genera. Uni- or binucleate; one genus multinucleate.

Trichomonadida. Three to six flagella per individual; rarely more. One flagellum typically trails and may border an undulating membrane. Inhabit digestive tract and other open cavities of various animals. Reproduction by binary or multiple fission. Cysts and sexual phenomena not known. Uninucleate or multinucleate.

Hypermastigida. Numerous flagella per individual. In many genera, food can be ingested by pseudopodia. Inhabit alimentary canal of wood-eating insects. Reproduction by fission, typically binary but multiple in some forms. Encystment and sexual stages occur. Uninucleate.

Order Rhizomastigida. These organisms are flagellated during most of their growth phase, but in all stages retain the potential for forming pseudopodia.

---

[1]Protozoologists usually include photosynthetic flagellates in this group, as the class Phytomastigophorea.

In some cases, flagellated and ameboid forms interconvert, a larger proportion of the population becoming flagellates when water is abundant. Such forms usually retract the flagella or pseudopodia as a step in conversion. In those forms that possess flagella and pseudopodia simultaneously, the latter may be withdrawn when the organism is disturbed; it then swims rapidly by means of flagella. Binary fission occurs in all active stages, and in many forms it also occurs within cysts. The cell size ranges from a few to 200 μm in longest dimension.

Most types are free-living; they occur in fresh water, being especially numerous in stagnant water, and in soil. A few are endocommensals in animals. One species, *Histomonas meleagridis,* causes blackhead (enterohepatitis) in fowl.

Mastigamoeba (Fig. 15-5) exemplifies a flagellated ameboid cell. One or two contractile vacuoles are present, depending on the species.

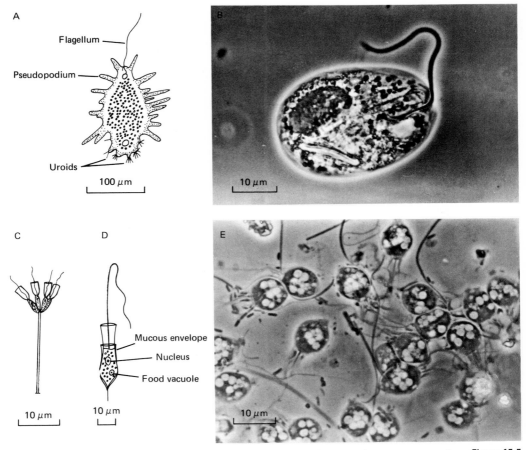

Flagellates: Rhizomastigida (*A*) and Protomastigida (*B–E*). *A. Mastigamoeba aspera,* an amebo- **Figure 15-5** flagellate. *B.* An unidentified flagellate. (Courtesy of P. Hirsch.) *C. Codosiga utriculus,* a choanoflagellate. *D. C. botrytis,* a choanoflagellate. *E. Codosiga* sp. in a mixed microbial population in lake water. (Courtesy of P. Hirsch.)

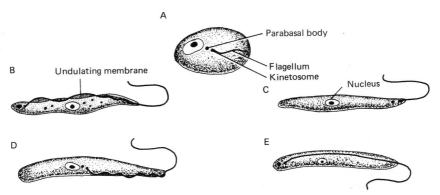

Figure 15-6 Five forms of trypanosomes. *A*. Leishmanial. *B*. Trypanosomal. *C*. Leptomonad. *D*. Blastocrithidial. *E*. Herpetomonad.

Order Protomastigida. Protomastigida includes a wide variety of relatively small (1 to 65 μm) organisms. Generally, the pellicle is delicate, and the shape of an individual may vary during locomotion.

One family (Codosigidae) comprises the choanoflagellates (collared flagellates). In *Codosiga* (Fig. 15-5), the collar is a thin membranous structure that can be retracted. Most of the choanoflagellates possess a gelatinous sheath, which may extend at the posterior end as a stalk. The cell ingests food by trapping particles between the collar and the sheath, contracting away from the sheath so that the particle can be moved below the collar, then forcefully expanding against the sheath. The particle is thereby forced against the protoplast, which invaginates to form a food vacuole. These organisms are usually sessile, but when accidentally detached from the substrate they can swim (stalk foremost) by means of the flagellum.

Included in this order is a family of animal parasites, the Trypanosomatidae, which are unusual (although not unique) among protozoa in that most types apparently do not ingest particulate foods at any stage of the life cycle. Representatives are responsible for several diseases of man and other warm-blooded vertebrates. They infect the circulatory system, spinal fluid, or internal organs. Human diseases resulting from trypanosome infections include Chagas' disease, African sleeping sickness, and kala-azar (leishmaniasis).

The parasites' life cycles are complex, and in the genus *Trypanosoma* the organism passes through four forms. Many types of trypanosomes are carried directly from one host circulatory system to another by blood-sucking arthropods such as fleas, flies, bedbugs, and ticks, within which they complete their life cycles. In some cases, the form that is infective for the vertebrate host appears in the mouth of the arthropod and is injected when the mouthparts pierce the vertebrate skin; in other cases, the infective form is discharged with feces deposited by the arthropod on the vertebrate's skin and enters the tissue when the vertebrate scratches the insect bite. Some species of trypanosomes infect only arthropods and other invertebrates. One genus (*Phytomonas*) parasitizes plants; like vertebrate parasites, these organisms are transferred between host plants by insects.

The form changes and host alternations of trypanosomes are illustrated in Figures 15-6 and 15-7. Trypanosome genera are distinguished by the number and types of forms that occur in the life cycle.

The trypanosome cell bears a single flagellum in each form. In the trypanosomal form, the flagellum arises in the posterior region of the elongated, flattened cell and extends anteriorly as the border of an undulating membrane.

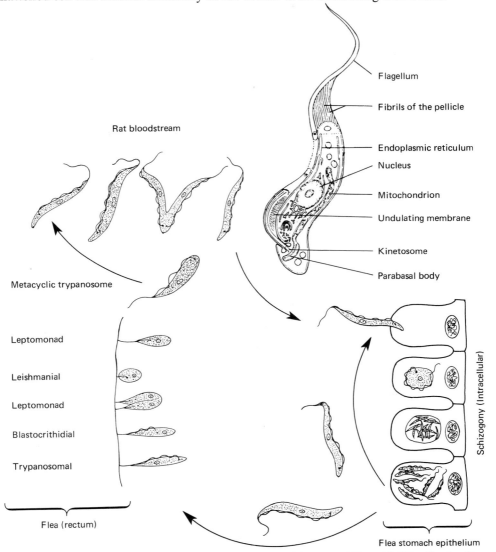

Life history of *Trypanosoma lewisi*. Multiplication occurs by schizogony within epithelial cells of the flea stomach, and by longitudinal binary fission of the leptomonad stage in the flea rectum and of trypanosomal stages in rat blood. Only the metacyclic, blunt trypanosomal stage is capable of infecting the rat. The herpetomonad stage does not occur in this species.   **Figure 15-7**

Inset: A generalized diagram of a trypanosomal form as it occurs in the vertebrate bloodstream. (Redrawn from Vickerman, K., 1962. *Trans. Roy. Soc. Trop. Med. Hyg.,* **56**:487. By permission of the Royal Society of Tropical Medicine and Hygiene.)

At the base of the flagellum is a kinetosome that contains DNA and divides during fission. The flagellum can serve as an attachment organelle in the crithidial and leptomonad forms, neither of which has a well-developed undulating membrane.

Trypanosomes were among the first protozoa to be isolated in pure cultures. They can be cultivated in a medium composed of soluble nutrients supplemented with blood.

Orders Polymastigida and Trichomonadida. The order Polymastigida is distinguished principally by the presence of three to eight flagella per individual; in two families, there are 12 or more flagella. Although at least one flagellum commonly trails, and some may adhere to the cell along its length, undulating membranes do not occur in this order. A cytostome is much more common among Polymastigida, in both free-living and parasitic forms, than in any of the other orders. A few genera include organisms that are ameboid through at least part of the life cycle.

The group is heterogeneous; the three examples in Figure 15-8 illustrate the range of form in this group. *Tetramitus* exists as two interconvertible forms, each of which reproduces by binary fission. The flagella and cytostome appear during conversion of the ameboid form to the flagellate form (Fig. 15-8*A–D*). Cells of *Giardia* are binucleate, flattened, and bilaterally symmetric. The cytostome is obscure. In *Chilomastix,* a flagellum and a groove lead to the cytostome. One of the four flagella undulates in the oral groove and presumably aids in directing the passage of food particles into the cytopharynx.

Trichomonads (Fig. 15-9) typically inhabit the digestive tract of various animals, including some insects and all classes of vertebrates. In form, they are similar to Polymastigida representatives, except that many of the trichomonads have an undulating membrane (Fig. 15-10), and none are binucleate. A modification of the usually close relationship between nucleus and flagella occurs in a few multinucleate trichomonads. In *Snyderella,* for example, there are 12 to 14 nuclei and as many as several hundred flagellar basal structures. Each structure includes four flagella and is not connected with a nucleus.

Binary fission, usually longitudinal, occurs in both orders. Budding has been reported in trichomonads; however, this process seems to be more accurately described as a prolonged multiple fission. During differentiation of a multinucleate organism into several incipient progeny, one new individual is released at a time.

Order Hypermastigida. The flagellates of Hypermastigida (Fig. 15-11) are uninucleate and bear large numbers of flagella. All are found in termites, cockroaches, or woodroaches where they inhabit the alimentary canal and assist in digestion of wood ingested by the animal. The flagellates ingest the wood chips by engulfing them in pseudopodia. Other particulate foods are also taken in by this means. Some representatives are as long as 200 μm, but others do not exceed 20 μm in maximum length. They are classified mainly according to the arrangement of the flagella.

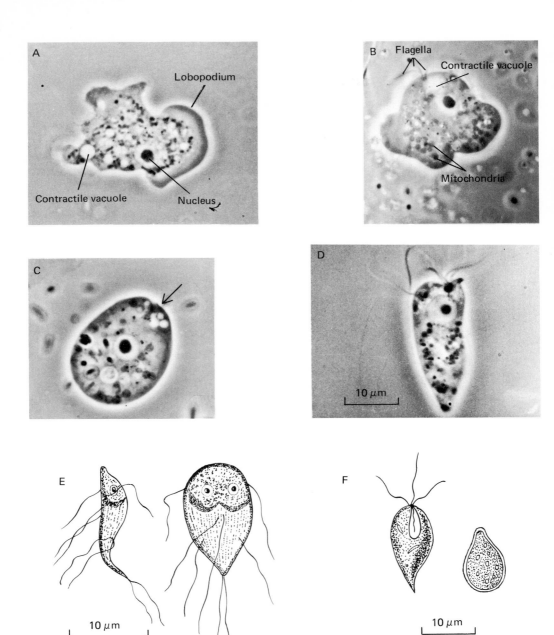

Flagellates: Polymastigida. *A–D.* Four successive stages in the transformation of the ameboid stage of *Tetramitus rostratus* to the flagellate stage (four individuals, sequence reconstructed). *A.* Ameba moving toward the right. *B.* An early stage of transition; the cell is still ameboid, while three of the flagella have appeared. The flagella typically arise near the contractile vacuole. *C.* A later stage. The arrow indicates the region that is developing into the anterior pole. *D.* Mature flagellate, with four anterior flagella. (From Outka, D. E., and B. C. Kluss, 1967. *J. Cell Biol.,* **35:**323. By permission of The Rockefeller University Press.)

E. Giardia intestinalis, an occasional inhabitant of human intestines. *Left:* side view; *right:* front view. *F. Chilomastix mesnili,* vegetative individual and cyst.

Figure 15-8

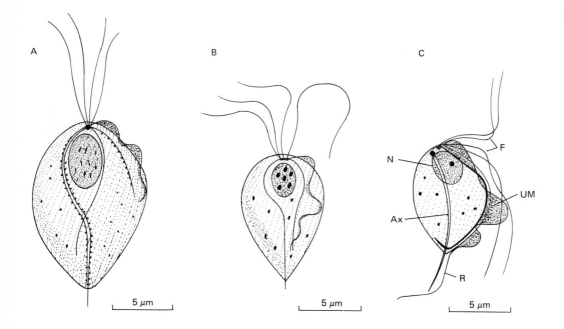

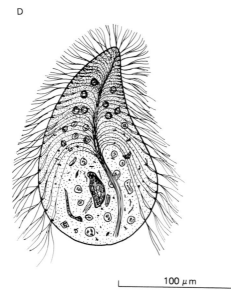

Figure 15-9   Flagellates: Trichomonadida. *N*, nucleus; *Ax,* axostyle; *F,* anterior flagellum; *R,* recurrent flagellum; *UM*, undulating membrane.

   A–C. Trichomonas species that occur in humans (see Chap. 22). *A. T. vaginalis. B. T. tenax. C. T. hominis.*
   D. Snyderella tabogae.

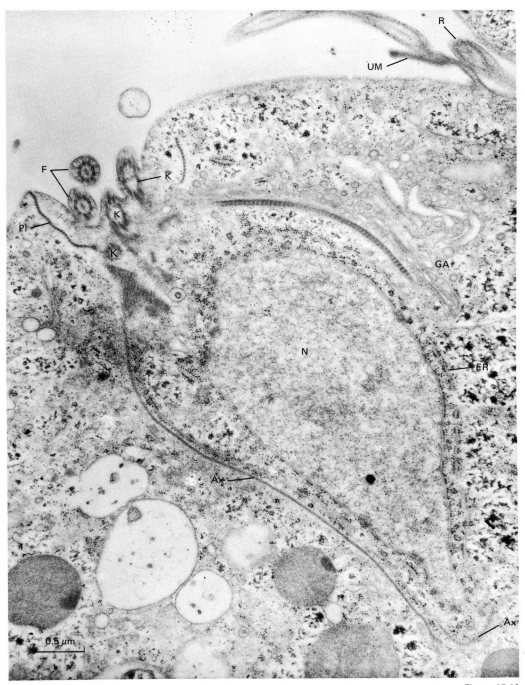

Longitudinal section of the anterior end of *Trichomonas gallinae* (see also Fig. 15-3) showing three **Figure 15-10** kinetosomes, *K*; two emergent flagella, *F*; nucleus, *N*; pelta, *Pl*; microtubules of anterior portions of the axostyle, *Ax*; endoplasmic reticulum, *ER*; and a membrane complex, *GA*, that is possibly a Golgi apparatus. The undulating membrane, *UM*, and recurrent flagellum, *R*, are seen in oblique section. Mitochondria are typically absent from sections of this trichomonad, which is found in the digestive tracts and internal organs of various avian groups. (From Mattern, C. F. T., B. M. Honigberg, and W. A. Daniel, 1967. *J. Protozool.*, **14**:320. By permission of The Society of Protozoologists and *The Journal of Protozoology*.)

A   B

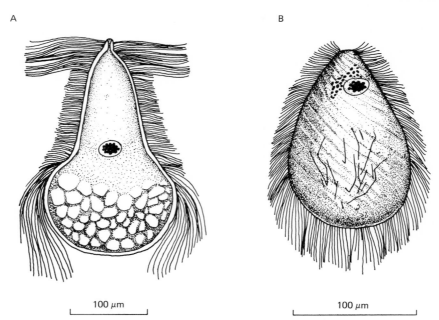

|__ 100 μm __| |__ 100 μm __|

Figure 15-11 Flagellates: Hypermastigida. *A. Trichonympha campanula;* representatives of the genus *Tricho-nympha* are found in the guts of termites and woodroaches. *B. Holomastigotoides hartmanni.*

In *Holomastigotoides,* the flagella are arranged in spiral rows. In other types, the flagella may arise in two, four, or several anterior tufts; over the anterior half of the cell surface; over the entire surface without any discernible pattern-ing; or in longitudinal rows, as in *Trichonympha.* Occasionally, tufts of flagella may be permanently fused, each bundle behaving as a unit. Binary fission may be transverse or longitudinal.

Observations on the behavior of a species of *Trichonympha* have revealed a coordination between metamorphosis of the host (the woodroach) and the life cycle of the protozoon. The roach periodically sheds its exoskeleton, and with it the lining of the hind-gut, which is inhabited by *Trichonympha.* Molting is initiated when the prothoracic glands of the roach begin to release the molting hormone, ecdysone. Some of the hormone is excreted through the malpighian tubules into the hind-gut. Because the gut contents move in only one direction, only those protozoa posterior to the excretory openings are exposed to the hormone. Each of these flagellates begins to construct a cyst wall. Within the cyst, the nucleus divides and the flagella disappear. New flagella are formed, and fission produces two new individuals. These are gametes, one male and one female. Because the nucleus of the male gamete stains more deeply than that of the female, the two can be distinguished within the cyst. These steps occur during the two or three days before molting; they can be induced artificially by injecting the insect with ecdysone preparations.

The cysts are eliminated when the exoskeleton is shed. Excystment occurs only after the insect reingests the gamete-containing cysts when it eats the shed hind-gut and thereby reinoculates its gut with the protozoa. The gametes emerge from the cyst into the lumen of the gut. The female gamete develops a posterior granular ring through which a fluid-filled vesicle protrudes. Upon contact with this vesicle, a male gamete enters it and becomes enclosed within the female. Except for the nucleus, the cellular organelles of the male become disorganized; the nucleus fuses with the female nucleus. Meiosis follows the nuclear fusion; each of the four resulting haploid nuclei is inherited by a vegetative cell derived from the zygote. Only the zygote nucleus, which does not divide mitotically, is diploid.

Phylum Sarcodina

The Sarcodina are protozoa that possess a thin, flexible pellicle, if any, and typically are motile by means of protoplasmic flow. Largely because of their dependence on living organisms as foods, very few types of Sarcodina have been grown in pure cultures. Many have not been cultivated in the laboratory and are known only from observations on natural materials. Some supposed Sarcodina may be ameboid stages of life cycles of other protozoa. Such stages are indistinguishable from Sarcodina that lack distinctive structures such as skeletons or shells.

Sarcodina are common in fresh water and moist soil; many species are marine, one large group (Radiolarida) occurring only in the oceans. Most parasitic amebae inhabit animal digestive tracts, although a few are plant parasites. All types ingest food particles, usually with the aid of pseudopodia. They are generally solitary organisms during the growth stages, with little tendency toward colony or aggregate formation.

Encystment is a common feature of development; some amebae form cysts that are both protective and reproductive. In one genus of parasitic amebae (*Entamoeba*), helical aggregates of ribosomes form during encystment; these may serve as a condensed reserve of protein-synthesizing organelles needed for germination (cf. nuclear cap of Blastocladiales zoospores).

The mature organism may have one, two, or several hundred nuclei. The number and staining properties of nuclei are used as taxonomic criteria for some genera.

Under a given set of conditions, a species produces pseudopodia of characteristic form. Some types produce only one kind of pseudopodium. Factors known to influence pseudopodial form include: contact with a solid surface, rather than being freely afloat; the nature and concentration of the organic food available; and the presence and concentration of certain inorganic salts. Four general kinds of pseudopodia are distinguished.

1. Reticulopodia. Typically, contain ecto- and endoplasm, but cytoplasmic regions may not be discernible in very slender reticulopodia; can fuse to form networks of flowing cytoplasm; function in ingestion, digestion, and locomotion. Also called rhizopodia or myxopodia.

2. Lobopodia. Contain ecto- and endoplasm; do not fuse; typically formed and retracted rapidly; function in ingestion and locomotion.

3. Filopodia. Contain ectoplasm only; do not fuse; function in capturing and bringing food particles to the cell surface for ingestion. Especially in Testacida, may also function in locomotion.

4. Axopodia. Contain ectoplasm and an axial core (or rod); do not fuse. Function in ingestion, apparently not in locomotion.

Motility in forms that do not produce locomotor pseudopodia is achieved by a directed flow of cytoplasm within the flexible pellicle; the cell surface is passively moved along as the protoplasm moves within it. Some Sarcodina are not motile; their pseudopodia function in gathering, in ingesting, and sometimes in initiating digestion of food.

Six orders are distinguished.

Proteomyxida. Produce radiating filopodia; pellicle typically thin. Many representatives are parasites of algae and plants. Others are free-living.

Amoebida. Produce lobopodia; pellicle often very thin.

Testacida. Produce filopodia or lobopodia; single-chambered test.

Foraminiferida. Produce reticulopodia that in some species may reorganize into axopodia; single- or multi-chambered test.

Heliozoida. Produce axopodia or slender pseudopodia that lack a core; ectoplasm vacuolated. Predominantly fresh-water, a few marine.

Radiolarida. Produce axopodia; protoplasm divided into outer and inner portions by a perforated membrane called the central capsule; marine.

Order Amoebida. This order contains the Sarcodina usually presented as typical examples of the phylum, and the term "amebae" is usually used to refer only to representatives of this order. They are more accurately present as examples of the least differentiated Sarcodina. The cells are highly plastic; their shape changes as the organism moves and feeds (see Fig. 15-12*A* and *B*). Skeletal structures do not occur, but a flexible pellicle is present in some forms. In laboratory cultures with bacteria or yeasts provided as food, the life cycles of amebae are relatively simple: individuals reproduce by binary fission, plasmotomy, or budding, or by more than one of these methods; encystment occurs, and each cyst typically releases one ameba upon germination.

Most Amoebida genera are usually accommodated in three families.

Naegleriidae. Free-living, dimorphic (amebo-flagellates).

Amoebidae. Most are free-living, monomorphic.

Endamoebidae. Parasites, monomorphic.

The flagellate stages of Naegleriidae possess two, three, or four flagella. The best characterized genus is *Naegleria,* which has been found in soil, stagnant water, and feces of vertebrates and invertebrates. The (protective) cysts contain only one or a few nuclei. Upon germination, an ameba moves out of the cyst wall. This stage can feed, reproduce by binary fission, encyst, and develop a pair of flagella. The flagellated form apparently cannot reproduce or encyst; it sheds or retracts its flagella in reverting to the ameba form after a period of swimming.

Representatives of Amoebidae can be found in almost any sample of water, fresh or salt; in moist soil, leaves, or moss; and in animal intestines or feces. Smaller microbes, e.g., bacteria and yeasts, may inhabit the cytoplasm of an ameba; they may be present in approximately constant number and location within the protozoon. The presence of such associates of amebae (and other protozoa, as well) presents a further difficulty in obtaining monotypic cultures for investigation of the protozoon's physiologic properties.

The most commonly studied Amoebidae are members of the genera *Amoeba, Pelomyxa, Chaos,* and *Acanthamoeba;* only the last of these is commonly encountered in natural materials. Species of *Amoeba* (Fig. 15-12) range in size from 20 to 600 μm and are uninucleate. *Pelomyxa* and *Chaos* are similar to *Amoeba* in appearance, but range from 500 to 5000 μm and are multinucleate; there may be fewer than 100 to more than 1,000 nuclei per individual. *Acanthamoeba* species are small (10 to 30 μm in diameter), uninucleate, and form double-walled cysts. All four types multiply by fission or plasmotomy and form protective cysts only.

Family Endamoebidae comprises parasitic amebae of animal digestive tracts. One human pathogen is placed in this family; this is *Entamoeba histolytica,* the causative agent of amebic dysentery (see Chap. 22). The Endamoebidae are similar in appearance to *Amoeba* species and of about the same size range. They multiply by binary fission and usually form protective cysts.

Order Testacida. The remaining four orders of Sarcodina contain free-living organisms that occur in water or in particular types of soil. The Testacida are found in water and in peat bogs and occasionally in other moist soils. Each organism lives within a single-chambered chitinous test, extending filopodia through an aperture in the test to capture food particles. The three families recognized are distinguished by the composition of tests.

> **Arcellidae.** Test chitinous, sometimes flexible; cytoplasm sometimes does not fill the test (Fig. 15-13*A*).
>
> **Difflugiidae.** Test composed mainly of foreign materials such as sand grains (hence the designation "arenaceous"), cemented on a base that is probably chitinous (Fig. 15-13*B*).
>
> **Euglyphidae.** Test constructed of scales typically composed of silica, apparently laid down on a chitinous membrane (Fig. 15-13*C–F*).

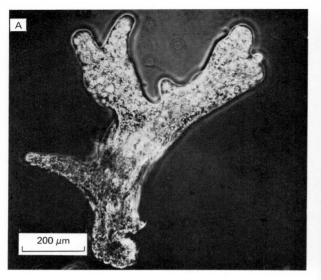

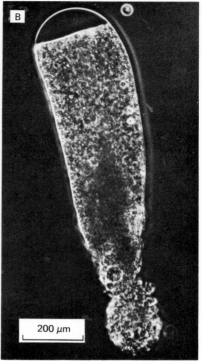

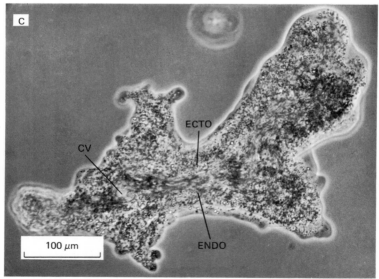

Figure 15-12 *Amoeba proteus. A* and *B.* Normal appearances of amebae in a single culture. The ameba in *A* is multipodial, the one in *B* is unipodial. Each organism is moving in the direction of the top of the photomicrographs. (From Czarska, L., and A. Grebecki, 1966. *Acta Protozoologica,* **4:**201. Courtesy of Lucyna and Andrzej Grebecki.) *C.* A multipodial ameba, photographed with a 0.2-second exposure so that the more rapidly moving endoplasm (*ENDO*) appears blurred and the more sluggish ectoplasm (*ECTO*) is distinct. *CV,* contractile vacuole. (From Schäfer-Danneel, S., 1967. "Strukturelle und funktionelle Voraussetzungen für die Bewegung von *Amoeba proteus,*" in *Zeit. f. Zellforsch. und mikroskop. Anat.,* **78:**5441–62. By permission of Springer-Verlag, Berlin, Heidelberg, New York.)

282

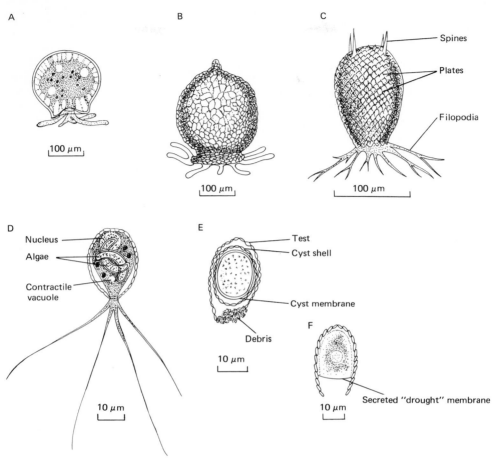

Testacida. *A. Arcella mitrata*, sectional view. *B. Difflugia urceolata*, surface view. *C. Euglypha* **Figure 15-13** *alveolata*, surface view. *D. Paulinella chromatophora*, with endosymbiotic algae (see Chap. 21). Individuals of this species typically lack food vacuoles. *E. Trinema enchelys* cyst. *F. Euglypha laevis* "drought" stage, an apparently dormant stage found attached to aquatic plants above the water line.

The Testacida are typically uninucleate. Diameter of the test ranges from about 20 to 200 μm. Motile forms move by extending pseudopodia that attach to a substrate, then contract, dragging the test in the direction in which the pseudopodia had been extended.

Reproduction is by binary fission, with one daughter cell retaining the old test and the other leaving as a naked ameba. The latter progeny may be provided with some of the materials for construction of a new test. For example, in *Euglypha*, scales are formed within the cytoplasm; at fission, practically all the intracytoplasmic scales are inherited by the naked progeny, which then adds them to the basal test membrane. In Difflugiidae, pseudopodia gather sand grains, which are stored within the cytoplasm prior to fission.

Encystment usually occurs within the test (see Fig. 15-13*E*). The pseudopodia are retracted, and the aperture may be sealed with debris. The cyst wall is laid down within the test by short pseudopodia.

Order Foraminiferida. The Foraminiferida also form shells covered by proto- plasm, but otherwise are quite different from Testacida. The shells are single- or, more commonly, multichambered. The pseudopodia are reticulopodia; they are extended through an aperture in the most recently formed chamber. The organism inhabits the entire shell, extending from chamber to chamber through apertures (foramina) in the intermediate walls. As the organism grows, a new chamber is formed to house the additional protoplasm. This construction is a function of the reticulopodia, which secrete the components of the shell or gather particles for arenaceous shells. Individual species may use particular materials—sand grains, sponge spicules, pieces of broken tests, echinoderm plates, or others—so that the composition is relatively constant for each such discriminating species. Secreted tests are usually composed chiefly of calcium carbonates. Several types of Foraminiferida shells are illustrated in Figures 15-14 to 15-16.

The life cycles of several Foraminiferida have been observed in entirety. The complex cycles involve an alternation of gamete-producing and non- gamete-producing generations, both of which are diploid. Meiosis precedes gamete formation.

Adult stages feed by means of reticulopodia, which usually are sticky and sometimes leave a trail of slime as they move. Food particles such as other protozoa, larval crustacea, and algae (usually diatoms) are engulfed by the reticulopodia and brought by protoplasmic flow to the main portion of the cell for digestion. In certain forms that develop relatively short, thick reticulo- podia, digestion is begun and often completed by the pseudopodia. Insoluble waste materials are deposited outside the shell by the reticulopodia.

These organisms are typically marine. Some are motile, whereas others are sedentary as adults and are often found on algae and plants. The shells of fossil Foraminiferida have been found in sea-bottom deposits from the Silurian Period; many of the extinct forms were much larger than modern species.

Order Heliozoida. The Heliozoida are predominantly fresh-water protozoa, although a few occur in the ocean. They are distinguished by the presence of numerous slender pseudopodia, usually axopodia, which radiate from a spheric cell, hence the "sunburst protozoa." The ectoplasm is typically vacuo- lated, whereas the endoplasm is not. Some species are naked, others possess an outer covering of gelatinous material or a lattice-like test, and others possess spicules of characteristic form. Simple tests are composed of chitin; compound tests are constructed of siliceous scales embedded in a gelatinous basal struc- ture. The spicules are of chitin or of silica. A few forms possess both types of skeletal components, but the majority of Heliozoida have only a relatively simple envelope of gelatinous or mucilaginous material. Most forms are free- floating, but a few occur attached to submerged surfaces by a stalk that is continuous with the envelope or test.

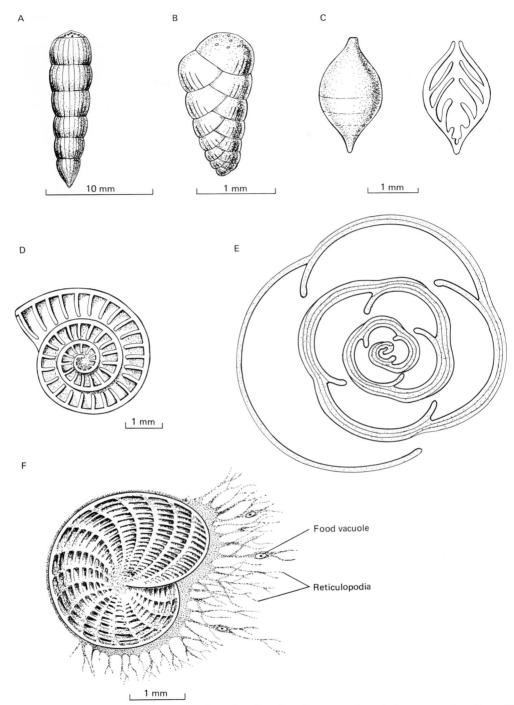

Foraminifera. *A. Nodosaria raphanus,* surface view. Pseudopodia emerge through the pores at the top of the shell. *B. Cribostomum textulariforme,* surface view. Pseudopodia emerge as in *A.* *C. Glandulina laevigata,* surface and sectional views. *D. Camerina elegans,* sectional view. *E. Rosalina floridana,* schematic sectional view to show the layered construction of the walls. The heavy line represents the organic lining of the shell; the additional layers are of calcite. (Redrawn from Angell, R. W., 1967. *J. Protozool.,* **14**:299. By permission of The Society of Protozoologists and *The Journal of Protozoology.*) *F. Elphidium crispum.*

Figure 15-14

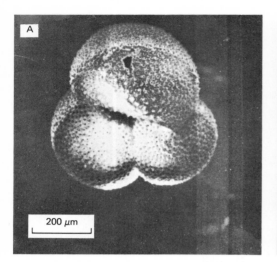

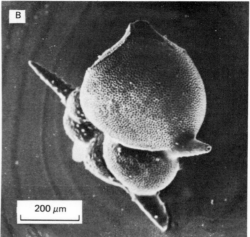

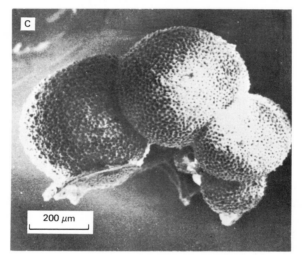

Figure 15-15 Scanning electron micrographs of foraminifera shells. *A. Globigerinoides rubra. B. Hantkenina alabamensis. C. Globigerinella siphonifera.* (From Honjo, S., and W. A. Berggren, 1967. *Micropaleontology,* **13**:393. By permission of the Department of Micropaleontology of the American Museum of Natural History.)

The axopodia function mainly in gathering food, which consists chiefly of other protozoa and of algae. Living prey have been observed to cease moving on contact with axopodia, which may reflect the production of a toxic substance by these pseudopodia. After a food particle adheres to an axopodium, protoplasmic flow carries the particle to the body surface, where ingestion by lobopodia occurs. Digestion occurs within a food vacuole.

The axial rod of an axopodium consists of numerous fibrils arranged parallel to the long axis of the pseudopodium. The fibrillar bundle originates internally at a location that is characteristic of the genus. The bundles may be associated

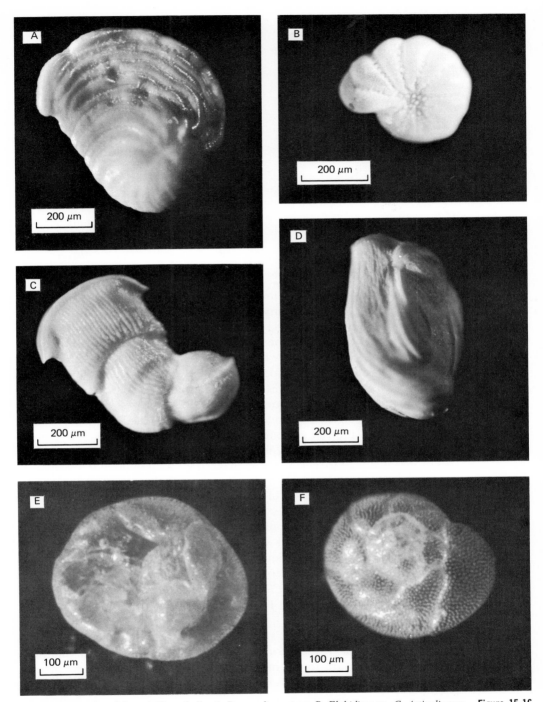

Photomicrographs of foraminifera shells. *A. Peneroplis proteus. B. Elphidium* sp. *C. Articulina* sp. **Figure 15-16**
D. Quinqueloculina sp. (*A, B, C,* and *D* courtesy of R. W. Angell.) *E* and *F. Rosalina floridana.*
Ventral (*E*) and dorsal (*F*) views. (From Angell, R. W., 1967. *J. Protozool.,* **14:**299. By permission
of The Society of Protozoologists and *The Journal of Protozoology.*)

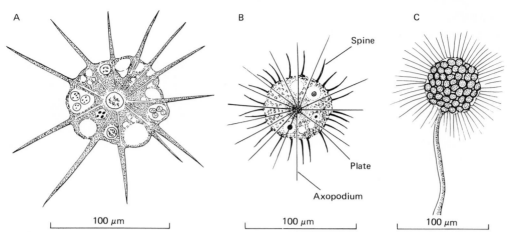

Figure 15-17   Heliozoa. *A. Actinophrys sol. B. Acanthocystis aculeata. C. Clathrulina elegans.*

with nuclei. All axial rods of a uninucleate type may converge on the single, central nucleus; each rod may originate at a different nucleus in multinucleate forms. Alternatively, the rods may arise from a zone between the endo- and ectoplasm; somewhat more commonly they arise from within the endoplasm.

Reproduction occurs by binary fission or by budding. In fission, the envelope is usually shared by the two progeny. In a few types, fission is not followed by separation, and small colonies develop. Budding is more common among the types with tests. In the most completely described process (in *Acanthocystis*, Fig. 15-17*B*), the single parent nucleus undergoes repeated divisions. Progeny nuclei migrate to the cell periphery and are included in units of cytoplasm to form buds. Spicules arise within each bud before it leaves the parent shell. This process is similar to schizogony, with one important difference: one nucleus remains behind with the residual protoplasm, and the parent survives as an individual. Meiosis and fusion of pairs of the reduction products have been observed; the zygote secretes a cyst wall.

Three types of Heliozoida are illustrated in Figure 15-17. *Actinophrys* occurs in still water and often contains symbiotic zoochlorellae (see Chap. 21). The organism is naked, vacuolated, and uninucleate. *Acanthocystis* is covered with a thin envelope in which siliceous scales are embedded; spicules are also composed of silica. The test of *Clathrulina* is a secreted structure of unknown composition, but not siliceous. The stalk is composed of the test material.

Order Radiolarida. The greatest structural differentiation among Sarcodina is found in Radiolarida. These are marine protozoa whose Silurian or Cambrian ancestors' skeletons are found in the ocean bottom. The skeletons of most Radiolarida are composed chiefly of silicates deposited by the organism to form distinct and elaborate spiny structures; in some forms, lattice-like shells are also formed. In one group (suborder Actipylina), the spines are composed of strontium sulfate, rather than silicates, and shells are not present.

Four types of modern Radiolarida are illustrated in Figure 15-18. Although these four organisms vary in skeletal organization, they share several distinctively radiolaridan features of protoplasmic organization. The cytoplasm is separated into two zones by a perforated, mucinoid, or pseudochitinous membrane called the central capsule. The capsule is typically spheroid and concentric with the surface of the organism. Food vacuoles are found only in the outer cytoplasmic zone. The inner zone contains the nucleus (or nuclei), reserve foods, any pigments that may be formed by the organism, and crystals of unknown composition.

Immediately external to the capsule is a mass of alveoli called the calymma. The alveoli function in maintaining or changing the buoyancy of the organism. While the organism is afloat near the ocean surface, the alveoli are filled with a fluid that is saturated with CO_2. In order to descend in the water, the cell retracts its pseudopodia and the alveoli collapse, expelling the fluid.

The diet of Radiolarida includes other marine organisms—algae, other

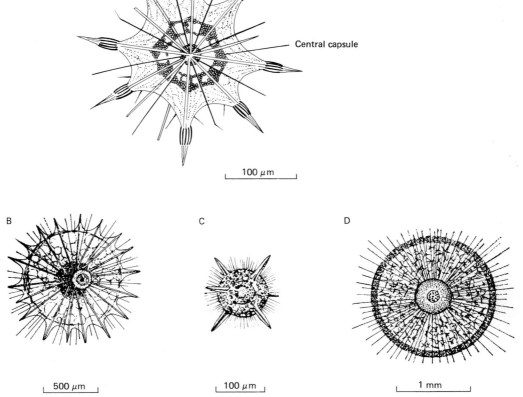

Radiolarians. *A. Acanthometra pellucida* (Actipylina). *B. Aulacantha scolymantha* (Tripylina). **Figure 15-18** *C. Hexacontium asteracanthion* (Peripylina). *D. Lampoxanthium pandora* (Peripylina).

protozoa, copepods—which are captured by the axopodia and carried to the main part of the cell in the same fashion as in heliozoidan feeding.

Although the life cycles of Radiolarida have not yet been observed, certain reproductive events have been reported. These include binary and multiple fission and budding. During these processes, the central capsule becomes indistinct and may largely disintegrate. It is presumably resynthesized or reorganized in the new individuals. In binary fission, the two progeny often share the skeletal structures, each regenerating the missing half of the skeleton as it grows. Naked buds may be formed, each of which organizes its own skeleton; if the skeleton consists solely or largely of spicules, the bud may be provided with some spiny material. Some Radiolarida remain clustered in colonies.

The Radiolarida are classified on the basis of composition of the skeleton and morphology of the central capsule and skeletal elements. Four suborders are recognized.

Skeleton of strontium sulfate:

> **Actipylina.** Skeleton usually composed of rods radiating from the center of the cell (Fig. 15-18*A*).

Skeleton not of strontium sulfate:

> **Monopylina.** Central capsule perforated only within a zone at one pole.
> **Tripylina.** Central capsule with three openings—one at one pole, and two smaller openings at the opposite pole (Fig. 15-18*B*).
> **Peripylina.** Central capsule with numerous, uniformly distributed perforations (Fig. 15-18*C* and *D*).

Phylum Sporozoa

All Sporozoa share two characteristics: they produce spores that serve as disseminative units, and they lack flagella and cilia in growth stages. All are parasitic, and the spores are usually an infective stage. Each spore contains one to eight sporozoites, which are released upon germination of the spore. They are typically motile. Other stages in the life cycle may also be motile. Except for flagellated gametes of a few species, locomotion is achieved by gliding, which may be effected by cell undulations. Some cells possess myonemes, usually situated within the ectoplasm and sometimes present in large numbers. However, myonemes have not been seen in all motile Sporozoa examined with the electron microscope; hence, myonemes may aid, but apparently are not necessary for, this sort of gliding motility.

The phylum as presented here comprises one class with three orders. This class, Telosporidea, seems to comprise a single phylogenetic group. The differences among the organisms included can be regarded as results of selection by the respective host environments.

Among Telosporidea, spores are derived from zygotes. Meiosis has been observed in only a few genera; in most of these, meiosis follows nuclear fusion, and all stages other than the zygote are haploid. In three genera, meiosis occurs at another stage so that some diploid mitotic nuclear divisions occur within the life cycle.

Three orders are distinguished on the basis of developmental characteristics and relationship to host cells, as indicated below. The term "syzygy" is used to designate prolonged direct contact of cells that precedes gamete formation. Cells in syzygy neither fuse nor conjugate; instead, they produce or differentiate into gametes.

Gregarinida. Most or all of growth occurs extracellularly within the host; typically parasites of invertebrates, inhabiting the digestive tract and body cavities. Sporozoites are enclosed in a spore membrane. Syzygy is a regular feature of the life cycle.

Coccidia. Intracellular parasites during most of the life cycle; occur in epithelial cells of invertebrate and vertebrate animals, and in white and red blood cells of vertebrates. Sporozoites are enclosed in a spore membrane. Syzygy occurs in only one of the two suborders.

Haemosporida. Intracellular parasites that occur in blood of vertebrates and alimentary canal and associated organs of blood-sucking invertebrates. Sporozoites are not enclosed in a spore membrane. Syzygy does not occur.

Order Gregarinida. This order is usually subdivided into two suborders. In suborder Eugregarinina, reproduction is accomplished solely by formation of spores. In suborder Schizogregarinina, reproduction occurs by sporulation and by fission or budding of growth stages.

The cell form of gregarines varies greatly, but the most common form is spindle-shaped, approximately circular in cross-section. Cell length ranges from approximately 10 to 3,000–4,000 μm in different species. Typically, the growing cell is uninucleate until shortly before reproduction (either asexual or through production of gametes). Multiple mitotic divisions precede reproduction, which is usually by schizogony; binary fission is rare. Gregarines are illustrated in Figure 15-19.

Order Coccidia. Coccidia occur as intracellular parasites of vertebrates as well as invertebrates; they are most often found in epithelial cells lining the host's digestive tract and in cells of glands associated with digestion. The Coccidia seem to obtain their nutrients as dissolved substances; they are not known to possess any mechanism for ingestion.

Two suborders are distinguished by the behavior of the gametocytes, as exemplified in the two life cycles diagrammed in Figure 15-20. *Adelea* is a representative of suborder Adeleina, and *Eimeria* of suborder Eimeriina; both species illustrated parasitize centipedes. The sporozoite emerges from the sporocyst and enters a host cell. Growth and schizogony occur; the host cell ruptures, typically releasing numerous uninucleate protozoa. These usually

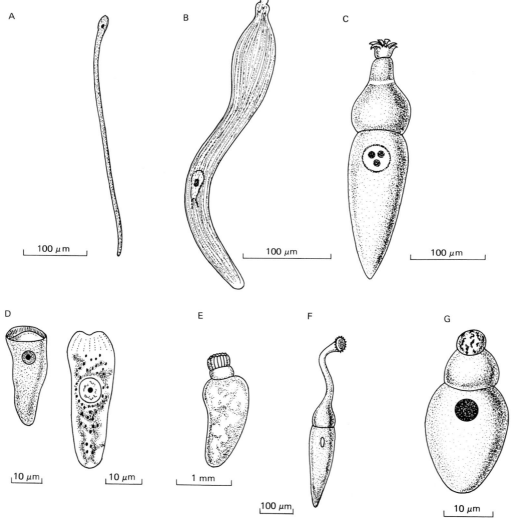

Figure 15-19 Gregarines. *A. Rhyncocystis porreata. B. Monoductus lunatus. C. Corycella armata. D. Stomatophora simplex. Left,* sucker retracted and *right,* sucker extended. *E. Anthorhynchus sophiae. F. Menospora polyacantha. G. Gregarina rigida.*

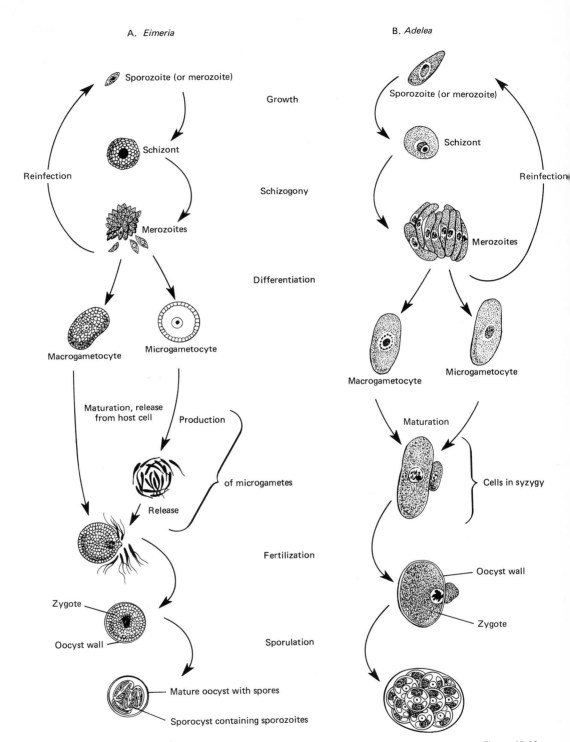

A. *Eimeria*

Sporozoite (or merozoite)

Growth

Schizont

Reinfection

Schizogony

Merozoites

Differentiation

Macrogametocyte

Microgametocyte

Maturation, release from host cell

Production

of microgametes

Release

Zygote

Oocyst wall

Fertilization

Sporulation

Mature oocyst with spores

Sporocyst containing sporozoites

B. *Adelea*

Sporozoite (or merozoite)

Schizont

Reinfection

Merozoites

Macrogametocyte

Microgametocyte

Maturation

Cells in syzygy

Oocyst wall

Zygote

Two types of life histories of Coccidia. *A. Eimeria schubergi. B. Adelea ovata.*

Figure 15-20

293

repeat the asexual cycle at least once; two to four asexual generations occur, depending on the species. The individuals in the last generation differentiate into gametocytes and initiate the sexual phase in the gut lumen.

In Adeleina, one macro- and one microgametocyte associate in syzygy as they complete their differentiation. The macrogametocyte becomes a macro-gamete, and just before or after fertilization it produces an oocyst membrane. The microgametocyte meanwhile produces a few (rarely more than four) microgametes, which in some genera are biflagellated. One microgamete enters the macrogamete, and the oocyst membrane is completed. Within the oocyst, the nuclei fuse; meiosis follows the fusion, and the haploid nuclei are included with cytoplasm within sporocyst membranes. Sporozoites (usually two to eight) are formed within each sporocyst. Infection of a new host results from its ingestion of either oocysts or sporocysts. The oocysts are thick-walled and can survive for long periods outside the host. Their viability in environments such as soil is largely responsible for the difficulty in eradicating coccidian diseases of livestock and poultry.

The life cycle of Eimeriina does not involve syzygy. Apparently, as a compensation to ensure fertilization, these organisms produce large numbers of microgametes.

Most Coccidia complete their life cycles in one type of host. A few, however, pass through the sexual stages in one host and the asexual stages in a different type of animal.

Order Haemosporida. Species in this order typically pass part of their life cycle within vertebrate erythrocytes, hence the name Haemosporida. Generally, schizogony occurs within cells of a vertebrate host. The first generation after inoculation of the host with sporozoites is typically produced in cells of the reticuloendothelial system. Succeeding generations are produced in erythrocytes, and sometimes also in the reticuloendothelial cells. Gametocytes arise only in the erythrocytes; completion of the sexual phase depends on ingestion of gametocytes by blood-sucking insects. Gamete production and fusion and derivation of sporozoites from zygotes occur in the insect by processes similar to those in the other Telosporidea, invariably without syzygy.

One major difference between Haemosporida and the other Telosporidea is the absence of sporocysts in Haemosporida. The sporozoites are formed by schizogony in the oocyst; they leave the oocyst while still in the insect host. Further development of the sporozoites occurs only after they are injected into the bloodstream of a suitable vertebrate when the insect feeds again. A second difference is that the intraerythrocyte stage has been observed to feed through a surface indentation that encloses a mass of host protoplasm.

The family Plasmodiidae includes the genus *Plasmodium,* at least four species of which cause malaria in man (see Chap. 22). The species vary in the symptoms they elicit and in susceptibility to therapeutic drugs. The insect host for all species that parasitize humans is the female mosquito of some species of *Anopheles.* Other genera of mosquitoes include vectors for malarial parasites of other vertebrate species.

The life cycle of one human parasite, *Plasmodium vivax,* is presented in Figure 15-21. The sporozoite enters the human with the saliva of a feeding mosquito. The exoerythrocytic development is initiated when the sporozoite is ingested by a reticuloendothelial cell in the spleen or liver. After at least one generation in such cells, some of the progeny enter erythrocytes. There they grow into the typical multinucleate plasmodium stage, which eventually nearly fills the blood cell. Schizogony produces 20 to 30 uninucleate cells (merozoites), which, upon release from the disintegrating blood cell, infect more erythrocytes.

Some progeny of each erythrocytic generation differentiate into gametocytes when they re-enter erythrocytes. When withdrawn with blood into the female mosquito, the gametocytes complete their development; each either releases a number of microgametes or develops into a macrogamete. The fertilized macrogamete (the ookinete) is motile; it migrates through the lining of the mosquito stomach wall, where it forms an oocyst membrane. Within the oocyst, schizogony results in thousands of uninucleate sporozoites. When the mature oocyst ruptures, some of the motile sporozoites migrate to the salivary gland, where they remain until inoculated into a human.

Phylum Ciliophora

The most extensive subcellular differentiation among protozoa is found in Ciliophora. All these protozoa possess cilia at some stage, and, as recognized here, the phylum includes all ciliated protozoa. With the exception of one small, presumably primitive group, the ciliated protozoa share two other distinctive characteristics: (1) each cell possesses two types of nuclei, and (2) sexual events involve conjugation, rather than fusion, of cells. Reproduction is typically by transverse binary fission or, in some forms, by budding.

The cilia of more primitive types of ciliates function solely or mainly as locomotor organelles. In structurally more complex ciliates, ciliary function is more commonly restricted to feeding, or to locomotion in the disseminative stage of the life cycle. In some sessile forms, cilia serve only to gather food by directing water and suspended particles toward a cytostome.

Cilia are the structural units of three types of compound organelles. An **undulating membrane** is formed by fusion of cilia in one or more longitudinal rows. These structures are usually associated with the oral region and help to direct food and fluid into the cytostomal area. A **membranelle** is generally flat and triangular in shape and is formed by fusion of cilia in transverse rows. Membranelles also function in feeding. The third type of ciliary organelle is the **cirrus,** which consists of a tuft of cilia embedded in a matrix; cirri function in feeding and locomotion.

The nuclei of most ciliates are differentiated as **micronuclei** and **macronuclei.** Micronuclei are smaller and usually approximately spheric. They serve as the repository of genetic information that can be exchanged during conjugation, and they periodically give rise to new macronuclei. Macronuclei are large and of various shapes: spheric, ovoid, elongated, beaded; they function to direct

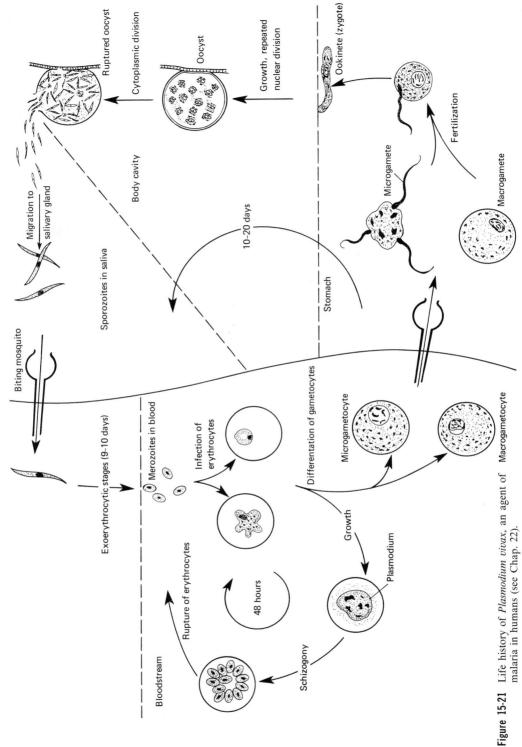

IN MAN

IN FEMALE ANOPHELINE MOSQUITO

Ruptured oocyst

Cytoplasmic division

Oocyst

Growth, repeated nuclear division

Ookinete (zygote)

Fertilization

Body cavity

Migration to salivary gland

Microgamete

Macrogamete

Sporozoites in saliva

10-20 days

Biting mosquito

Stomach

Exoerythrocytic stages (9-10 days)

Merozoites in blood

Infection of erythrocytes

Differentiation of gametocytes

Microgametocyte

Macrogametocyte

Growth

Plasmodium

Rupture of erythrocytes

48 hours

Bloodstream

Schizogony

296

Figure 15-21 Life history of *Plasmodium vivax*, an agent of malaria in humans (see Chap. 22).

metabolism. Although the number of nuclei per individual varies among species, the majority possess one nucleus of each type.

The most common means of reproduction in ciliates is transverse binary fission. Due to the complexity of the individual ciliate, fission is accompanied by considerable reorganization of internal and surface structures. In some forms, organelles are resorbed prior to fission and re-formed for each of the progeny. Because rows of cilia are typically arranged longitudinally, transverse fission results in inheritance of an equal number of rows by each progeny. During or following fission, each basal granule divides into two. One progeny granule retains the old cilium; the other produces a new one and thereby re-establishes the normal number of cilia per row. In organisms in which one of the progeny retains the original oral apparatus, a new apparatus is formed by differentiation of an area within the ciliary rows posterior to the older cytostome; this is usually accomplished before fission is completed. Adoral organelles are derived from the basal granules of certain cilia in these rows.

Micronuclei divide mitotically prior to or during fission and migrate to opposite poles of the cell. The macronuclei become elongated in the long axis of the cell and divide by equatorial constriction. Condensation of macronuclear material into chromosomes does not occur. Like many other protozoa, most ciliates can become dormant by encysting.

Three classes are distinguished.

Class Protociliata. This group comprises ciliates that lack a cytostome. Cilia are uniformly distributed without specializations. Nuclei are of only one type. Reproduction by oblique or longitudinal binary fission or plasmotomy. Sexual events involve cell fusion, rather than conjugation. The one characteristic this group shares with all other ciliates is cilia.

Class Ciliatea. Cilia, ciliary organelles, or both are present in adult stages. Ingestion typically through a cytostome. Reproduction by transverse binary fission or budding. Sexual exchanges involve conjugation. Two types of nuclei.

Order Holotrichida. Cilia of uniform length; they may arise over the entire surface of the cell. Some genera lack a cytostome.

Order Spirotrichida. Zone of membranelles along oral surface winding clockwise toward cytostome. Cilia may cover entire organism or may be restricted to a few areas.

Order Peritrichida. Anterior end of cell is flattened and bears a zone of cilia that winds counterclockwise toward the cytostome. Additional cilia absent in adult stages or present as a girdle near the posterior end.

Class Suctorea. Cilia present in young forms, absent in adults. Cytostome absent; ingestion typically through tentacles. Reproduction by budding. Sexual exchanges occur during conjugation. Two types of nuclei.

Phylum Ciliophora / Class Ciliatea

Most Ciliatea are unicellular and free-living in fresh or sea water. Some parasitic forms are known, however, and some of the sessile types grow attached to the surface of particular aquatic organisms including fishes and crustaceans. Their food usually consists of other microbes. Some ciliates display highly selective appetites (in the laboratory) and feed almost exclusively on microbes of one genus or species.

The surface of a ciliate is covered with a pellicle sufficiently rigid to maintain a distinctive cell shape. In a few ciliates, shape can be modified to some extent by contraction of ectoplasmic fibrils. The ectoplasm contains the basal structures of cilia, and trichocysts, if present. The endoplasm contains the nuclei, mitochondria, Golgi apparatus, food vacuoles, reserve food granules, and contractile vacuole(s).

Most Ciliatea possess a cytostome that may be situated at the inner end of an oral groove elaborately provided with cilia or ciliary organelles; the cytostome typically opens into a cytopharynx. Cell shape varies considerably among genera, but is not spheric in any group. Generally, under a given set of conditions, individual ciliates reach a characteristic size, which ranges from a few micrometers to 2 mm. Size, shape, and extent of development of organelles are influenced by environmental factors, especially by the sort of food available.

In spite of the awareness that ciliate morphology is markedly affected by the environment, their classification is based primarily on morphology, and to a more limited extent on habitat. For most ciliates, very little further information is available. However, some types have been grown in pure cultures with killed cells or dissolved foods, or with living yeasts or bacteria, but no other protozoa present.

Order Holotrichida. *Bütschliella* (Fig. 15-22*A*) represents the suborder Astomina, which comprises parasites of body cavities and digestive tracts of animals. These ciliates lack a cytostome and apparently feed by absorption. The anterior pole of the cell often possesses an attachment organelle that anchors the ciliate to the lining of the host cavity or gut. The macronucleus is typically elongated; there is usually one micronucleus. The contractile vacuoles may be aligned along one side, as in *Bütschliella,* or there may be a single, elongated, channel-like contractile vacuole. Fission, although binary, often results in progeny of different sizes; in such instances, the one derived from the anterior end of the parent is larger. Successive progeny may remain

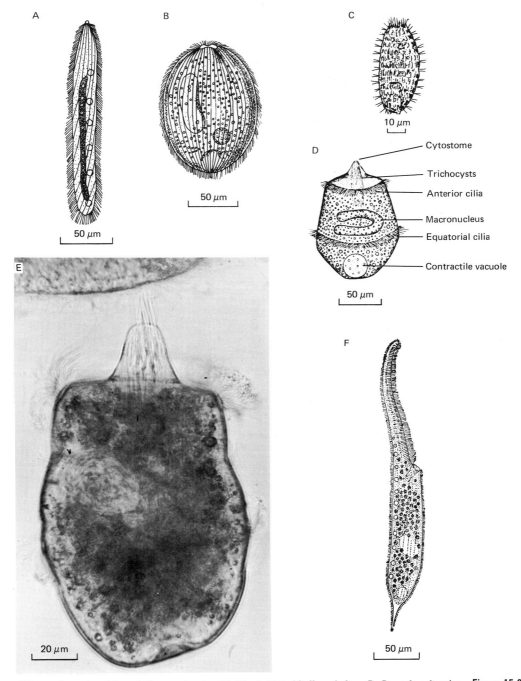

A

B

C

10 μm

D

Cytostome

Trichocysts

Anterior cilia

Macronucleus

Equatorial cilia

Contractile vacuole

50 μm

50 μm

50 μm

E

20 μm

F

50 μm

Ciliates: Astomina (*A*) and Gymnostomina (*B–F*). *A. Bütschliella opheliae. B. Prorodon discolor. C. Coleps hirtus. D. Didinium nasutum. E. D. nasutum* attached by trichocysts to a paramecium, prior to ingestion of the paramecium (see also Figs. 18-6 and 18-7). (From Schwartz, V., 1965. *Zeit. f. Naturforsch.,* **20b**:383. By permission of Verlag der Zeitschrift für Naturforschung.) *F. Dileptus anser.*

Figure 15-22

attached so that a chain of cells accumulates. Eventually, the chain breaks up into individuals.

Representatives of the suborder Gymnostomina (Fig. 15-22*B–F*) possess cytostomes that are often provided with trichites. A filament may be extruded explosively from each trichite during feeding; the filament seems to aid in holding the prey. Cilia over the rest of the cell are of uniform size except for a single long posterior cilium that occurs in a few genera, e.g., *Coleps* and *Ileonema*. Most Gymnostomina are free-living organisms found in fresh and salt water. The surface of most types is usually smooth in contour; cortical plates are peculiar to the family that includes *Coleps*. In the species of *Coleps* most closely examined, the plates are composed of calcium carbonate, and the pellicle lies external to the plates.

The anterior pole of some Gymnostomina is drawn out like a (ciliated) forward arm. The cytostome is located at the base of the arm, as illustrated in *Dileptus*. The side of the arm nearest the cytostome typically possesses trichocysts. In a related genus (*Paradileptus*), a wide, curved arm forms a rudimentary peristome.

In suborder Trichostomina, a higher degree of ciliary specialization occurs in the oral region. Usually, this consists of a dense zone of elongated cilia situated along the lip of a groove that leads to the cytostome. The side of the organism on which the groove is situated is designated ventral. *Balantidium* (Fig. 15-23*A*), a representative of this suborder, includes species that occur in human intestines and can cause dysentery.

The precytostomal groove of suborder Hymenostomina (Fig. 15-23*B–E*) is provided with an undulating membrane and membranelles. The number and arrangement of the organelles vary among genera. Two of these organisms, *Tetrahymena* and *Paramecium,* display small organelles, although in some species the organelles occur alone in the oral region without additional free cilia. The undulating membrane in *Pleuronema* is much larger than in the other two genera, and the peristome may extend two thirds of the cell length.

Tetrahymena (Fig. 15-24) and *Paramecium* have been used extensively in studies of protozoa, particularly in genetics. Conjugation in both groups occurs only between cells of compatible mating types, and as many as eight mating types may occur in one species. The sequence of events during conjugation in *Tetrahymena pyriformis* is illustrated diagrammatically in Figure 15-25. The conjugants form a bridge as their micronuclei undergo meiosis. One haploid nucleus from each cell migrates through the bridge into the other conjugant. During migration, each nucleus becomes contorted, and it seems that the nucleus is neither pulled nor pushed, but moves by an ameboid mechanism. Each migrated nucleus fuses with a haploid nucleus native to the reciprocal conjugant; this fusion re-establishes the diploid condition that is maintained throughout the remainder of the life cycle. New nuclei are derived from each zygote nucleus. Fission occurs after separation of the conjugants and restores the typical number of each type of nucleus in the progeny of the exconjugants. The number of nuclei, particularly of micronuclei and their meiotic products, that arise and degenerate during conjugation varies among species; in all

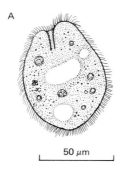

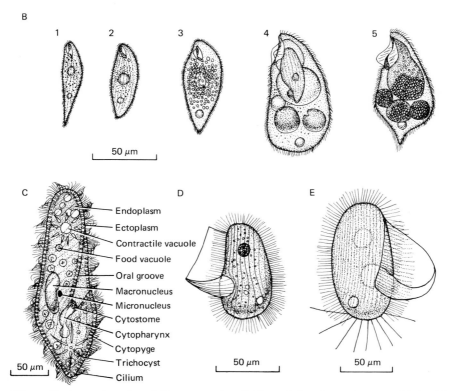

A

50 µm

B

1   2   3   4   5

50 µm

C

Endoplasm
Ectoplasm
Contractile vacuole
Food vacuole
Oral groove
Macronucleus
Micronucleus
Cytostome
Cytopharynx
Cytopyge
Trichocyst
Cilium

50 µm

D

50 µm

E

50 µm

Ciliates: Trichostomina (*A*) and Hymenostomina (*B–E*). *A. Balantidium coli,* agent of balantidial   **Figure 15-23**
dysentery of humans.

  B. Five forms of *Tetrahymena* (*Glaucoma*) *vorax.* The form, size, and proportional development
of the oral region vary according to the type of food available. *1.* Fed on living bacteria. *2.*
Cultivated in broth with soluble nutrients. *3.* Fed on killed ciliates (*Colpidium* sp.). *4.* Fed on
living ciliates (*Colpidium* sp.). *5.* Fed on living yeasts. (From Kidder, G. W., D. M. Lilly, and
C. L. Claff, 1940. *Biol. Bull.,* **78:**9. By permission of *The Biological Bulletin of the Marine Biological
Laboratory,* Woods Hole, Mass.)

  C. Paramecium caudatum. D. Pleuronema crassum. E. Pleuronema marinum.

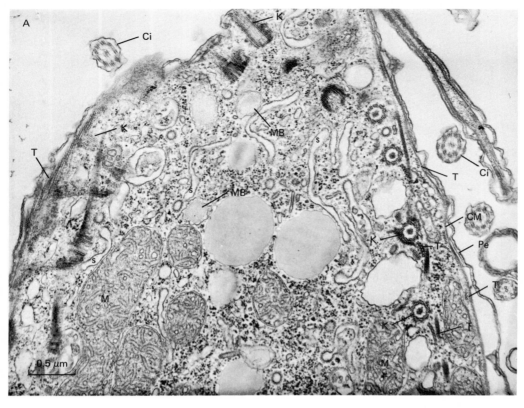

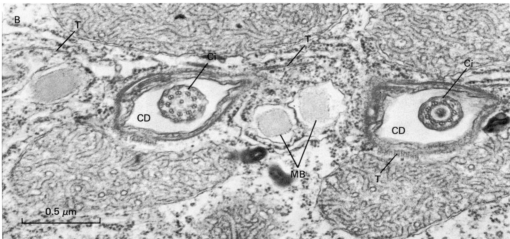

Figure 15-24 *Tetrahymena pyriformis* (see also Figs. 6-9*B* and 6-10*C* and *D*). *A*. Tangential section showing pellicle (*Pe*) in which the layers have separated, several kinetosomes (*K*) in transverse and longitudinal section, cilia (*Ci*), microtubules (*T*) in transverse and longitudinal section, mitochondria (*M*), muciferous bodies (*MB*), and flattened sacs (*S*) of unknown function. Each kinetosome is typically associated with a group of microtubules, and groups of microtubules also occur immediately within the cell membrane (*CM*) in the ectoplasm. *B*. Transverse section through two ciliary depressions (*CD*) in the cell cortex. Each cilium (*Ci*) emerges through such a depression. (From Allen, R. D., 1967. *J. Protozool.*, **14**:553. By permission of The Society of Protozoologists and *The Journal of Protozoology*.)

302

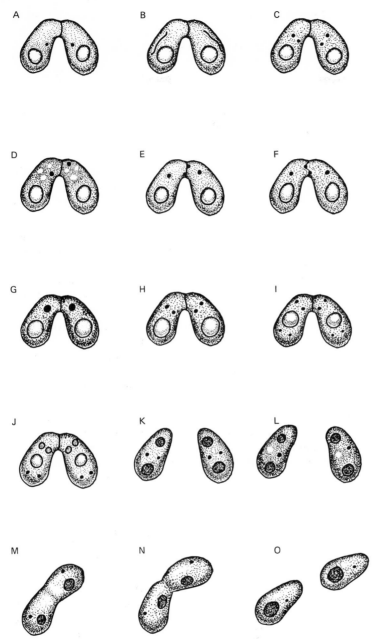

Nuclear events during conjugation in *Tetrahymena*. *Dark bodies,* micronuclei and their division products. *Lightly shaded bodies,* pre-existing macronuclei. *Heavily shaded bodies,* macronuclei derived from recombined gamete nuclei. *A.* Initiation of mating. *B.* Crescent stage of micronucleus. *C.* First prezygotic nuclear division completed; during this division, chromosomes are visible in the dividing nuclei. Presumed to be a reductive division. *D.* After second prezygotic nuclear division, three micronuclear products degenerate. The fourth becomes associated with the membrane between the conjugants. *E.* Third prezygotic nuclear division completed; one product remains associated with the membrane. *F.* Exchange of micronuclear products (the gamete nuclei). *G.* Nuclear fusion. The two zygote nuclei are genetically identical and presumably diploid. *H.* First postzygotic nuclear division; the products of this and all subsequent nuclear divisions are presumably diploid. *I.* Second postzygotic nuclear division completed. *J.* In each conjugant, two of the products of zygote nucleus division begin to develop into macronuclei; the pre-existing macronucleus degenerates. *K.* Continued development of the new macronuclei and termination of mating. *L.* Degeneration of one micronucleus in each exconjugant. *M–O.* First fission in an exconjugant, resulting in two individuals, each with one micro- and one macronucleus.

Figure 15-25

instances, however, each conjugant donates one and receives one gamete nucleus.

In many ciliates, conjugal nuclear exchange results in a pair of genetically identical zygote nuclei, one in each exconjugant. Whereas it is generally recognized that the advantage of sexual processes is the promotion of variation among interfertile organisms, nuclear exchanges in ciliates such as *T. pyriformis* decrease heterogeneity within a population.

Order Spirotrichida. The order Spirotrichida comprises organisms apparently derived from holotrichous types mainly by increased development of adoral organelles and reduction of ciliation. Four examples are illustrated in Figure 15-26.

Blepharisma species occur in water as free-living organisms that feed mainly on bacteria. The cell is covered with cilia of uniform length, as is common among holotrichs, but possesses a long, spiral peristome with a well-developed undulating membrane. Just within the cytostome is a distinct funnel-shaped pharynx. The peristome of *Stentor* occupies the entire anterior pole of the organism; along its rim is a field of membranelles that direct currents toward the cytostome, deep within the peristomal depression. Numerous myonemes are present in the ectoplasm, and the organism is contractile.

Diplodinium and closely related genera occur as endosymbionts in the rumen (see Chap. 21) or intestines of herbivorous animals. The suborder (Entodiniomorphina) in which they are placed accommodates organisms that lack free cilia, except as syncilia (tufts of cilia that behave temporarily as units); they possess membranelles as organelles of both locomotion and feeding. One zone of membranelles is situated near the cytostome, and another on the aboral surface. In some genera, there may also be one or more tufts of membranelles on the posterior half of the organism.

Stylonychia represents the suborder Hypotrichina, which accommodates protozoa with cirri. These organelles occur in groups along the peristome and at other sites on the ventral surface; their distribution varies among genera. An individual cirrus arises from a base plate within the ectoplasm; the kinetosomes of the component cilia lie external to the plate. The cirri of *Stylonychia* are quite sturdy and allow locomotion on a solid surface by a process similar to walking—only the tips of the moving cirri contact the surface.

Order Peritrichida. This group includes many types that are sessile and some that are colonial. The peritrich (see *Vorticella,* Fig. 15-27A) often possesses a posterior stalk, derived from pellicle and ectoplasm, by means of which it can attach to a substrate. During growth, cilia occur only in the anterior, flattened peristomal area. When reproduction occurs by external budding, the bud develops a girdle of cilia that are used for locomotion. The swimming bud eventually loses the equatorial cilia; in stalked types, the bud usually settles onto a surface and develops a stalk as its locomotor cilia disappear.

Reproduction in a large proportion of peritrichs occurs by binary fission. In stalked, colonial forms, the stalk branches at the time of fission. The resulting

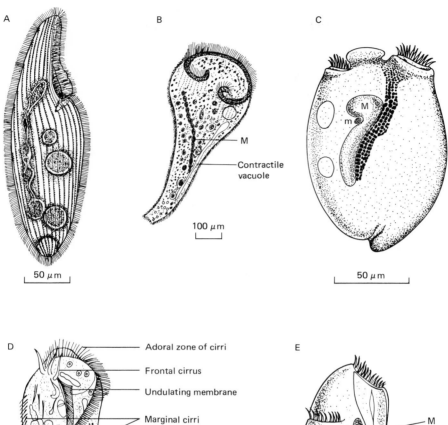

A

B

C

M

Contractile
vacuole

100 μm

50 μm

50 μm

D

E

Adoral zone of cirri

Frontal cirrus

Undulating membrane

Marginal cirri

Ventral cirrus

M

m

Anal cirrus

Caudal cirri

100 μm

50 μm

Ciliates: Spirotrichs. *M,* macronucleus; *m,* micronucleus. *A. Blepharisma undulans. B. Stentor* **Figure 15-26** *coeruleus,* partly contracted. *C. Eudiplodinium maggi,* a rumen organism (see Chap. 21). *D. Stylonychia mytilus. E. Ophryoscolex bicoronatus,* a rumen organism.

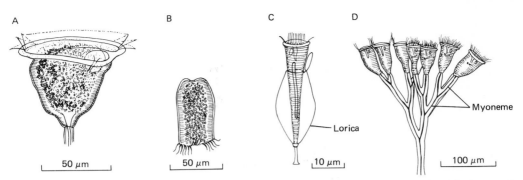

Figure 15-27 Ciliates: Peritrichs. *A. Vorticella campanula*, mature individual. *B. V. campanula*, juvenile (swarmer) stage. *C. Caulicola valvata. D. Zoothamnium adamsi.*

colony consists of a dichotomously branched stalk with a ciliate at the end of each branch. Within the stalk in certain genera is a system of myonemes that effect contraction of the stalk. In some genera, the myonemes are discontinuous at each branch point, and branches contract individually. In others, e.g., *Zoothamnium* (Fig. 15-27*D*), the myonemes are continuous, and the colony contracts as a unit. These colonies can reach a height of 4 mm.

Most peritrichs are free-living in fresh or salt water. Although sessile forms are commonly found attached to the surface of aquatic animals and plants, they do not parasitize their living substrates.

Phylum Ciliophora / Class Suctorea

Like peritrichs, the Suctorea are probably descendants of holotrich-like ancestors, but the two higher groups probably have evolved independently. Motile stages of suctoreans may possess cilia over most or all of the cell surface. Adult stages, however, do not possess cilia or ciliary organelles of any kind. They occur as free-floating individuals or, more commonly, as sessile organisms attached to the surface of submerged plants and animals, often by means of a non-contractile stalk.

Reproduction occurs by budding. The young bud possesses cilia and lacks tentacles. During metamorphosis, which may be completed within 60 minutes, the bud loses its cilia, but not the kinetosomes. The kinetosomes later divide and some will be inherited by each of the progeny. Neither stage has a cytostome; the adult feeds exclusively by means of its tentacles. The usual prey of suctoreans are ciliates, which appear to be immobilized upon contact with a suctorean tentacle. The tip of the tentacle produces a hole in the cortex of the ciliate; the protoplasm of the prey moves through the tentacle into the body of the suctorean (see Figs. 15-28 and 15-29). The driving force for this transport of material has not been identified. It is presumed to be suction, which would depend on the creation of a negative (or relatively low) pressure within the suctorean. It has been observed that the contractile vacuole of a feeding suctorean becomes very active, and it seems possible that the consequent elimination of water could maintain a low or negative pressure.

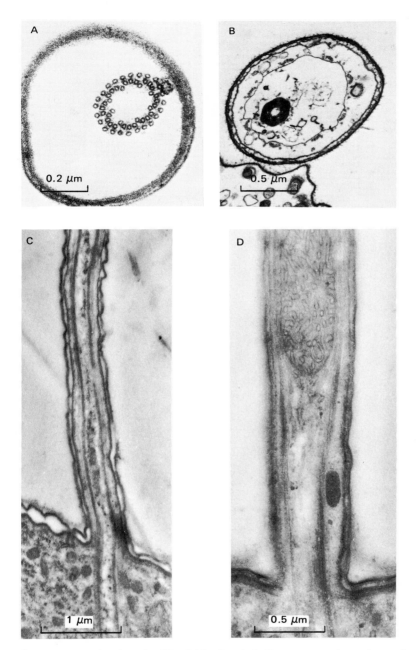

Suctorean tentacles (see also Fig. 6-11). *A* and *B*. Transverse sections of tentacles of *Acineta*   **Figure 15-28**
tuberosa. When the tentacle is not feeding (*A*), eight groups of four microtubules lie at the center
of the tentacle surrounded by an outer row of evenly spaced microtubules. During feeding (*B*),
the eight groups are evenly spaced around a central membrane (see Fig. 15-29*B*). (From Bardele,
C. F., and K. G. Grell, 1967. "Elektronenmikroskopische Beobachtungen zur Nahrungsaufnahme
bei dem Suktor *Acineta tuberosa* Ehrenberg," in *Zeit. f. Zellforsch. und mikroskop. Anat.,* **80:**108–23.
By permission of Springer-Verlag, Berlin, Heidelberg, New York.) *C* and *D*. Longitudinal sections
of tentacles of *Tokophrya infusionum,* during inactivity (*C*) and during feeding (*D*). The mitochondrion in *D* is from the prey, not the suctorean. (From Rudzinska, M. A., 1965. *J. Cell Biol.,*
25:459. By permission of The Rockefeller University Press.)

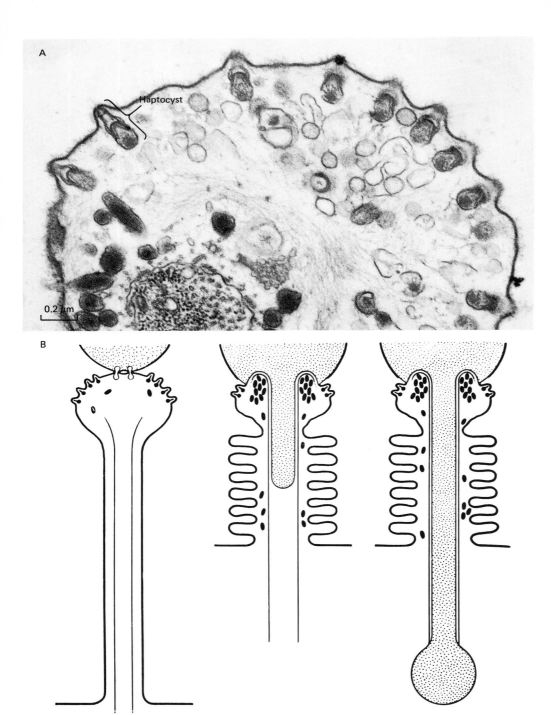

Figure 15-29 Suctorean tentacles. *A*. Transverse section through the knob of a tentacle of *Acineta tuberosa*. The haptocysts are discharged during capture of prey and help to hold the prey during feeding. (Courtesy of C. F. Bardele.) *B*. Diagram of an interpretation of three stages in tentacular feeding in *Acineta tuberosa* suggesting that the central membrane is derived from the cell membrane of the knob of the tentacle in a manner similar to formation of food vacuoles during ingestion in organisms such as amebae. (From Bardele, C. F., and K. G. Grell, 1967. "Elektronenmikroskopische Beobachtungen zur Nahrungsaufnahme bei dem Suktor *Acineta tuberosa* Ehrenberg," in *Zeit f. Zellforsch. und mikroskop. Anat.,* **80:**108–23. By permission of Springer-Verlag, Berlin, Heidelberg, New York.)

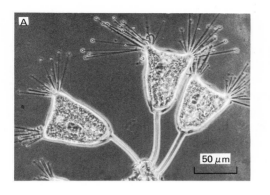

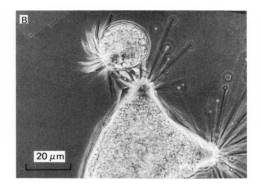

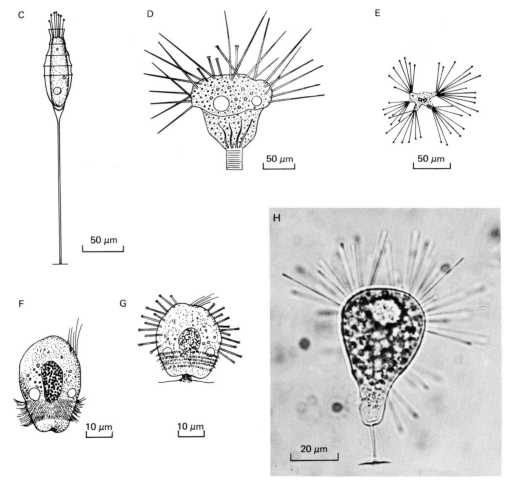

Suctoreans. *A* and *B. Acineta tuberosa.* The individual in (*B*) has captured a ciliate (*Strombidium* **Figure 15-30** sp.). (From Bardele, C. F., and K. G. Grell, 1967. "Elektronenmikroskopische Beobachtungen zur Nahrungsaufnahme bei dem Suktor *Acineta tuberosa* Ehrenberg," in *Zeit. f. Zellforsch. und mikroskop. Anat.,* **80:**108–23. By permission of Springer-Verlag, Berlin, Heidelberg, New York.) *C. Thecacineta gracilis. D. Ephelota gemmipara. E. Trichophrya epistylidis.*

F–H. Tokophrya infusionum. F. A young, ciliated swarmer. *G.* A juvenile, with tentacles; the cilia have not yet been lost. *H.* An adult. (From Rudzinska, M. A., 1965. *J. Cell Biol.,* **25:**459. By permission of The Rockefeller University Press.)

Five types of Suctorea are illustrated in Figure 15-30. *Acineta* possesses a stalk and slender knobbed tentacles. *Ephelota* possesses two types of tentacles; the pointed tentacles apparently serve mainly to capture and hold the prey, and the knobbed appendages serve as sucking tentacles. *Trichophrya* (*Platophrya*) cell form is not constant, even within a clone; the number of protrusions, each of which bears a fascicle of tentacles, is variable. Individuals are typically free-floating. An individual of *Tokophrya* may bear one to four fascicles of tentacles.

The life cycles of most Suctorea have been observed only incompletely. Motile stages typically occur, encystment is fairly common, and conjugation has been reported. The stages and events that have been described are similar to analogous phenomena in Ciliatea. However, since suctoreans feed on ciliates, and few ciliates are available in pure culture, pure cultures of Suctorea have not been obtained. Consequently, they—like most other protozoa—have not yet been studied in a defined or moderately well-controlled environment. Without such studies, neither their fundamental physiologic properties nor their role in chemical processes in nature can be evaluated.

Chapter 16

Slime Protists

Four groups of organisms are known that seem intermediate between fungi and protozoa. These are the net slime molds, the endoparasitic slime molds, the plasmodial slime molds, and the cellular slime molds. Like typical fungi, each type develops a fruiting structure that contains uninucleate units that remain dormant for long periods of time. Like typical protozoa, some of these types can ingest particulate foods.

Only a small amount of information is available about the net slime molds (Labyrinthulae) and the endoparasitic slime molds (Plasmodiophoromycetes). The former exist as epiphytes or parasites on marine algae and plants. They grow as naked, unicellular, uninucleate spindle-shaped cells, which produce slime filaments over (within?) which they move by gliding. The Plasmodiophoromycetes are obligate parasites of aquatic algae, fungi, and flowering plants; they develop intracellularly within their host. The principal growing stage is a **plasmodium**[1]—a naked, multinucleate organism—which probably develops from a uninucleate unit.

The other two groups have been more extensively investigated. Under laboratory conditions, the developmental stages of the plasmodial slime molds are the same as those that occur in nature. The cellular slime molds, however, form fruiting bodies in the laboratory that are not seen in nature. It is presumed that the fruits are formed, but are rapidly dissipated under natural conditions because of their fragile construction. Both these groups comprise free-living organisms that occur on such substrates as dung, soil, and dead wood. They feed on bacteria and other particulate materials and absorb dissolved nutrients from the substrate.

The plasmodial slime molds are called Myxomycetes by mycologists and

[1]See footnote p. 202.

Mycetozoa by protozoologists. They probably comprise a very old group that has descended independently of protozoa and filamentous fungi from an ancestral form common to all three groups. The propagative unit is dormant, thick-walled, approximately spheric, and resistant to adverse conditions such as drying. Upon germination, it releases typically one (although there may be as many as four) haploid, uninucleate, naked cell. The wetter the environment in which germination occurs, the greater the probability that the cell will be or will soon become flagellated. There may be one or two flagella, invariably of the whiplash type and located at the anterior end of the cell. The non-flagellated cell is ameboid; it produces pseudopodia that provide a means of locomotion and of ingesting particulate food. Pseudopodial feeding also occurs at the posterior end of flagellated cells.

Flagellated cells eventually either fuse in pairs after contacting each other posteriorly or change into ameboid stages which can reproduce by binary fission, encyst, or fuse with other ameboid units. Within the cells resulting from pairing of either type of cell, nuclear fusion occurs and the major vegetative stage of the organism is initiated.

As the diploid cell feeds and grows, nuclear divisions occur and the organism develops into a plasmodium. Additional diploid individuals may be incorporated into the plasmodium by fusion; in some strains, this seems to be so common that most plasmodia originate by successive fusion of several zygotes, rather than by growth of only one. Within one nuclear generation after the establishment of the plasmodium or addition of another by fusion, all the nuclei, regardless of source, undergo mitosis synchronously; this synchrony is maintained throughout the remainder of this stage. In laboratory cultures, mitoses have been observed to occur approximately once every 12 hours.

The plasmodium of some species reaches a maximum size of not more than 1 mm. If environmental conditions are favorable for further growth, the plasmodium divides, and growth continues in the smaller units. Plasmodia of other types may grow to more than 20 cm in diameter. These usually comprise networks of protoplasm developed by elongation, branching, and fusion of portions of the plasmodium. The cytoplasm is continuous within the network and is differentiated as an outer, gel-like layer of ectoplasm and an inner, mobile endoplasm. The endoplasm flows rapidly in one direction; then, about once every 60 seconds, it reverses the direction of its flow. The largest plasmodia are fan-shaped; they move over the surface of the substrate predominantly in the direction of the wider edge of the plasmodium (Fig. 16-1).

Eventually, the plasmodium ceases feeding and begins to form fruiting bodies. The environmental factors that stimulate this stage of development are still unidentified, although exhaustion of the food supply is often suggested as a major stimulus. Myxomycetes are typically holocarpic; the entire plasmodium is converted into one or several fruiting bodies.

The type of fruiting body formed by the plasmodium is characteristic of the genus and has one of four general forms: a column possessing small projections, each one bearing a single spore; a single sporangium, often borne on a stalk; a mass of sporangia more or less fused into one body; or a sporangium-like

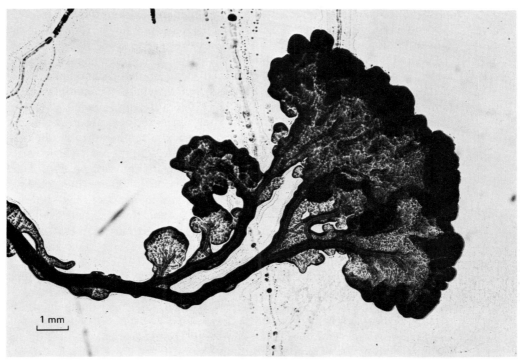

Physarum sp. Leading, fan-shaped portion of a plasmodium. (Courtesy Carolina Biological Supply   **Figure 16-1**
Company.)

structure that retains the approximate shape of the plasmodium at the time
of fruiting.

One or two nuclear divisions usually occur as the fruiting structures develop.
The cytoplasm included within a developing fruiting body wall is cleaved in
such a way that the spores are uninucleate (see Fig. 19-3). The spore walls
contain cellulose, and possibly also chitin. When the spores germinate, the
haploid cells emerge.

The life cycles of the cellular slime molds, or Acrasiae, differ from those
of plasmodial types in four principal ways: (1) flagella do not appear in
any stage; (2) the individual amebae constitute the entire vegetative stage;
(3) reproduction occurs by binary fission; and (4) aggregated cells do not
fuse. As in the Myxomycetes, the organization of fruiting structures is characteristic of the genus; species are distinguished by the shape of the fruiting structure and of the spores.

Crowding seems to be the factor that precipitates the fruiting process. This
does not necessarily mean a large population; as few as 100 cells, if crowded,
will aggregate to form a fruiting structure.

The first indications that fruiting is imminent are the cessation of feeding
by the amebae and their migration toward one cell or a small group of cells
from which an attraction substance called acrasin is diffusing. This substance

has been found within amebae that are still feeding; apparently, it is secreted into the environment when the cell stops feeding. As amebae respond to the acrasin, they also cease feeding and begin to release acrasin.

Eventually, practically all the individuals within a given area begin to migrate toward a central point. The aggregated cells heap up on one another to form an oblong mass, which may be nearly 1 mm in length, depending on the number of cells that have aggregated. This mass of cells is called a **pseudo-plasmodium;** it behaves as a unit, migrating over the substrate toward light, if present, and toward warmer regions, if there is a temperature gradient in the environment. After a period of migration, the duration of which varies among species, the pseudoplasmodium halts, and the anterior portion of the population (the "prestalk" cells) backs up on top of the others (the "precyst" cells). The prestalk cells begin to migrate down into the mass of cells, secreting a cellulose core for the stalk as they move. In two genera, the stalks are acellular; in all others, the cells that deposit the core remain as part of the stalk. The precyst cells move upward on the outside of the developing stalk and mass at its peak. These cells then form cellulosic walls as they encyst.

The pseudoplasmodium, which also occurs in a few species of Sarcodina, is of interest to biologists as an example of a primitive multicellular state. It can be disrupted into individual amebae without any effect on their ability to reaggregate, yet it behaves as a unit composed of two types of cells—prestalk and precyst cells. Pseudoplasmodia composed of mixed populations of distin-guishable strains can be made in the laboratory; these behave normally during migration and form fruits. The different strains are segregated into separate masses of cysts in the mature fruiting body; this is interpreted as a reflection of specific surface adhesions among precyst cells that segregate them from their own prestalk cells as well as from precyst cells of another strain.

Whether nuclear fusion and meiosis occur is still debated. Haploid strains of *Dictyostelium* have been isolated that possess seven chromosomes; diploid isolates have 14 chromosomes. The latter can give rise to haploid progeny with different traits, which reflects heterozygosity in the diploid strains.

Three stages in the life cycle of *Dictyostelium polycephalum* are illustrated in Figure 16-2. The mature fruiting structure of *D. discoideum* (Fig. 16-3) may be several millimeters tall; in other Acrasiae, it may reach only several microm-eters. A variety of fruiting structures is illustrated in Figures 16-4 and 16-5.

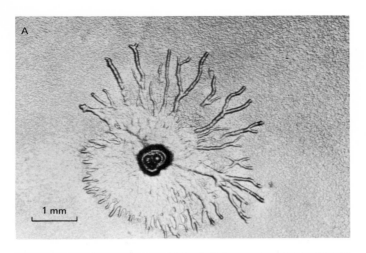

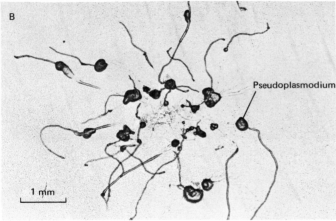

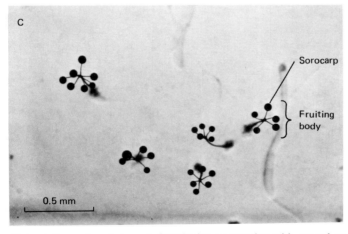

Dictyostelium polycephalum. A. Developing aggregation with several paths of migration to the center. *B.* Migrating pseudoplasmodia; several of these develop from a single aggregation. *C.* Sorocarps. Each fruiting body, consisting of several sorocarps, has developed from a single migrating pseudoplasmodium. (Courtesy of K. B. Raper.)

Figure 16-2

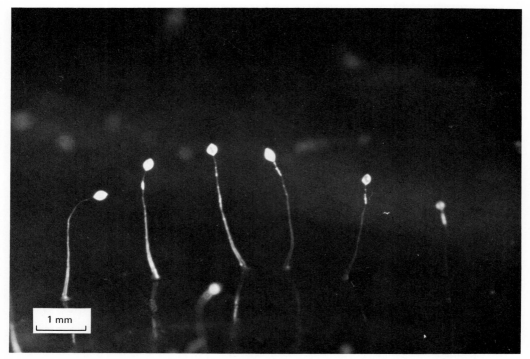

1 mm

Figure 16-3 *Dictyostelium discoideum.* Several sorocarps, one sorocarp per fruiting body, each fruiting body from one pseudoplasmodium. (Courtesy Carolina Biological Supply Company.)

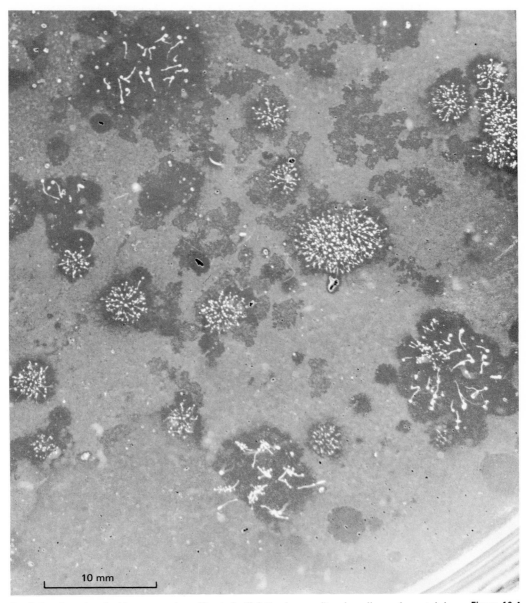

10 mm

Petri plate inoculated with a suspension of bacteria (light background) and a soil sample containing **Figure 16-4**
acrasiae. Acrasian fruiting structures arise in areas where the bacteria have been consumed. Other
areas of clearing of the bacteria presumably contain acrasiae that have not yet aggregated or
free-living soil amebae. (From Cavender, J. C., and K. B. Raper, 1965. *Amer. J. Botany,* **52**:294.
By permission of the Botanical Society of America and the *American Journal of Botany.*)

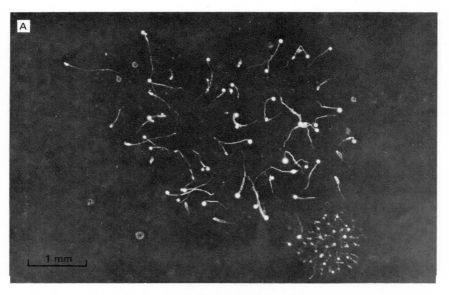

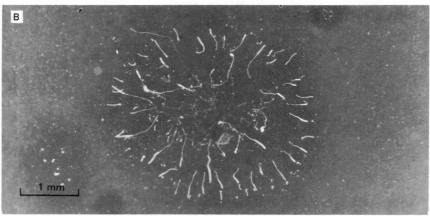

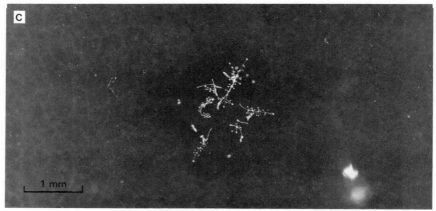

Figure 16-5 Higher magnification of fruiting acrasian colonies on plates such as the one in Figure 16-4. *A.* The larger colony is *Dictyostelium mucoroides,* the smaller is *D. minutum. B. Polysphondylium violaceum. C. P. pallidum.* (From Cavender, J. C., and K. B. Raper, 1965. *Amer. J. Botany,* **52:**294. By permission of the Botanical Society of America and the *American Journal of Botany.*)

Chapter 17

Algae

The algae are photosynthetic protists that contain chlorophyll a as a photo-synthetic pigment and can evolve O_2 as a by-product of photosynthesis. The group includes procaryotic and eucaryotic organisms. Some of the latter are highly developed and display a distinct trend toward tissue differentiation. The proposition that one group, the green algae, gave rise to the plants is widely accepted by biologists. The biochemical properties of photosynthesis and starch formation and the organization of photosynthesizing cells are basically the same in green algae and plants. The principal differences lie in the organization of the individual: the green algal thallus is not differentiated, whereas the plant body is composed of differentiated tissues; and the sex organs of algae are unicellular, whereas those of plants are multicellular.

Classification

The primary taxon used to classify algae is the division. The divisions are defined on the basis of two types of biochemical properties: identity of pigments and of reserve foods. On the basis of these characteristics, it seems that the procaryotic algae gave rise to the eucaryotic forms. There were probably at least six separate lines of descent, as implied in Table 17-1. Each division is characterized by its own array of pigments in addition to chlorophyll a, which occurs in all algal groups, at least one of which occurs in procaryotic algae but may not occur in any other group of eucaryotic forms.

Most of the groupings arrived at by using biochemical properties as the primary taxonomic criteria are homogeneous with regard to flagellation, but less homogeneous with regard to other structural properties. Since algae have persisted throughout their history predominantly as inhabitants of watery

319

TABLE 17-1. Properties of Algal Divisions

Division	Pigments*			Phycobilins‡	Reserve Foods	Flagellation	
	Chlorophylls	Carotenes	Xanthophylls†			Number/Cell	Position
Cyanophyces (blue-green algae)	a	β-	An,Apn,Apl,Flc,L,Mn,Ml,O,Z	PE,PC,alloPC	Cyanophycean starch, proteins	—	—
Chlorophyces (green algae)	a, b	±α-, β-	As,L,N,±S,±Sx,V,Z	—	Starch, oils	1,2,4 or many	Apical
Euglenophyces (euglenids)	a, b	β- and unidentified	An,As,L,N	—	Paramylon, oils	1,2 or 3	Apical
Chrysophyces (golden algae)	a, probably c, possibly d or e	β-	Dd,Dt,Dn,F,L	—	Chrysolaminarin, oils	1 or 2	Apical
Bacillariophyces (diatoms)	a, c	±α-, β-, ε-	Dd,Dt,F	—	Chrysolaminarin, oils	1	Apical
Xanthophyces (yellow-green algae)	a	β-	An,As,L,N	—	Chrysolaminarin, oils	2	Apical
Cryptophyces (cryptomonads)	a, c	α-, ε-	Z	PE,PC	Starch, oils	2	Lateral
Pyrrophyces (dinoflagellates, phytodinads)	a, c	β-	Dd,Dn,P	—	Starch, oils	2	Lateral; rarely apical
Phaeophyces (brown algae)	a, c	±α-, β-	Dt,Flx,F,L,V	—	Laminarin, soluble carbohydrates, oils	2	Lateral
Rhodophyces (red algae)	a, ±d	±α-, β-	L,T	PE,PC,alloPC	Floridean starch, oils	—	—

*"±": present in some representatives.

†Abbreviations: An (antheraxanthin), Apn (aphanicin), Apl (aphanizophyll), As (astaxanthin), Dd (diadinoxanthin), Dt (diatoxanthin), Dn (dinoxanthin), Flc (flavacin), Flx (flavoxanthin), F (fucoxanthin), L (lutein), Mn (myxoxanthin), Ml (myxoxanthophyll), N (neoxanthin), O (oscilloxanthin), P (peridinin), S (siphonein), Sx (siphonoxanthin), T (taraxanthin), V (violaxanthin), Z (zeaxanthin).

‡In some algae, the presence and amounts of phycobilins vary with the wavelength and intensity of illumination during growth. Abbreviations: PE (a class of phycoerythrins), PC (a class of phycocyanins), alloPC (allophycocyanin).

environments, the evolution of each line of descent has occurred in this environment. Consequently, similar morphologic variations suited for photosynthetic organisms in this environment have arisen and been perpetuated within each biochemical type.

Modern representatives of each of the proposed lines of descent seem to reflect a history of at least one of the following trends toward greater morphologic complexity, each presumably descending from a motile unicellular ancestral type.

1. To motile colonies.

2. To non-motile unicellular forms and non-motile colonies in which individual cells are capable of cell division.

3. To undifferentiated filaments, to filamentous forms with base-apex differentiation and/or with principal and subsidiary branches.

4. To non-motile unicellular and colonial forms in which individual cells are not capable of cell division, to coenocytic forms (multiple nuclei in an uninterrupted cytoplasm; see p. 202).

The descent of non-motile photosynthetic forms from motile ancestors is suggested by the occurrence of non-motile palmelloid forms (see p. 332), in which individual non-motile cells occasionally develop flagella and thereby become motile, and by the persistence of motility of spores and gametes in almost all major types of eucaryotic algae. In each line of eucaryotic algae except the Rhodophyces, in which flagella do not occur, some types are motile as adults, in other types only the reproductive units are motile, and in others only certain of the reproductive units are motile.

Photosynthetic eucaryotic protists that are unicellular or colonial and that possess one or more flagella in the adult stage are classified by protozoologists as Phytomastigophorea (Phylum Mastigophora). However, it seems clear that motile photosynthetic organisms have given rise to motile non-photosynthetic organisms as well as to non-motile photosynthetic organisms. Colorless counterparts are known for representatives of all algal divisions except Phaeophyces and Rhodophyces. Viable non-photosynthetic organisms can be derived from photosynthetic algae (motile and non-motile) in the laboratory by exposure of the algal cells to certain chemicals, radiations, or combinations of these. The colorless derivatives are in some cases indistinguishable from naturally occurring colorless algae, which, if free-living, are typically motile.

General Characteristics

Morphology. Algal cells typically possess fairly rigid walls and many also possess sheaths that lie external to the walls. These two structures, either or both of which may be composed of more than one layer, seem generally to be of different chemical composition. Walls and sheaths are often difficult to distinguish microscopically and usually difficult to separate, which would be necessary in order to obtain purified preparations that could be analyzed chemically. Nevertheless, some information is available about the occurrence of certain structural materials. Many of these, particularly those of which sheaths are composed, are complex polysaccharides containing several types of subunits in each polymer molecule. Materials that have been identified include pectin, cellulose, silica, alginic acids, fucin, chitin, and mucopeptide. Certain of these occur only in particular groups of algae, whereas others are of variable occurrence among and within divisions.

In all eucaryotic algae, the pigments are contained within discrete subcellular organelles. The color of the organism is determined by the relative proportions of the various pigments in these bodies. The pigment-containing organelles of Chlorophyces and Euglenophyces are designated **chloroplasts,** a name that indicates that their color is typically predominantly green. The same term is used to designate the photosynthetic organelles of plants, which are also green and which are presumed to have descended from the chloroplasts of chlorophycean ancestors. The other-than-green organelles of other algae are designated **chromatophores.** In addition to chlorophyll(s) and other pigments, chloroplasts and chromatophores contain the enzyme systems involved in photosynthesis.

Reproduction, Sex, and Dormancy. Most instances of reproduction in algae occur without change in ploidy, i.e., are asexual. Asexual mechanisms include fission, sporulation, and release of nucleated fragments (in multicellular forms).

Fission is commonly binary and occurs within the parental cell wall, if present. In some types, the original wall is discarded, and each of the progeny constructs a new wall before or after release from the parent wall. In other types—notably diatoms and certain dinoflagellates—the original wall is shared by the progeny, and each new individual constructs the missing portions. Fission products formed by non-motile unicellular algae that are morphologically similar to the adult at the time they are released are called **autospores,** although they are vegetative cells and capable of assimilation and growth. Multiple fission occurs in many types of algae, usually as a sequence of alternating nuclear and cell divisions (see the first mechanism[1] of multiple fission, Fig. 10-1).

Most types of non-motile algae produce zoospores as the principal means of asexual reproduction. A vegetative protoplast may differentiate into a single zoospore by developing flagella, or it may subdivide by multiple fission or by progressive cleavage into smaller units, each of which develops flagella. Zoospores are typically naked; if the vegetative cells of the species possess walls, the zoospore develops a wall as a first step in germinating into a vegetative organism.

Many multicellular algae can reproduce from fragments that are accidentally or regularly released from the multicellular unit. Within the multicellular unit, individual cells usually can divide, and they do not lose this capacity when the unit is disrupted.

---

[1]This mechanism differs from binary fission principally by the delay in separation of sibling protoplasts. In algae, separation is usually simultaneous with release from the parental cell wall. The construction of cell walls for the progeny may be initiated before the series of fissions is completed (see Chap. 18, *"Chlorella"*).

Sexual processes have not been reported for procaryotic algae (Cyanophyces) or unequivocally demonstrated in eucaryotic algae of Euglenophyces, Chrysophyces, or Cryptophyces. In each of the groups in which sexual fusions have been demonstrated, the processes vary in specialization from involving fusion of entire adult organisms (in unicellular forms) or indistinguishable gametes (in multicellular forms), to fusion of dissimilar motile gametes, to fusion of distinguishably male and female gametes and/or their nuclei. These unions are designated, respectively, **isogamy, anisogamy,** and **oogamy.**

With respect to nuclear fusions and reductive divisions, three basic life histories are observed among algae.

1. Principal vegetative phase haploid:

$$\text{Haploid adult} \longrightarrow \text{Gametes} \xrightarrow{\text{fusion}} \text{Zygotes} \xrightarrow[\text{division}]{\text{reduction}} \text{Four}$$

(or a multiple of four) unicellular units, each of which develops into a haploid adult.

2. Principal vegetative phase diploid:

$$\text{Diploid adult} \xrightarrow[\text{division}]{\text{reduction}} \text{Gametes} \xrightarrow{\text{fusion}} \text{Zygote} \longrightarrow \text{Diploid adult.}$$

3. Alternation of haploid and diploid vegetative phases:

$$\text{Haploid adult} \longrightarrow \text{Gametes} \xrightarrow{\text{fusion}} \text{Zygote} \longrightarrow \text{Diploid adult} \xrightarrow[\text{division}]{\text{reduction}}$$

Unicellular units, each of which develops into a haploid adult.

The third pattern is referred to as an alternation of generations, because there are two independent vegetative phases of different ploidy. They may or may not be morphologically similar.

The most common type of dormant stage in algae is the akinete. An akinete is derived from a vegetative cell and is either the same size as or larger than the undifferentiated cell. Its wall consists of a cyst wall fused with the original cell wall. Some algae form cysts—dormant stages whose walls are physically and sometimes chemically distinct from the wall of the vegetative cells from which they are derived. Many types of algae that produce zoospores also produce aplanospores; aplanospores possess walls and may be dormant. As in many lower fungi, the zygotes (zygospores, oospores) of some algae are thick-walled and dormant. Other types of resting stages (e.g., statospores; see Division Chrysophyces) are unique to certain groups of algae.

Distribution

Algae are widely distributed in nature. They occur in every type of water: fresh water, the open sea, along the shore and in estuaries, in brines, and in fields of snow and ice. All known major types of algae can be found in bodies of water. A somewhat narrower variety of algae occurs in terrestrial habitats, including soils and wet aerial habitats such as on the trunks of trees and the surfaces of rocks. Only a minor proportion of terrestrial algae are non-motile, attached types. Viable algae are also carried in the air, particularly on dust (soil) particles. Procaryotic algae are invariably among the first living systems to colonize newly habitable environments such as islands that arise in the sea or the surface of volcanic ash as it cools.

Each of the generalized environments is a composite of habitats among which the following environmental factors that influence the growth of algae will vary: rate of flow of water, intensity and wavelength of illumination, temperature, availability of mineral nutrients (particularly nitrogen and phosphorus sources), salinity, and pH; pH is directly related to the availability of ions of minerals such as Fe, Mg, and Ca. The conditions especially suitable for the development of any one type of alga are fairly constant with regard to each of these factors.

The majority of algae are free-living, but many occur in associations with other algae and as symbiotic partners of plants, animals, protozoa, and fungi. They are parasitized by bacteria, fungi, protozoa, and slime protists, but only rarely occur as parasites of other organisms. Most algae are beneficial to the animal kingdom. They serve as the major source of food for small marine and fresh-water animals, which in turn are the food of larger animals. Some algae are harvested from the sea and fed to livestock, eaten by humans, or used as sources of certain substances employed in the preparation of foods and pharmaceuticals.

Although the algae as a whole are widely distributed in nature, three groups—Cyanophyces, Chlorophyces, and Bacillariophyces—account for the majority of individuals encountered in algal habitats. In some habitats, algae can be observed macroscopically. A familiar form is pond scum, a macroscopic mass of algae that usually consists mainly of representatives of the three most common groups. Seaweeds include Rhodophyces, Phaeophyces, a minor proportion of Chlorophyces, and about six genera of plants. Algae are also obvious as the "moss" on the trunks of living trees.

Division Cyanophyces (Blue-Green Algae)

These are the procaryotic algae. They occur as sessile (often epiphytic) or free-floating organisms in fresh and sea water and in soils and aerial habitats such as rocks wet by the splash from waterfalls or runoff water from soil. Many types accumulate as macroscopic masses, usually slippery, on submerged rocks or the surface of ponds. Although they are informally referred to as blue-green algae, they may also be colorless, gray, green, olive, yellow, orange, pink, purple, brown, violet, or red in appearance. Only one type of phycobilin is present in certain representatives, although the majority possess all three phycobilins. The variety of colors is due mainly to the variation in presence and proportions of the phycobilins.

The structure of cells varies little among representatives of this division. Generally, the photosynthetic pigments are localized in membranes that occupy much of the periphery of the protoplast; the central area is occupied mainly by nuclear material. Other cytoplasmic elements occur between nuclear area and photosynthetic membranes and interspersed among the latter. The cells possess walls, and the walls that have been analyzed contain mucopeptide as a principal structural material, as do bacterial walls. The cell of almost every kind of blue-green alga is surrounded by a sheath of gelatinous materials of any of various textures. In representatives of one genus (*Nostoc*), cellulosic fibrils occur within the sheath; the presence of cellulose in other blue-greens has not been unequivocally established, and there is considerable evidence that cellulose does not occur in most types. Sheath materials are generally pectic substances.

Blue-green algae occur predominantly as colonial and filamentous forms, although a few types are unicellular. The colonies generally arise when cells remain embedded in a common mass of gelatinous materials as cell divisions occur. Morphologically, the individual cells of colonies are similar to those of the unicellular forms; they are spheroid or cylindric and may have individual sheaths that are distinguishable from the gelatinous matrix of the colony. Most of the filamentous types also possess sheaths; those with firmer sheaths tend to accumulate in colonies of filaments. A few filamentous representatives do not possess sheaths; they occur as naked trichomes that are not different from the trichomes of the sheathed forms.

Among algae, the life cycles of blue-greens are relatively simple. Sexual processes are unknown, and flagellated stages have not been found. Unicellular and colonial forms reproduce by cell division and, in the latter, by fragmentation that is accidental. Colonies of many types attain macroscopic dimensions in their natural habitats. In most filamentous representatives, cell division occurs throughout the filament; reproduction of the filament occurs by more or less regular fragmentation into smaller multicellular units called hormogonia. Fragmentation may be caused by external forces (water currents, movement of animals) or may result from weakening of the filament at points where a cell has died or at the juncture of a heterocyst (see below) and a vegetative cell or another heterocyst; in a few types that do not form heterocysts, disjunctor cells or discs are produced between cells, which then separate. Restriction of cell division to particular portions of filaments occurs in a few genera.

A few types of specialized cells are produced by blue-green algae. The most frequently encountered are akinetes. Some filamentous blue-green algae form heterocysts; each heterocyst is derived by morphogenesis of a single vegetative cell. Apparently, this type of specialized cell serves different functions in different genera in which it occurs. In some genera, the heterocyst contains cytoplasm, including photosynthetic elements, and can germinate and develop into a vegetative filament. In others, the heterocyst is colorless, and the contents are amorphous. Such heterocysts may serve as disjunctor cells, but in many cases their role is not understood; they have not been observed to germinate.

The division is subdivided as three to six orders of various composition; three of the orders are described here.

> **Chroococcales.** Unicellular or colonial, not filamentous. Reproduction by cell division and colony fragmentation. Non-motile.

Nostocales. Filamentous, unbranched or with false branching. Reproduction by release of akinetes and hormogonia (see Fig. 17-2). Gliding motility.

Stigonematales. Filamentous, true branching. Reproduction by release of akinetes and hormogonia. Gliding motility.

Order Chroococcales. This is a heterogeneous assemblage of blue-green algae. Individual cells may be spheroid, cylindric, or tapered and range from 2 or 3 μm in diameter to about 20 or more μm. Whereas the lower part of this range is typical of bacteria, most blue-green algal cells are at least several micrometers in diameter.

Genera are distinguished by the number of cells per colony, the shape of individual cells, the presence of sheaths around individual cells, and the arrangement of cells within the colony. The representatives diagrammed in Figure 17-1 illustrate these variations.

Order Nostocales. The order Nostocales comprises filamentous blue-green algae in which cell division occurs transversely only. Accordingly, branches do not arise by longitudinal division of cells within a trichome. Such "true branches" are the distinguishing trait of the order Stigonematales. Nostocales representatives are typically motile by a gliding movement; hormogonia are generally more actively motile than vegetative filaments, and in some genera only the hormogonia are motile.

Representatives of four families are illustrated here.

Oscillatoriaceae. Trichomes of constant diameter. Reproduction by hormogonia only; heterocysts (see Fig. 17-3) and akinetes are not formed. (Fig. 17-2A-F.)

Beggiatoaceae.[2] Non-photosynthetic counterparts of Oscillatoriaceae types. Reproductive units may be unicellular (gonidia) or multicellular (hormogonia). (Fig. 17-2G.)

Nostocaceae. Trichomes of constant diameter. Hormogonia, heterocysts and akinetes occur. (Fig. 17-3.)

Rivulariaceae. Trichomes tapered from base to apex or from center to each end. Hormogonia, heterocysts, and akinetes occur. (Fig. 17-4A and B.)

Order Stigonematales. The order Stigonematales comprises the filamentous blue-green algae in which cell division may occur longitudinally as well as transversely. Only a few genera are recognized, and in some systems they are classified as a family of Nostocales. However, because the occurrence of longi-

---

[2]This family approximates order Beggiatoales in Bergey's *Manual of Determinative Bacteriology;* see Table 13-1.

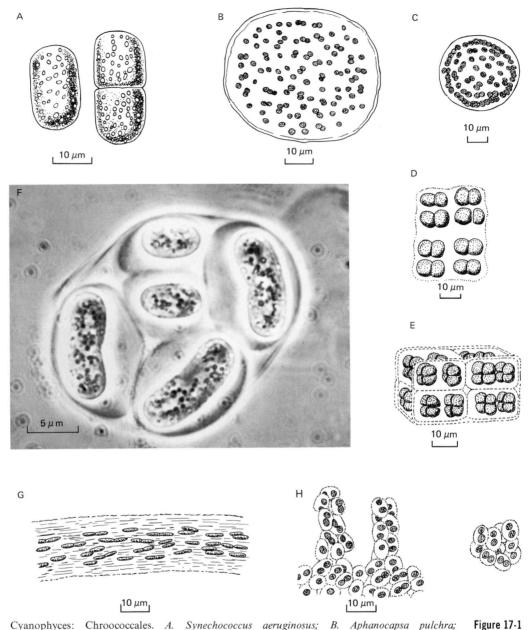

Cyanophyces: Chroococcales. *A. Synechococcus aeruginosus; B. Aphanocapsa pulchra; C. Coelosphaerium kuetzingianum; D. Merismopedia elegans; E. Eucapsis alpina. F.* An unidentified ensheathed, coccoid unicellular blue-green alga. (Courtesy of M. M. Allen.) *G.* Part of a colony of *Bacillosiphon induratus. H. Entophysalis magnoliae. Right,* a small colony; *left,* part of a large colony.

Figure 17-1

327

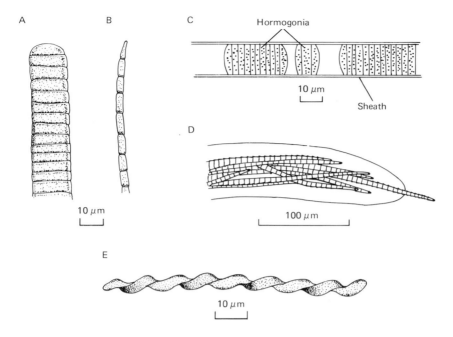

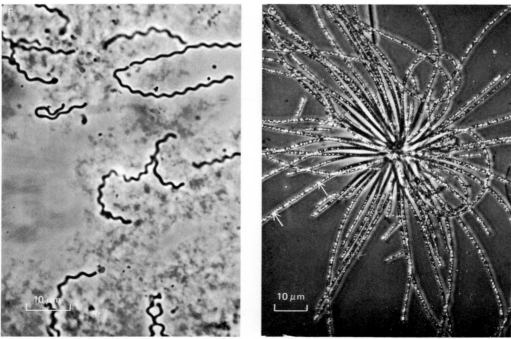

Figure 17-2 Cyanophyces: Oscillatoriaceae (*A-F*) and Beggiatoaceae (*G*). *A. Oscillatoria limosa. B. O. splendida. C. Lyngbya birgei.* The hormogonia are short, multicellular units that are released from the trichome and serve as disseminative units. *D. Microcoleus vaginatus.* Species of this genus are commonly found in soil. When these algae bloom in ponds, the water becomes toxic for animals. *E. Spirulina* sp. *F. Arthrospira* sp., a colorless organism similar to *Spirulina.* (Courtesy of R. A. Lewin.) *G. Thiothrix* sp. The arrows indicate sulfur granules. (Courtesy of E. J. Ordal.)

328

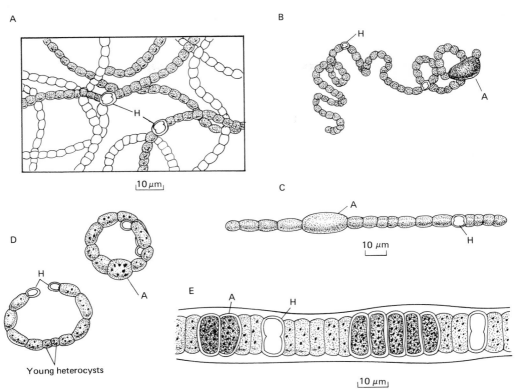

Cyanophyces: Nostocaceae. *H,* heterocyst; *A,* akinete. *A.* Portion of a thallus of *Nostoc linckia;*   **Figure 17-3**
the filaments are embedded in a mucilaginous matrix. *B. Anabaena spiroides. C. A. levanderi.*
D. Anabaenopsis elenkinii. A heterocyst is at each end of each filament, and subdivision of a
filament typically occurs by disjunction between a pair of heterocysts. *E. Nodularia spumigena.*

tudinal cell divisions results in a distinctive change in the structure of the
filament and the total organization of the individual, these genera are recognized here as constituting a major subgroup of the division.

   There are two potential structural consequences of longitudinal cell division
in a filamentous organism. The first of these is that the trichome can be
parenchymatous; i.e., the cells may be aligned along a dominant axis, but the
cross-section of the filament is multicellular. This potential is realized in the
genus *Stigonema;* in older portions of the main filament or of branches, cells
accumulate across the long axis as a consequence of longitudinal (vertical) cell
divisions.

   The second potential consequence of longitudinal cell divisions is the formation of branches that are continuous with the main filament. This true branching is characteristic of Stigonematales representatives and is illustrated for both
genera in Figure 17-4 (*C* and *D*). The importance of this development is that
branches are potentially specialized portions of a thallus. Among Stigonematales, such specialization occurs only to the extent that in certain species,
heterocysts arise only as or on branches, and in others, hormogonia are released
only from the branches.

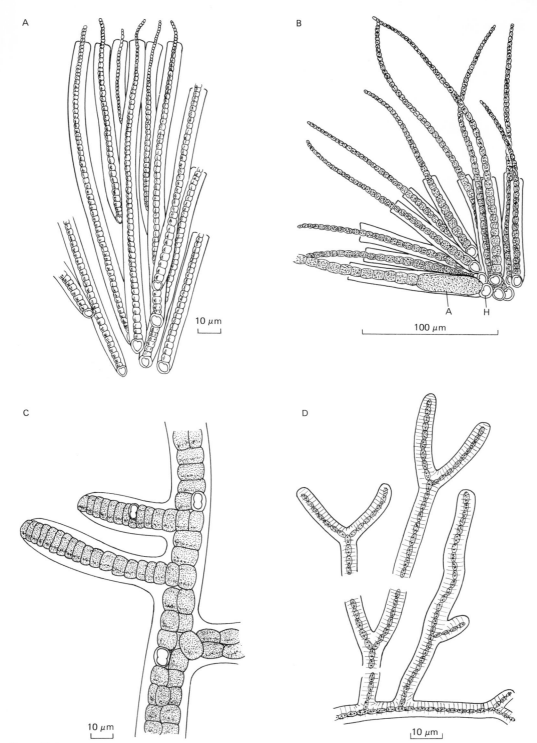

Figure 17-4 Cyanophyces: Rivulariaceae (*A* and *B*) and Stigonematales (*C* and *D*). *A*. Sector of a colony of *Rivularia dura*. *B*. Portion of a colony of *Gloeotrichia echinulata*. Akinetes (*A*) typically occur adjacent to the basal heterocyst (*H*). *C. Stigonema turfaceum*. *D. Colteronema funebre*, an alga found in hot springs.

As in Rivulariaceae representatives, there is some evidence that cell divisions are restricted to certain portions of the filaments of Stigonematales representatives that are unicellular in cross-section. In the latter organisms, cell divisions are more frequent in the tips of branches, although they may occur occasionally in other areas. The limited amount of branch specialization and the tendency of certain cells within a filament to cease cell division represent the highest level of differentiation achieved by procaryotic algae.

Division Chlorophyces (Green Algae)

Green algae can be found in every algal habitat except at the sources of hot springs. Some individual genera and species are ubiquitous; others occur only in particular types of habitats.

Within this group, all four proposed lines of structural evolution can be recognized, and modern representatives exhibit almost as great a variety of forms and reproductive and developmental processes as can be found throughout the subkingdom. Only the tendencies toward internal differentiation of vegetative tissues that are exhibited by brown and red algae do not occur among green algae. This is the only algal division in which all three types of life histories occur.

The majority of green algae contain one chloroplast per cell; it may be cup-shaped, laminate, or reticulate. In a minority of types, the chloroplast is stellate. The presence of numerous, small, discoid chloroplasts is most frequently encountered in green algae of multinucleate or coenocytic organization.

The distinguishing characteristics of nine orders of Chlorophyces are presented in Table 17-2. The green algae described in the following sections have been chosen to illustrate the major variations among green algae and to provide a summary of the characteristics of eucaryotic algae.

TABLE 17-2. Characteristics of Orders of Chlorophyces

Line*	Order	Chloroplasts	Nuclei	Flagella
		Typical Characteristics		
1	Volvocales	Cup-shaped	One	2; 4 or 8
2	Tetrasporales	Cup-shaped, stellate, discoid	One	2; 4
3	Ulvales	Cup-shaped, laminate	One	4/zoospore, 2/gamete
3	Ulotrichales	Laminate	One	2,4
3	Oedogoniales	Reticulate	One	Whorl
3	Cladophorales	Reticulate, discoid	Many	4
3†	Zygnematales	Laminate, stellate	One	——
4	Chlorococcales	Cup-shaped, laminate, discoid	One or many	2
4	Siphonales	Discoid	Many	2 or whorl; rare

*Proposed evolutionary line; see p. 321.
†Independently of the other orders of this line.

Order Volvocales. The Volvocales are flagellated and motile in the vegetative phase. One genus, *Chlamydomonas,* is considered the archetype of green algae. This unicellular, uninucleate, biflagellate alga possesses a single large chloroplast that in most species is cup-shaped, but in others may be laminate or stellate. There is a definite cell wall containing cellulose and, in many species, an additional external gelatinous layer. Reproduction occurs by longitudinal fission of the protoplast to form two, four, or eight daughter protoplasts. The flagella of the parent cell disappear at an early stage in reproduction. Before release of daughters from the parent cell wall, each daughter develops two flagella and constructs a cell wall.

Release of daughters typically occurs by gelatinization of the parent wall. In some instances, the daughter cells do not develop flagella and escape, and many generations may occur within a more or less gelatinized envelope or matrix. These masses of cells are called **palmelloid** stages; their development seems more dependent on environmental conditions, particularly conditions unfavorable for motility but not inimical to growth, than on the species of *Chlamydomonas.* Any cell can develop flagella and escape from the mass as a solitary, motile individual. Palmelloid stages occur in many eucaryotic algae as occasional or as predominant phases of development.

Species of *Chlamydomonas* generally are capable of sexual fusions (see Fig. 17-7). Depending on the species, union may be isogamous, anisogamous, or oogamous. In each type, the zygote is dormant for some time. Reductive nuclear division occurs as the zygote germinates; typically four motile vegetative cells are released, but sometimes the number is a higher power of two. All individuals except the zygotes are haploid.

All representatives of Volvocales are similar to *Chlamydomonas;* in colonial forms, the individual cells are similar to chlamydomonads. The cells of the *Chlamydomonas* species (*C. moewusii*) illustrated in Figure 17-5*A* are ellipsoid; in other species they may be ovoid or nearly spheroid. Most of the cell volume is occupied by the chloroplast, which contains a pyrenoid and a stigma. There are typically two contractile vacuoles, similar in structure and apparent function to those that occur in flagellate protozoa, located within the anterior pole of the chlamydomonad cell.

Asexual reproduction of colonial Volvocales (Fig. 17-6) typically occurs by the conversion of individual cells to autocolonies. An **autocolony** is formed by successive binary, longitudinal fissions of the protoplast within a parent cell wall. The developing colony comprises a sheet of cells, all oriented in the same direction; in many genera, the sheet becomes curved, and the mature colony comprises a single layer of cells at the periphery of a hollow sphere. When the characteristic number of cells has been produced, cell walls are formed. The number of cells per colony is fixed at the time of release from the parent cell and is regularly a power of two.

The cells of a colony of *Gonium* are arranged as a flat plate and number 4 to 32 per colony. The colony is surrounded by a membranous envelope that gelatinizes at the time of reproduction. Reproduction usually occurs simultaneously in all cells of the colony. Sexual fusion is isogamous; gametes are

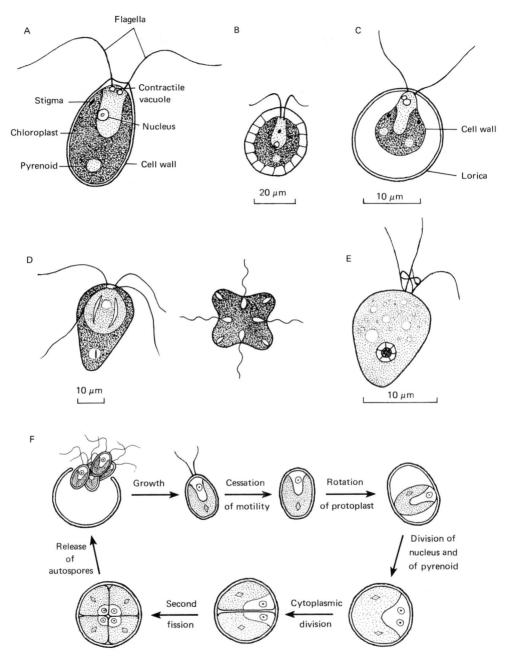

Chlorophyces: Unicellular Volvocales. *A. Chlamydomonas moewusii. B. Haematococcus lacustris.* **Figure 17-5** Cysts are colored red and are found as red films at the bottom of shallow fresh-water ponds. *C. Dysmorphococcus variabilis.* This individual appears in an early stage of cell division, with two stigmas and two pyrenoids. *D. Pyramimonas tetrarhynchus.* The cell lacks a wall and is organized as four lobes. *Left,* side view; *right,* anterior view. *E. Polytomella citri,* representative of a genus of colorless chlamydomonads. *F.* Asexual reproductive cycle in *Chlamydomonas eugametos.*

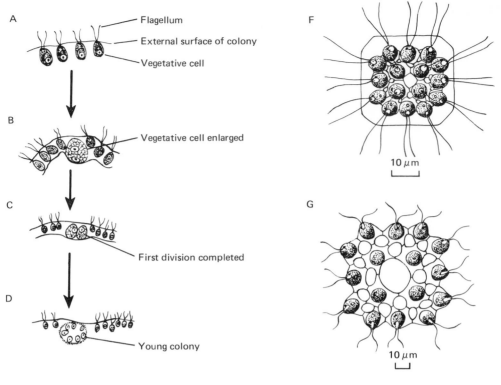

A
- Flagellum
- External surface of colony
- Vegetative cell

B
- Vegetative cell enlarged

C
- First division completed

D
- Young colony

F

10 μm

G

10 μm

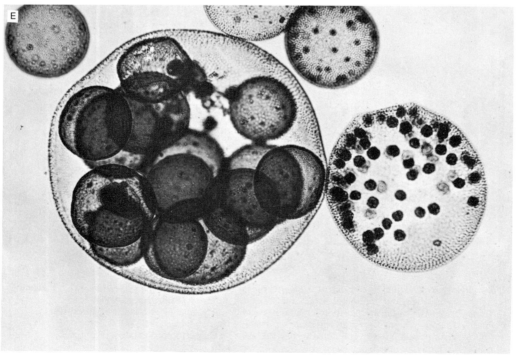

E

Figure 17-6   Chlorophyces: Colonial Volvocales. *A-E. Volvox.* *A-D.* Four successive stages in autocolony development. *E.* Colonies, which may be more than 0.5 mm in diameter. The largest colony contains autocolonies, the one to its right contains zygotes (see Fig. 17-7). (Courtesy Carolina Biological Supply Company.) *F. Gonium pectorale. G. G. formosum.*

produced in the same manner as are autocolonies, but the cells separate from each other upon release from the parent cell.

The spheric colonies of *Volvox* may contain as many as 5,000 or more cells and grow to nearly 1 mm in diameter. Only a few (sometimes only four, and not more than 50 in any species) cells in one hemisphere of the colony are capable of asexual reproduction. When first released from the parent cell into the gelatinous matrix of the center of the colony, the cells of an autocolony are oriented with their flagella toward its center. The autocolony then inverts by eversion of the sheet of cells through a pore in the surface of the autocolony; the flagella of a mature colony are oriented away from the center. When several such colonies have accumulated within a parent colony, the older colony disintegrates and its cells presumably die.

Most colonies of *Volvox* produce both male and female gametes, and fusion is oogamous (see Fig. 17-7). Heterothallism is common. Generally, many or nearly all cells of a colony can divide to produce motile male gametes, whereas only a few cells can differentiate into eggs. Fertilization occurs within the colony; like autocolonies, the zygotes are released when the parent colony decays. Each zygote eventually germinates and develops into a single colony. Generally, a colony reproduces either by forming autocolonies or by producing zygotes, so that the two types of reproductive units do not occur together in one colony (see Fig. 17-6*E*). There are usually more asexual than sexual generations in a given line of sister colonies.

Order Tetrasporales. These green algae presumably descended from motile ancestors by prolongation of the palmelloid stage; filamentous green algae presumably descended from these types by restriction of all or most of cell division to one plane. In the vegetative phase, the cells are non-motile, but each individual cell is capable of developing flagella and becoming motile. Even when non-motile, cells of many species possess structures usually associated with motility, viz., contractile vacuoles and stigmas. The cup-shaped chloroplast of typical vegetative cells is also found in zoospores, which are morphologically similar to chlamydomonads and usually have two, rarely four, flagella.

The majority of representatives have spheroid or ovoid cells that are united in irregular, gelatinous colonies that may grow to macroscopic size; a few types occur as solitary cells or in colonies of distinctive form. Many species of Tetrasporales have been designated that were later recognized as palmelloid stages of other green algae, especially Volvocales.

In Tetrasporales, growth of a colony results from cell division of all individuals within the colony. Reproduction of the colony occurs by fragmentation of the colony, by conversion of one or more cells to flagellated cells that escape and develop into independent colonies, and by formation of zoospores by fission of an individual cell into 2 to 16 spores. Many genera also form akinetes. Sexual processes have been observed in several genera; in all cases, union involves biflagellate isogametes.

Representatives of three genera are illustrated in Figure 17-8.

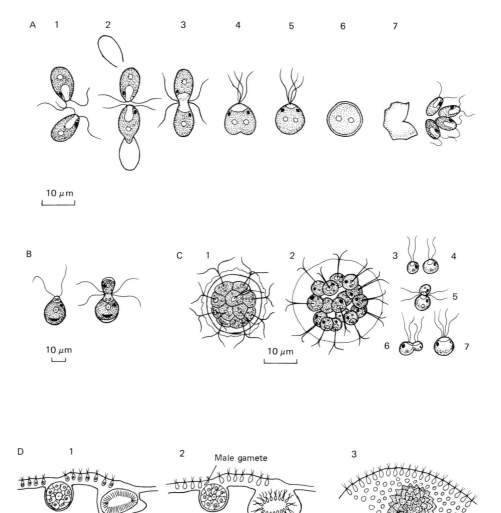

Figure 17-7   Sexual fusions in Volvocales. *A.* Isogamy in *Chlamydomonas snowiae.* (*1*) motile vegetative cells; (*2*) emergence of protoplasts from cell walls; (*3*) copulation; (*4*) fusion of gametes; (*5*) quadriflagellate zygote, motile for a while; (*6*) dormant zygote; (*7*) germination of zygote. *B.* Anisogamy in *Chlamydomonas monadina. Left,* vegetative cell; *right,* fusion of gametes. *C.* Anisogamy in *Pandorina morum.* (*1*) vegetative colony (a hollow sphere); (*2*) a colony of female gametes; (*3*) a male gamete; (*4*) a female gamete; (*5*) copulation; (*6*) fusion of gametes; (*7*) quadriflagellate zygote. *D.* Oogamy in *Volvox* sp. (1) gametangia within a colony; (2) release of male gametes, one male approaching the female gametangium; (3) zygote, an oospore. Mating may be homo- or heterothallic, depending on the species.

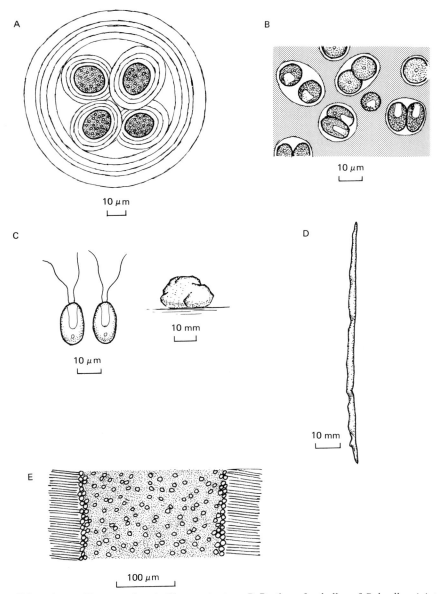

Chlorophyces: Tetrasporales. *A. Gloeocystis gigas. B.* Portion of a thallus of *Palmella miniata,* the **Figure 17-8**
cells embedded in the matrix of the thallus. *C. P. miniata* zoospores. *D. P. miniata* thallus, external
view. *E.* Thallus of *Tetraspora cylindrica;* thalli may be nearly a meter in length. *F.* Portion of
a thallus of *T. cylindrica;* the projections are flagella-like in size and external appearance, but
do not function in locomotion.

337

Orders Ulvales and Ulotrichales. These two orders are sometimes classified as families within one order. The principal distinction between the two groups is the form of the thallus. In Ulvales, cell divisions occur in two perpendicular planes, and cells within a thallus are arranged as a sheet of cells that may be one or more cells thick and flat and membranous or arranged as a hollow tube. The thalli of Ulotrichales are basically filamentous in organization.

Most Ulvales representatives are marine, but some fresh-water forms are included; certain species occur in habitats of various salinities. Two marine organisms are illustrated in Figure 17-9. Any one macroscopic thallus of *Ulva* may be haploid or diploid, since the life cycle involves an alternation of morphologically similar generations. Diploid thalli produce haploid, quadri-flagellate zoospores by meiosis followed by fission of individual vegetative cells. The zoospores develop into haploid thalli that produce haploid, biflagellate gametes. Most species are heterothallic. The zygote germinates shortly after fusion and develops into a diploid thallus. Most species of *Enteromorpha* exhibit life cycles similar to that of *Ulva*.

In Ulotrichales, thalli range in complexity from unbranched filaments only somewhat more regular than chains of cells in certain Tetrasporales representatives, to branched filaments in which zoospores are produced only on secondary, relatively small branches and which do not readily reproduce by fragmentation. Many of the more advanced types develop thalli that are differentiated as prostrate and erect portions.

Sexual processes are known for many genera, and, depending on the genus, union may be isogamous, anisogamous, oogamous with the egg cell released from the thallus, or oogamous with the egg cell retained in an oogonium until fertilized. In the majority of genera, meiosis occurs during germination of the zygote; however, in two genera a diploid generation may occur.

Several genera of Ulotrichales are illustrated in Figures 17-10 and 17-11. The genera *Ulothrix* and *Protococcus* (*Pleurococcus*) are relatively simple in organization. In *Protococcus,* one of the most ubiquitous of algae, reproduction occurs only by cell division; this organism is considered a reduced descendant of a filamentous type of Ulotrichales. In *Ulothrix,* cells other than the basal holdfast cell are undifferentiated and may divide vegetatively or cleave to produce quadriflagellate zoospores or biflagellate gametes. Sexual fusion is isogamous. Reproduction can occur by fragmentation of the filament; fragments that lack a holdfast cell continue development as free-floating organisms.

The thalli of *Stigeoclonium* and *Draparnaldia* are differentiated as prostrate and erect portions. The prostrate portion is typically a mass of interwoven, branched filaments; the erect portions are branched. Reproduction in both genera occurs by production in the secondary branches of quadriflagellate zoospores that swim away from the parent thallus, attach by their anterior poles to solid substrates, and then develop into vegetative thalli. Sexual fusions involve quadriflagellate isogametes.

Coleochaete and *Trentepohlia* represent more advanced types of Ulotrichales. Depending on the species, the thallus of *Coleochaete* may be a branched filament or a flat parenchymatous disc. Reproduction occurs by release of naked

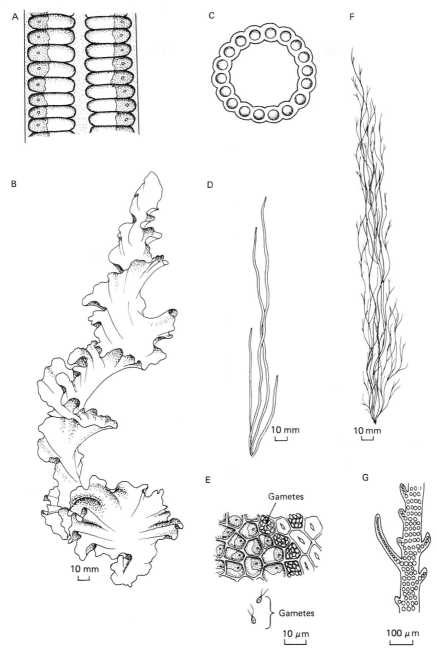

Chlorophyces: Ulvales. *A* and *B. Ulva lactuca. A.* A section showing the two layers of cells and the position of the chloroplasts toward the surface of the thallus. *B.* An entire thallus. *C-G. Enteromorpha* spp. *C.* Transverse section showing single layer of cells arranged as the periphery of a hollow tube. *D. E. intestinalis,* thallus. *E. E. intestinalis,* gamete-producing region of a thallus and freed gametes. *F. E. clathrata,* a young thallus. *G. E. clathrata,* detail of origin of branches.

Figure 17-9

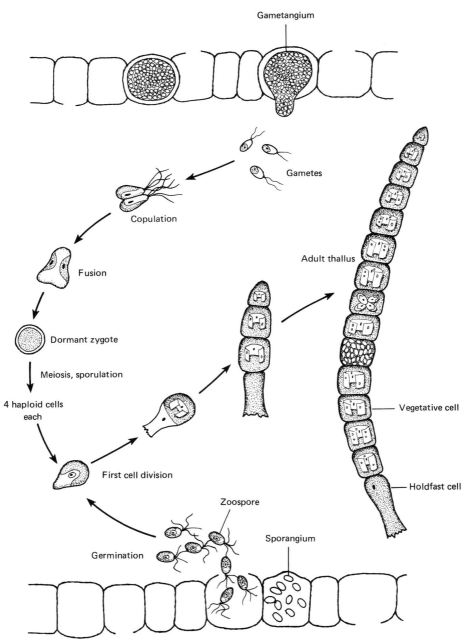

Figure 17-10 Life history of *Ulothrix*. The holdfast cell is a product of the first cell division of a germinating spore; it does not divide.

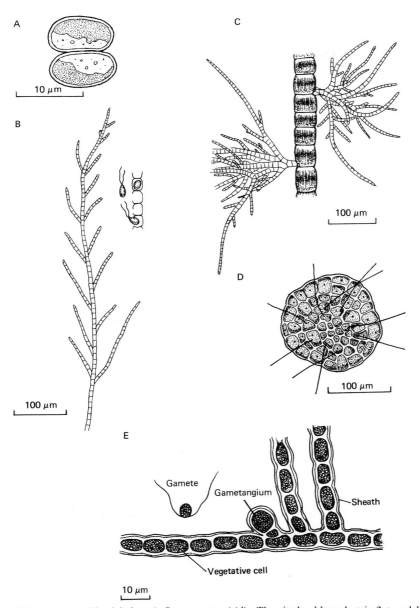

A

10 μm

B

C

100 μm

D

100 μm

100 μm

E

Gamete

Gametangium

Sheath

Vegetative cell

10 μm

Chlorophyces: Ulotrichales. *A. Protococcus viridis.* The single chloroplast is flat and lies at the periphery of the protoplast. *B. Stigeoclonium tenue.* A portion of a filament and release of zoospores. *C. Draparnaldia glomerata. D. Coleochaete scutata.* The function of the cellular projections characteristic of this genus is not known. *E. Trentepohlia aurea.*

Figure 17-11

341

zoospores, formed one per vegetative cell; after a brief period of motility, the spore constructs a cell wall and develops into a vegetative thallus. Sexual fusions are oogamous and involve motile male gametes produced on special branches or within cells at a particular location on a discoid thallus. The egg cells occur individually within oogonia derived by differentiation of cells at the tips of short branches. Fertilization occurs within the oogonium. In most species, branches grow around the fertilized oogonium and form a fruiting structure that persists through the winter. Germination occurs in the spring accompanied by meiosis.

Trentepohlia typically occurs in wet aerial habitats and may form extensive patches on tree trunks or stones. The growth is often orange due to the presence of hematochrome and large amounts of beta-carotene. In warm climates this alga is associated with a fungus as the lichen (see Chap. 21) *"Coenogonium."* When growing independently, the thallus comprises a prostrate portion and an erect, usually branched portion. Reproduction occurs by differentiation of terminal branch cells into sporangia, which are shed and disseminated by air currents. When moistened, the sporangia produce quadriflagellate zoospores, or sometimes aplanospores.

Order Oedogoniales. The order Oedogoniales includes branched and un-branched filamentous forms. Most representatives are fresh-water organisms that occur attached or, if derived from a colonial fragment, free-floating; some are terrestrial. Reproduction is typically by means of zoospores formed singly within vegetative cells. Each spore possesses a colorless anterior pole around which occurs a whorl of flagella. In most instances, the spore attaches to a substrate by its anterior pole and then develops into a vegetative filament.

Sexual processes in each genus are similar to those illustrated in Figure 17-12 for *Oedogonium;* see also Figure 17-13. Union is oogamous; most representatives are hermaphroditic, and these may be homo- or heterothallic. In a few species, any individual thallus produces only male or only female gametes. Depending on the species, male gametes are produced in small cells within the filament or in apical cells of dwarf male filaments derived from specialized zoospores that attach to or near a female cell.

Order Cladophorales. These are filamentous algae composed of multinucleate cells; branching of filaments occurs in all genera. Genera are distinguished mainly by the manner in which branches arise and also differ in the form of the rhizoids (Fig. 17-14*D*) that mediate their attachment to substrates. All genera occur in water as sessile forms or as masses that lie on the bottom of shallow bodies of water. The filaments are not covered by gelatinous material. As a consequence, they are particularly suitable as substrates for the attachment of epiphytic organisms, particularly smaller algae. Representatives of most genera can be found in both fresh and sea water, but two (*Chaetomorpha* and *Spongomorpha*) occur only in marine environments.

The multinucleate cylindric cell characteristic of this order contains a single reticulate chloroplast or, less commonly, numerous discoid chloroplasts. Occa-

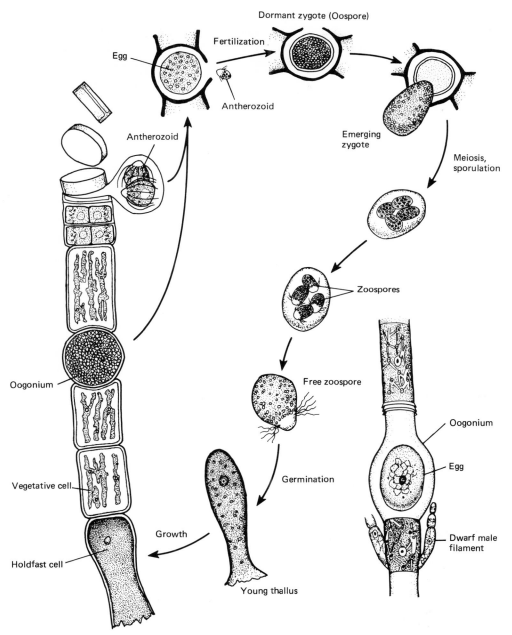

Sexual events in *Oedogonium*. *Lower right*, sexual development as in species in which dwarf male **Figure 17-12** filaments are formed.

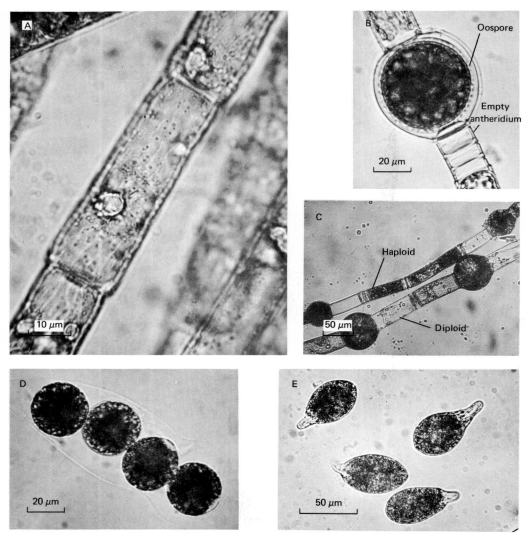

Figure 17-13 *Oedogonium foveolatum.* A. Vegetative cells, with parietal, laminate chloroplast, within a filament. B. An oospore and three empty antheridia in a haploid strain. Oospore germination occurs only in the light. C. Haploid and diploid filaments. Most strains isolated from nature are haploid, but diploid strains are encountered occasionally. Diploid strains can be produced under artificial conditions that interfere with meiosis during oospore germination (see Fig. 17-12) or as a consequence of spontaneous (i.e., unexplained) chromosome doubling in vegetative cells. D. Emergence of zoospores. The flagella become active before the spores emerge. E. An early stage in the germination of zoospores. (*A* and *C* courtesy of L. R. Hoffman. *B, D,* and *E* from Hoffman, L. R., 1965. *Amer. J. Botany,* **52:**173. By permission of the Botanical Society of America and the *American Journal of Botany.*)

344

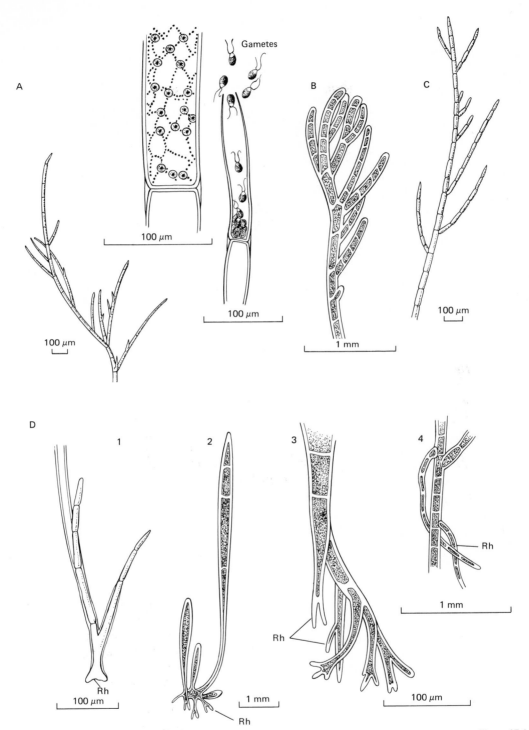

Chlorophyces: Cladophorales. *A. Cladophora kuetzingianum.* Portion of a filament, portion of a vegetative cell, and release of gametes. *B. C. trichotoma,* a coarse-filament species. *C. C. albida,* a delicate-filament species. *D.* Rhizoids (*Rh*) in (*1*) *Basicladia chelonum,* (*2*) *Chaetomorpha antennina,* (*3*) *Urospora penicilliformis,* and (*4*) *Spongomorpha arcta.*

Figure 17-14

345

sionally, both types can be found in one filament, reticulate chloroplasts occurring in younger cells. The chloroplast lies at the periphery of the protoplast, the nuclei lie internal to the chloroplast, and the central portion of the cell is occupied by a large vacuole that may be traversed by cytoplasmic strands.

Reproduction occurs by fragmentation and by production of quadriflagellate zoospores usually formed in large numbers by progressive cleavage of the protoplast of a vegetative cell. In some genera, cell division occurs throughout the filament, except in the basal cell, and zoospores may arise from any cell. In other genera (e.g., *Cladophora,* Fig. 17-14*A–C*), cell division occurs predominantly in apical regions, and zoospores are formed only from cells near the ends of branches. Aplanospores and akinetes also occur.

Sexual fusions involve biflagellate isogametes, which are formed in a manner similar to zoospores; many species are heterothallic. Depending on the genus or, in *Cladophora,* on the species, the life cycle may involve an alternation of generations of similar morphology. In *Urospora,* meiosis occurs during germination of the zygote, and all adult thalli are haploid. In one species of *Cladophora* (*C. glomerata*), adult thalli are diploid, but they may be asexual and produce diploid zoospores, or sexual and produce gametes. The asexual and sexual generations alternate regularly; the former arises from zygotes, the latter from zoospores.

Order Zygnematales. These are green fresh-water algae that seem to represent a phylogenetic line independent of the other three orders that include filamentous forms. The order includes unbranched filamentous forms and unicellular forms that usually occur as solitary individuals, but may accumulate in small colonies when gelatinous sheaths are present and confluent. The order is distinguished among green algae of these general morphologic types by the absence of flagellated cells and by the fusion of ameboid gametes.

Individual cells are typically uninucleate and possess one or two (rarely more) chloroplasts. In types with only one, the chloroplast is usually laminate; it may be situated centrally along the long axis of the cell or wound into a helix at the periphery of the protoplast. In types with two, the chloroplasts are commonly stellate.

Sexual fusions have been observed in many representatives. The protoplasts of vegetative cells serve as gametes. Union of gametes may occur within a conjugation tube formed between mating cells, or one gamete may migrate through the tube into the other cell. In filamentous types, nearly all the cells within each of a pair of filaments may fuse; when union occurs within one cell rather than within the tube, generally one filament behaves as recipient and the other as donor. In typical desmids (see Fig. 17-16), mating cells become associated and produce a common gelatinous matrix into which the protoplasts are released and within which they fuse. The zygotes are dormant, and meiosis occurs during their germination.

Conjugating filaments of *Spirogyra* are illustrated in Figure 17-15*G–E;* the mature zygotes are contained within the receptive filament. In typical desmids (Fig. 17-16), the wall is constricted at the equator of the cell, and the protoplast

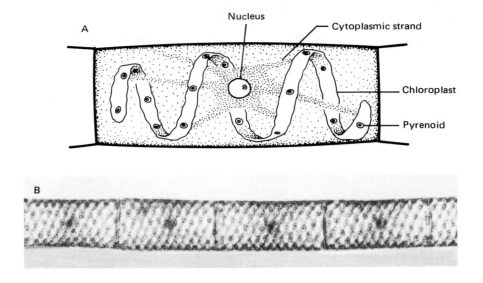

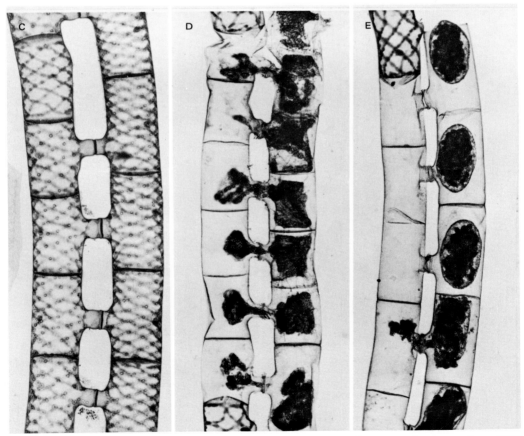

Spirogyra. A. Diagram of a vegetative cell. *B.* A vegetative filament. *C-E.* Three successive stages in conjugation. *C.* Formation of fertilization tubes between conjugating filaments. *D.* Migration of protoplasts (gametes) from donor to recipient filament. *E.* Young zygotes in recipient filament. (*B-E* Courtesy Carolina Biological Supply Company.)

Figure 17-15

347

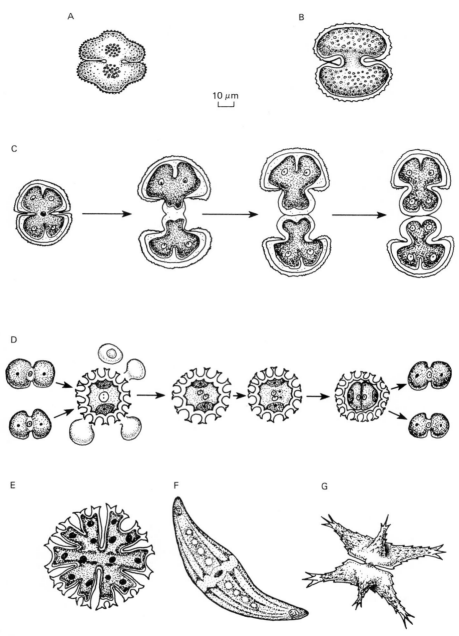

Figure 17-16 Chlorophyces: Unicellular Zygnematales (Desmids). *A. Cosmarium protractum. B. C. reniforme. C.* Successive stages in fission in *Cosmarium;* growth occurs in the newer semicell of each fission product. *D.* Successive stages in conjugation in *Cosmarium.* In most species, there are two chloroplasts per gamete and four in the zygote, two of which disintegrate as the zygote matures. The zygote nucleus divides twice (presumably reductively); two of the products of nuclear division disintegrate before germination. *E. Micrasterias crux-melitensis. F. Closterium ehrenbergii. G. Staurastrum anatinum.*

consists of two semicells united by an isthmus of protoplasm within the constriction. Binary fission occurs at the constriction; growth of each progeny regenerates a semicell (see Fig. 17-16C).

Order Chlorococcales. These green algae are non-motile unicellular and non-
filamentous colonial types that reproduce by production of zoospores, autospores, or both. Colonies arise by confluence of cell envelopes or as autocolonies.

The cells of the majority of uninucleate representatives contain one cup-
shaped chloroplast. In a few types, one or more laminate chloroplasts are
present and lie at the periphery of the protoplast. Multinucleate cells usually
contain either one large, reticulate chloroplast or a number of small, discoid
chloroplasts.

In several genera, autocolonies called coenobia are produced by aggregation
of the spores produced from the protoplast of a vegetative cell. Aggregation
may occur within the parent cell or within a vesicle in which the clone of spores
is released from the parent. This process is typical of one family (Hydro-
dictyaceae), in which a large number of zoospores is formed within an individual cell. The spores are released within a vesicle, within which they swarm
for a while. Eventually, the cells align in a pattern characteristic of the species,
cease motility, construct cell walls, and become united as a colony. Then the
vesicle ruptures, and the new colony is released and begins growth. Further
cell divisions do not occur; nuclear division may occur, and cells within a colony
may be multinucleate.

Most Chlorococcales are fresh-water, planktonic forms, but others occur in
snow fields, in soil, and in aerial habitats. One genus (*Chlorella*) in particular
is found in associations with other organisms, often invertebrate animals and
protozoa, where the algae (called zoochlorellae; see Chap. 21) may grow
intracellularly. One family comprises algae that grow among the cells of leaves
of green plants and in marine algae. A few representatives are illustrated in
Figures 17-17 to 17-20.

The organisms illustrated in Figures 17-18 and 17-19 reproduce by releasing
coenobia. The coenobia of *Hydrodictyon* are formed from zoospores, those of
Scenedesmus from autospores.

The organisms illustrated in Figure 17-20 represent a single large family of
Chlorococcales that reproduce by production of autospores that do not unite
in autocolonies. Zoospores are not formed; some representatives form akinetes.
Genera are distinguished by morphologic features of individual cells or of
colonies. About 30 genera are recognized, and representatives can be found
in a wide variety of habitats.

Order Siphonales. Siphonales representatives are typically coenocytic. The
protoplasm is usually contained as a peripheral sheet surrounding a large
central vacuole, which may be continuous throughout the cell or traversed by
protoplasmic strands. Numerous discoid chloroplasts occur in the peripheral

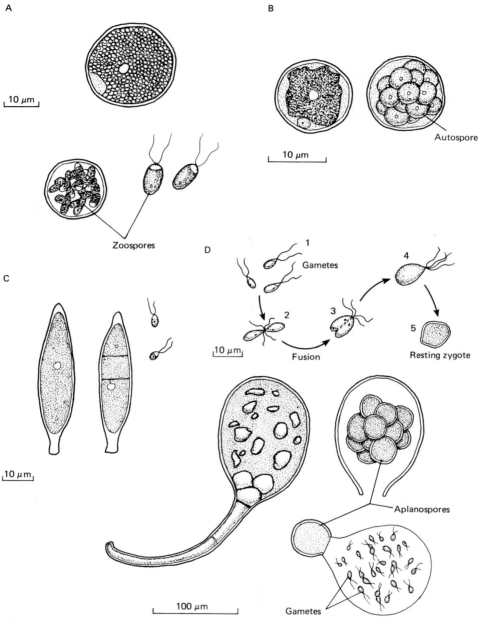

Figure 17-17 Chlorophyces: Chlorococcales. *A. Chlorococcum humicola.* Vegetative cell, cell with zoospores, and zoospores. *B. Trebouxia cladoniae.* Vegetative cell and cell with autospores. *C. Characium angustatum.* Vegetative cell, early stage of cleavage, and zoospores. *D. Protosiphon botryoides.* Vegetative cell, cell with aplanospores, a germinating aplanospore releasing gametes, and (1)–(5), successive stages in zygote formation.

350

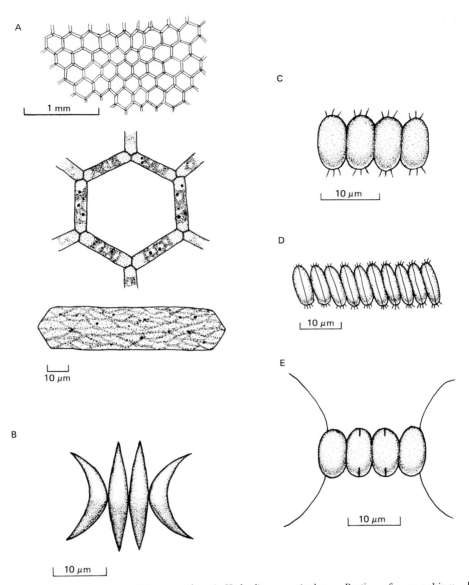

Chlorophyces: Coenobial Chlorococcales. *A. Hydrodictyon reticulatum.* Portion of a coenobium, **Figure 17-18** a group of young cells, and an older (larger) cell. *B-E. Scenedesmus* spp. (See also Fig. 17-19). *B. S. dimorphus. C. S. denticulatus. D. S. brasiliensis. E. S. armatus.*

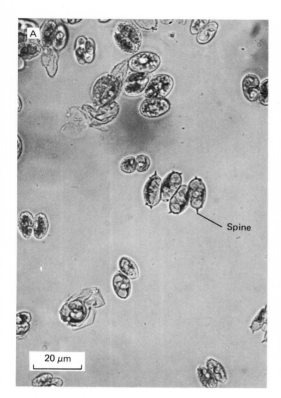

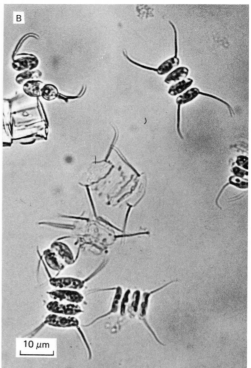

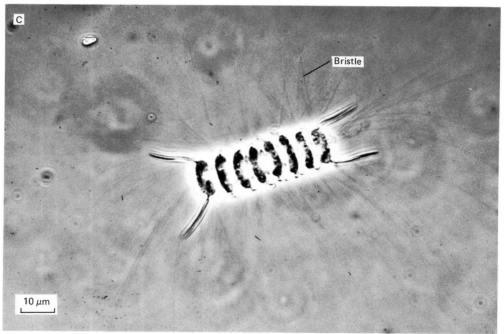

Figure 17-19 *Scenedesmus* spp. In this study, morphology of pure cultures was found to vary in many isolates according to environmental conditions and age of the culture. This implies that morphology alone is an insufficient basis for distinguishing species of *Scenedesmus*. *A*. An isolate in which the number of cells per coenobium and the presence of spines were variable. The cells were typically arranged alternately, as here. *B*. An isolate that showed morphologic features of three different species (*quadricauda, longispina,* and *armatus*). Here, it looks like *S. quadricauda*. *C*. An isolate that showed morphologic features of three different species (*longispina, armatus,* and *semipulcher*). This eight-celled coenobium possesses more than 100 bristles of unknown function. (From Trainor, F. R., 1966. *Amer. J. Botany,* **53**:995. By permission of the Botanical Society of America and the *American Journal of Botany*.)

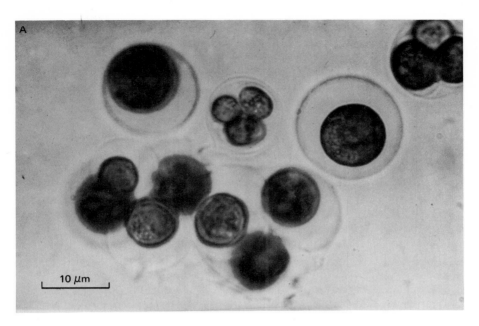

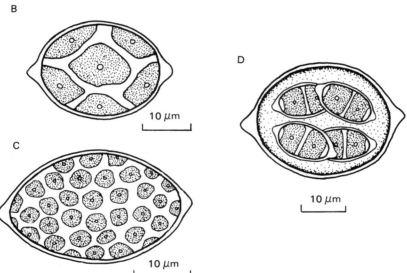

Chlorophyces: Immotile Chlorococcales. *A. Chlorella* sp. (Courtesy of P. Hirsch.) *B–D. Oocystis* **Figure 17-20** spp. *B. O. crassa. C. O. eremosphaeria. D. O. lacustris.*

protoplasm. The chloroplasts of all representatives that have been examined contain a xanthophyll peculiar to this group and called siphonoxanthin.

The single cell may grow to macroscopic dimensions and be externally differentiated in a variety of forms. Septation may occur by ingrowth of the cell wall to delimit reproductive structures or decaying portions of the thallus. The majority of representatives are marine, although two families include fresh-water types.

Reproduction only rarely occurs by production of zoospores or aplanospores. The more complex forms generally can reproduce by fragmentation, but sexual cycles provide the principal means of reproduction. In most types, sexual union involves flagellated anisogametes or, less commonly, isogametes; in one genus (*Dichotomosiphon*), union is oogamous. Most types are diploid in the vegetative phase; meiosis occurs during gamete formation.

A few representatives of this order that exemplify the variety of forms among these coenocytic algae are illustrated in Figure 17-21.

Division Euglenophyces (Euglenids)

The euglenids are unicellular flagellated algae of distinctive morphology that are frequently encountered in nature. They are particularly common in stagnant waters or other water with a high content of organic materials. Many representatives are colorless; besides lacking chloroplasts, they may also lack stigmas, which occur in most photosynthetic representatives. Two genera of euglenids are illustrated in Figure 17-22.

The cells do not possess walls. The outer surface of the cell membrane is differentiated as a pellicle that is often ornamented. The pellicle may be quite rigid, so that the cell has a constant shape, or so flexible that the cell shape changes as the cell moves. The protoplast typically contains one nucleus, one or two contractile vacuoles, one red stigma, and—in photosynthetic types— numerous small discoid chloroplasts. The anterior pole of the cell is invaginated; the invagination, called the gullet, is usually flask-shaped, with the narrower end (the neck) anterior to the wider end (the reservoir). The basal bodies of the flagella lie within the protoplast immediately internal to the reservoir, and the flagella extend through the reservoir to the exterior. There may be one, two, or three flagella; in several types originally described as uniflagellate, however, it has been found that there is a second flagellum that is short and does not emerge from the reservoir. Fluid from the contractile vacuoles is expelled into the reservoir, which apparently only passively releases the fluid to the exterior. In a few genera, the gullet is surrounded by pharyngeal rods similar to those of flagellate protozoa.

The majority of euglenids, whether or not photosynthetic, can assimilate organic substances, and many require them (particularly acetate) even for photosynthetic development. Several types can ingest particulate food through transient openings adjacent to (but not within) the gullet.

Reproduction occurs by longitudinal binary fission, which may occur while the cell is in motion or after it has come to rest and secreted a mucilaginous

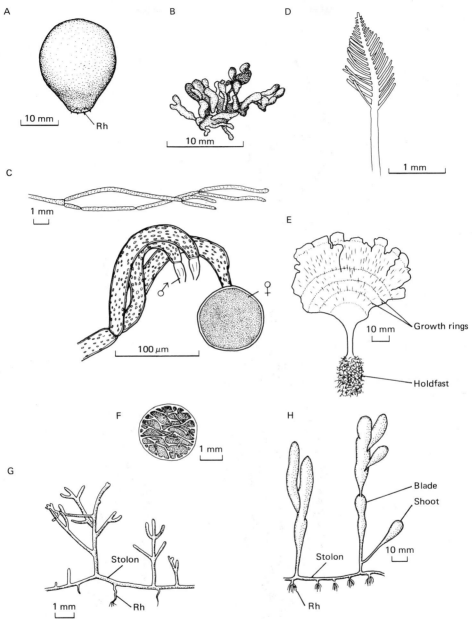

Chlorophyces: Siphonales. *A. Valonia ventricosa,* with unicellular rhizoids (*Rh*). *B.* Cluster of cells **Figure 17-21** of *Valonia aegagropila. C.* Portion of a thallus and detail of sexual structures of *Dichotomosiphon tuberosus,* a fresh-water form. *D. Bryopsis pennata,* upper portion of a thallus. *E. Udotea flabellum,* entire thallus. *F–H. Caulerpa* spp. *F.* Transverse section of axis showing network of internal filaments ("trabeculae"). *G. C. fastigiata.* Portion of a thallus with prostrate portion (stolon), erect branches, and rhizoids (*Rh*). *H. C. prolifera,* portion of a thallus with stolon, erect blades, rhizoids (*Rh*), and shoots. The shoots can separate from the parent thallus and develop as independent thalli.

355

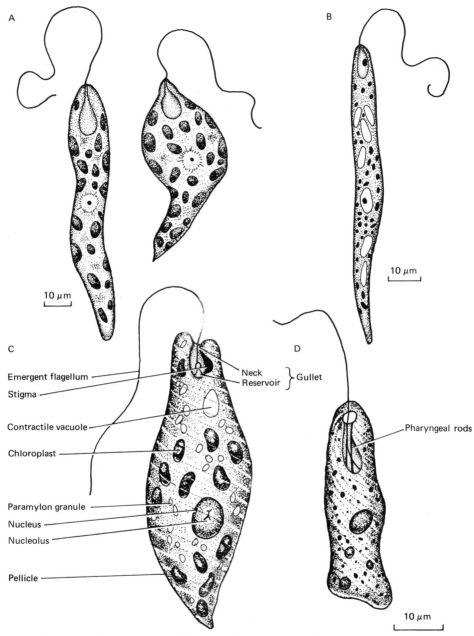

A

B

C

Emergent flagellum ——
Stigma ——

Neck
Reservoir

⎱
⎰ Gullet

Contractile vacuole ——

Chloroplast ——

D

Pharyngeal rods

Paramylon granule ——
Nucleus ——
Nucleolus ——

Pellicle ——

10 μm

Figure 17-22 Euglenophyces (see also Fig. 6-12). *A. Euglena intermedia,* a species in which the pellicle is delicate and flexible and cell shape changes during locomotion. *B. Euglena acus. C.* Diagram of a generalized photosynthetic euglenid. *D. Peranema trichoforum,* a colorless type.

envelope. In the latter case, palmelloid stages of short duration may arise. In one genus, the palmelloid stage is the principal vegetative phase; further evolution of euglenids toward multicellular organization has not occurred. Dormant cysts are formed by all types.

Euglenids seem intermediate between algae and protozoa, since they possess a combination of properties, especially photosynthetic capacity and ability to ingest, which are generally regarded as suitable for distinguishing the two types of protists. Photosynthetic euglenids are among the algae that can be bleached experimentally; however, neither colorless derivatives nor naturally occurring colorless counterparts can be induced to revert to phototrophy.

Division Chrysophyces (Golden Algae)

In many classification systems established before ca. 1960, this division also included Xanthophyces and Bacillariophyces. On the basis of the findings that the arrays of pigments vary among the three groups, they are now classified as separate divisions.

The three divisions do, however, share certain peculiar traits; these include the storage of foods as chrysolaminarin ("leucosin") and the formation of a dormant stage called a statospore. This type of spore is formed by nearly all types of golden algae, by centric diatoms, and by ameboid yellow-green algae.

The statospore is formed by delimitation of part of the protoplast of a vegetative cell within a membrane derived from the cell membrane. Generally, as the spore is completed, the remainder of the protoplast degenerates with the cell wall, and the spore is liberated; in one genus (*Chromulina*) of Chrysophyces, the excluded protoplasm migrates into the spore wall before the wall is closed. Statospores are typically uninucleate and dormant. Upon germination, the naked protoplast emerges and is motile by ameboid motion or may develop flagella.

The division Chrysophyces comprises predominantly flagellated and some ameboid organisms that occur singly or in colonies. The cells of these types are naked; the surface of the flagellated cell may be somewhat rigid due to presence of a pellicle. The naked ameboid types can ingest particulate foods by means of pseudopodia. Non-motile coccoid and filamentous types are also included in the division; these possess definite cell walls. Cells of golden algae generally are uninucleate and contain one or two, rarely many, chromatophores.

The flagella of vegetative and reproductive cells invariably occur at the anterior pole of the cell, but the number and length of flagella vary; there may be one, two (of equal or of unequal length), or three flagella per cell. These variations are reported for motile cells of single species, except that three flagella regularly occur in one family only.

The flagellates and amebae reproduce principally by binary fission, which is longitudinal in the flagellates; some of the amebae also form zoospores. The other types produce zoospores as one means of reproduction. Colonies can be regenerated from fragments or, in palmelloid forms, produced from individual flagellated cells.

Motile and non-motile Chrysophyces are illustrated in Figures 17-23 and 17-24.

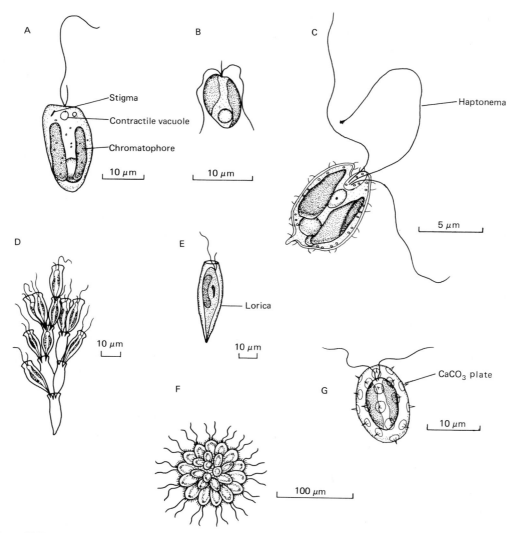

Figure 17-23 Chrysophyces: Flagellated types. *A. Ochromonas mutabilis.* A stigma is not always present and, depending on the species, there may be one or two chromatophores. *B. Prymnesium parvum.* The central, short appendage does not function in locomotion. Blooms of this species, with up to 500,000 cells per milliliter, are toxic for gill-breathing aquatic animals. *C. Chrysochromulina chiton.* The haptonema functions as an organelle of reversible attachment to submerged surfaces. *D. Dinobryon sertularia,* a colony of loricate individuals. *E. Dinobryon utriculus,* a solitary loricate individual. *F. Synura uvella.* Reproduction of individuals occurs by longitudinal fission of cells, and of colonies by subdivision of one into two colonies. *G. Syracosphaera* sp. The CaCO$_3$ plates are embedded in a secreted membrane. Typically marine.

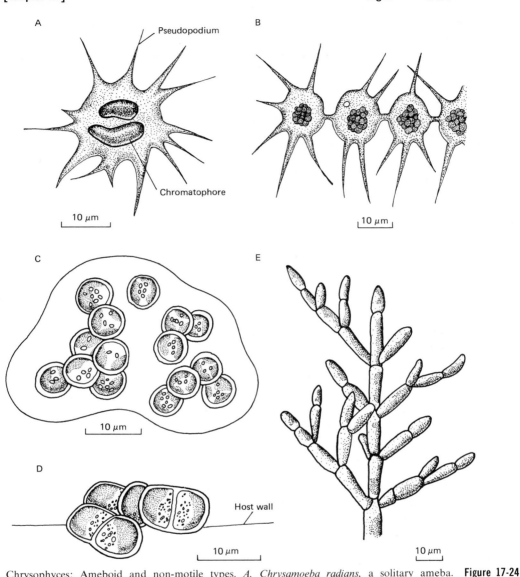

Chrysophyces: Ameboid and non-motile types. *A. Chrysamoeba radians,* a solitary ameba. **Figure 17-24**
B. Chrysidiastrum catenatum. There may be 2 to 16 amebae per colony, each with a single chromatophore. *C. Chrysocapsa planctonica. D. Epichrysis paludosa,* found on the surface of aquatic
plants. *E. Phaeothamnion confervicola.*

Division Bacillariophyces (Diatoms)

The diatoms possess cell walls composed of an organic, possibly pectic, base
in or on which hydrated amorphous polymerized silicic acid (silica) is deposited.
The wall consists of two parts, called **valves,** of not quite equal size and of
similar shape; the valves are united by a girdle that is less silicified and more

flexible than the valves. Typically, the valves are flattened, and one valve is slightly larger than the other; it overlaps the smaller valve like a lid on a box (Fig. 17-25A). Within the wall is a single protoplast that is typically uninucleate. The chromatophores of all types are brown or golden brown.

The two valves of the rigid, silicified wall of a diatom cell are formed in different generations. Cell division typically occurs as follows. The subcellular organelles are duplicated and migrate—if necessary—so that one set of duplicates lies within each valve. The protoplast then divides in a plane parallel to the flat (valve) surface of the cell. Each valve then contains one protoplast. Each protoplast then begins to construct a new silica valve on its surface adjacent to the other protoplast (Fig. 17-25B); completion of the valve is the final step in cell division.

The newer valve of any diatom cell is invariably the smaller valve, because it is constructed within the confines of the older valve. In some types, this results in a progressive decrease in the size of some of the cells in a reproducing population. The size approaches a minimum which is characteristic of the species, at which point the cells undergo auxospore formation (see below). In other diatoms, a fairly constant size is maintained by one of two mechanisms: (1) increase in size of the older valve to the maximum characteristic of the species so that the newer valve is not smaller than either valve of the parent cell; and (2) movement of the newly forming valve outward within the flexible girdle so that it is not significantly smaller than the older valve.

Auxospore formation occurs in all types of diatoms, although the frequency and details of the process vary in different types. In most forms, it occurs in cells of a particular size, which is small relative to the maximum size of the species. Because of this, it is generally interpreted as a means of re-establishing maximum size; it is also regarded as a rejuvenating process—one that allows internal reorganization while the protoplasm is not constrained within a size-limiting wall. The auxospore, or growth spore, is naked when first formed. It increases in size until considerably larger than vegetative cells and then constructs a siliceous wall. The protoplast then subdivides into protoplasts of maximum size. Each of these constructs a typical wall with two valves and is released when the auxospore wall disarticulates.

In one major subgroup of diatoms, viz., the centric diatoms (see Table 17-3), the auxospore is derived from a single vegetative protoplast that sheds its wall. In a few centric diatoms, it has been observed that, before the cell wall is shed, the nucleus of the cell divides twice; two of the progeny nuclei degenerate, and the other two fuse to become the auxospore nucleus. Apparently, the nuclear division is reductive, and the vegetative and auxospore nuclei are diploid.

In the second major group, the pennate diatoms, auxospore formation is usually a sexual process. Two vegetative cells become embedded in a common mass of gelatinous material and orient toward each other in a manner characteristic of the species (side by side, side to end, or end to end). Meiosis occurs in each cell. In some types, three of the four meiotic products disintegrate and each vegetative cell is transformed into a haploid gamete. In other forms, only

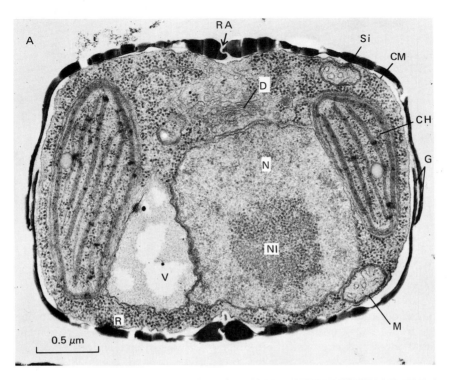

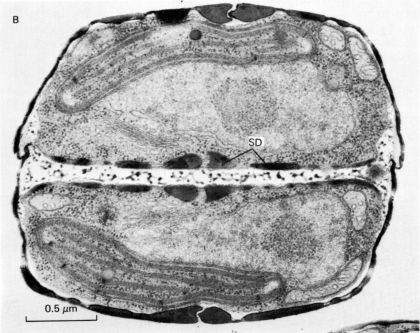

Bacillariophyces: *Navicula pelliculosa,* a fresh-water pennate diatom. *CH,* chromatophore; *D,* **Figure 17-25** dictyosome; *G,* girdle bands; *M,* mitochondrion; *N,* nucleus; *Nl,* nucleolus; *CM,* cell membrane; *RA,* raphe; *R,* ribosomes; *Si,* silica; *V,* vacuole. *A.* Transverse section. *B.* Transverse section of a dividing cell. Silica deposits (*SD*) appear at the site of formation of the new cell wall. (Courtesy of M. L. Chiappino and B. E. Volcani.)

TABLE 17-3.   Distinguishing Characteristics of Centric and Pennate Diatoms

	Centrobacillariophyceae	*Pennatibacillariophyceae*
Symmetry of ornamentation	Radial	Bilateral
Motility (vegetative cells)	Absent	Present in higher forms
Production of		
Statospores	Occurs	Does not occur
Microspores	Occurs	Does not occur
Auxospores	Occurs without cell fusions	Occurs following cell fusions
Typical number of chromatophores/cell	Many	Two; one or many in a few forms
Distribution	Predominantly marine, planktonic; a few exceptions	Wide: floating or sessile in fresh and sea water; in soils; in aerial habitats

two nuclei degenerate; the cell divides into two haploid gametes. The gametes emerge from the cell walls and fuse in pairs to become auxospores; the nuclei fuse, and the auxospores and their vegetative progeny are diploid.

Two other types of spores are formed by centric diatoms. Statospores (described in the section on Chrysophyces) occur in many types, but their germination has not been observed. The third type of spore is much smaller than a vegetative cell and bears one or two flagella. These microspores are produced by repeated binary fissions or by cleavage of a vegetative protoplast; one cell may produce 8 to 128 microspores.

The majority of diatoms occur as single cells or in colonies of more or less regular form in which the cells are embedded in a common mass of gelatinous material. In some diatoms, there are one or two small openings in each valve through which the gelatinous material that unites the cells is extruded. In a few types, the new valves formed after cell division remain attached to each other, and chains of cells accumulate. Diatoms that exist naturally as sessile forms attach to their solid substrates by means of gelatinous materials that are sometimes elongated and serve as stalks.

In the colder regions of the oceans, diatoms comprise the majority of planktonic algae and are the principal producers of organic material on which animals depend for their growth. Fresh-water forms are also somewhat more abundant in cooler waters; in temperate zones, they are present in greater numbers in spring and autumn than in summer. Some diatoms occur in terrestrial habitats; the vegetative cells of these types are resistant to desiccation and may survive in a dried state for several years.

The classification of diatoms at all taxonomic levels is based on the structure of the silica walls, called **frustules.** As illustrated in Figures 17-26*A* and 17-27, intricate sculpturings occur on the walls; these patterns are infinite in variety, and each pattern is characteristic of the walls of a species. The first subdivision of Bacillariophyces is based on the type of symmetry displayed by the ornamentation on the surface of the valve. Two classes are distinguished: Centro-bacillariophyceae, in which the symmetry is radial, and Pennatibacillari-ophyceae, in which the symmetry is bilateral. The basic symmetry is correlated with several other characteristics, as indicated in Table 17-3. Diatoms are illustrated in Figures 17-26 to 17-28.

The sagittal line of symmetry of pennate diatoms may be smooth, the ornamentation of the wall beginning on either side of the median strip; such a strip is called a pseudoraphe. In certain diatoms, the strip is slotted, and the protoplast communicates with the exterior through the slot; such an open strip is called a raphe. The raphe is invariably associated with gliding motility, and it seems that locomotion of vegetative diatom cells is accomplished by a flowing of cytoplasm along the raphe.

Division Xanthophyces (Yellow-Green Algae)

The algae placed in the division Xanthophyces are informally referred to as yellow-green or as heterokont algae. The former designation indicates the typical color of the chromatophores; the latter indicates the flagellation of a motile cell, which bears two flagella of unequal length. The longer, tinsel-type flagellum functions as a locomotor organelle. The shorter, whiplash-type flagellum is apparently passive and trails along the surface of the cell.

The majority of yellow-green algae are coccoid or ellipsoid cells that occur as individuals, as palmelloid colonies, or as colonies of cells situated at the tips of gelatinous branches. A smaller number of yellow-green algae occur that are almost as varied morphologically as are green algae. Some are flagellated and motile as adults; these may be walled cells or cells that have flexible surfaces and can produce pseudopodia. A few representatives are filamentous; they do not exhibit any differentiation within the chain of cells. Two genera include coenocytic forms; in one, the thallus is vesicular, in the other tubular.

Reproduction of colonial and filamentous types can occur by fragmentation. Ameboid types can reproduce by fission to give rise to two or more amebae, which may be flagellated. In addition, all yellow-green algae can produce zoospores, which usually contain at least one contractile vacuole and one to a few chromatophores. The number of zoospores produced by an individual cell varies from 1 to 200 or more, depending on the size of the cell at the time the protoplast cleaved.

Two other types of spores are produced by yellow-green algae. Most types can produce aplanospores, which are formed in the same manner as are zoospores. These types of spores are to some degree interconvertible; zoospores retained unusually long in the sporangium may become non-motile, and aplanospores of many types can alternatively germinate and develop into vegetative cells or produce zoospores. Filamentous forms also develop akinetes, which occur only rarely among non-filamentous forms.

Sexual processes have been reported in several types. Fusion is isogamous in filamentous types, isogamous or anisogamous in vesicular types, and oogamous (and homothallic) in tubular types. The zygote of the third type

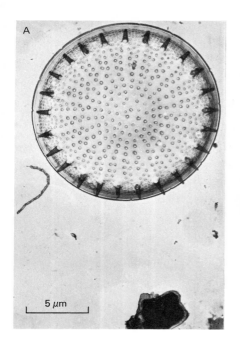

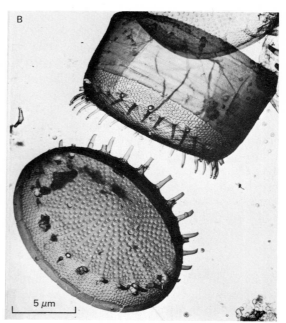

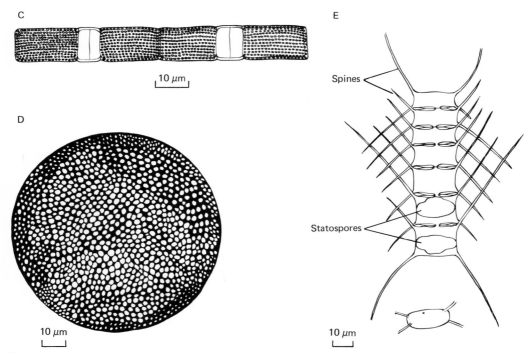

Spines

Statospores

Figure 17-26 Bacillariophyces: Centric diatoms. *A* and *B. Stephanodiscus hantzschii* frustules. (From Drum, R. W., 1969. *Österr. Bot. Zeit.*, **116:**321. By permission of Springer-Verlag, Berlin, Heidelberg, New York.) *C. Melosira granulata*, side view of two cylindric cells of a chain. *D. Coscinodiscus radiatus*, view of valve surface. *E. Chaetoceros elmorei.* Side view of a chain of cells. *Below,* valve view of a cell.

364

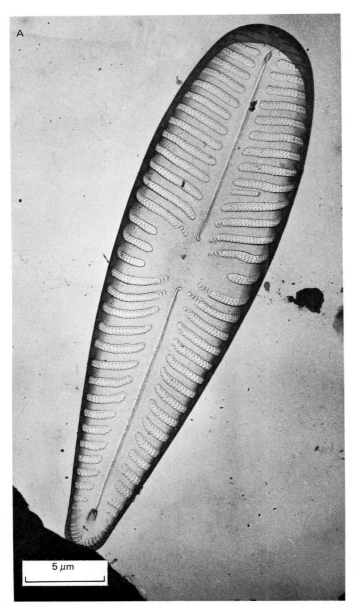

5 μm

B

5 μm

Bacillariophyces: Frustules of pennate diatoms. *A. Gomphonema olivaceum.* (From Drum, R. W., 1969. *Österr. Bot. Zeit.,* **116:**321. By permission of Springer-Verlag, Berlin, Heidelberg, New York.) *B. Nitzschia palea.* (From Drum, R. W., 1963. *J. Cell Biol.,* **18:**429. By permission of The Rockefeller University Press.)

Figure 17-27

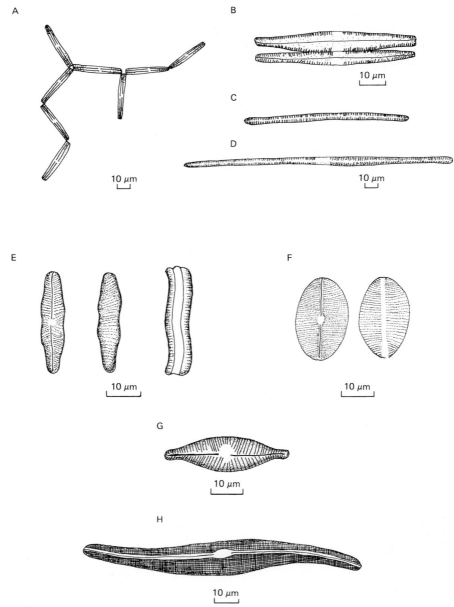

Figure 17-28 Bacillariophyces: Pennate diatoms. *A–D*. Family Fragilariaceae. *A. Tabellaria fenestrata,* a small colony. *B. Fragilaria crotonensis,* two cells of a chain. *C. Synedra splendens. D. S. subaequalis. E–F.* Family Achnanthaceae. *E. Achnanthes coarctata. Left to right,* surface of lower valve, surface of upper valve, girdle view. *F. Cocconeis pediculus. Left,* surface of lower valve; *right,* surface of upper valve. *G–H.* Family Naviculaceae. *G. Navicula rhyncocephala. H. Gyrosigma acuminatum.*

is dormant for several months, whereas the others can germinate shortly after fusion is completed. Apparently, reductive nuclear division occurs during germination of the zygotes; such yellow-green algae, and possibly all types, are haploid in the vegetative stage.

Most representatives of this division are fresh-water organisms. A few representatives occur in soil, and others in aerial habitats. Two examples of unicellular and colonial Xanthophyces are illustrated in Figure 17-29*A* and *B*.

The filamentous types are more commonly encountered in nature than are the simpler forms. They may be unbranched (as in *Tribonema,* Fig. 17-29*C*) or branched. Zoospores are formed within random cells in the filaments; depending on the genus, one to a few spores are formed per cell. The zoospores of some isolates have been observed to behave as isogametes. In *Tribonema,* aplanospores are more commonly formed than are zoospores, but this depends to some extent on the environment; excess water favors zoosporulation. Spores are released by disarticulation of the two parts of the wall; this also separates the filament into two multicellular portions, each of which continues to grow as an independent filament.

Botrydium (Fig. 17-29*D*) is a vesicular coenocytic yellow-green alga. It occurs typically as a soil organism; the vesicle remains on the soil surface, and the rhizoids grow into the substrate, anchoring the organism and absorbing water and dissolved nutrients.

Reproduction in *Botrydium* usually occurs by cleavage of the protoplasm of the vesicle to produce aplanospores. Alternatively, in the presence of water, cleavage results in production of flagellated cells; these are called zoospores, but they can alternatively behave as isogametes. Dormant spores are formed by migration of much of the protoplasm (most of the organelles) into the rhizoids and fragmentation of the rhizoids into thick-walled, unicellular units.

One genus, *Vaucheria* (Fig. 17-29*E*), accommodates all known tubular coenocytic yellow-green algae. The vegetative thallus is an elongated, branched tube within which the multinucleate protoplasm lies along the inner wall of the tube around a highly vacuolated center. The sexual structures are developed as short side branches; the male (antheridia) and female (oogonia) structures develop as adjacent branches, and gametes produced in adjacent structures can fuse. The fertilized egg cell develops a thick wall and becomes dormant; it is eventually released from the parent thallus by disintegration of the oogonial wall.

Septa can be produced to seal broken portions of the thallus, and reproduction can occur by accidental fragmentation of the tube. However, asexual reproduction usually occurs by the production of zoospores at the tips of branches. In most instances, a single zoospore is produced in a chamber separated from the rest of the thallus by a septum. The zoospore is multinucleate and bears two unequal flagella per nucleus. After release from the chamber through a terminal pore, the zoospore is motile for a period and then germinates into a vegetative thallus by producing one or more germ tubes.

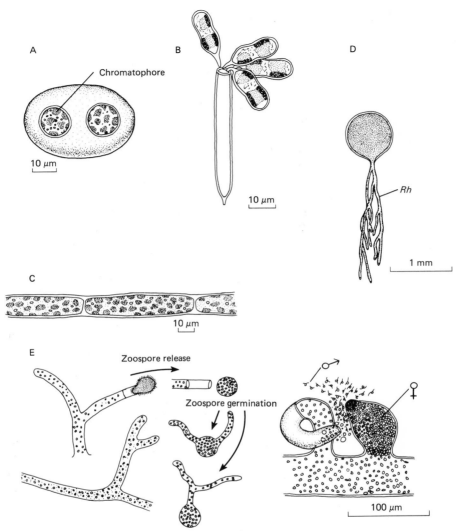

Figure 17-29 Xanthophyces. *A. Chlorobotrys regularis.* The cell wall of this organism is silicified and consists of two overlapping halves. *B. Ophiocytium arbusculum.* A colony results when zoospores attach to the open end of the parental cell wall, which disarticulates to release the spores. Spores that leave the parent cell wall develop into unicellular vegetative individuals. *C. Tribonema bombycinum,* a filamentous yellow-green alga. *D. Botrydium granulatum.* The bulbous region is the vegetative portion of the thallus; the filamentous appendages (*Rh*) are rhizoids. *E. Vaucheria sessilis.* Vegetative portion of a thallus, and zoospore release and germination, which results in production of one or two germ tubes. *Right,* release of antherozoids. The protoplasm of the female gametangium protrudes through the pore in the gametangial wall, which allows entry of the male gametes and subsequent fertilization.

368

Division Cryptophyces (Cryptomonads)

Almost all Cryptophyces are unicellular, biflagellate, somewhat flattened organisms that possess a semirigid pellicle; each cell typically contains one nucleus and two chromatophores, or a single bilobed chromatophore. These are the cryptomonads. The flagella seem to function separately, one being used as the principal locomotor organelle, the other often trailing. They typically arise together from one point a short distance behind the anterior pole of the cell; in a few types, the flagella are lateral. There may be a furrow in the cell surface extending back from the flagella; in some representatives, the groove is closed and is similar in form and location to the gullet of flagellate protozoa, but has not been demonstrated to function in ingestion.

Two unicellular representatives are illustrated in Figure 17-30. Palmelloid colonial types and non-motile unicellular types are also known; both these types reproduce by forming zoospores that are morphologically typical cryptomonads. Reproduction of motile types occurs by longitudinal binary fission; typically, the cell withdraws its flagella, becomes immotile, and secretes a gelatinous covering within which it divides. Both progeny leave the gelatinous covering, and cells do not accumulate in motile colonies.

Many Cryptophyces exhibit characteristics typical of flagellate protozoa. For example, in addition to possession of a pellicle and a gullet-like furrow, many cells also possess trichocysts; these may occur over the cell surface or, more commonly, along the furrow wall. Dormant stages are similar in structure and

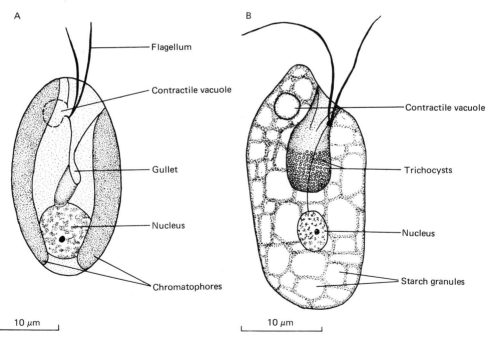

Cryptophyces. *A. Cryptomonas similis. B. Chilomonas paramecium,* a colorless type in which the **Figure 17-30** cytoplasm typically contains numerous angular starch granules, as here.

development to the encysted stages of flagellate and the lower ameboid protozoa.

Representatives of Cryptophyces, although not greatly varied in morphology,
occur fairly widely in fresh, brackish, and sea water. They are usually free-
living, but also occur as endosymbionts of radiolarians (Sarcodina) and sea
anemones. In these association they are usually referred to as zooxanthellae;
all such known symbionts possess chromatophores.

Division Pyrrophyces (Dinoflagellates and Phytodinads)

The division Pyrrophyces is represented predominantly by unicellular, flagellated algae, the dinoflagellates, and a smaller group of non-motile types, the
phytodinads, which produce zoospores morphologically similar to dinoflagellates. The dinoflagellates and phytodinads constitute the class Dinophyceae.
In photosynthetic types, the chromatophores are green-brown or light brown.
The majority of dinoflagellates that occur at depths of the ocean where light
does not penetrate are colorless.

The class Dinophyceae is subdivided into several (often eight) orders, which
are distinguished by structural features of the cell wall, relative duration of
motile and non-motile stages in the life cycle, and solitary or colonial existence.
All orders include both photosynthetic and colorless representatives.

In the dinoflagellates (Fig. 17-31) and the motile stages of the phytodinads
(Fig. 17-32), the cell form may vary from approximately spheric to elongated,
sometimes with conic poles, but there is invariably a furrow that encircles or
spirals around the lateral wall of the cell. Within this transverse furrow is a
flagellum that is more or less flattened; it undulates within the furrow, but
the effect of its movement on the motion of the cell is not clear. A second
flagellum arises within the transverse furrow or within a longitudinal furrow
that intersects the transverse one. This flagellum is approximately circular in
cross-section; it extends posteriorly and is responsible for the forward locomotion of the cell.

The surface of the dinophycean cell may be a firm pellicle (unarmored
dinoflagellates, order Gymnodiniales, Fig. 17-31A–D), a smooth, homogeneous
wall (phytodinads), or a set of articulated cellulosic plates (armored dinoflagellates, order Peridiniales, Fig. 17-31 E–G). Pectic substances rarely occur
in dinoflagellates, whereas a pectic sheath is common among phytodinads.

The chromatophores of photosynthetic representatives are varied and not
distinctive in shape or in number per cell. Most commonly, however, they are
cylindric, discoid, or band-shaped; numerous; and located near the periphery
of the protoplast. Most dinophycean cells are uninucleate.

Reproduction of dinoflagellates occurs by binary fission; in many representatives, the cell comes to rest and is not motile during division. The plane
of division is longitudinal or oblique, invariably passing through the plane of
the transverse furrow. Fission of armored types may involve the parent cell
wall, which separates into two portions. After separation of the progeny cells,
each regenerates the portion of the wall plates corresponding to those retained
by the other cell. Some dinoflagellates discard the parent wall; division of these

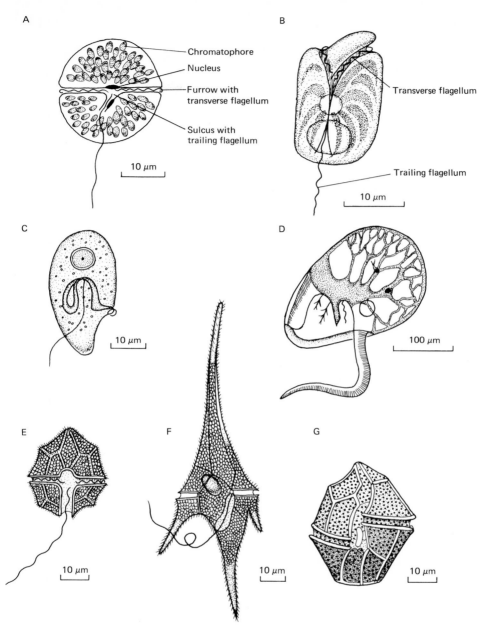

Pyrrophyces: Dinoflagellates. *A–D.* Gymnodiniales. *A. Gymnodinium neglectum,* with an equatorial **Figure 17-31** transverse furrow. The zoospores of phytodinads and naked stages of armored dinoflagellates (Peridiniales) are generally similar in cell form to vegetative cells of *Gymnodinium.* Such stages are called **gymnodinioid.** *B. Amphidinium klebsii.* The transverse furrow is near the anterior pole of the cell. *C. Oxyrrhis marina,* with rudimentary furrows. *D. Noctiluca scintillans,* which may be more than 1 mm in diameter. *Oxyrrhis* and *Noctiluca* are colorless. Representatives of these genera and of *Gonyaulax* (see *G*) and *Gymnodinium* occur in marine algal blooms called red tides. At night their presence is evident in breaking waves, where the water is highly aerated and the cells luminesce. *E–G.* Peridiniales. *E.* Peridinium tabulatum. Predominantly fresh water. *F. Ceratium hirundinella.* The cell form varies with depth, season, and salinity. Most species of *Ceratium* are marine, but several are found in fresh water. *G. Gonyaulax polyedra* (flagella not shown). Most species of *Gonyaulax* are marine.

371

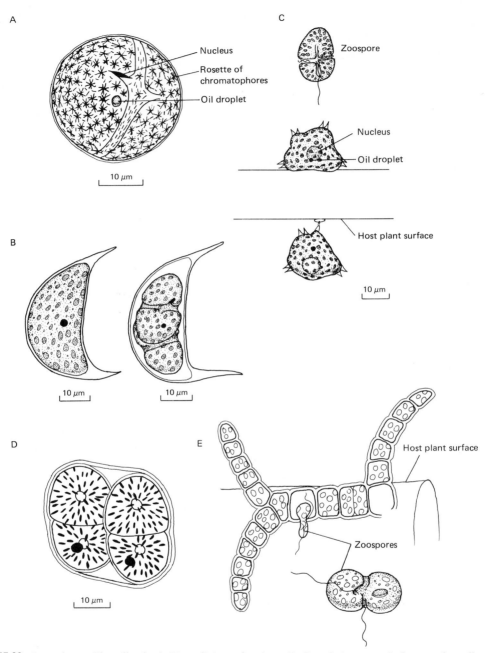

Figure 17-32 Pyrrophyces: Phytodinads. *A. Hypnodinium sphaericum. B. Cystodinium iners. Left,* vegetative cell; *right,* zoospore formation. *C. Tetradinium javanicum.* Two vegetative cells on the surface of an aquatic plant, and a zoospore. *D. Gloeodinium montanum.* Four to eight cells accumulate within a colony, then the envelope disintegrates and each individual develops independently. (*A, B,* and *D* and vegetative cells of *C* from Thompson, R. H., 1949. *Amer. J. Botany,* **36:**301. By permission of the Botanical Society of America and the *American Journal of Botany.*) *E. Dinoclonium conradi.* Vegetative filament on a host plant, and a zoospore enlarged relative to the filament.

types usually occurs within a gelatinous envelope, before or after the parent wall has been shed. Each progeny cell eventually reconstructs an entire wall, but may swim about for some time as a naked cell. Dinoflagellates may also form dormant cysts, typically one but rarely two per cell. Upon germination, each cyst releases a single naked, flagellated cell.

The phytodinad cells are coccoid or ellipsoid and non-motile. They reproduce by dividing into two, four, or eight zoospores. Phytodinads may alternatively produce non-motile spores, which are usually spheroid, but may be autospores.

Most Pyrrophyces representatives are marine and constitute, with the more numerous diatoms, a major proportion of the planktonic flora. In contrast to the diatoms, which are mainly cold-water organisms, the dinoflagellates occur in greatest abundance in warm waters. Fresh-water dinoflagellates are generally found in small bodies of water such as in pools, in ditches, and in ponds, and especially where there is heavy plant and algal growth. A few types of Pyrrophyces—both colorless and photosynthetic—are parasitic on fish.

Although some dinoflagellates (e.g., *Gonyaulax*) are strictly photolithotrophic, several photosynthetic forms can assimilate organic substances. Representatives of at least four genera of photosynthetic dinoflagellates can ingest particulate foods. Although the process of ingestion by the unarmored forms has not been observed, food vacuoles containing ingested microbes (algae, protozoa) can be found within the dinoflagellate cells. *Ceratium* representatives, which are armored, extend reticulopodia outward through pores in the wall; the reticulopodia engulf food particles, which presumably are digested before or as they are conveyed into the interior of the cell. Ingestion also is known to occur in certain colorless dinoflagellates.

Division Phaeophyces (Brown Algae)

These are marine algae, with the exceptions of only three or four genera whose representatives are rarely encountered. Three large subgroups of brown algae are distinguished: filamentous brown algae, kelps, and rockweeds. They are typically brownish in color, but may be olive-green or black.

In contrast to the other algal divisions, Phaeophyces is represented solely by multicellular organisms. Adult thalli are non-motile; motility occurs only in spores and gametes. Almost all brown algae are sessile on coastal rocks, the sea bottom, or other marine algae; in two large areas, the Sargasso Sea and the Gulf of Thailand, rockweeds that elsewhere occur as sessile organisms exist afloat. The thallus of each type of brown alga is differentiated at least to the extent of possessing a holdfast. Some thalli are unbranched filaments, but the group as a whole constitutes a series within which the thalli increase to considerable complexity.

The division also includes the largest algae. The giant kelps that occur in offshore areas of the ocean attached to the sea bottom reach lengths of as much as 150 m. All representatives of this type of kelp possess gas-filled bladders that increase the buoyancy of the thallus and typically a long stipe that joins the upper parts of the thallus with the holdfast. Such modifications allow these photosynthetic organisms to dwell attached in the dimness of the ocean bottom by extending into the regions to which light penetrates. Since most forms do not occur in waters deeper than about 30 m, a major proportion of the thallus may float at or near the surface and receive sunlight of intensity not significantly diminished by passage through water. Although other brown algae are much smaller than the giant kelps, they are characteristically macroscopic.

The division is subdivided into three classes according to the life histories of the organisms. One class accommodates those brown algae, all of the filamentous group, in which there occurs an alternation of morphologically similar generations. The second class, which includes a few filamentous browns and all the kelps, accommodates those types in which alternate generations are morphologically dissimilar; the diploid generation is dominant. The third class accommodates the rockweeds, in whose life histories only the diploid generation is free-living.

Filamentous Brown Algae.   The algae informally designated filamentous brown algae include, besides distinctly filamentous types, organisms whose thalli are multicellular in cross-section and which may be flattened and fan-shaped or lobed. In some of these types, the entire thallus adheres to the substrate, lying flat against its surface as a (wet) crust.

The group constitutes a series, probably a phylogenetic line, within which the structural complexity increases in parallel with increasing specialization of the reproductive processes. The simplest forms are unbranched or branching filaments in which sporangia develop by modification of individual cells within the filament. Somewhat more complex forms are branched filaments that develop sporangia as specialized side branches. This type is exemplified by *Ectocarpus* (Fig. 17-33*A*).

In *Ectocarpus* (order Ectocarpales), as in the simpler forms, the two generations are morphologically similar, and each generation is perpetuated by its own motile spores as well as by the alternate generation. As indicated in the diagram of Figure 17-33*A*, multi-chambered sporangia arise as branches; one motile spore is produced in each chamber. Each spore is of the same ploidy as the parent thallus and upon germination develops into an adult organism without change in ploidy. The spores produced by a haploid thallus can also behave as gametes; in *Ectocarpus,* mating is isogamous and usually heterothallic. The zygote resulting from gamete fusion develops into a diploid thallus. The only gross structural difference between the two generations is the single-chambered sporangium that is developed on the diploid thallus. Reductive nuclear division occurs within this type of sporangium, and the haploid spores that are formed complete the life cycle by developing into haploid thalli.

Some forms in which the life cycle is similar to that of *Ectocarpus* are pseudoparenchymatous. In a few of these, longitudinal cell divisions may occur in older portions of the thallus. In those representatives in which longitudinal and transverse cell divisions occur regularly and the thallus is parenchymatous, the diploid generation typically arises only from zygotes; diploid spores are not produced. Consequently, the two generations differ morphologically by the type of sporangia they develop. In some representatives, the haploid spores

produced following reductive nuclear division are non-motile, and there are
only four per sporangium; a haploid thallus is either male or female, and
mating is oogamous. In these types, neither generation produces spores to
perpetuate itself; each arises strictly as an alternation with the other.

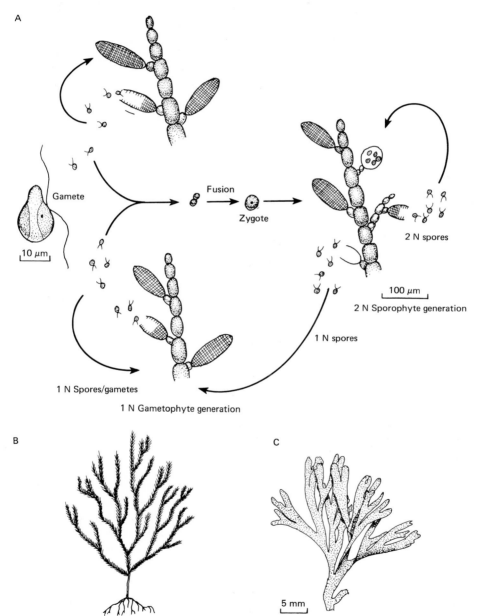

Phaeophyces: Filamentous brown algae. *A.* Life history of *Ectocarpus. B.* Thallus of *Ectocarpus* **Figure 17-33**
sp. *C.* Portion of a thallus of *Dictyota dichotoma.*

In simple and branched filamentous brown algae, growth typically occurs at several points along the filament; this also occurs in many of the pseudo-parenchymatous forms. In parenchymatous forms, growth is more often restricted to the margin of the flattened thallus and in forms such as *Dictyota* (Fig. 17-33*C*) is further limited to single cells or small groups of cells at the margin or the apex of a lobe of the flattened thallus.

Kelps. Representatives of kelps are illustrated in Figure 17-34. The young kelp is a single layer of cells that is anchored to the substrate by basal rhizoids. The organism gradually differentiates into a parenchymatous thallus consisting of holdfast, stipe, and blades. Eventually, growth that results in further elongation is restricted to the portion of each blade near its juncture with the stipe. The cells of the blade continue to grow; they divide in a plane perpendicular to the flat surface of the blade, thereby increasing the breadth of the blade.

The holdfast is typically large and may be a solid mass, but is usually composed of branching filaments. The stipe is usually unbranched. Internally, it is composed of at least two types of tissue: a central medulla in which the cells are non-photosynthetic and do not divide, and an outer cortex of photosynthetic cells that grow and divide. In at least two genera, a third type of cell structurally similar to sieve-tube cells of vascular plants occurs; there is some evidence that organic substances are transported along the stipe through these cells.

The large kelp thalli are the diploid generation. The haploid generation is small, usually microscopic, and composed of a small number of cells. This reduced haploid generation is illustrated in the diagram of the life cycle of *Laminaria* (Fig. 17-35). The haploid thalli are simple filaments that develop gametangia as short side branches. Each thallus is either male or female, and each gametangium produces one gamete. The egg cell may be fertilized within the gametangium, or, less commonly, after emergence from it. The zygote is released and develops directly into a diploid thallus. Sporangia develop within the blades of the diploid organism; reductive nuclear division precedes the formation of the motile, haploid spores, each of which develops into a small haploid thallus. This developmental pattern and life history are typical of the kelps.

Rockweeds. The rockweeds (order Fucales) are similar to kelps in external appearance, but are generally much smaller and are not markedly differentiated internally. Four examples are illustrated in Figure 17-36. Representatives of each of these genera are common along rocky shores, and practically every patch of shore-dwelling seaweeds includes some representatives of *Fucus*.

Reproduction of rockweeds frequently occurs by fragmentation of the thallus or detachment of shoots. The fragments regenerate holdfasts, attach to rocks, and continue growth, even though growth and cell division are normally restricted to apical cells or groups of cells.

Reproduction of rockweeds also occurs via a sexual cycle, as illustrated for

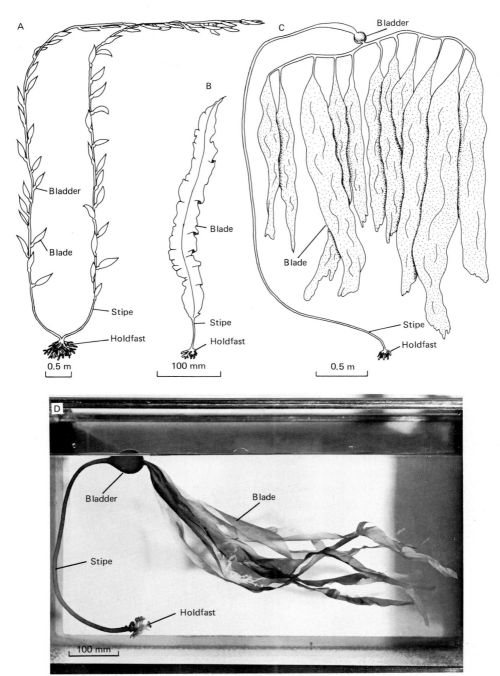

Phaeophyces: Kelps. *A. Macrocystis pyrifera. B. Laminaria agardhii. C. Pelagophyces porra. D. Nereocystis luetkeana.* (Courtesy Carolina Biological Supply Company.) **Figure 17-34**

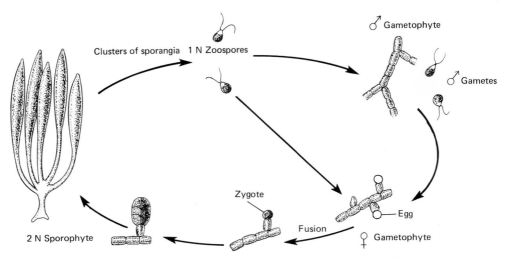

Clusters of sporangia 1 N Zoospores

♂ Gametophyte

♂ Gametes

Zygote

Egg

2 N Sporophyte

Fusion

♀ Gametophyte

Figure 17-35 Life history of *Laminaria.*

Fucus in Figure 17-37. Areas in the thallus become differentiated as reproductive structures; in *Fucus,* they are recognizable as swollen tips of branches,
in *Sargassum* as swellings within the blades, and in *Ascophyllum* as short,
swollen branches. The reproductive structure is a cavity within the thallus that
contains male and female sporangia and sterile filaments. Each type of sporangium begins as a single cell within which reductive nuclear division occurs.
Further nuclear and cell divisions follow; finally, 16 male gametes are produced
by the male structure, and as many as eight female gametes by the female
structure. The number of egg cells produced per female structure varies among
genera. The transient 16- or 8-celled stage is comparable to the haploid generation of other brown algae, except that in rockweeds, each cell of the haploid
generation differentiates into a gamete.

When the thallus is exposed at low tide, the multicellular sexual units are
released from the reproductive structure. As the tide returns and these units
become submerged, they release the gametes. The male gametes are motile,
and the female cells are spheric and non-motile. The male attaches to the egg
by means of one of its flagella; the second continues to move until the male
penetrates the egg. The zygote attaches to a rock and develops directly into
a diploid thallus.

Division Rhodophyces (Red Algae)

The majority of red algae are marine organisms that inhabit coastal waters
as intertidal and subtidal organisms. Like the brown algae, they occur as sessile
organisms except in a few areas; red algae occur afloat in the Black Sea and
in waters around Japan. The red algae that occur in the subtidal zones are
found at depths as great as 40 m; only short wavelength visible light (particularly violet) penetrates to such depths in any significant intensity. These wavelengths can be absorbed by red algae, but not by green or brown algae, and

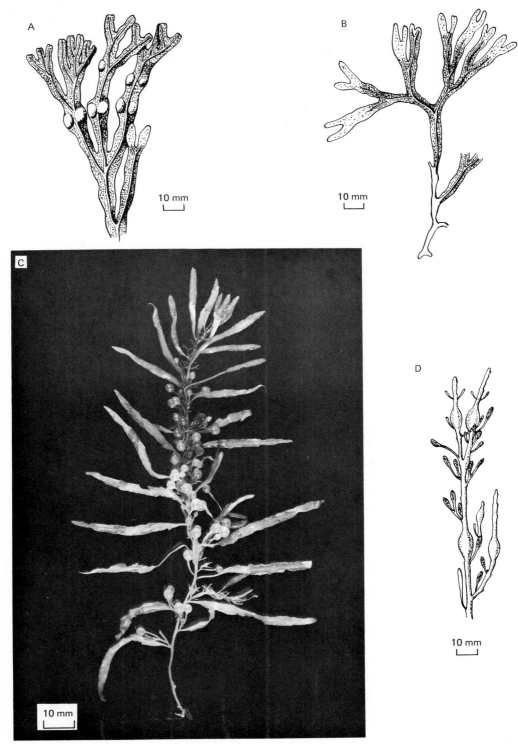

Phaeophyces: Rockweeds. *A. Fucus vesiculosus. B. F. edentatus. C. Sargassum filipendula.* (Courtesy **Figure 17-36** Carolina Biological Supply Company.) *D. Ascophyllum nodosum.*

379

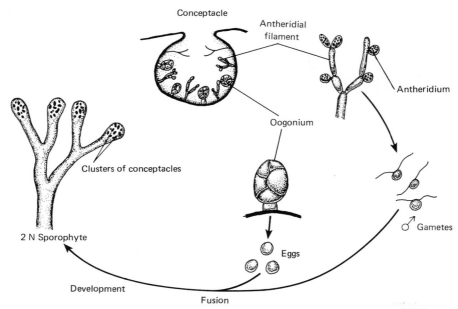

Figure 17-37 Sexual cycle in *Fucus*. Whether gametangia of one or both sexes occur in the same conceptacle depends on the species, as does the number of eggs per female gametangium.

the red algae are typically found in any area as the deepest dwelling seaweeds. They are generally much smaller than the kelps and do not possess flotation vesicles; the thalli of deep-dwelling red algae are entirely submerged at a considerable distance from the surface of the sea.

With the exception of one type, red algae are multicellular. The exceptional species are placed in the genus *Porphyridium,* whose representatives are spheroid, unicellular, non-motile algae that may accumulate in colonies as masses of cells irregularly arranged within a gelatinous matrix. These organisms reproduce solely by cell division, and sexual stages are not known. This genus, which is not accommodated by any order, includes the only terrestrial red algae; they grow on wet rocks, brick, soil, and woodwork.

Among the multicellular forms, the cells are typically uninucleate and possess one large chromatophore, often stellate, or numerous small discoid chromatophores. The latter type is more common among the higher forms of Rhodophyces, in which the cytoplasm occurs as a peripheral layer between a central vacuole and the cell wall.

The multicellular thallus of a red alga may be a simple or branched filament that grows throughout its length, or it may be a complex of two or three types of cells derived from a group of growing, dividing apical cells. Intermediate in complexity between these types of thalli are flat types composed of one or two layers of cells, filamentous forms of pseudoparenchymatous and of parenchymatous organization, and elongated types that are differentiated as colorless central axis (medulla) and outer photosynthetic cortex.

Rhodophyces differs from all other divisions of eucaryotic algae in two respects in addition to pigments and food reserves. First, flagellated cells are not known to occur in any stage of the life cycles of red algae. Second, sexual processes involve the union of a free, non-motile male cell with a female sex organ of peculiar structure called a carpogonium. Fertilization of the carpogonium is followed by the production of numerous uninucleate, unicellular spores called carpospores.

There are two principal types of sexual cycles among red algae. Each of these is diagrammed in Figure 17-38, the simpler type as it occurs in *Nemalion,* and the type that involves an alternation of generations as it occurs in *Gracilaria.*

In *Gracilaria,* three types of adult thalli occur: diploid thalli, which produce haploid spores; haploid male thalli, which produce male gametes; and haploid female thalli, on which the carposporangia and carpospores are formed. This type of life cycle is predominant among red algae; the haploid and diploid thalli are morphologically alike. The diploid carpospores are often borne within a structure that develops by proliferation of cells adjacent to the carpogonium. It serves as a protective envelope around the developing spores and has one opening, rarely two, through which the spores are released. Since the majority of higher Rhodophyces representatives are known to reproduce by means of carpospores, their classification is to some extent based on characteristics of the structures associated with this process.

In contrast to other multicellular algae, except kelps, reproduction of red algae by fragmentation of the thallus is not common. Asexual reproduction occurs by means of non-motile spores produced singly, in tetrads, or in large numbers in a sporangium derived from a single vegetative cell or produced as a specialized side branch. In lower forms, reproduction may occur by release of the protoplast of a vegetative cell. These and the sporangiospores are typically naked when first released; they develop cell walls before or after they attach to a substrate and before they develop into vegetative thalli.

One order, Bangiales, is recognized in the class Bangiophyceae or Protoflorideophyceae. These red algae are distinguished from higher forms by formation of complete septa between cells within the thallus and by the formation of carpospores by cleavage of the zygote rather than on special filaments.

The majority of red algae are placed in the class Florideophyceae. These organisms are distinguished among algae by the formation of perforated septa between cells; each septum has a central pore that is plugged (Fig. 17-39) so that the cytoplasm of adjacent cells is not continuous. During carpospore formation, the septum at the base of each filament is completed as the sporulating filaments arise.

Class Florideophyceae / Order Nemalionales. The developing carpospores of these algae are borne on single carpogonia without a protective envelope. Carpospore-forming filaments arise directly from the base of the carpogonium. The life cycle of most genera is the type illustrated above for *Nemalion.* Three genera are illustrated in Figure 17-40.

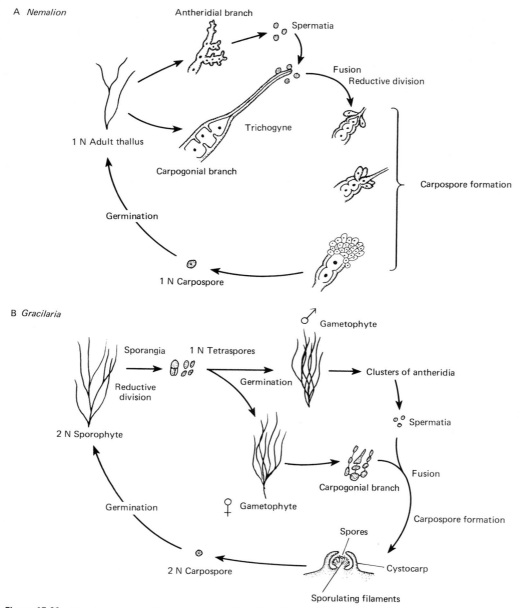

A *Nemalion*

Antheridial branch

Spermatia

Fusion
Reductive division

1 N Adult thallus

Trichogyne

Carpogonial branch

Carpospore formation

Germination

1 N Carpospore

B *Gracilaria*

♂ Gametophyte

Sporangia   1 N Tetraspores

Reductive
division

Germination

Clusters of antheridia

Spermatia

2 N Sporophyte

Fusion

Carpogonial branch

Carpospore formation

Germination

♀ Gametophyte

Spores

2 N Carpospore

Cystocarp

Sporulating filaments

Figure 17-38 Sexual cycles in Rhodophyces. *A. Nemalion. B. Gracilaria.*

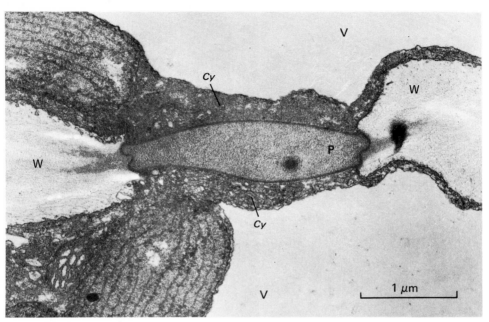

Vertical section of the center of a septum of *Laurencia spectabilis* showing the plug (*P*) that   **Figure 17-39**
completes the physical separation of protoplasts in adjacent cells. *W*, wall material of the septum;
Cy, cytoplasm; *V*, vacuole. (From Bisalputra, T., P. C. Rusanowski, and W. S. Walker, 1967.
J. Ultrastructure Res.; **20**:277. By permission of Academic Press, Inc., New York.)

The young thallus of *Batrachospermum* is a filament composed of a single longitudinal row of cells derived from an apical cell that divides transversely. As the filament elongates, by growth of the cells and by increase in the number of cells by repeated division of the apical cell, each older cell produces four short lateral branches. The basal cells of the branches later produce short filaments that grow downward along the parent axial cell and form a pseudo-parenchymatous cortex. The thalli of some species are highly branched; branching presumably results from longitudinal fission of the apical cell.

In *Nemalion*, the axial portion consists of a number of loosely associated filaments that arise from an apical group of dividing cells. The cells of the axial filaments are colorless; photosynthesis occurs in lateral tufts of branches produced from the axial filaments.

Class Florideophyceae / Other Orders. Five further orders of Florideophyceae are recognized, each represented only by marine forms. They are typically macroscopic, and many representatives grow to lengths of 20 or 40 cm. In many genera, only two types of spores are formed: the diploid carpospores formed on the haploid female thalli, and the haploid spores formed in tetrads on the diploid thalli following meiosis.

The thalli of most representatives of these orders are complex in organization, and cell division is typically restricted to an apical cell or, more commonly,

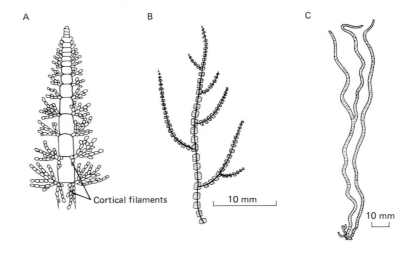

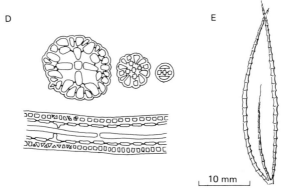

Figure 17-40 Rhodophyces: Nemalionales. *A. Batrachospermum* sp. Portion of a thallus showing origin of cortication. *B. B. boryanum.* Portion of a branched thallus. *C. Nemalion helminthoides.* Entire thallus. *D. Lemanea fluviatilis.* Three transverse sections (left to right, toward apex) and a longitudinal section in a fully developed region. *E. Lemanea annulata.* Entire thallus.

an apical group of cells. The majority are elongated, usually branched organisms that are multicellular in cross-section; they may be pseudoparenchymatous or parenchymatous in organization. Some are flattened and one, two, or several cells thick. Others, particularly the coralline types, are composed of a flattened portion, which lies on the surface of the substrate, and an erect portion.

The organisms illustrated in Figures 17-41 and 17-42 are classified in one order, Ceramiales; the thallus of representatives of this order is composed of a single axial filament and may have additional cortical filaments. Elongation and cortication occur much as in *Batrachospermum.*

The genera *Corallina* and *Lithothamnion* (Fig. 17-43*D* and *E*) exemplify

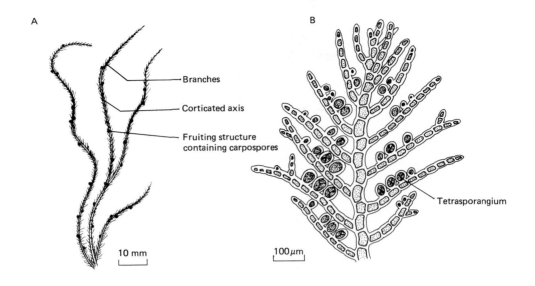

A

Branches

Corticated axis

Fruiting structure
containing carpospores

10 mm

B

Tetrasporangium

100 μm

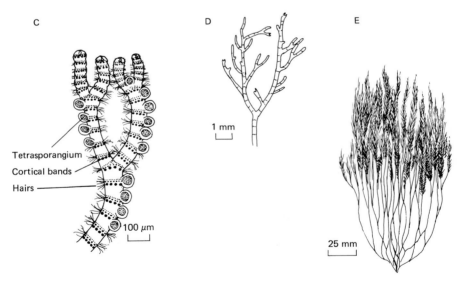

C

Tetrasporangium

Cortical bands

Hairs

100 μm

D

1 mm

E

25 mm

Rhodophyces: Ceramiales. *A. Dasya pedicellata. B. Callithamnion rupicolum.* Upper portion of   **Figure 17-41**
a thallus showing the regular, alternate branching, which occurs in one plane, *C. Ceramium avalone.*
Portion of a thallus. *D. C. rubrum.* The caliper-shaped tips of the branches in *C* and *D* are
characteristic of the genus *Ceramium. E. Polysiphonia denudata.* Entire thallus.

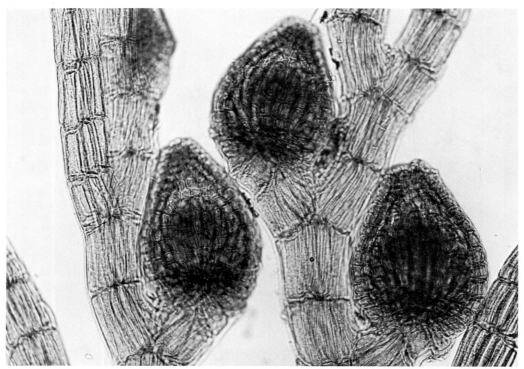

Figure 17-42 *Polysiphonia* sp., region of a completely corticated thallus bearing fruiting structures that contain carpospores. (Courtesy Carolina Biological Supply Company.)

the coral-reef algae. The erect portion of the thallus of organisms such as *Corallina* arises from an apical group of dividing cells; the resulting pseudo-parenchymatous mass of filaments may form a hollow tube, within which insoluble carbonates are deposited. In *Lithothamnium*, carbonates are deposited within the thallus, which is consequently very hard, even stony, in texture. When a coralline alga dies and disintegrates, the carbonate deposit remains intact in the approximate form of the thallus (Fig. 17-44*A*). The major proportion of a coral reef is deposited by such algae. Carbonates are also deposited by coral animals; almost all individuals of these animals contain endosymbiotic algae.

The red algae and the brown algae, although relatively complex in structure, typically macroscopic in size, and exhibiting cell divisions in localized portions of the thallus, nevertheless have not developed functionally specialized vegetative tissues composed of cells incapable of giving rise to progeny cells. For example, the (often colorless) axial cells of many red algae produce branches in which cell divisions occur. Accordingly, these organisms are recognizable as algae, as protists in which there is a tendency toward tissue differentiation, but in which this differentiation is in a primitive state relative to that of higher photosynthetic organisms.

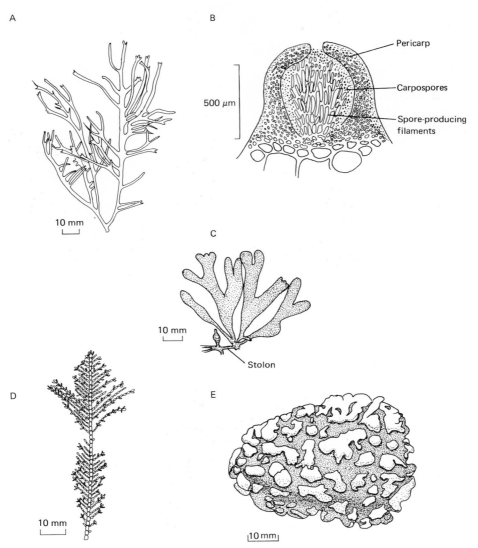

A

B

Pericarp

Carpospores

500 μm

Spore-producing
filaments

10 mm

C

10 mm

Stolon

D

E

10 mm

|10 mm|

Rhodophyces. *A. Gracilaria foliifera.* Entire thallus; branching occurs in one plane so that the **Figure 17-43** thallus is flat. *B. Gracilaria* sp. Vertical section through a carpospore-producing fruiting structure. *C. Rhodymenia pacifica. D. Corallina officinalis.* Part of the erect portion of a thallus (see also Fig. 17-44*A*). *E. Lithothamnium giganteum.*

Figure 17-44 Rhodophyces. *A.* CaCO$_3$ skeleton of a thallus of *Corallina* sp. *B. Chondrus crispus,* from which carrageenin is extracted for use as an emulsion stabilizer in foods such as chocolate products, syrups, salad dressings, and gelled desserts, and in cosmetic preparations. (Courtesy Carolina Biological Supply Company.)

388

Part 5

Variation

Chapter 18

Protistan Responses to Environmental Stimuli

Variation in living systems occurs at three levels: within an individual during its life span, within a population of similar organisms as differences among individuals, and within a line of descent as differences between generations. In the first instance, changes in the characteristics of an individual are determined in part by the developmental pattern of the type of organism (i.e., its genetic endowment) and in part by environmental factors to which it is exposed. This chapter is concerned with variations that occur within individual protists or within genetically homogeneous populations without change in the genetic endowment, particularly with those variations that are influenced by environmental factors.

The environment of a growing organism will inevitably undergo some change during the individual's existence. This is the case even for unicellular organisms that reproduce by fission so frequently that the life span of an individual is measured in minutes. The minimum amount of change in the environment will be those changes in chemical composition that result from the individual's own metabolic activities. Since only a few types of organisms complete their life cycles and cease to exist within minutes, and since most types of organisms of all sizes occur naturally in environments inhabited simultaneously by other individuals and usually other types of organisms, it is important that an individual be able to accommodate changes in its environment. The more advantageous type of accommodation is one that allows the individual to exploit environmental changes, but it is also advantageous for an organism to be able to protect itself from deleterious environmental changes it cannot exploit.

Whether an individual can accommodate a given environmental change and whether the accommodation is exploitative or protective are determined by its inherited capabilities. The environmental changes an individual can accommodate by modifying its activities can be regarded as **stimuli,** and the accommodations as **responses.** In the future, it may be possible to describe all such effects of environmental factors on protists in chemical or physical terms; at present, however, only a few systems of stimulation and response can be described in such terms, and then only partially.

Environmental factors whose appearance or quantitative change can elicit responses in a variety of protists are listed in Table 18-1. The table also lists the types of responses that can be made by protists. Some of the responses can be observed within individuals, others only in genetically uniform populations. In the latter case, either the response is slower than reproduction, or the response can be detected only in masses of living material considerably larger than an individual. With the exception of development of dormant or dehydrated, non-growing stages, the responses of protists by which they accommodate environmental factors or changes are exploitative.

The majority of environmental factors known to elicit responses in protists are chemical. In each such instance, there is a quantitative range within which

TABLE 18-1.   Types of Stimuli and Responses Observed in Protists

TYPES OF ENVIRONMENTAL FACTORS KNOWN TO ELICIT ACCOMMODATING
RESPONSES IN PROTISTS

Nutrients: availability, type, quantity, ratios of certain nutrients
Water: free, humidity
Heat: amount, fluctuation
Inorganic ions: pH, metal ions, inorganic anions
Gases: O_2, CO_2, H_2, motion of air
Light: presence, intensity, wavelength
Contact/crowding
Gravity
Specific chemicals: hormones of hosts or potential mates, substances produced by
    prospective prey

TYPES OF ACCOMMODATING RESPONSES OF WHICH PROTISTS ARE CAPABLE

Reproduction: cell division, formation or release of propagative units
Morphogenesis: overall form or size of individual or colony, thickness of cell walls,
    development and size of certain organelles, type of propagative unit, manner of
    germination, formation of flagella
Motion: orientation of intracellular organelles, activity of flagella or cilia, direction
    and rate of locomotion, orientation of fruiting structure, extension or withdrawal of
    pseudopodia, widening of cytostome, release of mucilage, release of trichocysts
Sexual activity: development of sex organs, differentiation of gametangia or gametes,
    release of gametangia or gametes, reduction division of nucleus
Metabolism: growth rate, respiratory rate, photosynthetic rate, synthesis of certain
    enzymes, synthesis of nucleic acids (particularly DNA), fermentation rate and iden-
    tity and proportion of fermentation products, accumulation or utilization of reserve
    foods, type of metabolism (litho- vs. organo-, photo- vs. chemotrophy)
Dormancy: encystment or sporulation, release from dormancy, dehydration or partial
    reduction in metabolic activities (quiescence)

the chemical is effective as a stimulus. When the factor is present but at levels below the lower end of the range, the protist is indifferent to its presence. Within the range, there may be an optimal quantity that elicits maximal response from the organism, or there may be a level at which maximum response is elicited and further increase in quantity of the stimulus neither increases nor decreases the response. The latter sort of quantity is designated the saturation level of the stimulus; the capacity of the organism to respond has been saturated.

The same sort of relationship probably holds for physical stimuli (heat, light, contact, and gravity). This relationship is well established for heat and light, but there is relatively little experimental evidence concerning the (quantitative) effects of contact and gravity.

Similarly, many protistan responses to environmental factors involve quantitative changes in the form, metabolic activities, or motion of the individual. This is not invariably the case, however, because certain types of responses are either self-limited (e.g., the cell becomes dormant or not; an intermediate stage does not occur) or are determined by genetic factors (e.g., induction of the synthesis of an enzyme may result in the production of a maximum amount of enzyme, regardless of the amount of inducer present).

Investigations of stimulus-response phenomena in protists (as in other organisms) are intended to determine causal relationships. In the natural environment, it is rare that a single factor will vary while all other possible stimuli remain constant; the appearance of a prospective mate or prey is an exception. Consequently, precise studies require controlled manipulations of well-defined environments of pure populations or solitary individuals. Only in this way is it possible to determine which environmental factor(s) is necessary for elicitation of a response, which is not involved in any way, and which single factor—if there is one—is sufficient to elicit the response under otherwise unchanged conditions.

Even when manipulation of a single factor under specified conditions invariably results in elicitation of a given response, that factor may not be the proximal stimulus. It may cause other changes in the environment that directly affect the organism. For example, an increase in incubation temperature of a culture will cause an increase in the humidity of the air immediately above solidified medium and a decrease in the solubility of gases in a liquid medium; introduction of CO_2 into a liquid culture will result in a decrease in pH, at least transiently, even if the medium is well buffered; flooding of a culture on solidified medium will decrease the concentrations of solutes present at the surface of the medium, as well as change the physical environment from solidified to fluid; addition of a specific nutrient will alter the ratios of nutrients in a medium; movement of air will increase the rate of removal of volatile metabolic products from the immediate environment of the organism and may also alter the humidity; and variation in pH will affect the ionization of weak acids or bases and hence the concentration of the undissociated molecules and the corresponding ions.

Similarly, the immediate response may be difficult to identify. A change in one process or structure within the organism may be sufficient to initiate a sequence of changes that culminate in the readily observed response. It is assumed at present that any response, from minor changes in metabolic activity to development of multicellular fruiting bodies, is mediated by biochemical changes within the organism. However, only one or a few of the changes may occur in direct response to an environmental factor, whereas the others are caused by the responses rather than by the stimuli.

In the following sections of this chapter, selected stimulus-response phenomena in protists that have been investigated experimentally are discussed. In these examples, the responses can be interpreted as advantageous to the organisms, especially in the context of their usual natural habitats.

Dimorphism in *Mucor*

The alternative development of certain fungi as mycelia or as yeasts, illustrated in Figure 18-1, was recognized as dependent on environmental conditions more than 150 years ago. In the mid-nineteenth century, such development was regarded by some as evidence that species characteristics of microscopic organisms were not constant and that such organisms thereby differed significantly from higher organisms. Others regarded it as evidence that microscopic organisms could modify their form and cellular composition in order to adapt to different environmental conditions, and that such adaptibility was a species characteristic and a response to specific environmental conditions.

The latter view has been substantiated by investigations with pure cultures. Depending on the isolate, dimorphism may be related to the presence of O_2, the presence of particular nutrients, or temperature of incubation. Depending on the environment, a given isolate will grow solely as yeast cells, solely as filaments, or as a mixture of the two forms, often with one or the other form predominating. Closely related fungi may grow only as yeasts or only as filaments, regardless of environmental conditions.

All representatives of the phycomycete genus *Mucor* can grow aerobically, and under aerobic conditions they develop as aseptate mycelial organisms that reproduce by formation of sporangiospores and, in many species, of arthrospores. Some representatives can also grow anaerobically when supplied with sugars, which they ferment and convert predominantly to ethanol and CO_2, as do many yeasts. Of those *Mucor* representatives that can grow fermentatively, some develop as mycelia that are not significantly different from aerobically grown forms. These are non-dimorphic types. Others may develop as yeasts, depending on other environmental conditions in addition to absence of O_2. These are the dimorphic types.

Among the factors known to be necessary for yeast-form development in anaerobic cultures of dimorphic *Mucor* isolates are: initial pH 4.5 to less than 6.0; a mixture of amino acids as the nitrogen source, rather than inorganic nitrogen compounds or a single amino acid; a heavy metal cation, probably Zn^{+2}; specific concentrations of unsaturated fatty acids; and probably a minimum concentration of CO_2. Under these conditions, arthrospores germinate by budding and thereby give rise to yeast cells; sporangiospores swell, then

200 µm

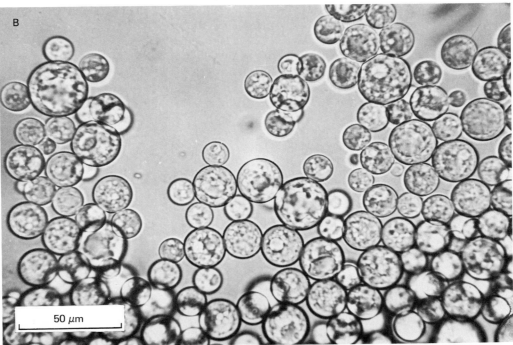

50 µm

Dimorphism in *Mucor rouxii. A.* Filamentous form; aerobic cultivation. *B.* Yeast form; anaerobic cultivation under CO_2. (From Barnicki-Garcia, S., and W. J. Nickerson, 1962. *J. Bact.,* **84**:829. By permission of the American Society for Microbiology.)

Figure 18-1

give rise to yeast cells by budding. Hyphae continue to grow by elongation; they give rise to yeast cells only through the formation of arthrospores. Accordingly, these conditions prevent the initiation of polarized growth and production of elongated germ tubes, but not the continuation of such growth.

The inability of *Mucor* isolates to develop as yeasts in the presence of even small amounts of O_2 has been noted since this dimorphism was first observed. However, it is still not certain whether CO_2 is also necessary. Part of the difficulty in assessing the involvement of CO_2 is due to the unavoidable presence of CO_2 as a product of fermentation. Another difficulty is the variable quantitative effect of exogenous CO_2 on different species of *Mucor* and on different isolates of a single species. Examples of morphologic differences among four *Mucor* isolates cultivated from spores under different environmental conditions are presented in Table 18-2. All conditions known to be necessary for yeast development were provided by the basal medium and anaerobic conditions; only the amounts of exogenous CO_2 and of glucose, the source of endogenous CO_2, were varied.

The observations presented in the table indicate the variability of the morphologic response of dimorphic strains to CO_2. Yeastlike development was induced in *M. subtilissimus* NRRL 1743 only at high concentrations of exogenous plus endogenous CO_2; further, this response was lost over a period of several years of artificial cultivation, and the strain recently has behaved as though non-dimorphic. The *M. rouxii* (see Fig. 18-1) and *M. racemosus* isolates grew as yeasts when either the endogenous or the exogenous level of CO_2 rose above an undetermined minimum. *M. subtilissimus* NRRL 1909 developed as yeasts under all conditions tested, although some filamentous development occurred when both endogenous and exogenous CO_2 levels were very low. At glucose concentrations of 0.1 per cent or more, the rate of endogenous CO_2 formation was maximum and independent of glucose concentration; only when the sugar concentration was sufficiently low to retard metabolic formation of CO_2 was it possible for this strain to develop as filaments.

The dimorphic isolates of *Mucor* are unusually tolerant of high concen-

TABLE 18-2.   Morphology of *Mucor* Isolates Under Various Conditions of Cultivation*

Atmosphere: Concentration of glucose:	100% N_2 2%	70% N_2, 30% CO_2 0.01% 2%		100% CO_2 0.01% 2%	
Isolate					
M. subtilissimus NRRL 1743	F	F	F	O	Fy
M. rouxii IM 80†	Fy	F	YF	F	Y
M. racemosus NRRL 1427	Fy	F	YF	F	Y
M. subtilissimus NRRL 1909	Y	YF	Y	Y	Y

F: filaments; Y: yeasts; Fy: predominantly filaments; O: growth not detectable.

*Sources: Bartnicki-Garcia, S., and W. J. Nickerson, 1962. *J. Bact.,* **84:**829; Bartnicki-Garcia, S., 1968. *J. Bact.,* **96:**1586.
†IM 80 grows as Y in 8 to 10 per cent glucose.

trations of CO_2. Non-dimorphic isolates, like most other phycomycetes and fungi in general, cannot grow in atmospheres containing as much as 30 per cent CO_2. However, growth of *Mucor* representatives under anaerobic conditions is less efficient than under aerobic conditions; three to five times as much protoplasm is synthesized per unit of carbon and energy source utilized when respiratory, rather than fermentative, processes are used to obtain energy.

Accordingly, by reacting to the least tolerable sort of anaerobic conditions (viz., conditions of high CO_2 accumulation), by reducing the size of an individual from a multinucleate unit of indeterminate growth to a uninucleate unit of determinate growth, the organism increases the possibility that some of the individuals will become separated from the mass and be returned to an aerobic environment. By converting to yeast cells rather than remaining dormant, the spores exploit the anaerobic environment and grow without losing their potential for dissemination as relatively small units.

Sporulation in *Bacillus*

The observation that endospores (see Figs. 18-2 and 18-3) typically appear in cultures of *Bacillus* cells after exponential growth has ceased has encouraged the interpretation that sporulation is a response to one or a few environmental factors that cause the cessation of growth (prevent its continuation). According to this interpretation, sporulation is a mechanism by which the cells ensure their continued survival as individuals. Each cell produces one endospore, which is dormant, and so does not require nutrients for its maintenance, and which is resistant to chemical and physical agents detrimental to growing cells.

Extensive studies on the physiology of sporulation have revealed that it is particularly the exhaustion of essential nutrients other than O_2 (i.e., energy, carbon, or nitrogen sources or micronutrients) that is followed by sporulation. This is regarded as evidence that the induction of sporulation is a consequence of the reduction of intracellular pools of metabolites to a minimal level; conversely, the presence of higher levels suppresses sporulation and allows growth and multiplication.

Growth and sporulation seem to be mutually exclusive processes. This interpretation is supported by the observation that, at an early stage of sporulation, the cell becomes "committed" to that process; addition of nutrients or transfer to fresh medium cannot reverse the process. Also, under most conditions of cultivation, sporulation occurs at the expense of endogenous reserves and can proceed in a non-nutritive environment containing only certain inorganic ions utilized in spore development. Once sporulation has proceeded to a particular stage (stage II, septation; see Fig. 13-2), the process continues independently of the nutrient environment.

However, other environmental factors influence sporulation. The most important factor for *Bacillus* cells is O_2. Generally, sporulation requires more vigorous aeration of the culture than does growth, and during early stages of sporulation the cells respire more actively than during growth. (The reverse effect is observed with the anaerobic spore-formers, *Clostridium;* sporulation

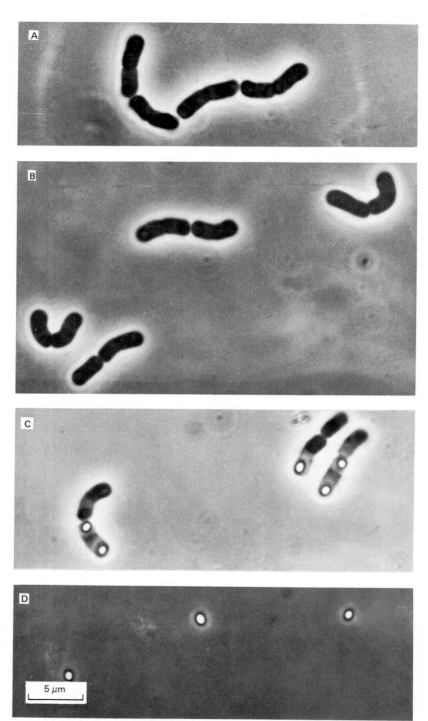

Figure 18-2 Sequence of stages in sporulation, *Bacillus megaterium.* Time is hours since the end of the exponential phase of growth. (See Fig. 13-2 for stage designations.) *A.* Stage III cells, engulfment (4.5 hours). *B.* Stage IV cells, cortex formation (6 hours). *C.* Stage V or VI, refractile spores (9.5 hours). *D.* Stage VII, free spores (21 hours). (From Hitchins, A. D., A. J. Kahn, and R. A. Slepecky, 1968. *J. Bact.,* **96:**1811. By permission of the American Society for Microbiology.)

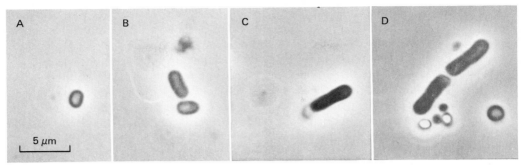

Sequence of stages in germination, *Bacillus megaterium*. *A.* Swelling, refractility already lost.   **Figure 18-3**
B. Elongation. *C.* Emergence and outgrowth, spore coat discarded. *D.* First fission. (From Hitchins,
A. D., A. J. Kahn, and R. A. Slepecky, 1968. *J. Bact.*, **96:**1811. By permission of the American
Society for Microbiology.)

is inhibited by traces of O_2 that may not interfere with growth.) In addition
to greater requirements for O_2, sporulation in *Bacillus* cells also requires specific
conditions of pH and temperature. Generally, the pH and temperature ranges
suitable for sporulation are narrower than those suitable for growth.

At least two environmental factors are known to affect sporulation by in-
fluencing the physiologic condition of the cells that sporulate. One of these
is Mn^{+2}; the other is the ratio of carbon to nitrogen sources in the medium
toward the end of exponential growth. Cells can grow without detectable
amounts of Mn^{+2} in the medium, but they cannot sporulate unless Mn^{+2} is
added by the time growth has ceased. Without Mn^{+2}, sporulation may begin,
but it halts before the spores are mature. When the carbon:nitrogen ratio of
the medium is high, cells synthesize large amounts of lipid reserve as they
proceed toward sporulation. This reserve is later used during spore development. When the ratio is low, little lipid is stored, and sporulation cannot
proceed without an exogenous supply of carbon and energy sources. Consequently, when cells are cultivated in a medium with a low carbon:nitrogen
ratio, sporulation does not occur in maximum stationary phase or occurs in
only a minor proportion of the population.

Although a single environmental factor cannot be designated the inducer
of sporulation, it is clear that completion of sporulation is dependent on several
factors and is a response to a particular kind of environment.

Germination of bacterial endospores occurs in two experimentally distinguishable stages. During the first stage, "initiation," the spore loses its heat
resistance and its refractility and becomes permeable to water and solutes such
as dyes; it swells, mainly as a consequence of the uptake of water. During
the second stage, "outgrowth," the cell begins to assimilate nutrients and to
grow. Water is essential for both stages; dry spores remain dormant indefinitely.
O_2 is also essential for both stages in *Bacillus* (and inhibitory for both stages
in *Clostridium*).

The environmental factors that stimulate or are essential for the two stages
of germination vary among *Bacillus* species. Generally, initiation can be in-

duced in a majority of a population of spores of any species by a combination of: heat shock (70 to 100° C for a length of time variable among the species, from less than 30 seconds to 30 minutes), trace metal ions (Zn^{+2}, Mg^{+2}, Ca^{+2}, Fe^{+2}—the amounts and specificity of metals again varying among species), and the amino acid alanine, and the nucleoside inosine for some isolates.

Outgrowth follows if phosphate is available; some species also require a source of sulfur. Alanine (and inosine) are not usually required. Development of the germinated spore beyond outgrowth occurs only in environments suitable for growth and multiplication.

The experimentally established correlation of this cycle of growth-dormancy-growth with specific environmental conditions suggests that sporulation in bacteria has evolved as a mechanism for surviving conditions unsuitable for growth by retirement into a dormant state, and that germination is a response to a favorable environment.

While the advantages of endospore formation seem obvious, the occurrence of this process in so few types of bacteria raises the question whether the advantages are realized. Since non-spore-forming bacteria survive in a wide variety of habitats in numbers comparable to those of spore-formers, does sporulation contribute significantly to the perpetuation of endospore-forming bacteria in nature? The answer seems to be affirmative for obligately parasitic spore-formers; most of these seem able to survive outside their hosts only as spores. An affirmative reply is also implied for many free-living types by two observations. (1) Vegetative cells of spore-formers, especially the aerobic types, are relatively (to many other types of bacteria) unstable when not growing; they tend to lyse when they do not sporulate, just as they do in the final stage of sporulation. Presumably, they contain the enzymes for their own destruction, and these enzymes eventually act on a non-growing cell whether or not it has sporulated. (2) The vegetative cells of many types of the anaerobic spore-formers are rapidly killed by O_2, whereas the spores are not affected. Consequently, dissemination of these types in most environments would be dependent on the development of the O_2-tolerant dormant stage.

Growth and Reproduction in *Chlorella*

Many types of algae reproduce at a particular time of day. This occurs in some types whose reproductive cycles are completed daily, as well as in others with longer cycles. In the latter case, only some individuals in a population will reproduce on any given day. This implies that reproduction in such algae is a response to some stimulus or composite of stimuli that occurs rhythmically within a period that coincides with the length of a day—i.e., is diurnal.

The principal diurnal environmental change is the alternation of light and darkness. Because sunlight provides heat as well as illumination, there is also a diurnal fluctuation in environmental temperature. The majority of experimental studies with pure cultures of algae have revealed that periodic illumination is sufficient to elicit a periodic response under conditions where all other factors remain constant. For many algae, periodic changes in temperature can elicit the same type of response under constant illumination. Cooler periods usually correspond, in terms of response, to dark periods, and warmer periods to periods of illumination. Apparently, modern algae can respond to either of these physical stimuli which fluctuate diurnally.

One of the most thoroughly characterized instances of diurnal behavior in algae is the reproductive cycle of *Chlorella*. This cycle is particularly suitable for biochemical investigation of growth and cell division because the organisms are unicellular during growth, and the reproductive cycle is not complicated by the development of dormant forms or specialized reproductive structures or by the occurrence of sexual stages. Representatives of several species have been investigated, revealing little difference among species. The cycle is summarized diagrammatically in Figure 18-4.

The seven stages that have been distinguished within the cycle are regularly observed in populations cultivated in an inorganic medium at a constant temperature with alternating periods of illumination and darkness. The characteristics of the cells at various stages are summarized in Table 18-3. These stages have been recognized in *Chlorella* cultures synchronized by incubating the cells under conditions of alternating light (or high intensity illumination) and dark (or low intensity illumination) periods and then selecting the smallest cells at the end of one of the latter periods. Selection is achieved by centrifugation and filtration procedures. The initial population in the cultures in which synchronous growth and reproduction occur consists of autospores of 2.7 to 3.3 μm diameter (D_s stage cells).

The time scale is indicated according to observations on cultures incubated at 21° C. The incubation temperature markedly affects the time course, but over a range from 9 to 30° C it does not affect the sequence of stages or the number of autospores produced. Maximum synchronization is achieved by illuminating the cultures for two thirds of the cycle period and incubating in the dark for the remainder of the period.

The effect of temperature as the principal environmental influence on generation time was indicated by studies on the influence of light intensity on synchronous development. At a given temperature, growth rate increased with light intensity over a range from 1,000 lux (meter-candles) to 10,000 lux; growth could not occur at intensities lower than 1,000 lux, and the rate did not increase further at intensities greater than 10,000 lux. The duration of the cycle, how-

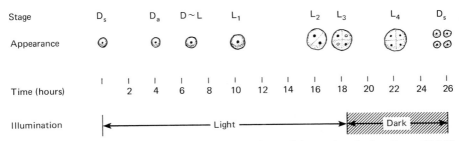

Sequence of developmental stages of *Chlorella* as observed in synchronized cultures (21° C).   **Figure 18-4**

TABLE 18-3. **Differential Characteristics of *Chlorella* Cells at the Distinguishable Developmental Stages**

Stage	Characteristics	Events Accompanying Transition to the Subsequent Stage
D_s	(Autospore) contains negligible endogenous reserves; photosynthetically active	Some growth; chlorophyll synthesis; increase in photosynthetic capacity
D_a	Contains maximum chlorophyll (per unit mass); maximum photosynthetic activity	Growth; chlorophyll synthesis retarded; photosynthetic capacity reduced
$D{\sim}L$	Transition stage	Growth; starch synthesis
L_1	Large; active in carbohydrate reserve synthesis	Growth; one nuclear division; first partition membrane begins to form
L_2	Binucleate; ca. maximum size	Growth ceases; second nuclear division initiated; photosynthetic capacity reaches minimum; second partition membrane appears
L_3	Bi- or tetranucleate; second (sometimes a third) nuclear division is in progress	Photosynthetic capacity low; starch utilization initiated; respiratory activity increases
L_4	Tetracellular	Cell division completed; daughter cells' walls are constructed; chlorophyll synthesis resumed, respiratory activity decreases, starch reserves practically exhausted, photosynthetic capacity increases. Autospores are released when parental cell wall disintegrates

ever, did not vary with light intensity. Since growth was slower at lower intensities while the duration of the growth period was the same at all intensities, the maximum size attained was proportional to light intensity. Apparently, *Chlorella* does not form autospores smaller than a certain size, and so the number of autospores was also proportional to light intensity. For example, at 16° C, two spores were formed at 1,000, two or four (an average of three in the culture) at 2,500, and four at 10,000 lux. The duration of the cycle at this temperature was approximately three days, regardless of light intensity.

The following discussion of growth and reproduction in *Chlorella* is based on studies of cultures incubated at constant temperature under saturating (10,000 lux) light intensity.

The D_s cells are autospores. They can initiate growth and rapidly synthesize chlorophyll as soon as they become independent units within the parent cell. These activities, however, require illumination. When L_4 cells are illuminated as the autospores are delimited, the D_s cells begin to grow even before they are released; the cells that are eventually released are more similar to D_a than to D_s cells. If the formation and release of autospores are allowed to occur in the dark, the small D_s cells are released.

Development of each of the stages from D_s through L_2 requires illumination. These are the growth stages; they are distinguished by (1) relative rates of chlorophyll synthesis (highest in D cells), (2) rates of starch formation (highest in L cells), (3) size and chlorophyll content, and (4) number of nuclei. At some point between the L_2 and L_3 stages, growth ceases. At this point, light is not necessary for further development. If illumination is continued after this point, the process of cell division is postponed for about 2.5 to 3.5 hours.

Whether or not light is present, L_3 cells eventually develop into L_4 cells. During this transition, the rate of photosynthesis becomes negligible and the cells consume O_2 more rapidly than in any other stage. They also begin to utilize the starch reserve accumulated during the photosynthetically active stages. This reserve is reduced to a minimal level by the time the autospores are formed. Oxidation of the starch by respiration provides the energy for the formation of autospores, and these stages (L_3 to D_s) can occur in the dark, but only if O_2 is available.

If illumination is discontinued when cells are in the L_2 stage, cell division can occur. However, only two autospores are formed, even though the L_2 cells are nearly as large as L_3 cells. During the transition from the L_2 stage to the L_3 stage in the light, a second round of DNA synthesis begins; it may be completed and the second nuclear division may be initiated. This implies that illumination of L_2 cells is required for initiation of DNA synthesis and/or of nuclear division; the amount of growth that occurs during this transition is small. It is also characteristic of cells during this transition that the molar ratio of CO_2 consumed to O_2 evolved by photosynthesis is reduced to approximately one third its value during growth. Apparently, photosynthesis is utilized at this time mainly as a source of energy, and less as a means of fixing CO_2. The requirement for energy is probably directly related to the nuclear events.

The influence of specific nutrients is variable. In a medium that does not contain a nitrogen source (NH_3, nitrate, or organic N), phosphate, potassium, or magnesium, D_s cells can initiate and complete one cycle. The number of autospores formed is proportional to the amount of growth that can occur at the expense of endogenous reserves. When sulfate is omitted from the medium, development is halted at about the L_2 stage. Addition of sulfate to the medium after development has halted allows cell division to occur. When sulfate is present throughout the cycle, it is taken up by the cells from late in the L_1 stage through the L_4 stage. Chemical analysis of sulfur-deprived and sulfur-nourished cells has revealed that three sulfur-containing nucleotides are formed as nuclear division begins. These substances are apparently essential for cell division; they are tentatively regarded as inducers of nuclear and/or cell division.

The availability of synchronized populations has made it possible to follow cytologic changes during this cycle. Electron micrographs of sections of cells in different stages are illustrated in Figure 18-5. Prior to the first nuclear division, each cell contains one chloroplast and one dictyosome. Soon after the first nuclear division is completed, two of each organelle are present, presumably as a result of division of the pre-existing organelles. The pair of dictyosomes is located between the nuclei, within which region there appears

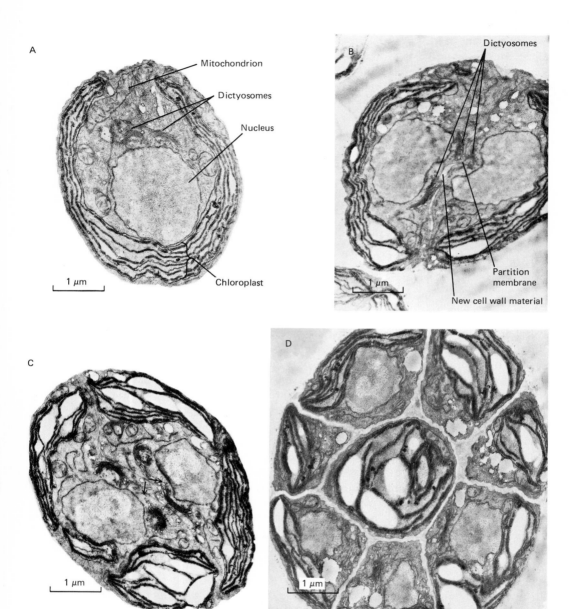

Figure 18-5 Electron micrographs of sections of *Chlorella* cells (L_2 to late L_4). *A*. L_2—one nucleus, one chloroplast, two dictyosomes. *B*. L_3—two nuclei, two chloroplasts, three dictyosomes visible; partition membrane and new wall material. *C*. L_3—two nuclei, four chloroplasts, four dictyosomes; partition membrane with lateral outgrowths (arrows). *D*. Late L_4—eight progeny, separated by walls. (From Bisalputra, T., F. M. Ashton, and T. E. Weier. 1966. *Amer. J. Botany,* **53**:213. By permission of the Botanical Society of America and the *American Journal of Botany.*)

404

a double unit membrane called the partition membrane. Vesicles released from the dictyosomes appear to fuse with the partition membrane, within which electron-transparent material accumulates. Whether this material is contained in the dictyosome vesicles and is deposited within the partition membrane when the vesicles fuse with it is not certain; however, it is clear that the material that accumulates is the cell wall material of the autospores or its immediate precursor. The second (and third, if it occurs) cell division is accompanied by the elaboration of the original partition membrane, which gives rise to additional partition membranes at right angles to itself.

Thus, during the stages of cell division (L_3 to D_s), new membranes and cell wall material, at least, must be synthesized. These syntheses, plus some chlorophyll synthesis, probably account for most of the utilization of reserve materials not consumed by respiration. The energy obtained by respiration supports these syntheses and the intracellular movements necessary for reorganization of the contents of one cell into two, four, or eight progeny of practically identical composition and organization.

In the *Chlorella* cycle, the processes of growth and reproduction are clearly separated in time and to some extent are mutually exclusive, as evidenced by the delay in initiation of cell division in illuminated L_3 cells. The two processes are also dependent on (stimulated by) different environmental factors. Growth requires light, CO_2, and, to reach the maximum otherwise possible, a nitrogen source and phosphate. Cell division, in contrast, requires O_2 and a sulfur source and is to some extent inhibited by light. It can occur in cells starved for certain nutrients (N, P, K, and Mg), even if very little growth has occurred, but the resulting autospores cannot grow in the absence of those nutrients.

The conditions required for completion of the *Chlorella* cycle imply that these algae are adapted to development under conditions of alternating light and dark, as occurs in nature. Growth in an inorganic environment is supported by photosynthesis; accordingly, the growth stages would occur during the daytime. When maximum size has been attained, the cell contains a maximum amount (per unit of mass) of reserve carbohydrate. Subsequent development can occur without the support of photosynthesis, at the expense of this reserve. Cell division, then, could occur at night, the main requirement being an aerobic environment.

Predation in *Didinium*

A significant proportion of protozoa that require particulate foods feed chiefly or exclusively on other protistan cells. In many cases, the prey must be living at the time they are ingested. Observation of such predaceous organisms in the presence of their living prey has repeatedly suggested that their feeding activities are stimulated by the proximity of suitable prey. In some instances, the presence of suitable prey apparently can be detected without direct contact between predator and prey. This implies that the predator is capable of detecting a soluble substance that diffuses from the prey. A motile predator may actively pursue the prey, which may exhibit little if any avoidance activity.

In other instances, the predator appears to react only to fortuitous direct contact with the prey. Such is the case with *Didinium nasutum,* a ciliate that, in the laboratory, can grow and multiply only when living individuals of certain species of *Paramecium* (e.g., *P. multimicronucleatum*) are available as food. When suitable paramecia are present in a culture with *D. nasutum,* the latter attaches to and ingests its prey only after a chance collision. It does not react to a paramecium that swims past it at a distance of only a few micrometers. Nevertheless, random collisions are frequent, and a culture initially containing both organisms will contain only well-fed *D. nasutum* after a few hours.

Once collision has occurred, the predator acts quickly, and ingestion may be completed in less than 60 seconds. When the predator is smaller than the prey, several minutes may be required for ingestion. If the predator cannot engulf the entire prey, it can break it and leave a portion of it uningested.

Regardless of the time required for ingestion, the same sequence of events occurs. The collision must involve the oral region of the predator, which is a protuberance at the anterior end of the cell (see Fig. 18-6*A* and 6*B*). Immediately upon collision, the predator extrudes short (8 to 10 μm) trichocysts from the oral region to establish a tight attachment between the two organisms. The stimulus for this extrusion has not been identified. It is at least apparent that, although necessary, contact alone is not the stimulus; collision of the oral region with objects other than paramecia does not elicit this behavior. Possibly the stimulus is a substance diffusing from paramecia and present in stimulating concentrations only at the cell surface, or a reaction between the trichocysts and a receptor material in the paramecium pellicle.

Attachment of the trichocysts to the prey elicits a similar response, and the paramecium releases trichocysts. The *D. nasutum* cell, in turn, acts to avoid the paramecium's trichocysts by drawing away, but it does not release its hold on the prey. Some of the cytoplasm from the oral region extends beyond the rim of the cytostome and maintains the connection between predator and its trichocysts; longer trichocysts from the oral region are also present in the connecting strand at this stage. Meanwhile, the pellicle and adjacent cytoplasm of the prey have become detectably disorganized (Fig. 18-7*A*). If the organisms are separated (e.g., with the aid of a micropipette) at this stage, disorganization of the paramecium continues until the entire organism appears abnormal (20 to 40 seconds); the cell disintegrates within two minutes.

Shortly after attachment has been effected by *D. nasutum,* a food vacuole begins to form. The cytostome widens to engulf the prey; it may extend to a diameter greater than that of the preying individual before ingestion began, especially if the predator happened to attach to the side, rather than one end of the prey, or to a relatively large individual. As the prey is brought in through the cytostome, it usually disintegrates and its protoplasm flows into the vacuole (see Fig. 18-7*B*).

The widening of the cytostome is a response to a substance that diffuses from dying paramecia. The existence of this substance or group of substances was demonstrated in the following way. When heat-inactivated (seven to eight seconds at 100° C) paramecia were offered to *D. nasutum* populations, the

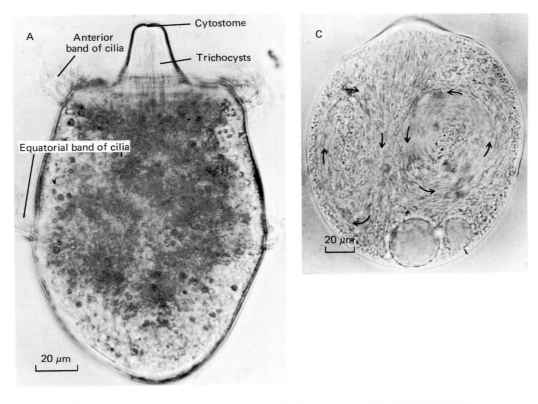

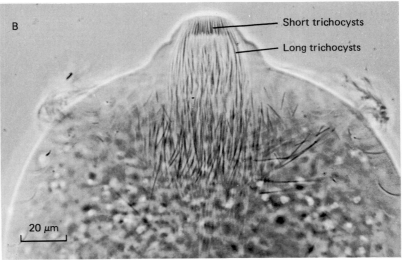

Didinium nasutum. A. Side view of an individual. *B.* The oral region of an individual. *C.* Protoplasmic streaming. The photomicrograph was taken with a one-second exposure so that the mobile endoplasm appears blurred. The arrows indicate the direction of flow as recorded by the observer. (From Schwartz, V., 1965. *Zeit f. Naturforsch.,* **20b:**383. By permission of Verlag der Zeitschrift für Naturforschung.)

Figure 18-6

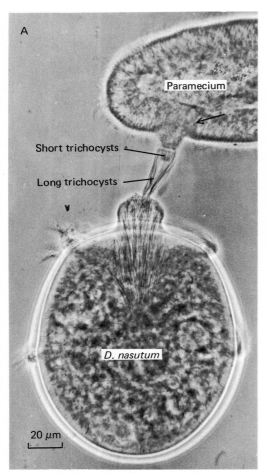

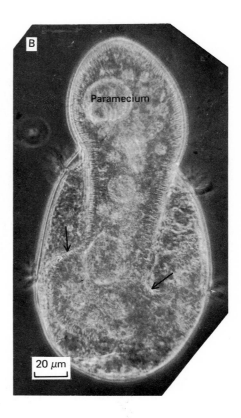

Figure 18-7   Feeding by *Didinium nasutum*. *A.* Attachment of trichocysts to paramecium surface, with localized disorganization of the paramecium cytoplasm (arrow). *B.* Engulfment, with generalized disorganization of the paramecium within the developing food vacuole (arrows). (From Schwartz, V., 1965. *Zeit. f. Naturforsch.*, **20b**:383. By permission of Verlag der Zeitschrift für Naturforschung.)

paramecia were ingested only in the presence of the medium in which the paramecia had been heated. That medium contained the substance that diffused from the dying paramecia. *D. nasutum* attached to killed, washed paramecia in the absence of this substance, but cytostome opening and engulfment did not follow. When the populations were mixed in diluted portions of medium in which the paramecia had been heated, the cytostomes opened to an extent proportional to the concentration of the medium containing the substance.

Cytostome opening could be elicited by this substance without prior attachment of the oral region to paramecia. When starved *D. nasutum* cells were mixed with disrupted, heat-killed paramecia in the medium in which the paramecia had been heated, the cytostomes of the predator cells opened. In many instances, the cytostome opened so far that endoplasm was everted from the cell. The naked endoplasm was not mobile nor did it respond to tactile stimuli (e.g., contact with a pipette) in any detectable way, but it could be retracted.

Movement of the food vacuole toward the posterior region of *D. nasutum* is apparently aided by protoplasmic streaming, which is observable in living specimens with the aid of phase-contrast microscopy (see Fig. 18-6C). The endoplasm streams forward within the cell periphery, turns toward the center of the cell below the oral region, and then flows backward along the central axis of the cell.

When *D. nasutum* cells are fed heat- or formalin-killed paramecia, ingestion proceeds to completion. However, such cells do not disintegrate within the vacuole and apparently cannot be digested. Instead, they are egested after about ten minutes, along with the short trichocysts, which remain attached to the prey. When offered an unsuitable ciliate (e.g., *P. bursaria*) as food, *D. nasutum* may occasionally ingest one of the cells. However, long before the *P. bursaria* population is decimated, the *D. nasutum* population encysts. The cysts can remain dormant for years; they germinate only in the presence of suitable prey.

Presumably, the specificity of feeding by *D. nasutum* is related to specific nutritional requirements, which are totally met only by living cells of certain types of *Paramecium*. Although other ciliates might satisfy some of the nutritional requirements of *D. nasutum*, it is to the advantage of *D. nasutum* that it feed only on an entirely wholesome diet, for at least two reasons. First, while occupied in the ingestion of a less suitable organism, the predator could not apprehend a suitable organism. Second, if the metabolism of *D. nasutum* is so regulated that it operates optimally on a properly balanced diet—as is well established in the nutrition of a great number of organisms at all levels of complexity—it probably could not make maximal use of utilizable components of partially suitable prey, since it might not have available the metabolic intermediates and cofactors essential for their utilization. All the necessary substances or their precursors would be available in the suitable paramecia.

Gametangial Development in *Achlya*

The responses described in this section result in sexual fusion of unlike nuclei, the necessary prelude to genetic recombination. Recombination is a means of increasing the variation among individuals, which increases the adaptability of the population. Accordingly, responses that increase the probability of mating are advantageous to the population, and to the line of descent.

Sexual activity in several phycomycetous fungi is stimulated by low molecular weight substances released by compatible thalli. Such substances, which function as sex hormones, have been recognized in representatives of *Achlya*, *Allomyces*, *Mucor*, *Phycomyces*, and *Pilobolus*, and proposed for some Pythiaceae. Depending on the organism, the substance may induce differentiation of gametangia, direct growth of gametangia so that contact can occur, or attract motile gametes.

Investigation of gametangial development in *Achlya* has revealed a system of hormones that stimulate sequential steps in maturation of sexual structures. These fungi are Oomycetes (see life cycle, Fig. 14-14); sexual fusions involve female nuclei of uninucleate oospheres in an oogonium and male nuclei that migrate from antheridia through fertilization tubes into the oospheres (see Fig. 18-8). Both the female and the male gametangia are non-motile; contact is established as a consequence of growth. In the two species most extensively studied, *A. bisexualis* and *A. ambisexualis,* any one thallus can develop only antheridia or only oogonia, and hence is either male or female. More limited investigations have revealed a similar system of hormones in hermaphroditic species.

Male and female thalli of *A. bisexualis* or *A. ambisexualis* are not distinguishable morphologically during vegetative growth and asexual reproduction. Individuals of both species develop as branched, coenocytic mycelia which reproduce by forming zoospores in terminal zoosporangia. When vegetative hyphae of opposite sex approach each other as a result of vegetative growth, however, development of sexual structures begins and the respective sexes of the thalli can be distinguished.

The first observable change is the elaboration of relatively slender and highly branched hyphae on the male thallus; these are the antheridial hyphae. Their development is stimulated by two substances, called hormones A and A_2, which diffuse from the vegetative hyphae of female thalli. The effects of the female A-hormones are augmented by hormone A_1, which diffuses from vegetative hyphae of male thalli. The male thallus also produces hormone A_3, which reduces the effect of the female-produced hormones on the male. Presumably, the presence of hormone A_3 prevents antheridial development if only small amounts of A and A_2 are present, thereby halting sexual development of the male unless the female thallus is nearby and growing.

During their development on the male thallus, the antheridial hyphae release hormone B. As this substance diffuses to the female thallus, it stimulates initiation of oogonial differentiation. The developing oogonia (oogonial initials) release larger amounts of the female A-hormones, and growth of the antheridial hyphae is directed toward the oogonial initials. When the immature gametangia contact each other, the antheridial hyphae develop septa that delimit the antheridia from the rest of the male thallus.

The delimited antheridia then release hormone D, which stimulates delimitation of each oogonium by septum formation at its base and, subsequently, cleavage of the oogonial protoplast to form oospheres.

The subsequent development of fertilization tubes and then the migration of male nuclei are not known to involve specific hormonal stimulation. The fertilized oospheres develop into thick-walled, dormant oospores. Meiosis precedes or accompanies germination, as in most Oomycetes.

The identification of the six diffusible substances, hormones A, A_1, A_2, A_3, B, and D, has been aided by their differences in solubility, which allow their

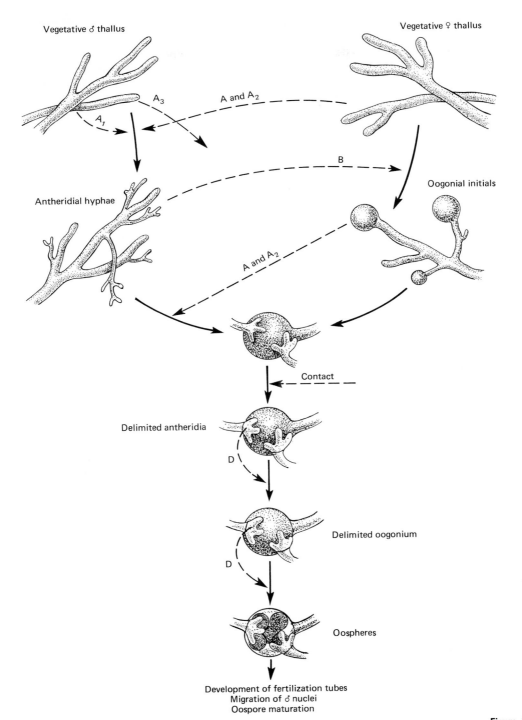

Vegetative ♂ thallus

Vegetative ♀ thallus

A₃

A and A₂

A₁

B

Oogonial initials

Antheridial hyphae

A and A₂

Contact

Delimited antheridia

D

Delimited oogonium

D

Oospheres

Development of fertilization tubes
Migration of ♂ nuclei
Oospore maturation

Development of sexual structures in *Achlya*.

Figure 18-8

411

separation by extraction of culture fluid with various solvents. Identification has also been aided by the availability of separately sexed thalli (uncommon among Oomycetes/Saprolegniales), since each type of thallus produces only some of the hormones. Purified preparations of the hormones have been used in determining the effect(s) of each hormone and quantitative assays of the hormones at different stages of sexual development.

Achlya representatives are typically aquatic fungi, yet they have evolved a type of sexual mechanism that involves non-motile gametangia borne on separate thalli. Most Oomycetes are hermaphroditic; oogonia and antheridia often develop adjacent to one another on the thallus. In an aquatic environment, the probability of contact between gametangia on separate thalli is low unless the population is exceptionally dense. The evolution of a system of sequentially produced stimulants of differentiation ensures that development of gametangia on a thallus will continue only in proximity to a compatible thallus on which gametangia are simultaneously developing.

Chapter 19

Genetic Systems

Inheritance

The study of inheritance in microorganisms has contributed substantially to the concepts of genetics[1] in general. The most significant contributions to date have been in the area called molecular genetics, which is concerned with the description of the chemical basis of inheritance. Most current studies in this area are concerned with the chemical composition of genetic material and the chemical reactions that result in its replication and in its expression. Microbial genetics has also contributed to concepts of the role of chromosomes in inheritance, of extrachromosomal mechanisms of inheritance, and of the dynamics of inheritance in populations of like organisms.

Among the contributions may be mentioned: the recognition that DNA is sufficient to carry fundamental information of inheritance; the concept that the sequence of amino acids in a protein directly reflects the sequence of nucleotides in the DNA of the gene for that protein; this is an elaboration of the "one gene–one enzyme" hypothesis, which was also formulated on the basis of studies with protists; the hypothetic model of gene expression by means of messenger-RNA synthesis followed by translation of the message by protein synthesis on the surface of ribosomes; direct corroboration of the genetic consequences of meiosis.

The advantages of employing microorganisms rather than plants or animals in genetic studies are related primarily to the smaller size, the higher reproductive rate, and the simpler organization of microbes. Because large numbers of individuals can be propagated within a small space in a short time, the physicochemical environment can be manipulated to allow the detection and

---

[1] A glossary of genetics terms used in this discussion is provided at the end of this chapter.

413

isolation of rare mutant or recombinant types in a population. Another advantage is that most microorganisms can reproduce asexually. Consequently, it is possible to determine the full range of phenotypes that can be informed by one genotype as well as the effects of environmental factors on the expression of that genotype. It is also possible to prepare a mass of genetically and physiologically homogeneous individuals for use in chemical analyses.

The principal function of a genetic system is to ensure the similarity of progenitors and progeny. In addition, however, if a line of descent is to evolve toward greater exploitation of and control over the environment (i.e., toward greater complexity of structure, function, and behavior), it is essential that it allow and perpetuate change. It is now reasonably well established that the ultimate source of inheritable change is chemical change in the genetic material. Such change is called mutation.

Mutation of any given gene occurs spontaneously at a frequency of usually less than once every 10^6 nuclear generations. It is detected as a change in the manner in which a gene is expressed, or as a loss or gain of expression. The similarity of the frequency of mutations among all types of organisms carries two major implications. One is that the stability and hence probably the chemical nature of the informational portion of the genetic material is the same in all organisms. The second is that any acceleration of the evolution of one line of descent relative to that of another with a similar generation time must result from the operation of additional mechanisms as sources of genetic variation.

Several such mechanisms are known among higher organisms (e.g., deletions, translocations, polyploidy), but by far the most common, regularly occurring mechanism is sexual fusion of nuclei. The fusion nucleus contains a mixture of genetic material derived from two separate and usually somewhat different individuals. This process, when coordinated with reproduction, results in progeny with a combination of inherited characters different from that of either parent. Such an offspring is referred to as a **recombinant.**

If the coordination of sexual fusions and reproductive events has acted as a major accelerating factor in evolution, one would expect to find a correlation between the coordination of reproduction with sexual fusions and relative evolutionary advance. The empiric argument in favor of this notion is based on the observation that the majority of individuals of most types of plants and animals are recombinants, whereas the majority of individuals of most types of protists are genetically identical with their parents.

It further seems that the evolution of mechanisms for the fusion and subsequent reduction of nuclei must have preceded the evolution of stable diploid nuclei. Most types of protists that are capable of sexual fusions are nevertheless haploid in the predominant developmental phase of their life histories.

It is assumed that diploidy evolved as a consequence of nuclear fusions. One of the major evolutionary advantages of diploidy is that mutations that are disadvantageous in the environment in which they occur can nevertheless be perpetuated, if recessive, in heterozygotes. As the environment changes or the organisms migrate, the mutant characters may become advantageous and contribute to the adaptation of the population to the changed or new environment, or to its ability to exploit the different environment. Thus, diploid organisms that do not develop at all as an independent haploid phase can accumulate greater potential for evolution than can organisms that develop as independent haploid individuals, even in only one phase of the life history. In this regard, it is significant that plants and animals are typically diploid in the predominant phase of development, whereas a large proportion of protists either do not form diploid nuclei or, if capable of sexual fusions, are haploid in the predominant developmental phase of their life histories.

Comparative Cytology of Nuclear Division

Various aspects of protistan existence described in Part 4 were noted as evidence of the similarity of modern protists to ancestors of plants and animals. Certain characteristics of nuclear division among eucaryotic protists also seem to be primitive relative to mitosis and meiosis as they occur in higher organisms. A summary of nuclear division typical of animal cells is presented in Figures 19-1 and 19-2. Nuclear divisions in higher plants differ from those illustrated principally by the absence of centrioles; the organizing center of their spindle fibers has not yet been identified with a discrete structure.

Observation of nuclear divisions in protists has been hindered by the following factors. (1) The nuclei of many protists are relatively small, many being smaller than an animal chromosome (typically more than 1 μm in length). The structures associated with the dividing nucleus are correspondingly small and difficult to visualize with the light microscope. (2) Staining procedures developed for the study of dividing nuclei in higher organisms are not always useful for protistan nuclei. Suitable methods are needed for different protists and for nuclei of different stages of the life history of a given protist. This is especially the case for fungal nuclei. (3) The nuclear envelope remains intact during nuclear division in many protists. This interferes with observation of nuclei in intact and especially in living cells and may be partly responsible for the need for special staining techniques. (4) A general pattern of nuclear division has not been recognized for any major group of protists. Consequently, there is not a general criterion for accuracy of an isolated observation.

Examination of dividing protistan nuclei with the aid of the electron microscope has revealed certain structures not detectable by light microscopy. In particular, fibrils and minute chromosomes have been detected. Electron microscopy has also revealed that the structural components associated with dividing nuclei vary among protists.

The features of protistan nuclear divisions described below apparently represent evolutionary levels intermediate between amitotic division by constriction of the nuclear envelope and divisions structurally similar to those typical of higher organisms. Both extremes occur among protists.

Nuclear Envelopes. As in higher organisms, the nuclear envelope in protists generally is composed of two closely apposed unit membranes. In protists in

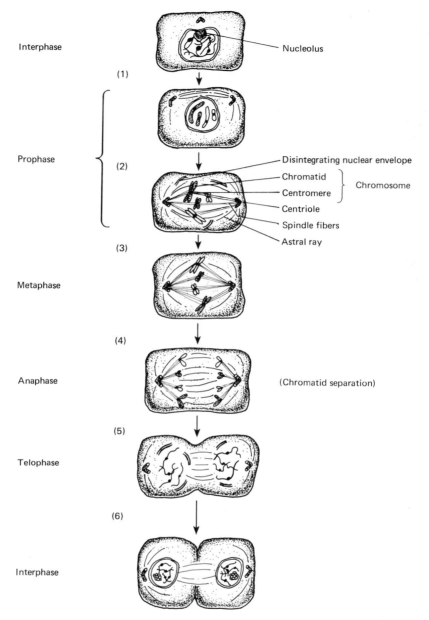

Figure 19-1   Mitosis in an animal cell.

(1) The chromatin of the interphase nucleus begins to condense. The centriole divides; the division products move to opposite poles of the nucleus and appear to generate fibrils. The fibrils that lie between the centrioles constitute the spindle; the fibrils that radiate into the cytoplasm are the astral rays. The nucleolus disappears.

(2) The nuclear envelope begins to disintegrate. The two chromatids of each chromosome appear separated except at the centromere.

(3) The chromosomes align across the equator of the spindle with their long axes perpendicular to the spindle fibrils. Some fibrils from each centriole are attached to the centromere of each chromosome.

(4) Each centromere divides. The chromatids (now chromosomes, since each has a centromere) of each prophase chromosome move toward opposite centrioles. The V shape of the chromosomes implies that the force that moves them is applied at the centromeres.

(5) The chromosomes begin to elongate, a nuclear envelope is organized around each daughter nucleus, and constriction of the cell begins at an equator whose plane is perpendicular to the spindle.

(6) Nuclear envelopes are completed by the time cell division is completed. A nucleolus appears in each daughter nucleus.

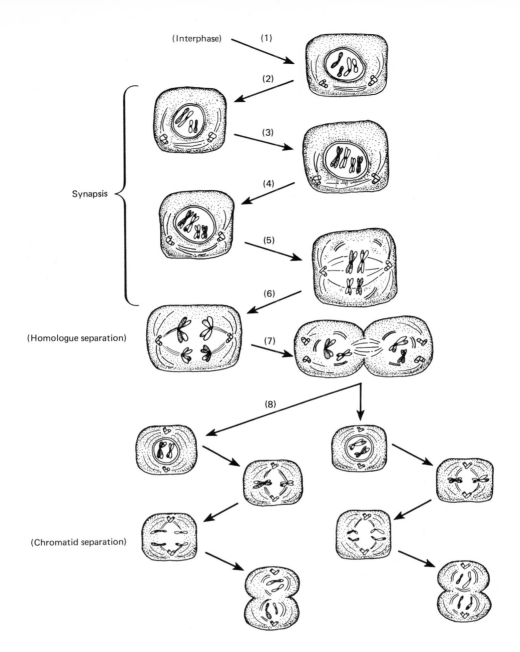

Meiosis in an animal cell.

Figure 19-2

(1) As in (1) of mitosis (Fig. 19-1).

(2) Synapsis: Chromosomes associate lengthwise in pairs with centromeres adjacent to each other. Each pair comprises homologues, chromosomes that contain the same array of genes at the same loci.

(3) The two chromatids of each chromosome appear separated except at the centromere. This is the "four-strand stage."

(4) Portions of chromatids of homologous chromosomes are exchanged. This is "crossing-over." As shown here, the process has been completed.

(5) The nuclear envelope disintegrates. Some fibrils from only one of the centrioles are attached to one centromere in each homologous pair of chromosomes. Fibrils from the other centriole are attached to the centromere of the other member of the pair.

(6) The chromosomes of homologous pairs move toward opposite centrioles.

(7) and (8) A nuclear envelope is reconstructed around each group of chromosomes. The centrioles divide. The chromosomes do not elongate as in telophase of mitosis. Cell division usually follows.

Subsequent events as in (2)–(6) in mitosis. Meiosis I comprises (1)–(7) of this figure, meiosis II the subsequent events.

which the envelope remains intact during nuclear division, the envelope of each daughter nucleus may arise in any of three known ways, depending on the organism.

1. The pre-existing envelope constricts at the equator, each half of it becoming the envelope of a daughter nucleus.

2. As the two masses of nucleoplasm accumulate at the poles of the elongated dividing nucleus, a terminal portion of the envelope closes around each polar mass. The intermediate portions of membrane and any included material (which may include fibrils of a spindle-like apparatus) eventually disappear.

3. New envelopes appear within the pre-existing envelope, one around each mass of nucleoplasm. Most of the intranuclear fibrils that may be present during division are excluded from the daughter nuclei. The old nuclear envelope ultimately disappears.

Chromosomes. Division of some protistan nuclei is not accompanied by the appearance of chromosomes. Such amitotic (without threads) divisions are more commonly reported for protozoa and fungi than for algae; however, such reports are usually based on light microscope observations, and it is possible that the persistence of nuclear envelopes during division has interfered with detection of the chromosomes.

Among protists in which they can be visualized, the chromosomes may differ in structure, arrangement, or behavior from chromosomes of higher organisms. Differences commonly encountered include the following.

1. Centromeres are not detectable. The chromatids appear completely separate early in metaphase or are joined end to end in a circle. Such chromosomes may move to opposite poles of the dividing nucleus with their long axes parallel to the direction of movement.

2. A distinct equatorial plate does not form at metaphase. Instead, the chromosomes gather in one area of the nucleus before the chromatids separate, but the outline of the mass of chromosomes and their orientation within the mass vary from one nucleus to the next.

3. Whether or not the chromosomes become aligned in a group with regular dimensions (e.g., as a disc), the separation of chromatids is not synchronous. One pair of chromatids may reach opposite poles even before another pair has separated. This asynchronous sort of anaphase is frequently reported for fungi, and seems to be typical of euglenid algae.

Fibrils. Intranuclear systems of parallel fibrils are found in dividing nuclei of a variety of protists. In some instances, the fibrils seem to serve primarily to stretch the nucleus into an elongated shape; presumably this is caused by growth of the fibrils, which would, therefore, have to be more rigid than the nuclear envelope. In other cases, some of the fibrils appear to terminate at chromosomes and presumably function to guide or cause the movement of chromosomes to opposite poles during anaphase. Both types of fibrillar systems may occur in one nucleus.

In addition to variation in apparent function of the fibrils, they differ in origin. Among the organisms whose dividing nuclei are illustrated in Figures 19-3 through 19-6, three origins can be observed. In the slime protist *Didymium* and the ciliate *Blepharisma,* the fibrils appear to originate from the inner surface of the nuclear envelope. In *Saccharomyces,* they originate from a thick, double, plate-like structure situated within the nuclear envelope. In the phycomycete *Catenaria,* intranuclear fibrils arise from an area within the nuclear envelope directly opposite an extranuclear centriole. In several types of Basidiomycetes, an extranuclear centriole is associated with the dividing nucleus as in *Catenaria;* the same centriole is also associated with (generates?) fibrils that radiate into the cytoplasm.

Mechanisms of Genetic Recombination in Bacteria

Three mechanisms for the transfer of genetic material in bacteria have been discovered: transformation, transduction, and conjugal transfer. Each can result in recombinant formation. All three mechanisms typically allow only a small portion of the genome of the donor to be transmitted to recombinant progeny.

Transformation. Transformation is observed as a change in heritable characteristics of a clone derived from a cell (the recipient) that incorporated into its genome a fragment of DNA released by lysis of another cell (the donor). By incorporating the DNA, the recipient acquired some of the genetic information contained in the fragment and transmitted that information to its progeny.

The discovery of transfer of genetic material between bacteria by cultivating recipients in the presence of disintegrated donors was first reported in 1928. This was the first report of genetic recombination in bacteria and also the first of the accomplishment of a specific, predetermined change in hereditary properties of an organism.

The original experimental studies of transformation were carried out with pneumococci. These bacteria occur naturally in the respiratory tract of mammals, in which they may cause pneumonia. When first isolated from a natural host, the bacteria possess capsules composed of polysaccharide. About 100 types of capsular polysaccharides can be distinguished, and any one isolate can be classified among pneumococci according to the type of polysaccharide present in its capsule. The types are designated by Roman numerals.

Under conditions of artificial cultivation, variants (which are mutants) that lack capsular material can be isolated. Pneumococci that lack capsules cannot infect the natural host and cause pneumonia. They are called R-variants because the surface of their colonies appears rough, whereas the colonies of encapsulated strains (called S) appear smooth due to the presence of large amounts of mucoid capsular polysaccharide. R-variants can revert to S by back-mutation; when this occurs, the type of polysaccharide formed by the revertants is the same as that of the S strain from which the R-variant was derived.

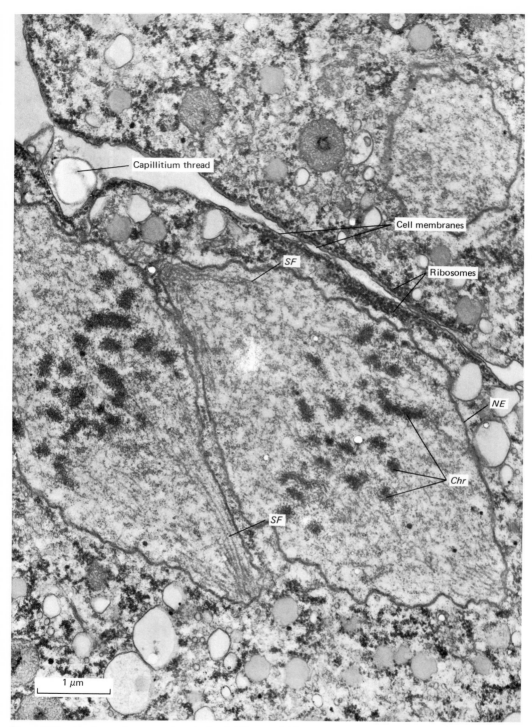

Figure 19-3 Sections of two synchronously dividing nuclei in a plasmodium of *Didymium nigripes* prior to sporulation. Cleavage of the protoplasm has begun, with the new cell membranes lined internally with ribosomes. (Courtesy of F. Schuster.)

Labels in Figures 19-3–19-6
NE, nuclear envelope; *SF*, microtubule-like spindle fibrils; *Pl*, plate within nuclear envelope; *Ce*, centriole; *Chr*, chromosome.

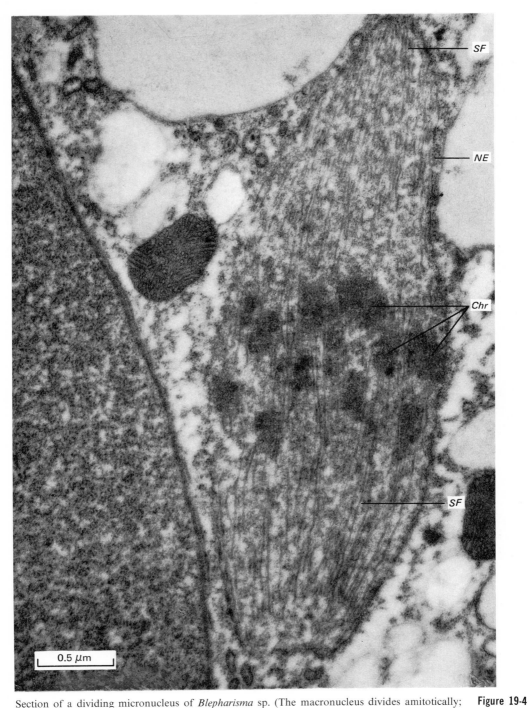

Section of a dividing micronucleus of *Blepharisma* sp. (The macronucleus divides amitotically; **Figure 19-4** intramacronuclear fibrils have not been observed, but fibrils do occur on the outer surface of the envelope of the dividing macronucleus.) (From Jenkins, R. A., 1967. *J. Cell Biol.*, **34**:463. By permission of The Rockefeller University Press.)

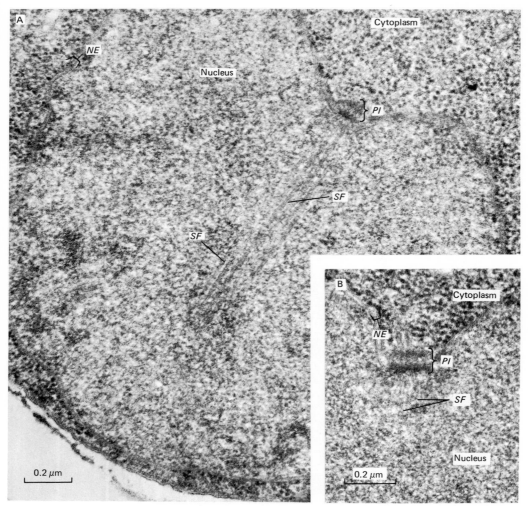

Figure 19-5   Section of a dividing nucleus of *Saccharomyces cerevisiae. Inset:* the plate within the nuclear envelope, somewhat higher magnification. (From Robinow, C. F., and J. Marak, 1966. *J. Cell Biol.,* **29**:129. By permission of The Rockefeller University Press.)

In the 1928 experiments, it was found that when a mouse was inoculated with large numbers of R cells, an infection occasionally resulted. Among the bacteria reisolated from the infected mouse, only encapsulated clones were found. It was further found that this result was more likely if heat-killed S cells were inoculated simultaneously with living R cells.

The first interpretation of this latter observation was that the R cells acquired some capsular polysaccharide from the dead S cells and subsequently could make more of it. This seemed to be supported by the results of the following type of experiment. Living R cells derived from type II encapsulated pneumococci were inoculated into mice simultaneously with heat-killed type III S cells.

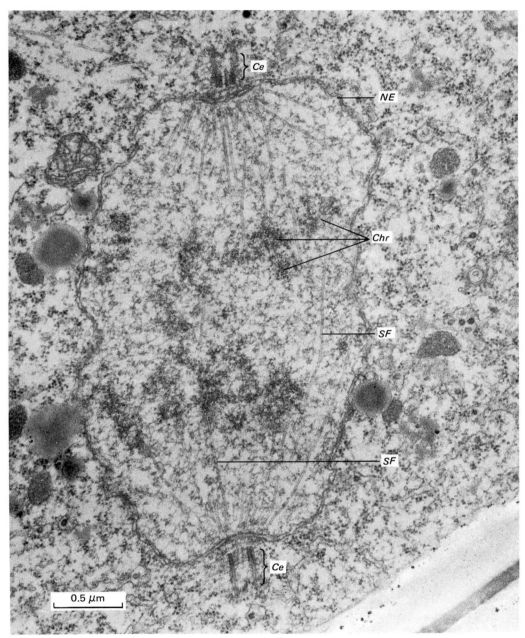

Section of a dividing nucleus of *Catenaria anguillulae* in early anaphase. (From Ichida, A. A., and M. S. Fuller, 1968. *Mycologia,* **60**:141. By permission of *Mycologia* and The New York Botanical Garden.)

Figure 19-6

After symptoms of infection appeared, living type III S cells could be recovered from the mouse. This phenomenon was designated "transformation" of R cells to S cells. Because the type of capsular polysaccharide formed by the transformed cells (the **transformants**) was the same as that present on the heat-killed cells and could be different from the type formed by the S progenitors of the R cells, the "transforming principle" was tentatively postulated to be the polysaccharide itself or a protein involved in its synthesis.

Some years after the initial report, it was found that transformation of pneumococci could occur in artificial cultures, as well as in mice. In 1944, the results of an investigation of the chemical nature of transforming principle active in artificial cultures were reported. Variously treated preparations of heat-killed type III S cells were added to cultures of viable R cells. Chemical or enzymatic treatments of the S cells that eliminated polysaccharide, lipid, protein, or RNA did not affect their transforming activity. A sterile preparation of material from S cells purified by elimination of small molecules, polysaccharide, lipid, protein, and RNA still contained a practically undiminished amount of transforming principle. The material consisted of DNA, as inferred from quantitative determination of its elemental composition and physicochemical properties.[2] Most significantly, the transforming activity of the DNA preparation was destroyed by enzymes known to degrade DNA from various organisms. The investigators concluded that the transforming principle was identical with DNA.

The same investigators also reported that transformed cells produced not only the specific capsular polysaccharide, but the transforming substance as well. That is, type III S transformants could serve as a source of DNA for transformation of other type II R cells. Prior to 1944, the DNA of eucaryotic cells was known to be localized in the chromosomes, but was believed to be a structural component that did not function biochemically and that lacked sufficient specificity to serve as genetic material.

Most of the chemical and physical studies on which the presently accepted hypothetic molecular structure of DNA is based were reported after 1944. According to current opinions, DNA meets each of the criteria that genetic material would fulfill: (1) it is replicated;[3] the pre-existing molecule serves as a template on which the new molecule is built, so that the new molecule is a copy of the pre-existing one; (2) the information it contains can be translated into biochemical activities within the cell; and (3) its fine structure is specific, being constant within a species and different in different species. Only very short segments, at most, of DNA molecules from different types of organisms are identical in fine structure. Such segments are called homologous, because they seem to occur in proportion to the general similarity of the organisms and are presumed to have been inherited from a common ancestor.

[2]The physicochemical properties determined included sedimentation behavior in the ultracentrifuge, light-absorption spectrum, electrophoretic behavior, heat stability, solubility, and viscosity.

[3]The term "replica" has been borrowed from fine art, where it is used to refer to a copy of a work of art prepared by the person who produced the original. In biochemistry, it is used to refer to a molecule that is synthesized only in immediate physical association with the molecule of which it is a copy.

As information concerning the chemistry and biologic activity of DNA accumulated, interest in transformation increased. Since 1944, transformation has been accomplished with bacteria of the genera *Haemophilus, Neisseria, Rhizobium, Acinetobacter,* and *Bacillus.* A description of the general features of experimental transformation can now be given on the basis of these studies.

Transformation involves the following steps.

1. Release of DNA upon lysis of the donor cell.
2. Fragmentation of the DNA to pieces whose molecular weight is about 5 to 15×10^6.
3. Adsorption of DNA to the surface of the recipient cell.
4. Penetration of DNA into the protoplast of the recipient.
5. Integration of the DNA into the recipient's genome.
6. Expression of the genetic information in the recipient and its progeny.

Penetration appears to be influenced markedly by the environment of the cells immediately prior to or during their exposure to transforming DNA. The cells must be in a receptive (also called "competent") state in order for the DNA to penetrate. The conditions under which cells become receptive must be determined empirically for any given strain of bacteria. For examples, some strains must be growing, others can be suspended in a non-nutrient fluid; some must be in a medium containing proteins or animal fluids, others need not be; and some strains must be in the early, others in the late, still others in the middle of the exponential phase of growth.

Integration of transforming DNA usually involves displacement from the genome of the homologous segment of the resident DNA, at least in the genetic material of progeny of a transformant. On the assumption that displacement occurs in the recipient cell, it is proposed that the transforming DNA is integrated into the genome by a process (Fig. 19-7) analogous to crossing-over between chromosomes of higher organisms. In the case of transformation, however, the two units of genetic material are not equivalent. One is the genomic DNA of the recipient; the other is a fragment of exogenous DNA that has penetrated the protoplast. The double-crossing-over-like process transposes a portion of the fragment into the recipient genome and the displaced portion of the genome into the fragment (see Fig. 19-7A). The fragment presumably is later destroyed by cell enzymes or spontaneously disintegrates; it is not replicated. This is the supposed mechanism by which relatively small segments of transforming DNA having extensive homology with recipient DNA are integrated.

Another mechanism of integration is proposed for those instances in which the transformants retain both the entire resident genome and some or all of the exogenous DNA fragment. This happens particularly when the transforming DNA fragments are long and/or only partly homologous with the recipient DNA (as in interspecies transformation). The DNA fragment becomes associated with the (approximately) homologous area of the recipient DNA, and one or more small portions become inserted (see Fig. 19-7B). The genetic information of the fragment is thereby added to the genome without displacement of resident genes from the genome, and it is replicated with the recipient

A

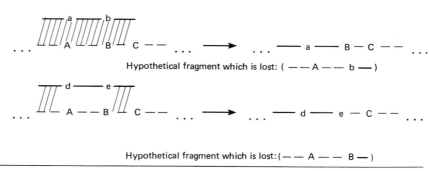

Hypothetical fragment which is lost: (— — A — — b —)

Hypothetical fragment which is lost: (— — A — — B —)

B

or

— — — — Recipient DNA

———————— Transforming DNA from donor

Area of homology

Figure 19-7   Proposed mechanisms of integration of transforming DNA. *A, B, C*, etc., are loci. In this chapter the use of upper- and lower-case letters to designate loci does not imply dominance or recessiveness; it indicates only that the alleles are detectably different. Upper-case letters are used for loci from one parent, lower-case for loci from the other parent.
   A. Integration by displacement. *B*. Integration by addition.

genome. Such transformants may carry two alleles of a given gene in one genome. For example, encapsulated strains (in pneumococci and *Haemophilus*) of one type can be transformed to produce capsules containing a mixture of two types of polysaccharides.

About 1 in 10^4 cells in a recipient population generates a clone transformed for a given character. In addition to capsule formation and type, the following kinds of characters have been transformed: drug resistance, tendency to form chains, endosporulation, lysogenic state (i.e., prophage genes can be transferred), synthesis of specific enzymes (i.e., nutritional markers), and infectivity for plants (in *Rhizobium*). Generally, only one marker is transformed in any recipient's progeny. A double-transformant clone can arise when a recipient integrates two different fragments of transforming DNA, or when it integrates a single fragment containing two markers.

Transduction. Transduction, bacteriophage-mediated genetic transfer, is similar to transformation in that (1) the donor of genetic material does not need to make contact with the recipient, and (2) the only cellular substance removed from donor to recipient is DNA. The principal difference is that transduced DNA is enclosed within virion protein during its transit from donor to recipient, rather than being free, as in transformation.

There are two important consequences of this difference. First, the DNA is protected from substances, particularly degradative enzymes, that could inactivate it as genetic material. Second, adsorption of the virion by the recipient can occur only if the cell surface contains receptor sites for that virus. Since receptors for a particular bacteriophage generally occur only in genetically related cells, this ensures that the transduced DNA will enter only cells in which it is likely to be incorporated into the genome.

Bacteriophages may be classified in three groups according to the events that follow entry of phage nucleic acid from a virion into a susceptible cell. The least virulent type of phage invariably lysogenizes[4] the infected cell. The second type usually initiates phage multiplication, but lysogenizes about 1 of every 10^5 cells infected. These two types are called temperate phages, because they can lysogenize. The third type is called intemperate; infection of every cell results in lysis.

All bacteriophages that can mediate genetic transfer ("transducing phages") are temperate. Cells infected with intemperate phages do not survive long enough after infection for any genes that might be carried by the phages to be expressed. In known transducing phages, the normal phage genome is contained in DNA. Whether RNA-containing phages transmit inheritable characteristics between bacteria has not yet been determined; from what is known concerning transduction (generalized; see below) at present, it cannot be concluded that this phenomenon must be limited to DNA-containing phages.

Two types of transduction are distinguished at present. The more common type, called generalized transduction, may involve any bacterial gene. The less common type is called specialized (or restricted) transduction; only one or two specific bacterial genes can be transduced, their identity being constant for a given transducing phage. Whether transduction is generalized or restricted is a property of the phage.

Generalized transduction is illustrated diagrammatically in Figure 19-8. A **transducing particle** is a virion that contains bacterial DNA. In generalized transduction, a transducing particle is formed when a fragment of bacterial DNA comparable in volume to a normal phage genome is assembled into a virion instead of a copy of the phage genome. This happens in about 1 in 10^4 virions. Most transducing particles contain only bacterial DNA and lack phage DNA. Such particles may be produced in lytic cycles resulting from exogenous infection by a transducing phage or from conversion of the prophage of a lysogenic cell to vegetative phage. The fragment of bacterial DNA may

[4]See Chap. 7, and Fig. 7-2.

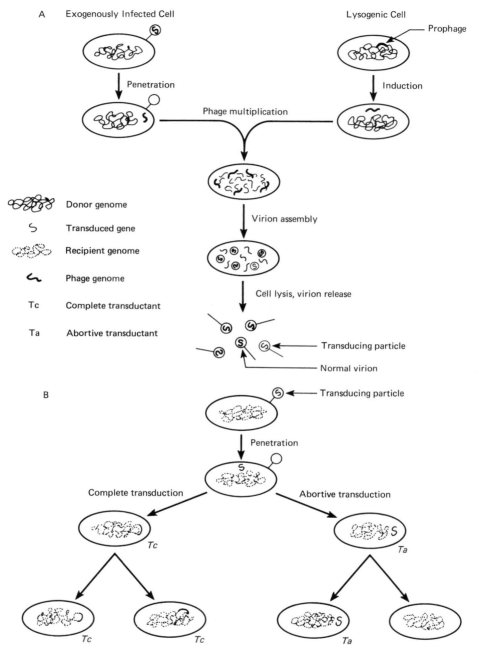

A   Exogenously Infected Cell

Lysogenic Cell

Prophage

Penetration

Induction

Phage multiplication

Virion assembly

Cell lysis, virion release

Transducing particle

Normal virion

Donor genome

S   Transduced gene

Recipient genome

Phage genome

Tc   Complete transductant

Ta   Abortive transductant

B

Transducing particle

Penetration

Complete transduction

Abortive transduction

Tc

Ta

Tc

Tc

Ta

Figure 19-8   Generalized transduction. *A.* Formation of transducing particle. *B.* Formation of transductant.

contain as many as three or four detectable bacterial genes, although most transducing particles contain only one.

Transducing particles are externally similar to normal virions. They can adsorb to cells susceptible to the phage, and the DNA they contain can be released into the protoplast. However, because the DNA usually does not contain any phage genes, neither lysis nor lysogenization results from entry of the DNA of a transducing particle into a cell. In most instances, it apparently does not have any effect on the cell. In some instances, a recipient cell generates progeny in which a bacterial gene contained in the virion-borne DNA is expressed. Such a cell is called a **transductant.**

About 90 per cent of transductants are abortively transduced. The DNA fragment persists in the cytoplasm of a recipient, but is not replicated. The character is expressed in only one cell of each subsequent generation, viz., the cell that inherited the DNA fragment. In the remainder of the transductants, the phage-borne DNA becomes integrated into the genome of the recipient. This phenomenon is called complete transduction. The transduced gene replaces the homologous gene in the genome of the recipient and subsequently is replicated with the remainder of the genome. The clone derived from the complete transductant possesses the transduced gene as a stable constituent of its genome, and the characteristic determined by the gene is expressed in every cell. The integration of a transduced gene into the genome is tentatively presumed to involve a mechanism similar to that proposed for transformation.

Restricted transduction is illustrated diagrammatically in Figure 19-9. This phenomenon has been studied extensively in the phage lambda–*E. coli* K12 system, and the description presented here is based on the observations and interpretations of this system.

Strain K12 of *E. coli* possesses a lambda-insertion site in its genome, situated between the genes for galactose utilization and biotin biosynthesis. The lambda prophage of a lysogenic cell is invariably inserted at this location. When a population of lysogenic cells is exposed to an agent, e.g., ultraviolet light, which provokes the conversion of lambda prophage to vegetative phage, approximately 1 in 10^5 induced cells produces transducing particles rather than normal lambda. Whether the induced cell is to produce transducing particles or normal phage apparently is determined at the time the prophage dissociates from the bacterial genome. If the prophage dissociates at the same points at which it originally was inserted, the dissociated DNA will consist only of the phage genome. If, on the other hand, dissociation occurs at different points, the dissociated DNA will consist partly of prophage DNA and partly of bacterial DNA. In either case, the dissociated fragment is replicated, and one copy is eventually assembled into each virion. Those virions that contain a mixture of phage and bacterial DNA are potentially transducing particles. The DNA is a single unit, with the bacterial portion in one end and the phage portion accounting for the remainder.

The dimensions of infective lambda virions are constant, and the head is filled when the entire phage genome is present. When some of the DNA within a lambda virion has been derived from the cell genome, an equivalent volume

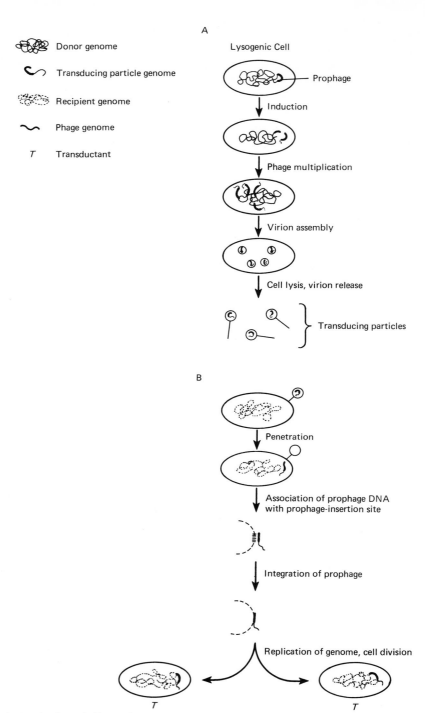

Figure 19-9   Restricted transduction. *A.* Formation of transducing particles. *B.* Formation of transductant.

of phage DNA must be excluded. Consequently, it is characteristic of lambda transducing particles that they do not contain complete phage genomes. If a phage gene essential for vegetative phage multiplication, virion assembly, or cell lysis is not present, the virion is called defective. It can adsorb to a susceptible cell, release its DNA into the protoplast, and establish itself as a prophage and confer immunity to lambda on the cell. However, it cannot initiate a lytic cycle of infection that results in release of phage particles, either as an exogenously infecting virion or from the prophage condition.

Lambda virions carrying bacterial genes for galactose utilization are typically defective. A cell incapable of utilizing galactose (gal—) to which the gene for galactose utilization (gal+) is transduced by lambda is defectively lysogenic. The phage portion of the virion-borne DNA becomes inserted at the lambda-insertion site. The gal genes can remain attached to the inserted prophage and be replicated with the recipient's genome, whether or not they are integrated into the main axis of the DNA molecule that constitutes the genome. Cells in which the gal+ genes are not integrated continue, through successive generations, to carry two sets of gal genes—the resident genes present before defective lysogenization, and the transduced genes.

It seems at present that the principal difference between generalized and restricted transduction lies in the events surrounding virion assembly. Restricted transducing phages apparently do not assemble DNA into virions unless it contains at least some phage DNA. Generalized transducing phages appear able to assemble any (D?)NA fragment that will fit into the virion coat.

Conjugation.[5] The third known mechanism of transfer of genetic material between bacteria involves a reversible physical association of cells. Cell fusion does not occur, and the cells eventually separate. The recipient contains the (partial) zygote nucleus, and the recombinants arise among the progeny of the recipient. This behavior is called conjugation, by analogy with mating in higher organisms.

Most isolates of any species in which conjugation can occur either cannot conjugate or can conjugate only as recipients. Occasionally isolates that can behave as donors are found. So far, the donor isolates have been found to inherit donor ability through a genetic determinant that is not associated with the nucleus (hence called a "cytoplasmic" or "extragenomic" genetic factor). Such isolates can be referred to as male+. The non-nuclear factors that determine maleness are transferred during practically every instance of conjugation of a male+ cell, whether or not nuclear markers are also transferred.

Ability of an isolate to conjugate as a recipient is usually attributable to lack of a maleness factor. Such an isolate can be designated male—. However, under certain conditions of mating, cells of a male+ strain can receive additional maleness factors or nuclear markers from another male+ strain. Generally, recombinants are more frequent in crosses between male+ and male— strains than in crosses involving two male+ strains.

[5] See footnote p. 445 in "Parasexuality" section concerning actinomycetes.

Genetic transfer during conjugation has been discovered in several genera of bacteria, including *Escherichia, Salmonella, Shigella, Vibrio,* and *Pseudomonas* (all are gram negative). Of these, genetic transfer associated with the F (for "fertility") factor of *E. coli* strain K12 has been most extensively investigated. Although the description of this system is still largely hypothetic, it is at present the most complete. The remainder of this discussion will be concerned with the F factor system in *E. coli.*

Conjugation and genetic transfer apparently occur as follows. Compatible pairs of cells collide at random and become united by a short bridge visible in electron micrographs. The only apparent pathway along which genetic material could pass between the cells is the single bridge. In many accounts of bacterial conjugation, this structure is referred to as a "cytoplasmic bridge." However, there is very little cytoplasm present, and it has been possible to detect transfer of cytoplasmic constituents from donor to recipient in only a few specific kinds of matings; transfer of any kind in the reverse direction has not been detected. Establishment of the bridge apparently requires less than five minutes after male and recipient populations are mixed, since transfer of markers can be detected at this time.

The type of genetic material that moves depends on the state of the F factor. The F factor can exist as a unit of genetic material separate (or separable) from the nuclear material. In this state, it replicates autonomously, but in approximate synchrony with the nuclear material. A cell containing cytoplasmic F factors is designated F+. In 99.999 per cent of mating pairs involving an F+ cell as donor, only the F factor is transferred to the recipient. This requires less than nine minutes of conjugation, and conjugation usually results in transfer of the F factor. The recipients generate F+ clones which are not recombinant for any other characters. All nuclear markers are inherited from the recipient.

Alternatively, the F factor can exist as an integrated portion of the genome. The genomic F factor inhibits replication of cytoplasmic F factors so that a clone of male cells contains F factors in one state or the other, but not both. A cell containing genomic F factors is designated Hfr (for high frequency of recombination). When the donor cell of a mating pair is Hfr, nuclear markers move from donor to recipient in about one of every ten mating pairs; only rarely is the integrated F factor transferred. All the evidence so far available is consistent with the following interpretation of events during conjugation involving an Hfr donor.

When conjugation is initiated, a replica of the circular DNA molecule that comprises the nuclear genome of *E. coli* K12 is or almost immediately becomes linear. The two free ends are formed within the F factor region in the genome. One end then begins to move into the recipient cell, with the remainder of the molecule trailing after it. If conjugation continues until both the initial and the terminal ends are transferred, the entire F factor enters the recipient. If the F factor is reconstituted as a unit, the progeny of the recipient may subsequently inherit the donor trait and be Hfr.

Generally, however, only a portion of the genome is transferred, and recombinants are male only if the recipient was male. The conjugating cells separate, on the average, after about 20 minutes. Within an hour after the termination of mating, some of the markers received from the male are incorporated into one of the nuclei of the recipient. Apparently, after this time, any unincorporated genetic material from the donor disintegrates or is destroyed by enzymes within the recipient; it is not replicated.

Incorporation of genetic material apparently occurs, as in transformation and complete transduction, by displacement of homologous regions from the recipient genome. The hypothetic fragment containing unincorporated donor genetic material and displaced genetic material is subsequently lost. One of the two to four genetically homogeneous clones generated by successive fissions of the recipient comprises cells containing recombinant nuclei derived from the zygote nucleus. A complete diploid genome is not formed, and only rarely does a partial diploid nucleus persist. The recombinant nucleus usually contains a single allele of each gene, and an equivalent of reductive nuclear division such as meiosis does not occur and is not necessary. Since only a portion of the donor genome is transferred, and only a fraction of the transferred material is incorporated, the recombinant clones inherit most of their genetic information from the recipient.

Hfr strains have not been isolated from naturally occurring *E. coli* populations; they have been obtained only as rare (less than 1 in 10^5) clones within F + populations. The transition from F + to Hfr is regarded as a consequence of a mutation-like event in the F factor that causes or allows it to become integrated into the genome. The change is reversible; about 1 in 10^5 cells in an Hfr population contains autonomous F factors.

Conjugal transfer differs from transformation and transduction in three significant ways. First, conjugation requires direct contact between two cells that differ genetically (or at least physiologically, in male + -by-male + crosses) in their ability to act as donors. They must, however, be closely related otherwise and usually are strains of one species. Second, larger amounts of genetic material can be transmitted; it is possible in rare conjugating pairs for the donor to transfer a complete copy of its genome to the recipient. Consequently, several markers from the donor may appear in the recombinant genotype. Third, the donor can survive.

Genetic Recombination in Haploid Eucaryotic Protists

Tetrad Analysis. Haploid organisms are valuable as subjects of genetic studies because all genes can be expressed in every individual, and the four products of meiosis serve as the nuclei of four (or a multiple of four) independent organisms that can reproduce asexually. According to the principles of mendelian inheritance, the genetic characters of the parents should segregate among the four nuclei and among the four types of clones subsequently generated by asexual reproduction. Since not all genes will be expressed in the same environment, the availability of clones representing the four meiotic products allows the detection of different kinds of genes. This can be accomplished by examining the properties of portions of a given clone cultivated under different conditions or analyzed by different methods. Consequently, a complete analysis of a single set of four meiotic products (a tetrad) can be performed without further matings.

A tetrad can be characterized as one of three types, according to the number of genotypes present and their similarity to the genotypes of the parents.

1. Parental Ditype (PD). Two genotypes, one the same as that of one parent, the other the same as that of the other parent.

2. Non-parental Ditype (NPD). Two genotypes, neither the same as that of either parent (i.e., both recombinant).

3. Tetratype (T). Four genotypes; two parental and two recombinant, or all four recombinant.

The manner in which each type of tetrad is generated in meiosis is illustrated schematically in Figures 19-10 and 19-11.

These figures illustrate the two principal uses of tetrad analysis in genetic studies: the detection of linkage and of crossing-over. The probability of PD's and NPD's is approximately equal when the genes are unlinked and therefore assort randomly at the first meiotic division. Linkage between two genes is implied when the proportion of ditypes accounted for by PD's approaches 100 per cent. NPD's arise only as a consequence of double (four-chromatid) crossing-over prior to the first meiotic division and so are relatively rare.

Whether or not genes are linked, a tetratype can arise only as a consequence of two-chromatid crossing-over so that the different alleles do not segregate until the second meiotic division. If the genes are unlinked, crossing-over must occur between at least one gene and its centromere. If the genes are linked, the crossing-over must occur between them. If crossing-over occurs for both of two unlinked genes, about 50 per cent of the tetrads could be PD's (see ordered tetrads, below), the others tetratypes. Nevertheless, the only source of tetratypes is crossing-over and second-division segregation, so that their appearance indicates that crossing-over occurred.

Chlamydomonas. Sexual fusion of *Chlamydomonas* may involve fusion of isogametes, anisogametes, or male and female gametes (see Fig. 17-7), depending on the species. The fusions are typically heterothallic. In isogamous species, the mating type is determined by a single gene (*mt*) for which there are two alleles, designated plus (*mt +*) and minus (*mt −*). Compatible gametes are of opposite mating type; consequently, the inheritance of the mt gene can be followed in the same manner as that of other genes.

In isogamous species, vegetative cells behave as gametes under certain conditions. Generally, the cells are cultivated on solidified medium in the light and then either transferred to a medium lacking a utilizable source of nitrogen or incubated in the dark for 12 to 24 hours. During this incubation, the cells deplete endogenous reserves, a process that increases their tendency to behave

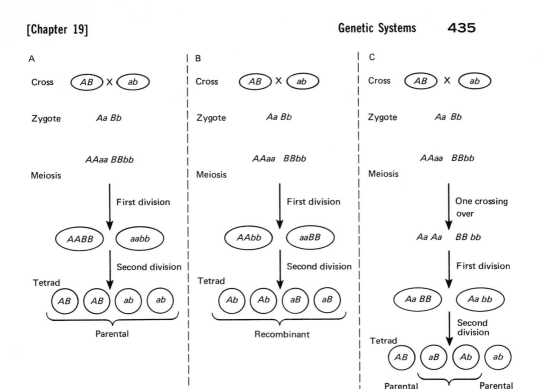

Generation of three types of tetrads—unlinked genes. *A.* Generation of a parental ditype. **Figure 19-10**
B. Generation of a non-parental ditype. *C.* Generation of a tetratype.

as gametes. After the starvation period, the cells are suspended in liquid (either nutrient medium or water). This "flooding" causes a marked increase in flagellar activity, which was inhibited on the solidified medium. Within a few minutes, practically all the cells are actively motile. If two such suspensions of cells of opposite mating type are mixed at this time, pairs of cells (or occasionally clumps containing larger numbers of cells) appear within a few minutes. The mating is allowed to continue for an hour or more and then the cells are transferred to solidified medium. Subsequent development of the zygotes requires first a period of illumination (generally, until the zygote wall is under construction), then a period of darkness, during which the zygote matures.

Sometime during the dark period, the zygotes, which are readily distinguished morphologically from vegetative cells, are manipulated (see Fig. 19-12) into well-separated sites on the surface of a plate of solidified medium. Six to eleven days after mating, depending on the genotype of the zygote, the wall of the zygote ruptures and exposes flagellated cells formed by fission of the zygote protoplast. These cells are manipulated into lanes cut into the agar and allowed to reproduce asexually until each cell has generated a colony. Each isolated colony comprises a clone; each clone is then isolated and tested for genetic homogeneity (see Chap. 11).

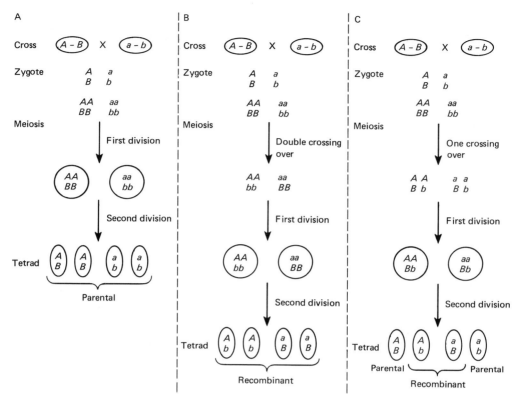

Figure 19-11 Generation of three types of tetrads—linked genes. *A*. Generation of a parental ditype. *B*. Generation of a non-parental ditype. *C*. Generation of a tetratype.

In this way, investigators obtain pure populations of asexually produced *Chlamydomonas* cells whose nuclei are direct descendants of the respective meiotic products. Each group of 4, 8, or 16 clones can be identified with a single zygote. Subsequent characterization of each clone in such a group provides a direct analysis of the tetrad that arose from the zygote.

An example tetrad analysis from a *C. moewusii* cross is presented in Table 19-1. This cross was performed with mutants obtained by ultraviolet irradiation of wild type strains, which were identical except for *mt*. Thus, the parents were genetically marked derivatives of strains of known genotype.

Zygotes 15, 21, and 18 yielded three different tetratypes. This is a common observation in tetrad analyses involving three or more unlinked genes, since any pair of the genes may occur as PD, NPD, or T. In the examples presented, the tetrad from zygote 15 is a tetratype combining *vol/mt* and *vol/pho* as tetratypes, and *pho/mt* as a PD; the tetrad from zygote 21 combines *vol/mt* as a NPD, and *vol/pho* and *pho/mt* as tetratypes; and the tetrad from zygote 18 combines all three pairs as tetratypes. Among the progeny of the three zygotes were seven different genotypes. Accordingly, even this very small sample of zygotes, involving only three genes of the species, illustrates the

Mating mixture of + and − cells

6 days in dark

1. A mixture of unmated vegetative cells and zygotes is spread on the surface of a solidified medium and exposed to chloroform vapor for about 30 seconds to kill vegetative cells.

2. Zygotes manipulated with glass needle under microscope.

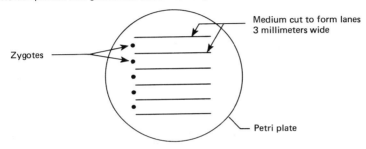

Medium cut to form lanes 3 millimeters wide

Zygotes

Petri plate

3. Incubated, observed for germination.

4. Upon germination the cells are manipulated with a glass needle under the microscope into the lanes.

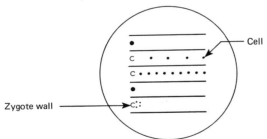

Cell

Zygote wall

5. The plate is incubated in the light until colonies are 0.75 millimeter in diameter. Samples from colonies are then used to inoculate individual cultures.

Isolation of zygotes and their immediate products in *Chlamydomonas.*   **Figure 19-12**

extensive variation possible among sexually produced progeny of one pair of genotypes.

The results of several other crosses between genetically marked *C. moewusii* strains were reported in the article from which the examples of Table 19-1 were selected. The inheritance of eight genes in addition to *mt* was studied. The behavior of the markers in the various crosses implied linkage between

**TABLE 19-1.   Analysis of Tetrads in *Chlamydomonas moewusii*,
Cross: (vol−pho+mt+) × (vol+pho−mt−)***

Zygote #	Clone #	Marker†: Volutin	Photosynthesis	Mating Type
15	7,8,11,13	vol−	pho+	mt+
	1,2,4,15	vol+	pho+	mt+
	3,5,9,10	vol−	pho−	mt−
	6,12,14,16	vol+	pho−	mt−
21	1,2,3,6	vol+	pho−	mt+
	8,9,11,14	vol+	pho+	mt+
	10,12,13,15	vol−	pho+	mt−
	4,5,7	vol−	pho−	mt−
18	2	vol−	pho+	mt+
	3	vol+	pho−	mt+
	1	vol+	pho+	mt−
	(Deduced	vol−	pho−	mt−)

* Data from Lewin, R., 1953. *J. Genet.,* **51**:543, Table 5.
† Markers other than mt: Volutin: wild type (vol+) accumulates a moderate amount of phosphate reserve; mutant (vol−) accumulates an abundant phosphate reserve. Photosynthesis: wild type (pho+) is capable of photosynthetic development; mutant (pho−) is not.

the markers *T* and *L* (see Table 19-2). Among the tetrads resulting from matings between cells carrying different alleles of these genes, only PD's and tetratypes were found. This means that recombination of the parental alleles of these genes occurred only by crossing-over, and not by independent assortment. This further indicated that the genes were so close together in their common linkage group that the probability of double (four-chromatid) crossing-over between them was very low. However, if a larger number of zygotes had been available for analysis, an occasional NPD would have been expected.

The numbers of tetrad types for the other gene pairs presented in Table 19-2 show PD:NPD ratios expected for unlinked genes.

The data presented above for *C. moewusii* illustrate three characteristics of mendelian inheritance. First, among the progeny of a single zygote nucleus, the maximum number of genotypes is four. Mendel recognized that four was the basic number of each of the ratios he had observed; it is now recognized that the number is determined by the number of copies of each gene present at the beginning of meiosis—viz., four (two identical alleles from one parent, two from the other, each pair contained in a duplicated chromosome composed of two chromatids and one centromere). Second, each gene segregates among the progeny in such a way that 50 per cent of the progeny receive the allele contributed by one of the parents, and the rest receive the other allele (from the other parent). Thus, in any tetrad, the ratio of occurrence of the two alleles of any one gene is 2:2. (It was on this basis that the fourth genotype of the tetrad of zygote 18 was deduced; see Table 19-1.)

Third, the high proportion of tetratypes in all crosses indicates that crossing-over occurs frequently during meiosis in *C. moewusii*. The phenomenon of crossing-over, discovered after Mendel's death and so not included in mendelian principles as he formulated them, occurs during most meioses observed in all types of organisms capable of sexual fusion and reductive division of nuclei. In general, the majority of tetrads generated by meiosis are tetratypes. This means that, even if only two genes are followed, not more than half the progeny of each zygote will be genotypically like a parent. The proportion of parental genotypes among the progeny decreases as the number of genes in which the parents differ increases.

Genetic studies have been performed with species of *Chlamydomonas* other than *C. moewusii.* The results are generally similar. However, at least two mutant characteristics of *C. reinhardi* have been found that are not inherited in a mendelian manner; specifically, they do not segregate during meiosis. All the progeny inherit the characteristic from one of the parents. Such non-mendelian inheritance can in many organisms be attributed to an unequal contribution of cytoplasm from the parents to the zygote (maternal inheritance). However, mating in *C. reinhardi* is isogamous, and each parent contributes the same amount of cytoplasm to the zygote and, subsequently, to the haploid cells that emerge from the zygote wall. The basis of non-mendelian inheritance in *C. reinhardi* has not yet been elucidated.

Neurospora. Another haploid protist in which both nuclear and non-nuclear inheritance have been investigated extensively is the ascomycetous fungus *Neurospora crassa.* This filamentous organism produces two types of conidia— multinucleate "macroconidia" and uninucleate "microconidia," both of which can function either as asexual propagative units or as male cells that fertilize ascogonia. The fertilized ascogonium develops into a perithecium containing numerous asci; each ascus contains eight ascospores, which are initially uninucleate. The ascospores are dormant, but they can be stimulated to germinate soon after maturation by exposure to heat (50 to 60° C for 10 to 60 minutes).

The ascus is elongated, and within it the ascospores are aligned in a single row. The eight nuclei are produced by meiosis of the zygote nucleus followed

TABLE 19-2.   Numbers of Tetrad Types Generated in *Chlamydomonas moewusii* Crosses Involving Pairs of Markers*

	Pairs of Markers†				
Tetrad Types	*T/mt*	*T/V*	*T/L*	*L/V*	*L/mt*
PD	14	9	8	4	3
NPD	10	9	0	2	3
T	24	32	11	13	12
Total number of tetrads analyzed:	48	50	19	19	18
Fraction of ditypes accounted for by PD's:	0.58	0.50	1.00	0.67	0.50

*Data from Lewin, R., 1953. *J. Genet.* **51**:543, Table 14.
†Markers other than mt: V: volutin (see footnote of Table 19-1). T: twinning; cell division in mutant type is incomplete. L: lazy; flagella of mutant type move sluggishly.

by one mitotic division before ascospore delimitation. During meiosis II, the spindles do not overlap; as a consequence, genetic factors that segregate during the first division of meiosis are contained in ascospores in one half of the row of spores. Accordingly, the eight spores comprise an ordered tetrad; each meiotic product is contained in a pair of adjacent, genetically identical spores. The spores can be removed from an ascus in order and germinated separately, and the genetic content of each spore can be determined from the properties of the clone it generates. The dissection of spores in order from an ascus is illustrated in Figure 19-13, and an example of reconstruction of meiotic events is diagrammed in Figure 19-14.

The example analysis in Figure 19-14 illustrates the three patterns in which any given character may be distributed among the spores. When the two alleles of a marker segregate at the first meiotic division, the marker is distributed in pattern I. When segregation occurs at the second meiotic division, the marker is distributed in pattern II-alt or II-sym, depending on the orientation of the

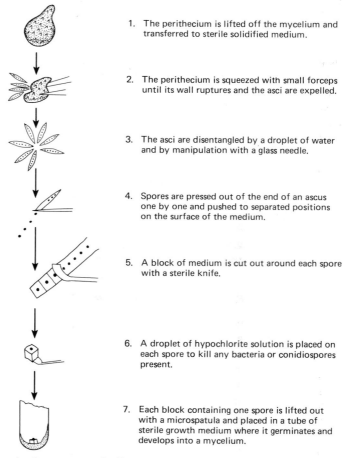

1. The perithecium is lifted off the mycelium and transferred to sterile solidified medium.

2. The perithecium is squeezed with small forceps until its wall ruptures and the asci are expelled.

3. The asci are disentangled by a droplet of water and by manipulation with a glass needle.

4. Spores are pressed out of the end of an ascus one by one and pushed to separated positions on the surface of the medium.

5. A block of medium is cut out around each spore with a sterile knife.

6. A droplet of hypochlorite solution is placed on each spore to kill any bacteria or conidiospores present.

7. Each block containing one spore is lifted out with a microspatula and placed in a tube of sterile growth medium where it germinates and develops into a mycelium.

Figure 19-13 Dissection of spores in order from an ascus in *Neurospora crassa.*

Ascospore:	8	7	6	5	4	3	2	1

Characteristics: Spores 1–4   mt+

                         5–8   mt–

           Spores 1, 2, 5, 6   brown

                         3, 4, 7, 8   colorless

                Spores 1, 2, 7, 8   adenine-requiring (ad–)

                         3, 4, 5, 6   adenine-independent (ad+)

Infer: Products of first division of meiosis

            Homogeneous for mt

            Heterogeneous for spore color and adenine requirement

        Products of second division of meiosis, in order

mt–	mt–	mt+	mt+
colorless	brown	colorless	brown
ad–	ad+	ad+	ad–

Spores:	8 and 7	6 and 5	4 and 3	2 and 1

Distribution patterns: mt, pattern I (– – – – + + + +)

                       Spore color, pattern II alternating (+ + – – + + – –)

                       Adenine requirement, pattern II symmetric (– – + + + + – –)

Reconstruction of meiotic events by analysis of an ordered set of eight *N. crassa* ascospores. **Figure 19-14**

alleles on the second division spindles. This orientation is random, so that the number of asci showing II-alt distribution of any given marker is approximately equal to the number showing II-sym distribution. Both II-patterns result from crossing-over between a marker and its centromere. Accordingly, even when only one marker is followed, crossing-over can be detected in an ordered tetrad.

The calculation of gene-to-centromere distance is based on the frequency of crossing-over in that region. On the assumption that the probability of crossing-over increases with the distance between two points on a chromosome, arbitrary units of distance along the chromosome are assigned so that the number of units increases with apparent frequency of crossing-over. The approximation involved in these calculations is reduced when the tetrad is ordered and first- and second-division segregations can be distinguished for every marker (see Fig. 19-15*A*).

The detection of linkage is also facilitated when tetrads are ordered. As illustrated in Figure 19-15*A* and *B*, linkage is apparent not only in the greater proportion of PD's among the ditype tetrads, but also in the distribution pattern of genotypes. Some of the PD tetrads involving linked genes result from crossing-over between the gene that is closer to the centromere and the centro-

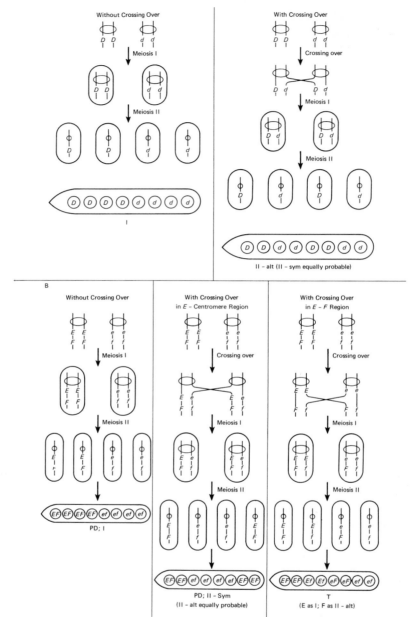

Figure 19-15 Discrimination of first- and second-division segregation in ordered tetrads: *A* of a single marker; *B* of two linked markers.

mere. In random (unordered) tetrads, these cannot be distinguished from PD's resulting from first-division segregation. In ordered tetrads, all tetrads, including the PD's, generated by crossing-over show a II-pattern of distribution (see Fig. 19-15*B*). As implied in Figure 19-15*B*, the positions of linked genes relative to the centromere can also be inferred from the distribution of markers in the ordered tetrads. For example, the frequency of tetrads showing a II-distribution of the E/e alleles will be lower than that of tetrads showing a II-distribution of the F/f alleles.

Non-mendelian inheritance of a few markers has also been found in *N. crassa*. Each of the known markers influences growth rate and respiratory activity; most of these are designated *mi*, because they affect the activities of mitochondria. The mutant alleles are associated with growth rate and respiratory activity lower than those of the wild type, and at least one of the mutant alleles is also associated with an altered enzyme content of the mitochondria. Differences between the inheritance of these characters and the inheritance of other characters can be detected in two types of crosses—in reciprocal sexual crosses, and in the recovery of homokaryons from experimentally produced heterokaryons.

In sexual crosses between a strain carrying a *mi* mutant allele and a wild type strain, all viable ascospores develop into mycelia that exhibit a growth rate and respiratory activity similar to those of the ascogonial (female) parent. Thus, when ascospores are formed from *mi* mutant ascogonia fertilized by conidia from the wild type strain, all progeny exhibit the *mi* mutant phenotype. Conversely, if *mi* conidia are used to fertilize wild type ascogonia, all progeny grow and respire at rates comparable to those of the wild type (see Fig. 19-16A). This is an instance of maternal inheritance, a phenomenon generally attributed to a non-nuclear location of the gene. Because most or all of the cytoplasm of the offspring (the ascospores) of the zygote is derived from maternal cytoplasm, the major or exclusive source of the gene is the female parent. In the case of the *mi* markers in *N. crassa*, the genes are probably contained in the mitochondria; it has been established that mitochondria in this organism (1) contain DNA and (2) arise, apparently exclusively, by fission of pre-existing mitochondria.

The conclusion that the *mi* genes are located in a discrete, self-perpetuating cytoplasmic structure is further supported by the behavior of these markers in heterokaryons. Certain strains[6] of *N. crassa* can readily develop as heterokaryons when their vegetative hyphae come into contact and fuse. Nuclei from both mycelia are distributed more or less randomly (depending on environmental conditions) through the hyphae that grow from the points of fusions. The nuclei segregate completely, however, when microconidia are formed (macroconidia can be heterokaryotic); from a heterokaryon formed by fusions of strains that are both wild type with respect to *mi* alleles, any one conidium contains genetic characters from one parent only.[7] However, if one of the strains carried a mutant *mi* allele, progeny of four types can be found, as illustrated in Figure 19-16B. Two types are the same as the parent strains; the other two are recombinant for the *mi* allele with all other traits. The occurrence of these

[6]Strains that carry identical alleles of three genes: mating type and two genes apparently concerned only with compatibility for heterokaryotic development.

[7]A parasexual cycle (see below) has not been found in *N. crassa*.

A

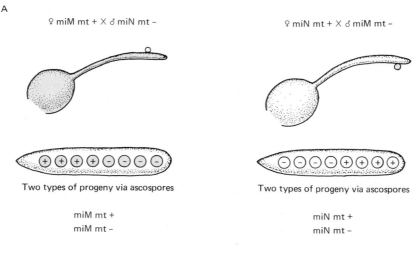

♀ miM mt + X ♂ miN mt –   ♀ miN mt + X ♂ miM mt –

Two types of progeny via ascospores   Two types of progeny via ascospores

miM mt +   miN mt +
miM mt –   miN mt –

B   XY miM X xy miN

Four types of progency via conidiospores

XY mi M ⎫
xy mi N ⎬ Parental

XY mi N ⎫
xy mi M ⎬ Recombinant

Figure 19-16 Behavior of *mi* markers in *N. crassa. A.* In reciprocal sexual crosses. *B.* In a heterokaryon. *mi*N, wild-type allele, unshaded; *mi*M, mutant allele, shaded.

particular types of recombinants implies only that the *mi* gene is located outside the nucleus, within which all the other traits are localized. The occurrence of recombinants at all implies that the *mi* genes are present in numbers not significantly greater than the number of nuclei; if they were, the probability that they would segregate in the uninucleate conidia would be very low. This is consistent with the notion that the *mi* genes are situated in mitochondria, since any microconidium contains only one or a few mitochondria.

Parasexuality. Parasexuality is a mechanism of genetic mixing and recombination known to occur in a variety of fungi, principally ascomycetous and imperfect types. In contrast to sexual mechanisms, if they occur in the same fungi, (1) nuclear fusion is followed by mitosis, rather than by meiosis; (2) recombination within linkage groups occurs by mitotic, rather than meiotic, crossing-over; and (3) eventual reduction in ploidy occurs by unequal mitotic divisions, rather than by meiosis. Nevertheless, the genetic consequences are the same as those of the sexual mechanisms, viz., parental characters are mixed in a single diploid nucleus (and its progeny) and later are reassorted among haploid progeny nuclei in recombinations resulting from random assortment of chromosomes and crossing-over.[8] However, the frequency of crossing-over recombination by this mechanism, as mentioned below, is much lower than in meiosis.

The genetic aspects of this phenomenon have been most thoroughly studied in the ascomycetous mold *Aspergillus nidulans.* The asexual propagative units of this fungus are uninucleate conidiospores. Several markers are known that determine conidiospore color, and any given spore exhibits a color according to the spore-color markers of its nucleus. Heterokaryons between strains carrying different spore-color markers (e.g., white and yellow; the wild type color is green) can be constructed by cultivation of the differently marked strains in a single culture. Hyphal fusions occur, and the nuclei of the two strains coexist in a common cytoplasm. Occasionally, two unlike nuclei fuse. When conidia are formed on heterokaryotic mycelium, they may be any of three colors: white, yellow, or (relatively rarely) green. Each green spore contains a diploid nucleus, and the spore volume is approximately twice that of a haploid spore. The diploid spores are heterozygous for each spore color marker, and their green color indicates that the wild type allele of each marker is dominant to the mutant allele.

When a diploid green conidiospore is allowed to germinate, it develops into a mycelial colony that exhibits characteristics predictable on the basis of the genotypes of the haploid parents. Dominance is typical of the known markers, so that the diploid exhibits each character in the same manner as the parent that contributed the dominant allele. An occasional character, e.g., spore color, is affected by more than one gene. When the parents differ in that character because they carry recessive alleles of different genes affecting that character, the diploid will differ from both parents in that character.

As the diploid mycelium develops conidiospores, the majority are diploid. Occasionally, a patch or sector of white or yellow conidiospores appears; a single conidiophore may bear spores of more than one color. These spores may be diploid recombinants in which the spore color markers have segregated, or they may be haploid. The formation of diploid segregants results from mitotic crossing-over and subsequent segregation as the chromosomes assort randomly. Mitotic crossing-over occurs in only about 1 of every 50 mitoses, and then it involves only one chromosome pair. This is a much lower frequency

---

[8]A genetically analogous mechanism of recombinant formation occurs in filamentous bacteria of the order Actinomycetales. In *Streptomyces,* compatibility is determined by an extragenomic factor similar to that described in the section on bacterial conjugation (above). In *Nocardia,* compatibility is determined by genomic factors.

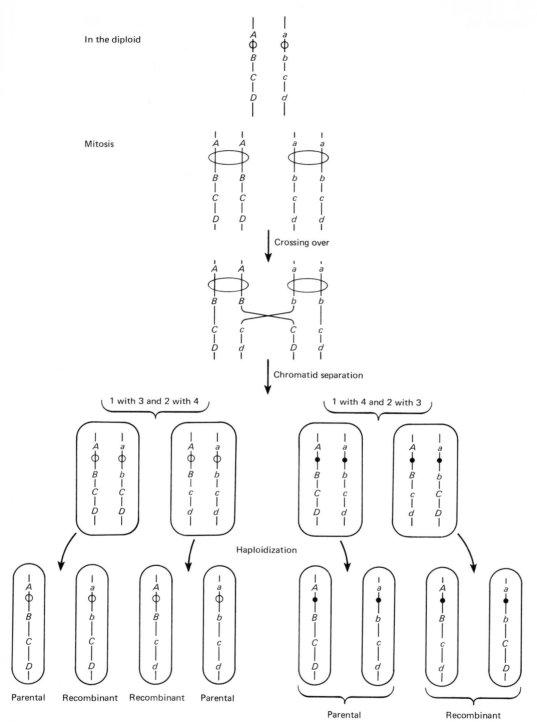

Figure 19-17 Haploidization products following mitotic crossing-over.

than in meiosis, in which crossing-over occurs in practically every pair of homologous chromosomes at every meiotic division. Crossing-over requires synapsis between the homologous chromosomes, an event typical of meiosis, but rare in mitosis. The genetic consequences of mitotic crossing-over are diagrammed in Figure 19-17.

Haploid nuclei are derived from diploid nuclei by a process called haploidization. Cytologic examination of diploid mycelia that produce haploid spores has revealed that some nuclei contain a number of chromosomes intermediate between the haploid and diploid numbers; such nuclei are called aneuploid. Meiotic divisions have not been detected. These observations imply that reduction of the diploid nuclei occurs in several steps. First, in about 1 of 50 mitoses, an unequal division occurs that results in one nucleus with more than the diploid number of chromosomes and one with less than the diploid but more than the haploid number. During subsequent mitoses, chromosomes apparently are lost so that the former type of nucleus is returned to the diploid number, and the latter is reduced to the haploid number.

Formation of haploid nuclei by haploidization is not associated with the development of a specialized fruiting structure, as meiosis is in ascospore formation. Consequently, the mycelium that develops from a diploid spore eventually becomes a heterokaryon containing predominantly diploid and fewer haploid nuclei. The diploid and haploid nuclei are sorted out only in the formation of conidiospores. The haploid and diploid spores may be distinguishable by differences in color and are usually distinguishable by the smaller size of the haploid spores.

Diploid mycelia of *A. nidulans* often produce numerous perithecia. Each ascus within a perithecium develops from a single diploid cell; i.e., mating is not necessary to stimulate the formation of asci. However, in contrast to perithecia formed on fertilized haploid mycelia, the perithecia formed on diploid mycelia usually contain few asci, and most of these do not contain viable ascospores. Meiosis is initiated in these asci, but usually cannot continue beyond the first metaphase. This is true even of diploid strains derived from a pair of haploid strains whose male and female gametes are fully fertile and yield large numbers of viable ascospores. This seeming paradox implies that there is a significant difference between the zygote nucleus of an ascus and a genetically identical diploid nucleus that can divide mitotically. The latter shows a tendency toward strictly vegetative (somatic?) behavior. The elucidation of this difference may provide important insight into the evolution of diploidy and of differentiation.

Terminology

This glossary, selected from the voluminous vocabulary of genetics, contains terms used in this chapter. This list is intended as a review, since the reader presumably was exposed to these terms prior to reading this text. The terms are not arranged in alphabetic order because designation of the reference of certain of the terms can be most economically achieved by employing others.

Gene. The functional unit of inherited information, expressed as a single trait.

Allele. One of the alternative forms of a gene; expressed as the quality of the trait or absence of the trait.

Marker. An allele known or assumed to have arisen by mutation.

Locus. The site of a gene in the genetic material.

Dominance. A quality of an allele that allows it to be expressed when present in a nucleus containing another allele of the gene and to prevent expression of the other allele.

Recessiveness. A quality of an allele that does not allow it to be expressed when present in a nucleus that also contains a dominant allele of the gene.

Linkage Group. A set of two or more genes that tend to be inherited together from one parent or the other, rather than independently.

Genome. A complete minimal set of genes contained in the nucleoplasm, comprising one allele of each gene. (Originally, this term was used to refer to the complete set of genes present in the haploid complement of chromosomes. The expanded reference designated here allows it to be used with regard to organisms whose nuclei divide amitotically.)

Ploidy. The number of genomes contained in a nucleus (haploid—one genome; diploid—two genomes).

Genotype. The genetic constitution of an individual.

Phenotype. The inherited characteristics displayed by an individual.

Clone. A line of asexually propagated organisms of one genotype, except as altered by mutation during the asexual propagation.

Chromatin. The cellular material that stains with specific basic dyes. In eucaryotic organisms, all the chromatin is located within the nucleus.

Chromosome. A discrete body of condensed chromatin usually apparent only during nuclear division. Generally elongated in shape, but may be nearly spheric, especially in protists. (It has been demonstrated in many types of eucaryotic organisms that the loci of all genes of any one linkage group are in the same chromosome. Accordingly, chromosomes are regarded as the physical structures identical with the linkage groups detected by genetic studies.)

Nuclear Division. Subdivision of one nucleus into two separate and equivalent nuclei.

Equational. Each of the product nuclei contains the same amount of genetic material (and information) as the predivisional nucleus had at the time it arose by nuclear division.

Reductive. Each of the product nuclei contains one half the amount of genetic material (and information) as the predivisional nucleus had at the time it arose by nuclear division.

Mitosis. Equational nuclear divisions during which chromosomes are distinguishable; diagrammed in Figure 19-1.

Meiosis. Two successive nuclear divisions during which chromosomes are distinguishable. The first division (meiosis I) is reductive; the second (meiosis II) is equational. Meiosis is diagrammed in Figure 19-2.

Segregation. The distribution of different alleles of one gene into separate products of nuclear division.

(For spindle fiber, chromatid, centromere, homologue, synapsis, and crossing-over, see Figures 19-1 and 19-2, legends and diagrams.)

Zygote. A nucleus formed by fusion of two nuclei; also used to refer to a cell, individual, or clone whose nucleus or nuclei are zygotes or were derived from a zygote by equational nuclear divisions.

Gamete. A nucleus that can fuse with another to form a zygote; also used to refer to a cell whose nucleus is a gamete.

Mutant. A cell in which a mutation has occurred; also used to refer to the gene itself or to the clone generated by the mutant.

Revertant. A cell (clone, nucleus, gene) that once displayed a mutant characteristic, but has returned to the original state.

Recombinant. An individual with a genotype comprising an assortment of alleles different from the assortment in the genotype of either of its parents; also used to refer to a nucleus, a genome, a genotype, or the clone generated by the recombinant.

(The context in which any of these last five terms is used usually implies whether the term refers to a nucleus, a cell, or other. In some instances, clarity of reference requires that the term be used attributively, as in "mutant allele" or "recombinant clone.")

Effects of Protists on Their Environments

Chapter 20

Metabiotic Activities

Metabiosis

Metabiotic activities are those activities of a living organism that determine the suitability of its environment for the growth and multiplication of other organisms. Almost all the metabiotic effects exerted by protists are chemical, although in certain situations their activities may affect physical factors such as temperature, humidity, light intensity, and mobility of water.

All these effects are realized within the **biosphere.** The biosphere is that portion of the earth inhabited by living organisms, wherein protists, particularly microscopic forms, are ubiquitous. The biosphere is only a small fraction of the earth's volume, comprising the surface waters, the upper few feet of the earth's crust, and the lower few thousand feet of the atmosphere. It differs from the non-biosphere in chemical composition and in the extent of chemical reactivity. As a consequence of selective accumulation by living systems, a few elements are present in the biosphere in higher proportions than on the earth as a whole; these include C, H, O, N, S, P, Na, K, Ca, Mg, B, and the halogens Br, Cl, and I. A great number of chemical transformations are constantly in progress in the biosphere; these transformations are the processes incidental to the growth of living systems.

Three major classes of transformations occur: conversions of inorganic substances to organic substances, interconversions among organic substances, and conversions of organic to inorganic substances. The first type, particularly as it relates to carbon, is called **primary production.** Primary production is mainly the result of activities of photosynthetic organisms. According to most estimates, slightly less than one half the primary production on earth occurs in the oceans, catalyzed by algae, and the remainder on land, catalyzed by plants.

453

In addition to formation of organic materials from inorganic substrates, photosynthesis results in the conversion of light energy to chemical energy. This energy is contained in the chemical bonds of the organic compounds produced by photosynthetic organisms. It is the source of all energy for living systems, which release the energy from the bonds through oxidation reactions and use the energy mainly to form the chemical bonds of their own components. As organisms feed on other organisms, both matter and chemical energy are reused.

However, metabolic energy is also used for motion, and some energy is converted to heat during the transformations of substances. The chemical energy content of the biosphere is diminished by the amount lost in motion and as heat. Consequently, the maintenance of life is dependent on a net input of chemical energy into the biosphere. In the modern biosphere, the mechanism by which this is accomplished is photosynthesis.

The second type of transformation comprises mainly those processes in which the components of one organism are converted into components of another by the metabolism of the latter organism. Some of the products of these conversions are by-products of metabolism that are not incorporated into the organism that formed them (e.g., organic products of fermentation). Such by-products may later be converted into components of a third organism.

The third type of transformation is called **mineralization.** Although the immediate products of mineralization processes are not components of living systems, the continual occurrence of these processes is essential to the maintenance of conditions compatible with life in the modern biosphere. Their substrates include materials that would interfere with animal life if allowed to accumulate, and their products are substrates of plant growth.

Protists participate in all known types of chemical transformations that occur in the biosphere. Some protists are exclusively or predominantly responsible for certain of these processes. In this chapter, protistan activities that condition the chemical composition of the environment of plants and animals will be discussed.

The Cycling of Elements

The participation of protists in the biologic cycling of the elements C, N, S, and P is related directly to the welfare of photosynthetic organisms and indirectly to the welfare of animals, which depend on photosynthetic organisms as their primary food source. Since plants are predominantly terrestrial organisms and draw most of their nutrients from soil, the protists of greatest importance to plants are those that grow and multiply in soil. All the processes whose sum is the cycling of these four elements occur in soil, catalyzed by soil-dwelling protists. The biologic cycling of C, N, and S is summarized in Figure 20-1. Similar processes occur in waters and bottom muds; there they directly affect the development of algae, whose inorganic requirements are basically similar to those of plants.

All the substrates necessary for plant development are inorganic. Of these,

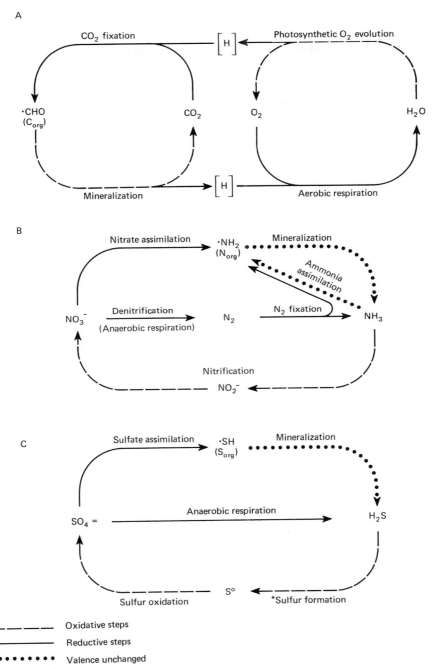

A

CO$_2$ fixation [H] Photosynthetic O$_2$ evolution

·CHO (C$_{org}$)   CO$_2$ O$_2$ H$_2$O

Mineralization [H] Aerobic respiration

B

Nitrate assimilation   ·NH$_2$ (N$_{org}$)   Mineralization

Ammonia assimilation

NO$_3^-$ Denitrification (Anaerobic respiration)   N$_2$ N$_2$ fixation   NH$_3$

Nitrification
NO$_2^-$

C

Sulfate assimilation   ·SH (S$_{org}$)   Mineralization

SO$_4$ =   Anaerobic respiration   H$_2$S

S°   *Sulfur formation
Sulfur oxidation

– – – – –   Oxidative steps

————   Reductive steps

• • • • • • •   Valence unchanged

Cycling of elements as catalyzed by living systems. *A.* Carbon and oxygen cycles. *B.* Nitrogen cycle. *C.* Sulfur cycle.   **Figure 20-1**

*In aerobic environments, this step can occur by chemical reaction between sulfide and O$_2$. In anaerobic environments, it occurs only as a result of bacterial activity.

CO_2, water, and phosphate enter directly into the photosynthetic reactions. Other known necessary substrates include the anions nitrate and sulfate; the major metal cations Ca, Fe, Mg, and K; and cations required in relatively small amounts ("trace metals"), Bo, Cu, Co, Mn, Zn, and probably Mo. The metals are generally supplied by the soil; their solubility may be affected by microbial activities, and small amounts are provided through the mineralizing activities of protists. However, protists probably do not play an essential role in providing metals as plant nutrients. In contrast, plants depend on microbial activities for each of their major nutrients other than water and sunlight, as described in the following sections.

The major products of plant development are plant substance and O_2. Plant substance represents two commodities in the terrestrial biosphere: (1) primary organic material and (2) primary biochemical energy. The organic substance and the energy enter the secondary processes of the biosphere when plant substance is utilized by other organisms as their food. Molecular oxygen (O_2) is the terminal oxidant in the respiration of most modern organisms.

Carbon / Oxygen Cycles (Fig. 20-1A)

CO_2 Fixation. In photosynthetic CO_2 fixation by plants, the electrons used to reduce ("fix") CO_2 are accounted for directly by the electrons removed from water. The overall process also involves excitation (increase in energy content) of the electrons by light energy and conversion thereby of the radiant energy into chemical energy. The chemical energy is stored in the organic compounds formed by CO_2 fixation and in high energy phosphate bonds. The energy in the latter compounds is utilized in the various synthetic reactions by which the plant converts fixed CO_2 into all its organic constituents (cofactors, enzymes, structural materials, nucleic acids, and so forth).

Molecular Oxygen. Molecular oxygen arises in nature as a by-product of photosynthesis and as a product of light- or electricity-catalyzed reactions (mainly in the atmosphere). However, the quantity of O_2 formed by abiologic processes is relatively small, and equivalent amounts would be consumed by abiologic oxidations that can occur naturally. The amount of O_2 required for the maintenance of aerobic organisms greatly exceeds that which is available from chemical reactions. Modern organisms, most of which are strict aerobes, are dependent on photosynthesis as the source of their respiratory oxidant, which is continuously required and for which there is usually not a suitable substitute.

Carbon Mineralization. Mineralization of carbon is catalyzed principally by bacteria and fungi. Respiration in other organisms and combustion of organic materials account for only an estimated 10 per cent of the CO_2 formed from organic carbon. Organic matter accumulates in soil and in muds at the bottom of bodies of water as plants die or shed their fruits or leaves and as animals die or deposit their excreta. These materials are the substrates of mineralization, and it is in these two environments that most natural mineralization occurs; a smaller proportion occurs in waters.

Organic carbon is symbolized in Figure 20-1 simply as "·CHO." This symbol represents a great variety of substances—viz., all the organic products of living systems. Some of these substances, such as sugars and low molecular weight organic acids, can be assimilated by the majority of types of organisms. A larger proportion of organic carbon is accounted for by complex substances, many of which are relatively insoluble in water and served as structural materials in the organism that formed them.

Every known naturally occurring organic compound can be mineralized by bacteria and fungi; many of these compounds cannot be attacked enzymically by other organisms. This does not, of course, mean that any one type of bacterium or fungus is so versatile in its degradative capacities; rather, it is a reflection of the physiologic diversity among the types of organisms in each of these groups.

Many types of fungi are presently described simply as "plurivorous," because any one type may be found in a number of habitats that differ in the kinds of organic substances present. In a few habitats, however, only certain types of fungi are found, and their degradative activities are inferred from their ability to develop on certain substrates. For examples, woody tissues are degraded by Basidiomycetes, keratin (the protein of nails, hoofs, and hair) by Ascomycetes and related imperfect fungi, and chitin (a structural material of many invertebrates and of some fungi) by various phycomycetes, many of which—especially the chytrids—can also degrade keratin. Some of the Basidiomycetes that grow on dead wood attack the cellulose of the tissue, others attack the lignin, and some can degrade both components. Many terrestrial molds, especially *Penicillium* and *Aspergillus* representatives, can grow on a variety of natural and processed materials; the latter include leather, rubber, paper, and paint.

Among bacteria, there are several types that have been recognized as the principal agents of degradation of particular organic substances. The cytophaga group of myxobacteria are the principal cellulose decomposers among bacteria; other myxobacteria can degrade chitin. Certain pseudomonads are particularly active in degradation of aromatic compounds, especially the low molecular weight substances released from woody tissue by fungi. Marine vibrios can solubilize and assimilate the pectins and other components of algae. Mycobacteria and actinomycetes and some gram-positive cocci are largely responsible for the natural mineralization of hydrocarbons.

This is only a partial mention of the degradative activities that occur in nature and can be attributed to specific groups of fungi or bacteria. Other types, chiefly of bacteria, are known to be specialized for degradation of proteins or of compounds that occur naturally only in the excreta of certain types of animals.

The organisms mentioned above are typically aerobic organisms that occur in soil or water and can oxidize most of their substrates to CO_2 and H_2O. Most of the mineralization that occurs in muds beneath bodies of water or in marshlands is carried out by anaerobic organisms, principally bacteria. Mineralization in anaerobic environments is generally slower than in soil, because only part of the organic carbon is oxidized to CO_2; the remainder accumulates as low molecular weight, highly reduced organic compounds. This is the case whether fermentative organisms or organisms capable of anaerobic respiration are active, because the latter typically release some of their organic substrates in incompletely oxidized form. Anaerobes are also active in soil, where the products of their metabolism are oxidized by aerobes.

Because of the physiologic diversity of soil microorganisms and the physical inhomogeneity of the habitat, it is technically difficult to enumerate and characterize the viable members of the population of a given soil sample. Nevertheless, estimates of microbial soil populations are available. There are generally an estimated several million bacteria per gram of soil (or mud). In soil, 90 to 99 per cent of these are aerobes; in mud, 50 to 75 per cent are anaerobes. The numbers of mycelial organisms (fungi and actinomycetes) are more difficult to estimate, because spores and mycelial fragments can develop into colonies. A recent estimate of fungal spores is 1 million or fewer per gram of soil. Actinomycetes seem to be the most numerous of bacterial types in various soils; there may be 2 million of these bacteria in a gram of soil. Algae and protozoa are present in smaller numbers than the other protists, usually at most 50,000 and 25,000 per gram, respectively. The numbers of each type of organism vary with the types and amounts of organic materials present; the moisture content, inorganic composition, and acidity of the basal soil; the amounts of CO_2 and O_2 in the atmosphere within the soil; and the general climate, particularly temperature and precipitation.

Nitrogen Cycle (Fig. 20-1*B*)

Nitrogen in organic compounds is usually at the oxidation level of ammonia nitrogen, and mineralization of nitrogen generally results in the release of ammonia. Most protists can assimilate ammonia as a source of nitrogen; consequently, a significant amount of nitrogen is cycled between organic and inorganic form without a change of oxidation state. However, the development of most higher plants, and in particular those cultivated by man as crop plants, is more rapid and more extensive when nitrate is available as a source of nitrogen.

Nitrification. Two groups of aerobic soil bacteria are in large part responsible for the conversion of ammonia to nitrate. Representatives of the *Nitrosomonas* group oxidize ammonia to nitrite; those of the *Nitrobacter* group oxidize nitrite to nitrate. Both types of bacteria are chemolithotrophic, and they usually occur together in soils. They obtain energy for CO_2 fixation and growth by the aerobic oxidation of these inorganic substances and are unable to oxidize organic substances for these purposes.

In addition to the lithotrophs, some organotrophs can oxidize NH_3 to nitrite or, less commonly, to nitrate. Isolates of the bacterial genera *Vibrio, Bacillus, Mycobacterium,* and *Streptomyces* and of the fungal genus *Aspergillus* can perform such oxidations. They do not depend on these reactions for their chemotrophic energy supply and in pure cultures produce much lower concentrations of nitrite or nitrate than do the lithotrophic bacteria. However, they are generally present in soils in greater numbers than the lithotrophs.

The respective contributions of the two groups of nitrifying organisms have not been evaluated, although in some soils the number of lithotrophs is sufficient to account for the quantity of nitrate formed. Often, however, microbial nitrification is insufficient to supply the amount of nitrate required for agricultural plant production, and then nitrates must be added to the soil to compensate for the absence of nitrifying protists or to supplement their activities.

Nitrate Utilization. Plants must compete with some protists for nitrate. Many bacteria, fewer fungi, and a few protozoa can assimilate nitrate as a nitrogen source. Because of this, a soil with a high content of organic matter may be unsuitable for plant cultivation; it supports the growth of a dense microbial population that assimilates inorganic nutrients such as nitrate (or phosphate) and thereby reduces the availability of these nutrients for plant growth.

In addition, many soil and water bacteria can utilize nitrate as a respiratory oxidant when O_2 is not available. Their anaerobic respiration results in the reduction of nitrate to gases, mainly N_2, which diffuse out of the soil into the atmosphere. Nitrogen as N_2 (or the other gases) is not available to most plants. Denitrification, as this process is called, results in a loss of nitrogen from the soil and its inhabitants. However, it is added to the atmosphere over the soil, rather than washed away into rivers and the ocean, as are salts such as nitrates. Consequently, the element is still accessible to the soil through the biologic soil process called N_2 fixation.

N_2 Fixation. Nitrogen is returned to chemical combination in the soil by N_2-fixing organisms. The product of N_2 fixation is ammonia or organic nitrogen; i.e., fixation is reductive, as is CO_2 fixation. Biologic N_2 fixation depends entirely, as far as known, on microbial activities; the microbes act either as free-living N_2-fixing agents or in symbiotic association with plants.

The free-living N_2-fixing microbes include several types of bacteria and blue-green algae. The contribution of the algae is significant in warm climates, where they are present in relatively large numbers. Also in warm climates, bacteria of the genus *Beijerinckia* (which includes species simultaneously classified in *Azotobacter*) are active as free-living N_2-fixing agents. Representatives of the bacterial genus *Azotobacter* were regarded for many years as the principal free-living agents of N_2 fixation in temperate zone soils. However, although these bacteria are widely distributed in cultivated soils, there are usually only 1,000 to 3,000 viable individuals per gram of soil. This number is not sufficient to account for the amount of N_2 fixation that can be detected. The number of anaerobic N_2-fixing bacteria, principally *Clostridium* representatives, is usually either as great as or as much as several thousand times greater than the number of *Azotobacter* cells. This implies that the contribution of the anaerobes to N_2 fixation is generally much greater than that of the aerobes.

N_2 fixation that occurs in anaerobic muds is performed principally by photosynthetic bacteria, both lithotrophic and organotrophic types. Other microbes that have been reported to be capable of N_2 fixation include a variety of soil, mud, and water bacteria (including *Pseudomonas, Spirillum, Aerobacter, Desulfovibrio*) and two types of yeasts. The distribution of this capacity among microorganisms has not been extensively determined; however, the studies of recent years, aided by the use of the isotope ^{15}N, have revealed that it is more common than was believed for many years.

Various types of plants have been found to be able to grow well—sometimes—in soils deficient in nitrate; one result of their growth is an increase in the nitrogen content of the soil. The central factor that determines whether they grow well and enrich the soil in nitrogen is the presence of specific types of bacteria. On the roots or leaves of these plants are nodules in which their bacterial associates grow and within which N_2 fixation occurs. Each species of plant must be associated with a particular type of bacterium. Most of these bacteria also exist as free-living organisms, but only a few can fix N_2 when not associated with a specific plant.

The most extensively studied plant-bacterial N_2-fixing associations are the legume-rhizobia systems. Legumes constitute a group of plants, including clover, alfalfa, peas, soybeans, and lupines, that bear their seeds in pods. Rhizobia are bacteria classified in a single genus, *Rhizobium* (see Chap. 13); they occur in soils as free-living organisms. When a legume and compatible rhizobia grow in the same soil, the rhizobia may develop as colonies on the root hairs of the plants. Enzymes released by the growing bacteria disintegrate the walls of some of the root hair cells. As the bacteria multiply, the colony expands into the root hair. Their presence stimulates cell division in the root hair, and a macroscopic knob of growth called a nodule develops. The mature nodule is composed of plant cells containing rhizobia (see Fig. 13-9).

If the invading bacteria and the plant constitute an effective pair, N_2 fixation occurs in the nodule. The plant assimilates the fixed nitrogen and does not need nitrate from the soil. The bacteria also assimilate the nitrogen and utilize substances produced or absorbed by the plant for their other nutrients. Many species of *Rhizobium* are distinguished only on the basis of their ability to establish effective nodules on particular species of plants. The basis of their specificity has not been elucidated.

Other symbiotic N_2-fixing systems are known, but they have not been investigated or exploited so extensively as nodulated legumes. Rhizobia are involved in some of these associations; other associations involve actinomycetes (apparently *Streptomyces*) or gram-negative bacteria similar to *Klebsiella* types as the bacterial partners.

Sulfur Cycle (Fig. 20-1C)

The natural cycling of sulfur is similar to that of nitrogen, with the principal exception that one step (the oxidation of sulfide to elemental sulfur) can and does occur abiologically as well as biologically. Bacteria can carry out each of the processes in the sulfur cycle; bacteria and certain colorless blue-green algae are the only known living agents of the steps involving interconversions of inorganic forms of sulfur.

Sulfate Formation. The oxidation of sulfide to sulfate, with elemental sulfur as one of the intermediates, is performed by at least two types of bacteria: by the chemolithotrophic thiobacilli in aerobic environments such as aerated soils, and by photosynthetic sulfur bacteria in anaerobic environments such as muds. The formation of sulfate in soil is beneficial to agricultural plants in three ways: (1) sulfate is the most suitable sulfur source for their development; (2) sulfate is the anion of a strong mineral acid (viz., H_2SO_4), and its formation prevents excessive alkalinity due to ammonia formation by mineralizing microbes; and (3) localized accumulation of H_2SO_4 immediately around thiobacilli results in solubilization of inorganic salts that contain plant nutrients such as metals and phosphates.

Sulfate Utilization. Sulfate can be assimilated as a sulfur source by most plants and by many types of protists. (Certain fungi and many protozoa are excepted; they require an organic source of sulfur, a nutritional requirement common among animals.) Sulfate is consumed in anaerobic environments by bacteria that utilize it as a respiratory oxidant. The majority of these bacteria are *Desulfovibrio* types which are unable to utilize any substance other than sulfate for respiration. They grow organotrophically and are particularly common in anaerobic environments rich in sulfate and organic materials, such as the sea bottom, coastal mud flats, and estuaries. Their presence in any number can be detected by the odor of H_2S and the blackening of the mud due to the accumulation of FeS. They also occur in fresh water and in soil, where the sulfide does not typically accumulate before being oxidized to sulfate.

Phosphate Cycle

Plant (and algal) development is more commonly limited by the supply of phosphate than that of any of the other major nutrients. In soils, phosphate is present as organic phosphate and as mineral phosphates. Most of the organic form is accounted for by nucleic acids in dead organisms and by substances called phytic acids (inositol phosphates) in plant debris. The nucleic acids are mineralized rapidly by microbial activities that release the phosphate as the inorganic ion. The phytic acids, however, are mineralized only slowly, partly because they combine readily with metal cations to form salts of low solubility. The phytic acids and their salts may accumulate in soils until they account for nearly 90 per cent of the organic phosphorus, and this phosphorus is not readily available to plants.

Inorganic phosphates are also present in most soils, usually as insoluble salts of Ca or Fe. The phosphate of the Ca-salts is made available to plants by the solubilizing activities of a variety of bacteria and fungi. Generally, Ca-phosphates are solubilized in areas where organotrophs are producing organic acids; as the acids accumulate, the hydrogen ion concentration of the micro-environment around the cells increases to levels at which the phosphate salts are soluble. When this occurs in the vicinity of plant roots, some of the PO_4^{-3} (or HPO_4^{-2} or $H_2PO_4^{-1}$) diffuses into the plants.

The release of soluble phosphate from insoluble inorganic salts by fungi and bacteria can be demonstrated in pure cultures of many soil isolates. It has also been demonstrated experimentally that the uptake of such phosphate by plants is enhanced by the presence of microbes in the soil surrounding their roots.

Relatively little analytic or experimental attention has been paid to the biologic cycling of phosphorus among oxidation levels other than phosphate (H_3PO_4, plus 5). Phosphite (H_3PO_3, plus 3), hypophosphite (H_3PO_2, plus 1), and phosphine (PH_3, minus 3) occur in nature, and bacteria and fungi are known that can oxidize or reduce the phosphorous atom of these compounds and phosphate. However, these processes do not, at present, seem to have a significant effect on the quantity of phosphate available to plants.

The Environment of Animals

Activities of protists influence the suitability of the environment for animal development in four general ways: (1) through effects on plant development; (2) by consumption and production of O_2; (3) by alteration of the quantity and quality of foods; and (4) by purification of the environment by disposal of noxious wastes, discarded parts, and carcasses. Since animals as a class of organisms depend on plants as their ultimate source of organic nutrients and of O_2, the protistan activities discussed in the first sections of this chapter are relevant to animal as well as plant development.

Oxygen. Protists compete with animals for O_2 in habitats where the supply of O_2 is limited by physical restraints on the amount of air that can enter (as in soil) or by the low solubility of O_2 in water (as in aquatic and marine environments, and in soil).

The competition is observable at the present time in fresh-water streams and rivers, where the growth-limiting nutrient for the primary (photosynthetic) organisms is often phosphate. When the water is polluted with industrial or agricultural wastes, in which phosphate is commonly an ingredient, multiplication of algae, then of bacteria and fungi, and finally of protozoa that feed on the other protists occurs at abnormally high rates. The resulting dense populations of microscopic protists consume O_2 so rapidly that O_2, rather than phosphate, becomes the growth-limiting factor. The evolution of O_2 by the algae is not sufficient in these situations to support even their own nighttime respiration. Aquatic animals, such as fishes, that require a continuous supply of O_2 suffocate and die. Decomposition of uncommonly large numbers of animal carcasses increases the concentration of organic materials (including N, S, and P sources) in the water, contributing further to the development of organotrophic, O_2-consuming protists.

Whereas microbial consumption of O_2 may affect animals adversely, some animals are dependent on O_2 production by protists. For example, in many types of fresh-water habitats, algal photosynthesis is the principal source of O_2 for aquatic animals. In recent years, this dependence has become more obvious in waters polluted with industrial wastes or chemical insecticides. Some of these materials inhibit algal development and thereby diminish O_2 production in the water. As a consequence, the aquatic environment becomes unsuitable for aerobic animal life.

Effects on Foodstuffs / Quantitative. Animals have evolved as organisms that eat other organisms (usually freshly killed), parts of living organisms, and/or products of living organisms. The majority of animals are predators: "hunters" (if their food organisms are motile) or "foragers" (if their food organisms are not motile). A few animals have evolved that cultivate their food organisms, and some have evolved that store dead or dormant organisms or their parts or products.

All creatures (including immature stages such as eggs, seeds, and spores) are foods for animals. Plant parts such as leaves and fruits and roots and subterranean storage organs such as tubers are widely used as foods by animals. Animal blood and plant sap can be used by animals specialized for penetrating and withdrawing fluids from the tissues of a living organism. Products used include metabolic by-products (exudates from plants, exudates and excreta from animals), nectar, and milk.

Any one kind of animal will utilize only some of these foods. Three general categories of feeding types are recognized: herbivores (eaters of plants), carnivores (eaters of animals), and omnivores (eaters of plants and animals). However, feeding habits are much more specific than these categories indicate, and, for example, a given kind of carnivorous animal will usually eat at most only a few different types of animals.

The selectivity of animals in their feeding increases their susceptibility to interference with their food supplies by protists. The protists that cause the greatest changes in the quantities of living organisms are the pathogens, particularly those that cause diseases that result in death or diminished reproduction. Such protists are usually specific for the organisms they damage and typically affect only one type of organism in any habitat at any time, i.e., under a given set of environmental conditions.

A pathogen may increase the food supply of a given animal by causing disease in its competitors. It may decrease an animal's food supply by destroying its food organism(s) or by interrupting its food chain. Diseases characterized by the stunting of growth also reduce the food supply represented by the diseased or recovered organism.

In some instances of plant diseases, only a portion of the plant is destroyed; this affects only those animals that eat that portion of the plant. For example, in many plant diseases caused by fungi and bacteria, only the fruit is affected. At the time in the growing season when the fruit normally matures, there may be in its stead only a mass of fungal or bacterial protoplasm, regarded as inedible by many of the animals that eat the normal fruit. Similarly, pathogens that cause wilt diseases of plants severely reduce the supply of healthy leaves on which certain insects, worms, and mammals feed.

Effects on Foodstuffs / Qualitative. Most of the effects of protists on the quality of animal foodstuffs involve stored foods and hence affect man and his domesticated animals to a greater extent than most other animals. Protistan activities affect food qualitatively in three general ways—by altering its palatability, its nutritive value, or its toxicity.

Palatability is a characteristic of foods that is determined in part by genetic characteristics of the animal that have evolved in a given geographic area. Those animals that preferentially eat foods that are both available in their area and especially nutritious for that type of animal survive and multiply. Man is not an exception to this, but palatability for humans is further determined by cultural practices of food preparation.

Some methods of food preparation by humans are dependent on the development of specific microbes in the foods. Most of these methods were initially used as means of food preservation that resulted from accumulation of acids or alcohol in the foods during microbial development. Foods prepared with the aid of microorganisms and the microbes that bring about the desired changes in the foods are listed in Table 23-8; many of these food products are more digestible or more nutritious for humans than the unaltered foods.

Most foods altered by microbial activities are regarded as spoiled (unpalatable). This is generally true of meats and fruits that are altered in undesirable ways when proteolytic or pectinolytic microbes, respectively, develop in them. Storage grains and other vegetable foods are also susceptible to spoilage by bacteria and fungi. However, many types of plant-derived foods can be stored for long periods without significant spoilage, due mainly to the presence of skins, rinds, hulls, or shells that are not readily penetrated by microbes. Foods such as apples, citrus fruits, and nuts are usually spoiled only if the protective covers are damaged by mechanical means. Meats, fish, and poultry spoil (putrefy) relatively rapidly as a consequence of the continued (and usually expanded) activities of the microbes that inhabited the alimentary and respiratory tracts, gills, and body surface of the living animal.

Specific types of fungi and bacteria that can grow in stored foodstuffs produce substances toxic to animals that ingest them. The presence of such microbes is often undetectable in the taste, odor, or appearance of the food; their presence becomes apparent only after symptoms of intoxication have appeared in animals that have consumed some of the foods. This is the case in two well-known types of human food poisoning—botulism (*Clostridium botulinum*) and staphylococcal food poisoning (*Staphylococcus aureus*). The former intoxication is often fatal as a consequence of irreversible damage to the central nervous system. The latter is usually only extremely distressing for several hours, during which severe vomitting, diarrhea, and abdominal pains occur.

A variety of fungi that are especially common in materials stored as livestock feeds produce toxins that affect vertebrates generally (livestock, humans, laboratory animals, fish, and cultivated animal cells). Toxins in the spores of *Pithomyces* cause facial eczema in cattle and sheep; the fungus is widely distributed and grows on dead plant material. Toxins elaborated on stored cereal grains by *Fusarium* cause edema and hemorrhage in various animals, and one of these toxins causes reduced milk production in cattle. The aflatoxins and other toxins produced in stored grains and peanuts by species of *Aspergillus* and *Penicillium* are lethal to livestock (notably poultry stock) in very small amounts. The aflatoxins accumulate rapidly in the liver, where their presence results in severe, often fatal, hemorrhage and/or malignancy (hepatoma).

Certain algae also contribute to the toxicity of animal foodstuffs and of drinking water. Three types of animal intoxication by algae have been documented. (1) Blue-green algae of the genera *Microcystis* and *Anabaena* occasionally develop as dense populations (blooms) in fresh-water ponds. Toxins are released that are lethal to cattle that drink the water. (2) Paralytic shellfish poisoning of humans is a consequence of their ingestion of animals such as mussels and clams that have ingested certain toxin-producing dinoflagellates. The algae are representatives of the genera *Gonyaulax, Gymnodinium, Prorocentrum,* and *Pyrodinium.* (3) Aquatic gill-breathing animals such as fish and mussels are killed by toxins released into the water by certain chrysomonads, viz., *Prymnesium* and *Ochromonas.*

Purification. It is generally characteristic of living organisms that they release into their environment substances they have taken up or synthesized, but cannot further metabolize. In quantitative terms, as proportion of foods released, this is especially characteristic of animals. Many such substances are toxic to the organism that produces them (autotoxic) when they accumulate within the organism or in its immediate environment. Most of the potentially autotoxic substances released by animals are organic compounds that can be metabolized by fungi and bacteria. Microbial metabolism converts the substances to non-toxic materials. Most of these transformations occur in soil and in water and mud, where animal excreta are deposited.

In general, the mineralizing activities of fungi and bacteria are as important to the welfare of animals as of plants. Digestive and metabolic wastes and the discarded parts (e.g., outgrown exoskeletons and shells) of animals usually cannot be digested by animals. Animal carcasses may serve as foods for insect larvae and carrion animals, but a considerable proportion of this type of food is utilized by microbes.

Whenever the rate of deposition of animal discards or carcasses exceeds the rate of consumption by other organisms, and especially the mineralization by protists, the immediate environment becomes unfavorable for animal life. This is due in part to O_2 consumption by the protists and by auto-oxidizable substances in the accumulation, and in part to the accumulation of products of the decomposition. For example, sulfur is released from organic combination as H_2S, which is toxic for many animals above certain concentrations. When the H_2S is produced slowly, it dissipates in the atmosphere, precipitates as metal sulfides, or is used as an energy source by sulfur-oxidizing chemo- or photo-lithotrophic bacteria.

If mineralization is to be effective in maintaining a non-toxic environment for animals, it must be sufficiently rapid to prevent accumulation of animal substance and products. In this sense, microbial activities are urgent with regard to the welfare of animals, while only essential to the welfare of plants.

Chapter 21

Associations

Symbiosis

Most kinds of protists share their natural habitats with a variety of other protists and with higher organisms. The relationships among the organisms in a given habitat vary in intimacy, dependence, and antagonism. Some of the major kinds of indirect interactions of protists with higher organisms were discussed in Chapter 20. More direct interactions, which involve specific kinds of organisms existing as contemporaries, will be discussed in this chapter.

Symbiosis is the phenomenon of different kinds of organisms existing in a constant and intimate association. Most symbiotic relationships involve direct physical association of two individuals, two clones, or an individual and a clone; three or more different kinds of organisms are involved in some symbioses. Different "kinds" means that the associates (called **symbionts**) are not classified in the same species. That is the minimum difference; many associations involve organisms classified in different kingdoms.

Three general classes of associations are distinguished on the basis of the physical relationship between partners. In endosymbiosis, one symbiont dwells within the other. If the latter is multicellular, the endosymbiont may inhabit intercellular spaces, a body cavity, or the interior of cells. If the host is uni-cellular, the endosymbiont is intracellular. In ectosymbiosis, the ectosymbiont dwells on the surface of its partner. In parasymbiosis, the partners share a common habitat and interact constantly, but may not be in direct physical contact.

In any symbiotic association, one symbiont is usually larger and/or more highly organized than the other. Occasionally, biologists refer to the larger or more complex organism as the host (or the morphologic host). This usage implies that it is invariably the smaller or more primitive organism that derives greater benefit from the association. This implication is misleading, since the interaction of symbionts is predominantly physiologic, and their association may be beneficial to either or to both partners.

The benefits potentially derived from symbiosis by one or both partners include the following.

A source of nutrients in the absence of competitors.

A source of specific micronutrients, especially vitamins or amino acids.

A waste-disposal system.

Protection, by virtue of structural properties of the partner, from adverse environmental conditions such as scarcity of water, extremes of temperature, or intense illumination.

Mobility and consequently wider, more frequent dispersal; or, conversely, sessility in a favorable environment.

Increased ability to absorb water and soluble nutrients.

Three categories of relationships are recognized according to the derivation of benefits from symbiosis.

Mutualism. Both partners benefit from association.

Parasitism. Only one partner (the parasite) benefits; most parasitic associations are destructive for the other partner (the host), which is disadvantaged or damaged by association.

Commensalism. The partners share a food source; either the respective partners utilize different portions of the food, or one utilizes the food only after it has been modified by the metabolism of the other.

As in all biologic classifications, the categories are only convenient concepts. The natural phenomena grade without significant discontinuity from one category to the next.

Any association involving living organisms is dynamic; the designation of any association as a particular type is meaningful only with respect to a point in time (in particular, a point in the development of that individual association) and to a given environment. The environment is the ever-present third partner in a biologic association. This point is relevant even to endosymbionts, which may interact with the environment only indirectly, through the effects of environment and of endosymbiont on the partner.

Any environmental change that greatly favors only one of the partners may disrupt the association by altering the physiologic balance typical of prolonged associations. Similarly, the balance may be upset by environmental conditions unfavorable for both partners. Many mutualistic associations, in particular, can be established only within a narrow range of environmental conditions; once established, they may become parasitistic whenever a change in environmental conditions results in an increase in the relative numbers of one partner or a change in its activities.

Organisms may be designated obligate symbionts for either or both of two reasons: (1) they cannot be found in nature as free-living organisms; they can be found only in symbiotic association with other organisms; and (2) they cannot be cultivated in the laboratory in inanimate environments. The concept of obligatory symbiosis serves as an explanation of these negative observations. It proposes that the organisms have evolved to so great a dependence on their associates that they do not occur commonly or develop readily outside the association. It might be that obligate symbionts are dependent on activities of their partners that are specifically stimulated by activities of the obligate associates.

In the following sections, particular symbiotic associations in which at least one symbiont is a protist are described as illustrations of principles stated above. Three symbioses are described in detail; several others are treated only briefly, to illustrate the variety of ways in which protists are known to associate with other organisms.

Lichens: Protist-Protist Symbiosis

Until late in the nineteenth century, lichens were regarded as a kind of plant. The notion of symbiosis (1873) and the suggestion that lichens were composites of organisms (1867) were proposed at about the same time. All subsequent studies of lichens (which are still classified as plants by some authors) have substantiated their dual nature. They are now regarded as one of the clearest examples of symbiosis known.

The partners in a lichen are an algal clone (the "phycobiont") and a fungus or fungal clone (the "mycobiont"). The association is not obligatory for either organism. The same organisms (as species) are found free-living, and both algal and fungal partners in lichens can be cultivated in artificial media as pure populations. However, lichens grow in many habitats that do not support growth of either partner alone. The broader distribution of lichens than of the partners as free-living organisms is a priori evidence that both partners derive some sort of benefit from association.

Lichens occur from the tropics to the arctic and are particularly abundant in regions of high humidity and moderate to low temperatures. Unlike most free-living organisms, they can survive and grow when their only source of water is the atmosphere, such as in fog or mist.

The lichen algae are usually representatives of lower Chlorophyces or of Cyanophyces; one xanthophycean phycobiont has been reported. They are either unicellular or simple filamentous types; in the latter case, the organism may be filamentous when free-living, but develop as separated unicells in the lichen thallus. The algal cells generally have thinner walls, are more permeable, and are smaller relative to cells of the same strain growing in pure culture; certain types also contain considerably less pigment when in the lichen.

The lichen fungi are chiefly Ascomycetes; the fungi of some tropical lichens are Basidiomycetes. When the mycobiont is separated from a lichen and cultivated without its algal symbiont, it often is unable to form fruiting bodies (ascocarps).

Thus, the morphology and pattern of development may be altered for either partner when in association. In addition, lichens display chemical and physiologic properties that are not predictable on the basis of the sum of the properties of the partners when growing separately.

The overall shape and internal organization of lichens vary with the identity of the partners. Each association has its peculiar morphology and pigmentation, as well as habitat. The bulk of the lichen is fungal protoplasm. The lichen thallus may be crustose (developing as a thin crust on the surface of rocks), foliose (flattened, often ribbed), or fruticose (attached at one point and growing away from the point of attachment, like a shrub in appearance). Internally, the algae may be scattered randomly among the hyphae or they may be restricted to one region, usually a flat layer (see Fig. 21-1). In both types, the outer surface is typically a pseudoparenchymatous cortex derived from hyphae. Additional hyphal layers may be present, as well as hyphae that extend out from the thallus to anchor it and/or to absorb water and nutrients.

In some lichens, the hyphae surround the algae, but do not penetrate the cells. More commonly, hyphal tips or lateral haustoria grow through the algal cell wall; they do not penetrate the cell membrane, and the algal protoplast remains intact. The walls of the penetrating mycobionts are relatively thin where they are within the algal walls. This type of penetration allows an intimate association between cell membranes of the partners, and nutrients should be able to diffuse through these contacts more readily than they would through cell walls of normal thickness.

Reproduction of lichens occurs in three principal ways. (1) Formation of fruiting bodies, e.g., ascocarps, characteristic of the fungus and containing only fungus spores. A new lichen may be established by each spore that germinates; the phycobiont may be different from the alga of the parent lichen. (2) Fragmentation. This is a regular feature of some lichens, and each fragment contains both partners. Accidentally produced fragments can likewise re-establish individual lichens. (3) Formation of soredia. These are spheroid bodies released from the surface of the lichen. Each soredium contains at least one algal cell that is enclosed in hyphae. Soredia are wind-dispersed and upon germination develop into lichens of the same type as the parent.

The structural dominance of the mycobionts and the ability of lichen algae to grow in nature without their partners have led some authors to regard lichens as an instance of parasitism of algae by fungi. However, algae do not occur in nature in all kinds of environments to which their propagules conceivably have access. Particularly in lichen habitats such as the surface of inland rocks, the amounts of moisture and soluble inorganic nutrients may be low and illumination intense; these conditions are unsuitable for free-living development of the types of algae that occur in lichens. Further, rock-inhabiting lichens demonstrably solubilize components of the rocks by the production of organic

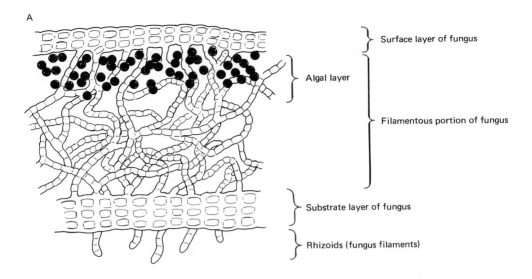

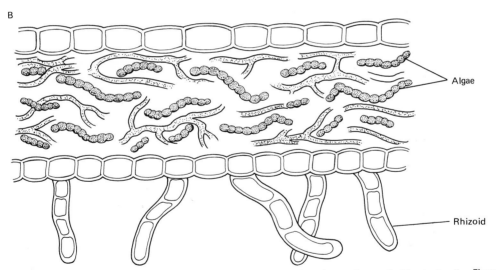

Diagrams of lichen constructions. *A. "Sticta"* type, with the algae in one layer. *B. "Leptogium"*   **Figure 21-1**
type, with the algae scattered through the interior. (Courtesy of P. Hirsch.)

acids; inorganic nutrients are thereby made available to both partners. Many of these acids are also chelating agents, which bind metal ions in soluble forms that can be absorbed by the lichen.

Phycobionts in pure cultures show a greater susceptibility to inactivation by heat or drying than they do in lichens. They also grow better at low than at high light intensities. Most phycobionts can grow organotrophically in the dark and grow poorly on purely inorganic media. Although they have retained their photosynthetic capacity, lichen algae seem to have evolved toward an organotrophic nutrition.

Most mycobionts in pure culture require or are definitely stimulated by the vitamins biotin and thiamine. They utilize various carbohydrates readily and can also digest more complex organic substances. They can utilize various nitrogen sources with equal readiness.

From studies of pure cultures of lichen organisms, of lichens reconstructed from pure cultures, of natural lichens in culture, and of the natural distribution of lichens, it can now be concluded that both partners derive benefits from the association. The algae are supplied with water and soluble inorganic nutrients, e.g., phosphate, which are absorbed by the hyphae; they are protected by the fungal pseudoparenchyma from high light intensities and from desiccation; and probably utilize organic nitrogenous compounds such as amino acids synthesized by the mycobiont. The fungi are supplied with organic nutrients for which they do not compete with other organotrophs (except parasites of lichens, which include bacteria and fungi), and with organic micronutrients, e.g., vitamins, which mycobionts have been found to release into the medium of pure cultures. Lichens in which the phycobiont is a type of N_2-fixing bluegreen alga (e.g., *Nostoc*) can fix N_2; this is clearly an advantage to its mycobionts, none of which can fix N_2 alone. In addition, when phycobiont cells (which are shorter-lived than the fungal cells) die and disintegrate, the fungus can digest and reabsorb their components. This results in an internal conservation of scarce nutrients, particularly nitrogenous substances.

Similarly, portions of the mycobiont of some lichens serve as storage areas for products of photosynthesis, and these carbon reserves are available to both partners under conditions unfavorable for photosynthesis.

An individual lichen in its natural habitat may be very long-lived. Some terrestrial lichens are estimated to have existed for at least tens of years. They grow slowly, increasing in diameter at most only a few millimeters per year, often less than 1 mm per year; an exceptional lichen ("*Peltigera*" spp.) can grow 2 to 4.5 cm per year. Such slow growth is partly attributed to the low water and nutrient supply of the habitat and the frequent desiccation of the thallus. However, even aquatic and coastal lichens of the tropics grow at these rates. Environmental changes that favor the growth of one or both partners usually result in dissociation of the lichen. Prolonged wetting particularly favors the phycobiont, which multiplies giving rise to cells not contacted or penetrated by the fungus, and which can become separated from the lichen thallus.

Constant levels of nutrients, water, or illumination, even if low, that favor uninterrupted growth also result in dissociation.

On the other hand, under some conditions of prolonged starvation, the fungus digests the algal cells. This digestion occurs periodically in some types of lichens, but typically involves only a fraction of the phycobiont population. It appears to be one mechanism available to the fungus for obtaining sustenance from the alga.

Generally, the lichen is an association that permits survival of both partners in environments unsuitable for the growth of either symbiont. This is survival allowed not by dormancy, but by mutualistic growth.

Mycorrhizae: Protist-Plant Symbiosis[1]

Mycorrhizae are associations between plant roots and filamentous fungi. There is a distinct specificity among mycorrhizal partners, such that particular fungi are regularly associated with particular plants. A particular developmental pattern is characteristic of each pair of associates. In nature, all known types of plants have been found to associate with mycorrhizal fungi; the fungi of mycorrhizae include representatives of two of the major groups (viz., phycomycetes and Basidiomycetes) and imperfect filamentous types that usually bear clamp connections and presumably are Basiodiomycetes.

Two principal organizational types of mycorrhizae are recognized: ectotrophic, in which most of the fungal protoplasm surrounds the root as a sheath, and endotrophic, in which most of the fungal protoplasm is within the root. In both types, the root tissue is not disorganized, as it usually is when roots are parasitized by fungi, and the composite organ—the mycorrhiza—is typically long-lived, some surviving and functioning for years. Only ectotrophic mycorrhizae are discussed here.

An ectotrophic mycorrhiza is initiated when a fungal hypha or germ tube contacts a young feeding rootlet of a suitable tree or seedling. The fungus develops as a pseudoparenchymatous sheath tightly apposed to the lateral surface of the root. This sheath is macroscopic when mature and is the most conspicuous portion of the mycorrhiza. In addition, hyphae grow into the root and ramify among the cortical cells. They do not invade the plant beyond this region, and they do not penetrate cells of the cortex. Wefts of hyphae also grow outward from the mycorrhiza into the soil. The external mycelium of a mycorrhiza may extend for several meters beyond the trunk of the tree; most of it is subterranean, but some may extend upward and develop within the loose layer of plant litter and other organic materials on the surface of the soil.

Ectotrophic mycorrhizae are found in many forest trees, both deciduous and coniferous. They were first described in beech (*Fagus*), subsequently in pine (*Pinus*), and are now known for more than a dozen genera. Individual trees are rarely found in the natural habitat without mycorrhizae. Generally, these trees are photolithotrophs as adults, and their seeds contain sufficient organic nutrients to provide the energy for germination and development of photosynthetic capacity. Under certain conditions, notably in fertilized agricultural soils, they can develop without mycorrhizae without any detectable decrease in growth rate or ultimate yield.

The fungi of these associations are usually Basidiomycetes that are found in vegetative condition in nature almost exclusively in the neighborhood of trees with which they can form mycorrhizae. Soil-dwelling mycelia can often

[1]See also Chaps. 13 and 20 concerning rhizobia and legumes.

be traced to tree roots, and fruiting bodies can be traced through such mycelia (at least presumptively) to roots. The fungi can be cultivated as pure populations in artificial laboratory media, but they do not form fruiting bodies in culture. Artificial cultivation of these fungi employs simple organic compounds, particularly sugars, as carbon sources and ammonia or organic nitrogenous compounds as nitrogen sources. They are generally incapable of utilizing complex organic substances such as cellulose and lignin. Most isolates require the vitamin thiamine and many also require one or more other vitamins, e.g., biotin, pantothenic acid, and nicotinic acid. Their growth in cultures is stimulated by mixtures of amino acids, extracts of plants, and root exudates. Some of this stimulation has been attributed to specific, though unidentified, factors (in pine) that are not identical with known micronutrients.

At present, ectotrophic mycorrhizae are regarded as mutualistic associations. The respective partners differ in their dependence on the association. The fungus is provided with growth substrates and growth factors, and with morphogenetic stimulation on which its germination and sporulation depend. The fungi are not competitive, and their development is usually inhibited in mixed microbial cultures. Lack of ability to compete with other microbes presumably is the reason that they do not proliferate in soil at large.

The benefits derived by the plant are related to the soil environment. The trees seem to have some resistance to infection by mycorrhizal fungi when nutrients are plentiful in the soil. However, when the supply of N, K, or P is low, but other conditions of moisture, pH, and illumination are generally favorable for the plant's development, mycorrhizae appear on the roots. Growth of each mycorrhiza increases the absorptive surface of the root and also, by means of the externally radiating hyphae, increases the volume of the soil from which the plant, through its associate, can obtain soluble nutrients. In addition to benefiting the plant by absorption, the mycorrhizae store solutes during periods of abundance; when the environmental supply decreases, the nutrients are transferred to the plant. Thus, the mycorrhiza provides the tree with a higher level of mineral nutrients in nutrient-poor soils or during periods of nutrient scarcity in generally favorable soils.

The Rumen: Protist-Animal Symbiosis

The rumen is a chamber in the anterior part of the alimentary tract of certain herbivorous animals (the ruminants) that is inhabited by a dense population of microorganisms whose identities and relative proportions are characteristic of the animal and of its diet. All the ruminants are mammals: cattle, sheep, goats, deer, giraffes, pronghorns, and mouse deer. The microorganisms are protozoa and bacteria. The microbes are transferred from animals with mature rumens to weanlings mainly by mouth-to-mouth contact, and also via air-borne droplets and drinking water ingested by the young.

Developmentally, the rumen is a modification of the esophagus (see Fig. 21-2), and like the esophagus its wall does not contain glands that release digestive enzymes. The rumen is rudimentary in a suckling animal, and its

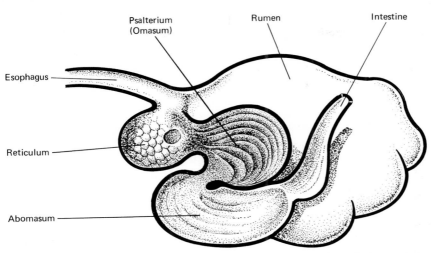

Psalterium   Rumen   Intestine
(Omasum)

Esophagus

Reticulum

Abomasum

Diagram of the upper alimentary tract of a ruminant. Food passes through the esophagus into   **Figure 21-2**
the rumen, is regurgitated through the reticulum, and is chewed as cud. It is swallowed again
and enters the psalterium (omasum) and then the abomasum (stomach), within which most of
the digestive processes catalyzed by the animal's enzymes occur.

maturation is stimulated by the establishment of a normal rumen microbial population. In cattle reared without contact with rumen microorganisms or maintained on a milk diet, development of the rumen is abnormal; specifically, the size is below average and the absorptive tissues of the wall are incompletely developed. There is evidence that certain of the organic acids produced by the microorganisms stimulate normal development. The volume of the mature rumen in cattle and sheep is approximately one tenth the volume of the animal (100 liters and 6 liters, respectively, when filled).

In the mature normal rumen of cattle (the most thoroughly characterized system), conditions fluctuate regularly within a narrow range as the animal feeds, the foods are transformed by the microorganisms, the rumen contents are removed to the bloodstream and the stomach, and the animal feeds again. The temperature is ca. 38° C and is maintained by the thermoregulatory system of the ruminant. There is very little dissolved O_2 (E_h ranges from -420 mv up to -360 mv); any O_2 that enters the rumen is rapidly consumed by the facultative anaerobic bacteria present.

The pH is somewhat less than neutrality (ca. 6.5), and not normally less than 6. The saliva of the animal is the principal fluid other than ingested water; it contains large amounts of bicarbonate (0.1 M) and phosphate (0.026 M), which serve as buffers, at an initial pH of 8; the cation Na^{+1} (at 0.18 M) provides electrostatic balance. The saliva does not contain digestive enzymes. The pH in the rumen is lowered by the accumulation of acids produced by the microbes and raised by the microbial production of NH_3 by hydrolysis of urea and protein. Urea may be present in the foods, but the major source is the wall of the rumen, through which urea is released from the bloodstream.

All the enzymatic activities of the rumen are attributable to the microorganisms. With the exception of a few facultative anaerobes, these microorganisms are anaerobes that obtain energy for growth by fermentation of carbohydrates. The major products of their fermentations are organic acids (predominantly fatty acids, e.g., acetic, propionic, butyric, and higher straight- and branched-chain fatty acids; most are saturated acids), CO_2, and H_2. Methane (CH_4) is also produced in significant amounts by one type of bacterium (*Methanobacterium ruminantium*) from CO_2 and H_2 and from formic acid. Of these substances, the acids are absorbed by the ruminant, and the CH_4 is released from the rumen by belching. Some of the CO_2 is consumed in organotrophic CO_2 fixation reactions in the rumen, and the H_2 serves as the principal reductant in terminal fermentation reactions. Some of the CO_2 and H_2, which are produced in greater quantities than can be used by the microbes, is released with the CH_4.

The substrates of these fermentations include low molecular weight carbohydrates present in plant materials, and—most important—plant structural carbohydrates, including cellulose, xylans, and pectins. Lignin is not decomposed in the rumen. The complex carbohydrates are degraded in two general ways: (1) by soluble enzymes released by a small proportion (usually less than 5 per cent of the population) of the bacteria, and (2) within protozoa that ingest particles of the food. The soluble carbohydrates released by the action of the bacterial enzymes are available to all the inhabitants of the rumen. Starches present in the food are attacked in the same general ways.

The majority of the bacteria grow by fermenting the soluble carbohydrates available either in the ingested food or released from it by some of the bacteria. Some of these organisms occur only in the rumen (e.g., *Butyrivibrio, Lachnospira, Ruminococcus, Succinimonas, Succinivibrio,* and several species of other genera). Others also occur in non-ruminant digestive tracts, in soil, or in plant materials decaying outside the rumen; these include lactic acid bacteria, various gram-positive cocci, corynebacteria, *Desulfovibrio* types, and certain spirochetes. They comprise a morphologically varied group, and, except for basic similarities in their fermentative (energy) metabolism, their nutritional properties are varied.

All the rumen protozoa that have been studied are ciliates. Flagellates are sometimes reported, but they do not seem to be regular rumen inhabitants. The ciliates are representatives of two orders: *Dasytrichia* and *Isotricha* of Holotrichida, and *Diplodinium, Endodinium, Entodinium, Epidinium, Eudiplodinium, Ophryoscolex,* and *Polyplastron* of Spirotrichida (suborder Entodiniomorphina), which are generally larger than the holotrichs. These are unusual among protozoa in their ability to grow anaerobically. The products of their fermentations are qualitatively similar to those of rumen bacteria. It is estimated that they perform about 20 per cent of the digestion and fermentation that occur in the rumen, the remainder being performed by the bacteria. However, the activities of the protozoa are not essential to normal functioning of this digestive system; when the pH of the cattle rumen drops below 6, the protozoa disappear, and the rates of bacterial processes per unit volume of rumen contents increase to compensate for the activity lost with the protozoa.

The numbers of microorganisms present in the rumen contents vary primarily with diet. The total counts of protozoa vary from a few thousand to 1 million or more per gram of rumen contents. The smaller forms (the holotrichs) are especially numerous when the feed is high in soluble carbohydrates, as in fresh plant material. The others are most numerous when the diet is rich in starch, as in grains. They can digest cellulose, but their contribution to this digestion is small relative to that of bacteria.

The total counts of bacteria range from 10^{10} to 10^{11} per gram. Viable counts approach the total counts in rumen material from animals fed on a grain diet, but are only ca. 10^9 in animals fed on hay. It could be that 90 to 99 per cent of the bacteria in a hay-fed rumen are of a physiologic type not yet cultivated; however, it seems more likely that they are not viable, although still metabolically active.

The density of the microbial population in the rumen is not exceeded in nature and is greater than can usually be attained in artificial cultures. Comparable microbial densities are found in other portions of vertebrate alimentary tracts, particularly of other types of herbivores and of omnivores. Generally, vertebrates are capable of digesting animal tissues without the aid of microbes, and carnivorous animals carry smaller numbers of microorganisms in their alimentary tracts.

The multitude of activities that occur in the rumen have been extensively documented, unquestionably because of the importance of the welfare of domesticated ruminants to human nutrition. The contributions of the ruminant and of the microbes are summarized in Figure 21-3 and Table 21-1.

The microbial population itself constitutes a parasymbiotic community, within which certain interactions have been inferred from studies of mixed rumen populations and of pure and two-membered cultures in defined media. (These are in addition to some already mentioned above, e.g., the hydrolysis of cellulose to low molecular weight carbohydrates, an instance of commensalism, and consumption of O_2 by facultative anaerobic bacteria, which detoxifies the environment of the strict anaerobes.)

1. Hydrolysis of urea, which yields NH_3 and CO_2. The enzyme urease is produced by gram-positive rumen cocci. The NH_3 can be utilized as a nitrogen source by most of the rumen microbes.

2. Production of specific fatty acids that are growth factors for some of the bacteria.

3. Production of vitamins. Although this is generally regarded as an advantage to the ruminant, many rumen microbes also require vitamins as growth factors.

4. Hydrolysis of pectin to galacturonic acid and methanol by holotrichs. These protozoa cannot use the hydrolysis products; they are utilized by other, non-pectinolytic microbes present.

Also within this community are predators and their prey. The protozoa can and do ingest bacteria, usually showing a preference for certain bacterial types.

On the whole, the rumen is regarded as a mutualistic association in which

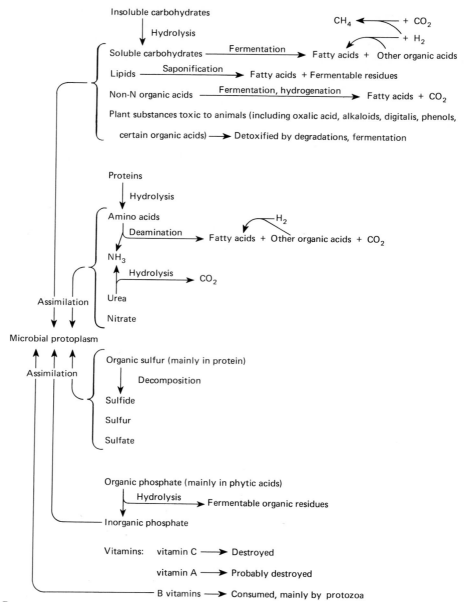

Figure 21-3   Rumen processes.

all the participants are benefited. The ruminant benefits nutritionally; in contrast to other vertebrates, including other types of herbivores, it can survive on a diet that is high in its content of plant fibrous material; is low in N, S, and P compounds usually required by vertebrates; and lacks B vitamins.

The microorganisms are provided with a habitat in which the physical and chemical conditions and population are unusually constant. Further, in contrast to the situation of microbes growing fermentatively in inanimate environments, the metabolic waste products of rumen microorganisms are continually removed from their habitat by the animal. The acids, in particular, do not accumulate to concentrations that would inhibit microbial activities. It is considered a significant indication of the ability of the various bacterial types to cohabit the rumen that none of them produces antibacterial antibiotic substances. Further, neither the bacteria nor the protozoa typical of the rumen produce dormant, resistant stages. They are perpetuated in the vegetative state, transferred from parent ruminant to the young.

TABLE 21-1. Major Rumen Products and Their Fates

1. Undigested plant materials	1. Eventually eliminated with little further alteration
2. Fermentation products a. Fatty acids	2. a. Approximately 75% is absorbed through the rumen wall into the bloodstream; remainder is absorbed through walls of intestines; constitutes principal assimilable carbon and energy source for the ruminant
b. Gases—CO_2, H_2, and CH_4	b. Some CO_2 and H_2 is consumed in rumen reactions; excesses of all three gases are eliminated by eructation
3. Microbial protoplasm	3. Digested mainly in the stomach and partly in the intestines by ruminant enzymes; digestion products absorbed through walls of intestines; constitutes principal source of N, P, S, amino acids, and vitamins for the ruminant*
4. Substances added by ruminants a. Bicarbonate and phosphate	4. a. Serve as pH buffers; some of each is consumed by microbes and later reassimilated by the animal
b. Urea†	b. Hydrolyzed in the rumen to NH_3 and CO_2; the NH_3 is consumed by microbes; the nitrogen is later reassimilated by the animal

*The microbial cells contain proteins that are more readily digested by the animal than are plant proteins and contain higher proportions of those amino acids specifically required by the animal. The vitamins provided by the rumen microbes (within their cells plus as solutes in rumen fluid) are known to include the fat-soluble vitamin K and the water-soluble vitamins B_1 (thiamine), B_2 (riboflavin), B_6 (pyridoxine), B_{12}, folic acid, nicotinic acid, pantothenic acid, and biotin. These vitamins are dietary requirements of the young ruminant until its rumen population is established.

†Urea is a waste product of the animal's nitrogen metabolism. When dietary nitrogen is plentiful, much of the urea is excreted in the urine. When dietary nitrogen content is low, most of the urea is recycled to the rumen.

Other Associations Involving Protists

The following sections contain brief descriptions of a few additional symbiotic associations that have been recognized. Several other examples and some of their characteristics have been mentioned in earlier chapters.

Mycoparasites. Parasitism of one type of fungus by another, called mycoparasitism, is known to involve representatives of all major groups of fungi both as hosts and as parasites. These associations comprise a full spectrum of host-parasite interactions. There are mild, non-destructive parasitic associations; associations that are initially non-destructive and result in damage to the host only after prolonged association; and associations that are destructive from the time they are initiated and that usually progress rapidly to death of the host.

Most of the obligate mycoparasites known establish the mild, prolonged type of association. Dependence of a mycoparasite on its host usually seems to involve specific soluble substances synthesized by the host. These substances may be required by the parasite for spore germination, vegetative growth, or sporulation. A few types of fungi resist being parasitized, either by formation of walls that cannot be penetrated, or by failure to synthesize the specific substances the parasite requires for germination or growth.

Some mycoparasitic associations are endosymbiotic, especially those involving Chytridiomycetes as parasites. More commonly, withdrawal of nutrients or components from the host is mediated by haustoria. Depending mainly on the parasite, the haustoria penetrate the host only near its hyphal tips, where the wall is of minimum thickness, or randomly along its hyphae. In both cases, penetration appears to be aided by enzymes that produce holes in the host wall by dissolving it at the points of contact with developing haustoria; in some associations, appressoria are also formed.

Once the parasite has penetrated the host wall, and, less commonly, the cell membrane, it grows by utilizing as nutrients substances absorbed by the host from the environment or synthesized by the host. If the host can continue its development, it may show disease symptoms such as reduced growth rate, inability to sporulate, or disintegration of hyphae due to digestive activities of the parasite.

Mycoparasitism in nature may account for certain successions—sequential predominance of types in one habitat. For example, Basidiomycetes generally succeed Ascomycetes and Deuteromycetes in dead wood. This succession has in the past been attributed to the relatively rapid growth rates of the Ascomycetes and Deuteromycetes, and to the early exhaustion of nutrients they can utilize; their development leaves the more resistant components of wood for the slower-growing Basidiomycetes. Recently, however, several wood-inhabiting Basidiomycetes have been recognized as capable of parasitizing wood-inhabiting Ascomycetes and Deuteromycetes and apparently depend on their hosts mainly as a source of nitrogen. Thus, destruction of the early inhabitants of the niche may be an additional factor in this type of succession.

Entomogenous Fungi. Fungi are known to be parasitically associated with many types of insects. The insect parasites include representatives of all major fungal groups. Some associations are ectoparasitic; most of the thallus of the parasite develops on the surface of the insect, and nutrients are withdrawn from the host body through haustoria. Many of these relationships are not fatal, although they are typically destructive.

Infection of an insect by an endoparasitic fungus is, in contrast, usually fatal. The host may become infected in any of its developmental stages, and death typically occurs within two weeks of infection. The course of this brief association commonly follows the following general pattern.

1. A spore germinates on the surface of the host body, producing a germ tube that penetrates the body's integument and enters the hoemocele (the principal body cavity); many of these fungi, when grown in pure cultures, have been found capable of hydrolyzing chitin, the major structural component of the middle layer of the (mature) insect integument.

2. The fungus grows as unicells or short filaments in the hoemocele, multiplying by fragmentation or by budding.

3. As fungal protoplasm increases within the hoemocele, the host displays disease symptoms—it ceases feeding, becomes restless, often climbs (in soil or on a plant), then loses coordination, and eventually becomes immobile.

4. Shortly before or only after death of the host, the fungus develops as elongated hyphae, which may penetrate the host body and extend outward from it.

5. The fungus sporulates, usually from the hyphae that are outside the host; asexual spores such as conidia are formed more commonly than sexual spores or resting stages such as chlamydospores, but the manner of sporulation may also be affected by environmental factors such as illumination and/or humidity.

Contact of a fungus spore and a suitable host does not inevitably result in infection. Infection in practically all known pairs of endoparasitic fungus and susceptible insect requires humid conditions. Susceptibility to infection has been reported to increase during periods of physiologic stress in the host. Stresses may be due to hormonal changes at particular stages of metamorphosis, food deficiencies, extremes of environmental temperature or water content, crowding, injury, or exposure to certain chemicals.

The environmental and developmental factors that influence susceptibility are currently of major interest to insect pathologists because of the growing public concern about the possible detrimental effects of chemical insecticides on humans and wildlife. It is hoped that, with sufficient information concerning natural insecticidal agents such as endoparasitic fungi (and some bacterial parasites and some viruses, as well), these agents could be used to control insects that damage agricultural plants. The major advantage of microbial and viral insecticides is their specificity for insects.

Fungus-Cultivating Ants. Several species of ants are known that are associated mutualistically with filamentous fungi in a manner parallel to man's relationship to his crop plants (or, more precisely, his table mushrooms). Depending on the ant, the fungi are provided with bits of fresh leaves or of plant debris (mulch) or with ant excrement (manure) as nourishing substrates. Certain workers among the ants tend the fungus beds within the ant colony and remove fungi which that type of ant does not eat (i.e., the weeds). The fungi may be carried to a new ant colony by the young queen, sometimes in a special body pouch and usually as hyphal fragments. Most of the fungi that have been identified are Basidiomycetes. The hyphae and/or spores are eaten by the ants as part of their diet, and the fungi are provided with utilizable nutrients in the absence of fungal competitors. The presence of growing fungi in the colonies also apparently serves as a mechanism for maintenance of a constant level of humidity.

Insects other than ants are known to cultivate particular fungi as foods. These include certain termites and beetles. The insects involved usually construct their nests in decaying plant materials, which are invariably inhabited by fungi. In all probability, feeding on fungi was at one time not specific, but the nutritional advantages to a particular type of animal of utilizing certain fungi resulted in the evolution of lines that fed on and maintained only one kind of fungus.

Phytopathogenic Bacteria. Every individual plant growing in nature can be expected to be associated with bacteria. Most of these bacteria do not harm the plant and are present on its aerial or subterranean surfaces as a consequence simply of their presence in air and soil. The roots of many, probably most, plants support a population of non-invasive bacteria and fungi in their immediate (up to about 1 mm) environment, the rhizosphere, as a consequence of the exudation of organic materials from the roots into the soil. The population of this rhizosphere is not specific for the plant, but usually differs from the general bacterial soil population in its higher proportion of amino acid-dependent bacteria. Rhizosphere microbes seem to contribute to the welfare of the plant, largely through the solubilization of inorganic substances, especially soil phosphates.

Certain types of bacteria[2] can, under favorable conditions of temperature, moisture, and nutritional state of the plant, invade plant tissue and develop as parasites. The usual result of any extensive development of bacteria within the tissues of a living plant is disease of the plant. According to the manner of its transmission from plant to plant, the site(s) through which it can enter a new host, the degree of its invasiveness, its predilection for certain tissues, and the manner in which it causes destruction (occlusion of vascular tissues, release of pectinolytic or cellulolytic enzymes, or production of toxins), the parasite may cause localized or generalized disease in the host.

Transmission may occur through the soil or the air or via insect vectors. The roots, aerial portions, or sites of insect feeding, respectively, will be initially invaded. Bacteria may also be included in the seeds of an infected plant and thereby be transmitted (overseason) to the next generation. Air-borne parasites

[2]Bacteria are discussed here, but the principles of infection, resistance, and pathogenesis apply to fungal phytopathogens as well.

may invade the plant through natural openings on the plant, such as leaf stomata, or through wounds, including those caused by feeding of insects that are not vectors, by accidental damage caused by wind or animal movement, or by agricultural implements, which can serve as inanimate vectors—fomites.

The most important defenses of plants against microbial invasion seem to be the ability of the plant to exclude a wounded and/or infected site from the general circulation, such as by deposition of insoluble materials resistant to microbial degradation (lignin, suberin) around the site, or to produce or accumulate antimicrobial substances such as phenolic compounds at the site.

Plant diseases that result from bacterial infection are various, and the symptoms of any one host-parasite association are influenced further by environmental factors during infection. Generally, under environmental conditions that favor development of disease symptoms, infection by *Agrobacterium* results in galls (hypertrophies of stems or roots), by *Corynebacterium* in spot or vascular diseases, by *Pseudomonas* in leaf diseases and wilts, by *Streptomyces* in scab diseases of tubers or roots, and by *Xanthomonas* in necrosis (soft rot) of various tissues. Infection by *Erwinia* results in a variety of diseases. Each bacterial species as presently recognized generally can infect and cause disease in only one or a few related plant species, with the notable exception of *Agrobacterium*, which can infect a variety of unrelated plants.

Algae-Associated Bacteria. Many algae (and protozoa) contain endosymbiotic bacteria, and it is typical of colonial forms that their colonies are inhabited by one or several types of bacteria. Sheathed forms usually carry a number of types of bacteria in their sheath materials.

In one association that has been studied in laboratory cultures, the algae have been found dependent on the presence of certain bacteria. The colonies of the green alga *Volvox aureus* are normally inhabited by large numbers of unicellular bacteria and actinomycetes. In laboratory media, most of the bacteria are lost as the cultures are transferred, but *Pseudomonas fluorescens* persists, apparently maintained in some way by the algae in all kinds of environments. When the algae can be freed of *P. fluorescens,* e.g., by micromanipulation, the algae die after a few generations. The living bacteria cannot be replaced by extracts of their cells or by known growth factors. It has been inferred from this that the pseudomonads either provide the alga with unidentified growth factors or utilize (and thereby detoxify) products of algal metabolism that inhibit algal development.

Endozoic Algae. A variety of coelenterates (including hydras, corals, sea anemones) possess endosymbiotic algae. The advantages to the coelenterates are: an endogenous source of primary (i.e., photosynthetically produced) organic nutrients, known to include amino acids; an endogenous system for elimination of respiratory CO_2, both through CO_2 fixation and by deposition of insoluble carbonates by the algae; and possibly a source of O_2. Animals with endosymbionts are demonstrably more capable of surviving periods of starvation than are animals of the same type that do not possess algae. Most of the algae are dinoflagellates (zooxanthellae); some are chlorellae (zoochlorellae). In pure cultures, algae isolated from coelenterates can utilize a wide variety of element sources (e.g., any of nitrate, ammonia, or organic nitrogenous compounds as nitrogen sources), although they often require vitamins as growth factors. Whether the algae derive any benefit from association with coelenterates, other than possibly protection from high light intensities, is not clear; similar types occur as free-living organisms.

Many other invertebrates (including annelids, molluscs, tunicates, and sponges), as well as numerous protozoa (notably foraminifera, plus many radiolarians and some ciliates; see Fig. 21-4) are similarly associated with unicellular algae. Some of the protozoa possess blue-green algae as endosymbionts. These algae have occasionally been described as subcellular organelles called "cyanelles." Like some lichen phycobionts, the "cyanelles" lack sheaths when in association, but develop extramural structures typical of the species when artificially cultivated as free-living organisms.

These associations could be regarded as instances of nutritional parasitism of algae by organotrophs, since most of the algae grow well in inorganic media (some require vitamins) and are more widely distributed in the sea than are their non-photosynthetic associates. However, some of these latter organisms are unusually capable of accumulating inorganic nutrients present in low concentrations in sea water, and this should benefit the algae nutritionally.

Organotrophs of all types that contain endosymbiotic algae respond to light. Most of these organisms are motile and can respond to variations in light intensity by migrating to positions where illumination is optimal for their endosymbionts. Responsiveness to light is absent when the organism is experimentally deprived of or occurs naturally without its algae. This implies that the algae, many of which are not motile as adults, benefit from association with motile organotrophs that can transport them to their energy source.

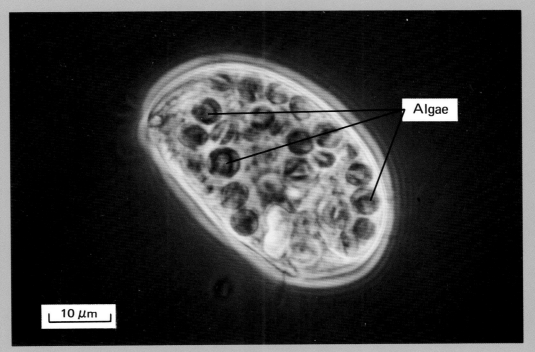

An unidentified ciliate protozoon with endosymbiotic chlorellae. (Courtesy of P. Hirsch.) **Figure 21-4**

Chapter 22

Inhabitation of Man

Like all other higher organisms, humans are inhabited by a variety of protists during most of their existence. Depending on characteristics of the individual human and of the protists with which he becomes associated and on environmental conditions prior to and during their association, the consequences of the association may be beneficial, harmful,[1] or innocuous for the host. As a biologic system, man and his microbial associates are basically similar to other vertebrates (especially other mammals) and their microbes. Accordingly, much of the discussion in this chapter is relevant to animals other than man. Only the "names" of some of the microorganisms would need to be changed.

An important consequence of this basic similarity is the usefulness of studies of infectious diseases in animals such as guinea pigs, rabbits, rats, mice, hamsters, dogs, cats, pigeons, and chickens in understanding infectious diseases of humans. Since the work of Pasteur with livestock and of Koch with mice, animal studies have contributed major concepts in medical microbiology and have greatly reduced the necessity of employing humans as subjects. Much of our present understanding of defense mechanisms and other aspects of the interaction of humans with infective microbes was first inferred from animal studies and later substantiated by studies of humans, with much less risk for the individuals who volunteered.

The Host

The normal unborn human is free of microorganisms. His first contact with them occurs as he passes through the birth canal, and from that time until

[1]According to vital statistics as of the late 1960's, the major cause of deaths among the principal expected readership of this book (viz., U.S. college students) is the automobile. Suicide is the distant second, followed by malignancies. Infectious diseases are of minor influence in the matter of survival for this group of humans; their prevention, by individuals and by the society, is a daily activity.

485

his death he harbors a microbial population that varies only slightly during his lifetime. The long-term, or indigenous, population is either non-destructive (non-pathogenic) or beneficial to the otherwise healthy human. It is acquired mainly from other humans and is restricted to body regions exposed to the environment. Some of these organisms and related types are even better suited for multiplication within the host body, e.g., within cells, in certain tissues, or in the bloodstream; their invasion of such regions usually results in impairment of function (disease) of the host. Consequently, the normal functioning of the host is dependent on continuous defense against invasion by microbes.

Three lines of defense are recognized in the human body, distinguished by the stages at which they can arrest invasion. The first two lines are innate characteristics of humans and operate independently of previous contact of the individual with specific microorganisms. The third mechanism involves a response by the individual to microorganisms that pass the first two lines of defense; it is specifically active against those invading microorganisms.

Primary Defenses. The primary defenses include mechanical factors that act as physical barriers to penetration of host tissues by potential invaders, or as means of removing the invaders from areas where penetrable tissues are accessible to them; and chemical factors that kill or inhibit the growth of microbial cells.

The respiratory and alimentary tracts are lined with mucus, which serves as a physical barrier between microbes and host cells. It is adhesive and traps the microbes, preventing them from moving farther along the tract. In the trachea and bronchi, cilia on the cells beneath the mucus move it upward toward the pharynx from which the mucus is expelled by sneezing or coughing; it may also be swallowed. The stratified epithelium of the skin is effective as a barrier to penetration; desquamation of the outer layer removes surface microbes. The motion of fluids—tears in the eyes moving downward through the lacrimal ducts, saliva in the mouth being swallowed, and urine moving out of the body—serves to wash the eyes, mouth, and urethra, respectively, and remove microbial cells from those regions.

The acids and digestive enzymes of the stomach kill most of the microbes that enter with food or with mucus from the respiratory tract. An empty stomach is practically sterile. Organic acids present on the skin maintain a surface pH of 3 to 5, which is unsuitably low for the growth of many microorganisms; the acids themselves may be toxic. These acids are produced both by the host and by the normal microbial population. Tears, nasal secretions, and saliva contain lysozyme, an enzyme that degrades cell wall components of bacteria, causing disintegration of the cells. Semen contains spermine, a basic organic compound, at a concentration that is lethal for many pathogenic bacteria.

Secondary Defenses. Phagocytosis—ingestion of particles such as microbial cells by specialized host cells—is the principal component of the second line of defense. The body contains several types of cells that are capable of phagocytosis, including: wandering macrophages, which move out from blood vessels to patrol extravascular tissues; polymorphonuclear leukocytes normally present in the blood, but which can migrate to extravascular tissues in response to injury or invasion; and endothelial cells of the lining of the lymphatic system, which are especially numerous in the sinusoids of lymph nodes, spleen, and liver.

Phagocytosis is an effective defense if the ingested microbes can be killed by the phagocytes. This process has been studied particularly in polymorphonuclear leukocytes, within which destruction of ingested bacteria occurs as follows. Shortly after the phagocyte has ingested one or a few particles, lysosomes collide with the food vacuole, and the limiting membranes of the two structures fuse in such a way that their contents mix. The digestive enzymes contained in the lysosome are known to include phosphatases, nucleases, lysozyme, and a proteolytic enzyme; these attack the microbes in the food vacuole and cause their disintegration. Different types of phagocytes differ in their digestive capacities, so that their effectiveness against particular microbes varies.

When microbes invade extravascular tissue, the macrophages are the first phagocytes to act. If the number of invading microbes is greater than the macrophages can accommodate, **inflammation** of the invaded site occurs. This process is characterized by increase in diameter and permeability of adjacent blood vessels and migration of leukocytes into the tissue. Microbes that resist this defense enter the lymph fluid and are carried to lymph nodes. If not eliminated by the stationary phagocytes of the lymphatic system, the microbes eventually are carried to the bloodstream. There they may be eliminated by blood phagocytes or attacked by the third line of defense.

Specific Acquired Defense—The Third Line. The introduction of certain types of substances into the body of a human elicits the appearance in the blood of soluble proteins that react specifically with the eliciting substance. The proteins are called **antibodies,** and substances that evoke their appearance are called **antigens.**

Except in special circumstances that will not be discussed here, a substance is antigenic only if it is foreign to the body. An individual does not form antibodies that react with his own constituents or with substances from another source that are chemically identical with his own constituents. In addition to being foreign, the substance must also be a macromolecule in order to act as an antigen. Most proteins are antigenic; some polysaccharides are antigenic, but many behave as antigens only when complexed with proteins; and nucleic acids are usually antigenic only when combined with proteins.

The cells of any one type of microorganism contain several antigenic substances, including structural components of wall, cell membrane, flagella, capsules, enzymes, ribosomes, and internal membranes. The effects of reaction with antibody depend on the nature of the antigen and its function in the microbial cell. For example, antibodies specific for cell wall components may cause the cells to clump or (usually in combination with other blood constituents) to lyse; antibodies that react with flagella may immobilize the cells;

antibodies active against the capsules may increase susceptibility of the cells to phagocytosis; and antibodies that react with soluble proteins may neutralize toxins or inactivate enzymes that could attack host constituents.[2]

Antibodies are found in the gamma-globulin fraction of the blood, a fraction distinguished from other blood proteins by solubility characteristics. All evidence available at present implies that the protein molecules that act as antibodies against a particular antigen are synthesized only after the antigen has entered the body; they do not exist preformed, to be released into the bloodstream when the antigen appears. Specific antibodies are probably synthesized within cells of the lymphatic system; the antibodies appear first in lymph fluid, in which they are transported to the bloodstream. Once a cell has been stimulated to form a particular antibody, it apparently gives rise to progeny that can synthesize that same antibody.

The continued presence in the lymphatic system of living cells capable of forming a particular antibody is probably related to two important characteristics of this defense mechanism: persistence of antibodies in the blood and the anamnestic response. Antibody can be detected in the blood for some time after the inciting antigen has disappeared from the body. The concentration of persistent antibody and the duration of its persistence, which may be several weeks to several years, depend mainly on the antigen[3] and the amount of antigen (dose) that enters the body. During this time and sometimes even after antibody has disappeared from the blood, a second exposure to the antigen will stimulate a secondary, or anamnestic (recall, recollection), antibody-forming response. This response differs from the response to the first exposure to an antigen in several ways: antibody synthesis is elicited by a smaller minimal amount of antigen, is initiated sooner after the antigen enters the body, and continues for a longer period; when net synthesis ceases, the maximum concentration of antibody in the blood is higher, the concentration declines more slowly, and the persistent residual level is higher. Primary and anamnestic responses to an antigen are illustrated in Figure 22-1. This response is especially well suited as a defense against invading microorganisms, which, unlike inanimate antigens, can multiply in the body. Its occurrence is the principal theoretic basis of artificial immunization against infectious diseases (see below and Chap. 23).

The Concept of Immunity.   A person is regarded as **immune** to a given infectious disease if he does not contract the disease when exposed to the causative microorganism under natural conditions. Immunity to many diseases is a consequence of recovery from disease symptoms; in some such diseases, immunity is life-long; in others it is lost after a period that is characteristic mainly of the disease. Antibodies that react with the microorganism and/or

---

[2]Some toxins are enzymes.

[3]Antibody persistence depends mainly on the antigen and the dose in a given host species. However, both formation and persistence of antibody for a given antigen may vary considerably among types of vertebrates. This variation presents a major difficulty in evaluation of the significance for humans of immunization studies in experimental animals.

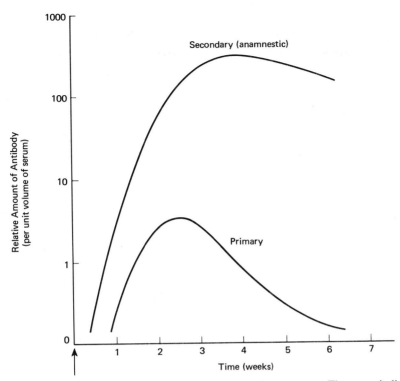

Primary and secondary (anamnestic) antibody-formation responses. The arrow indicates the time **Figure 22-1** of exposure to antigen. The time scale is as commonly observed in humans and rabbits.

its noxious products can often be detected in the blood of an immune person, whether or not he has previously displayed symptoms of the disease. The presence of specific antibodies or the capacity to respond anamnestically is presumptive evidence of current or past invasion of the individual by the corresponding microorganism.

Circulating (bloodstream-borne) antibodies and the immunity they usually confer may be acquired actively, by response of the antibody-forming mechanism to the presence of antigen, or passively, by entrance into the bloodstream of antibodies formed in another individual. Active immunization occurs naturally as a consequence of infection or intoxication (entrance of an antigenic toxin into the body). It can be acquired artificially in response to injection into the body of a preparation of the antigen(s) that can elicit antibody formation, but not disease symptoms. Such preparations may contain viable cells of a non-pathogenic strain, fractions of cells of a pathogenic strain, or heat- or chemical-inactivated pathogenic cells or toxin (called toxoid). Artificial immunization is now available as a means of decreasing susceptibility to several infectious diseases (see Chap. 23).

Passive immunization also occurs both naturally and artificially—naturally, when maternal antibodies pass through the placenta into the circulatory system of the fetus; these antibodies provide some degree of immunity for an infant for the first two or three months after birth;—artificially, in serum from the blood of experimental animals (usually horses) artificially immunized, actively, with a specific antigen, or in serum or gamma-globulins from blood withdrawn from humans during convalescence from a known disease (convalescent serum).

In addition to circulating antibodies, coproantibodies may be formed; these antibodies are found in higher concentrations in the feces than in the blood and are regarded as especially effective in combating infections originating in the intestines.

Some persons who do not display any evidence of previous invasion or other active immunization are nevertheless relatively **resistant** to certain diseases or to infectious diseases generally. Less is known about this type of person than the types that show unusually low resistance. The latter include persons with unusually low amounts of gamma-globulins and hence weak antibody responses; with phagocytes in which the lysosomes are surrounded by an extra membrane and cannot fuse with food vacuoles to digest ingested microbes; or with very low numbers of one or another type of phagocyte. In each case, one of the basic defense mechanisms on which the sterility of the interior of the human body depends is impaired. The discovery of these conditions in persons who frequently display symptoms of infectious diseases has provided circumstantial evidence of the effectiveness of those defense mechanisms when they operate normally.

The Inhabitants

The protists that can be found multiplying on most healthy humans regardless of climate, diet, personal hygiene, and public sanitation can be regarded as the indigenous microbial inhabitants of humans. This group of microbes seems to include only certain bacteria and yeasts. Other types of bacteria and yeasts as well as other fungi and protozoa are found occasionally in healthy humans; the frequency of incidence of these microbes in a population varies with the environmental factors just mentioned, particularly climate, hygiene, and sanitation. Once established as inhabitants, however, these microbes often become residents of prolonged tenure and in some human populations are as frequent as the more generally occurring indigenous protists. The presence of representatives of a third group of bacteria, fungi, and protozoa is usually associated with disease of the host. This group comprises the microbial pathogens of humans and seems to include approximately 300 species of protists.

The distinction between a pathogen and a non-pathogen is somewhat arbitrary. Any parasite or any free-living organism capable of parasitism is a potential pathogen. For most purposes, it is suitable to designate as a **nonpathogen** an inhabitant whose presence on an otherwise healthy host does not typically result in disease, and as a **pathogen** an inhabitant whose presence in an otherwise healthy host typically results in disease. This conditional distinction will be used in the present discussion.

Indigenous Protists. In order for a protist to be recognized as indigenous to a particular region of the body, it should be found in that region in a significant proportion of the individuals of any human population and in numbers greater than could occur as a consequence of external contamination. The latter criterion is necessary to distinguish between organisms frequently present as transient contaminants and those that can multiply in association with the body region.

The regions of the body that are normally inhabited by multiplying microorganisms (are "colonized") and the microorganisms that commonly inhabit each region in adults are indicated in Table 22-1. The population of any region may be augmented by organisms from an adjacent region, depending on climatic factors, personal hygiene, and variations among individuals with regard to such factors as amounts and chemical composition of particular secretions and the pH maintained in a given region.

Establishment of the indigenous population is initiated a few hours after birth. The microorganisms acquired by the infant during passage through the birth canal are transient; they are soon replaced by microorganisms derived from the persons who attend the infant and from ingested foods. During the first day of life, many of the bacteria and yeasts that will be present in the individual during his lifetime can be detected in the regions they colonize in the adult, although several months to nearly two years may be required for the numbers and relative proportions of types to become adjusted to adult levels. Only three developmental changes are associated with marked changes in microbial populations, viz., weaning, the eruption of teeth, and onset and later cessation of ovarian function. These result in changes in the populations of mouth and lower intestine, mouth, and vagina, respectively.

The skin is not a single region, and the population of an area of skin varies according to its proximity to other colonized regions and to the presence and density of sweat and sebaceous glands. Microbes that colonize the nose and pharynx are found on the skin of the face, intestinal inhabitants are found on the perineal surface, and the mycobacteria that grow in earwax (not listed in the table) are found on outer regions of the ear. Regions of the body that contain greater densities of sebaceous glands, in which anaerobes grow, contain a higher proportion of anaerobic to aerobic skin microbes. Fungi are more common in areas of the skin that are relatively moist (axillae, palms of the hands, and feet). The staphylococci of the skin are usually identical with those found in the nose; because the staphylococci become established in the nose earlier than on the skin, it is assumed that the anterior nares are the initial source of skin staphylococci.

The microbial population of the mouth varies greatly among individuals, presumably due to variations in chemical composition of saliva and condition of the teeth and gums, and probably also to variation in diet. Oral disorders (especially dental caries, gingivitis, and extractions) are usually associated with quantitative changes among the resident microbiota. It is not yet clear whether microbes alone are responsible for caries or gingivitis, but it is clear that they

TABLE 22-1. Microorganisms Indigenous to Man

BODY REGION NORMALLY INHABITED:	Conjunctiva	Skin	Nose	Pharynx	Mouth	Lower Intestine	Vagina
A. MICROBES FOUND IN 40% OR MORE OF HUMANS							
Bacteria							
Staphylococci		+	+*				+
Hemophiles	+	+	+	+	+		
Corynebacteria	+	+	+++		+		+++
Viridans streptococci				+	+	+	
Mycoplasmas				+	+	+	
Neisseriae			*	+	+	++	
Pneumococci				+	+		
Bacteroides spp.				+	+	+++	
Anaerobic streptococci				+	+	+++	
Spirochetes				+	+	+++	
Enteric bacilli					+	+++	
Fecal streptococci					+	++	
Lactobacilli				+	+	+	++
Clostridia					+	+	
Mycobacteria						+	
Unidentified gram-negative rods		++					
Veillonellae		+		+	+		
Actinomycetes					+		
Yeasts							
Candida albicans		+		++	++	++	++
Torulopsis glabrata							
Pityrosporum ovale		+					
B. MICROBES FOUND IN SOME HUMANS (RARELY AS MANY AS 40%)							
Bacteria							
Meningococci				++			
Staphylococcus aureus							
Beta-hemolytic streptococci				++†			
"Pathogenic" pneumococci				+			

492

Fungi

Candida spp. + + +
Saccharomyces
Oidium +
Dermatophytes
Pityrosporum spp.

Protozoa

Trichomonas vaginalis
Trichomonas tenax +
Entamoeba gingivalis + + + ‡
Trichomonas hominis +
Giardia lamblia + + +
Entamoeba coli + + §
Endolimax nana + +
Iodamoeba bütschlii + +
Chilomastix mesnili + +
Enteromonas hominis + +
Retortomonas intestinalis + +
Dientamoeba fragilis +

C. POPULATION DENSITIES AND ORGANISMS TYPICALLY PREDOMINANT

	Aerobes	Anaerobes	Predominant
Conjunctiva	(Few)	(Few)	*Corynebacterium xerosis*
Skin	$10^2/cm^2$ generally; up to $10^6/cm^2$ on face	10^4–$10^6/cm^2$; up to 10^7/ml of sweat	*Staphylococcus albus*, *Corynebacterium acnes*
Nose	10–10^4/ml of 20-ml washing	10^2–10^5/ml of 20-ml washing	*Staphylococcus albus*, diphtheroids
Pharynx			Naso: viridans streptococci and neisseriae; Oro: also mouth organisms
Mouth	10^6/ml of teeth scrapings; 10^7/ml of saliva or gingival scrapings	10^6/ml of teeth scrapings; 10^7–10^8/ml of saliva or gingival scrapings	Mixed
Lower intestine	10^7–10^8/gm of wet feces	10^9–10^{10}/gm of wet feces	*Bacteroides*; *Escherichia coli*, the predominant coliform, ca. 10%
Vagina	10^7–10^8 bacteria/ml of secretions		Lactobacilli or corynebacteria

*Incidence correlated with presence in attendants during infancy.
†Lower in populations without tonsils.
‡May be as high as 40 per cent on feet; also on hair and nails.
§Occurs in ca. 10 per cent of healthy mouths, in up to 95 per cent of gingivitis patients.
‖May be more than 40 per cent in tropical regions.

493

intensify and/or prolong such disorders; they are usually present in much larger numbers in unhealthy than in healthy mouths.

The regions of the alimentary tract between mouth and lower intestine normally contain microbes that pass through, but do not colonize, those areas. The partial sterilization of foods accomplished in the stomach reduces the number of viable ingested microorganisms that enter the upper regions of the intestine; the food is moved relatively rapidly through these regions, and the microorganisms that survive the stomach action do not remain long enough to multiply. Most of the microbes found in feces are derived from the population of the lower intestine, through which the contents move relatively slowly. The most dense and varied microbial population of the body inhabits this region. These microbes are predominantly anaerobic bacteria of the *Bacteroides* group; several other types are present in large numbers, though low proportion.

The upper respiratory tract carries two distinct populations: predominantly aerobic types (staphylococci and diphtheroids) in the nose, and predominantly anaerobic types (streptococci and neisseriae) in the nasopharynx. The lower part of the pharynx, which is common to the alimentary and respiratory tracts, harbors a combined population derived from the mouth and nasopharynx. The number of microorganisms in the larynx and lower respiratory tract is small, being continuously controlled by the upward movement of mucus and the activity of phagocytes in the alveoli of the lungs.

Most of the microorganisms of the urinary tract and external genitalia reflect the intestinal and skin populations of the region. Microbes do not normally colonize the posterior portion of the urethra or the bladder. The preputial secretions in both sexes are usually inhabited by several microorganisms, one of which (*Mycobacterium smegmatis*) occurs on the body only in this material. The immature and postmenopause vagina carries a mixed population that is similar in composition to the population of external genitalia (staphylococci, corynebacteria, mycobacteria, yeasts, sarcinae, coliforms; rarely any pathogenic microorganisms).

When the ovaries are active, the lining of the vagina is rich in glycogen. This is an especially suitable substrate, in this habitat, for a variety of lacto-bacilli collectively known as Döderlein's bacilli. They are often predominant in the adult vagina; corynebacteria predominate in some individuals. In addition, streptococci, diphtheroids, *Oidium*, and *Saccharomyces* are often present. This population also appears transiently in newborn females during the first month of life; when hormones derived from the maternal circulation are excreted, glycogen and the associated microbial population disappear from the vagina until puberty.

Non-Pathogens of Minor Frequency as Indigenous Protists. In the second portion of Table 22-1 are listed some of the microorganisms that occur in at most about 40 per cent (and usually less than 20 per cent) of the humans in populations surveyed. Some of these are potential pathogens whose presence in most humans is associated with disease. Individuals who harbor such microbes without developing disease symptoms are regarded as **carriers,** because they can transmit the organisms to individuals who are susceptible to disease due to infection by these organisms.

This portion of the table includes several fungi, certain of which are harbored for long periods without disease symptoms. However, disease symptoms may appear intermittently and then disappear spontaneously (i.e., without specific treatment) when conditions in the body, many of which are undefined, favor multiplication of these organisms. These situations are usually regarded as inapparent or latent infections.

This list also includes the non-pathogenic protozoan inhabitants of humans. With the exceptions only of the flagellates *Trichomonas tenax* and *T. vaginalis,* which inhabit the mouth and vagina, respectively, and the ameba *Entamoeba gingivalis,* which inhabits the mouth, the protozoa are usually found only in the lower intestine. The frequency of incidence of protozoa in human populations has so far been found to vary mainly with latitude. In the tropics and subtropics, intestinal protozoa may be present in 40 to 50 per cent of the population. In temperate zones, less than 10 per cent of the population harbors any of the protozoa. Several of the protozoa cannot be found among humans native to arctic regions.

The frequency of incidence of intestinal protozoa in adults cannot be correlated with sanitary practices of the community or with personal hygiene. This is in contrast to the incidence of intestinal metazoan parasites (especially helminthic worms), whose frequency in a population can be greatly reduced by the introduction of sanitary and hygienic practices, particularly with regard to sewage treatment, toilet habits, and food preparation. The increased incidence of intestinal protozoa nearer the equator is possibly due to the increased transmissibility of the organisms resulting from their longer survival outside the host, and from the greater number of flies present in warmer climates. The flies serve as vectors, carrying protozoa from feces to foods.

The oral and vaginal protozoa, particularly the latter, have been implicated as pathogens. However, an increasing amount of survey information obtained in the past decade has revealed that the majority of hosts to these organisms do not display disease. Nevertheless, the protozoa are commonly present and present in their highest numbers in individuals with gingivitis or vaginitis. Because elimination of the protozoa by treatment with drugs or other chemicals usually is followed by relief of the symptoms, it seems that the protozoa at least aggravate these conditions.

Beneficial Effects of Resident Protists. Since the 1930's two developments in medical microbiology have revealed that some (all of which are bacteria) of the resident microorganisms of animals and of man are distinctly beneficial to the host. These two developments were (1) the discovery and use for treatment of infectious diseases in man and other animals of chemicals that inhibited or destroyed certain microorganisms, and (2) the development of methods for cultivation of animals free of microbial inhabitants ("germ-free") or inhabited by only one or a few known microorganisms ("gnotobiotic").

The beneficial activities of resident microbes demonstrated by or inferred from studies of animals or persons deprived of some or all of their indigenous population include the following.

1. Antagonism of multiplication of non-indigenous microbes.
2. Elicitation of antibodies to antigens common to indigenous microorganisms and related pathogens.
3. Production of growth-stimulating substances.
4. Stimulation of maturation of certain tissues.

The first of these is a general and often non-specific function of resident microorganisms. Skin inhabitants produce organic acids, particularly fatty acids, that are inhibitory for many types of microbes; the acids also contribute to the maintenance of a low pH (3 to 5) on the skin surface. In the adult vagina, the lactic acid bacteria convert glycogen to lactic acid; the higher the proportion of Döderlein's bacilli among the vaginal microbes, the lower the pH (ca. 4.5 when these organisms predominate). In both habitats, the low pH discourages colonization by non-acid-tolerant microorganisms.

In the intestine, fermentation products (especially fatty acids) of the resident anaerobes and facultative anaerobes probably prevent development of some microorganisms. In this habitat, however, it seems more likely that inhibition of exogenous microbes is due mainly to the high density of the resident population. Most adventitious microbes cannot compete with the resident population, under the anaerobic conditions in the colon, for nutrients.

Resident microorganisms that contain antigens in common with pathogens include the staphylococci, streptococci, pneumococci, and enteric bacilli. Apparently, their antigens occasionally reach the circulatory system, probably due to absorption through the intestinal wall of components of disintegrating bacterial cells. This can result in a low level of antibodies that react with the corresponding pathogens and should increase the probability that the host could respond anamnestically to invasion by the pathogen.

Intestinal bacteria, mainly the enteric bacilli, provide some or all of certain vitamins required by man. These are believed to include biotin, pantothenate, pyridoxine, riboflavin, and vitamin K. Nicotinamide, nicotinic acid, and thiamine may also be provided in part by the metabolic activities of intestinal bacteria. Because the intestinal population also usually includes vitamin-consuming microorganisms, there is some competition between host and inhabitants for microbial products, as well as for growth-stimulating substances in the diet.

Stimulation of structural and functional development has been inferred entirely from animal studies (see, e.g., Chap. 21, "The Rumen"). Mammals reared without intestinal microbes often develop an unusually large lower intestine with a relatively thin wall. In rats, at least, this can be reversed by inoculation of the alimentary tract with intestinal bacteria normally present in rats. Intestinally germ-free animals are much more susceptible to enteric pathogens than are normal animals; at least two factors contribute to their increased susceptibility—absence of microbial antagonism in the intestine and greater penetrability of the thin wall by the pathogens.

Certain host defenses are also less well developed in germ-free animals. In particular, the amount of lymphatic tissue of mammals and of fowl is abnormally small and the level of gamma-globulins in the blood is low. Intestinal bacteria seem to be the most important of indigenous microbes in stimulating development of the lymphatic system and gamma-globulin synthesis; certain viruses[4] also stimulate lymphatic development in fowl. These observations are consistent with the notion that proliferation of antibody-forming cells of the lymph nodes is stimulated by antigenic substances.

Pathogens. Inhabitation of a region of the human body by pathogenic microorganisms is called **infection.** At the present time, it is believed that pathologic symptoms of infection result primarily from chemical interaction of host components and microbial products (within or released from the microbial cells), i.e., that the basis of infectious pathogenesis is chemical. Physical effects such as disintegration of a tissue or organ are regarded as consequences of chemical attack on its component cells or intercellular substances.

The specific symptoms associated with infection by a given microbe are determined by the accessibility to microbial products of host components susceptible to chemical alteration by them. Accordingly, the symptoms depend on:

1. The site at which the pathogen multiplies (this may vary according to the site that happened to be contaminated by the pathogen).
2. Whether the pathogen releases toxic substances from its cells.
3. Whether the toxic substances diffuse from the site of their production.
4. The sites affected by diffusible toxic substances.
5. The stability of such substances in transit from site of production to site of toxic action.

With regard to site of multiplication, three main classes of pathogens can be distinguished.

1. Non-invasive. These cause disease while inhabiting body regions normally inhabited by protists.

2. Invasive. These cause disease if, and usually only if, they multiply in regions of the body normally free of microorganisms. They gain access to such regions by overcoming host defenses against invasion.

3. Opportunistic. Only when host defenses are reduced or inactivated due to other factors do these gain access to sites in which their multiplication results in disease. This class of pathogens would include many indigenous microbes. Conditions that prepare the way for such pathogens include wounds, infection by invasive pathogens, and administration of certain drugs. Pathogens that enter the host through insect bites are a specialized class of opportunistic microbes.

[4]Virions are antigenic.

Invasiveness is a property of host-pathogen interaction and not strictly a microbial property. In general, pathogenic and non-pathogenic microorganisms cannot be distinguished from each other in the absence of a host susceptible to the pathogen. In a few instances,[5] pathogenicity of a given microbe can be correlated with a microbial trait; i.e., the trait is present in all pathogenic and absent from all non-pathogenic strains of the same species. However, with the exception of toxin production (the detection of which requires a susceptible host), disease production is not always attributable to the distinguishing trait.

Infection and disease production by a given organism may be limited to only one or a few types of animals that seem physiologically quite similar. For example, of infectious diseases of man, typhoid fever cannot be produced experimentally by ingestion of typhoid bacilli, the usual manner in which humans contract typhoid fever, in any healthy individual of the usual group of experimental mammals; syphilis can be produced only in rabbits; respiratory disease due to *Haemophilus influenzae* can be produced only in monkeys; and laboratory animals are generally not susceptible to neisserial diseases such as meningitis and gonorrhea. In some instances, the human pathogens can infect experimental animals, but they either do not produce disease or produce a different disease from that which they cause in humans. From such observations has risen the notion of host specificity, a concept important in the control of infectious diseases in populations of any type of organism—human, other animal, protist, or plant.

Several infectious diseases of humans and the microbes associated with the diseases are listed in Table 22-2. In each of these diseases, it has been demonstrated that infection of a given region of the body by the particular microorganism is a necessary condition for development of the disease symptoms. In the following section of this chapter, a few of these diseases are described in order to illustrate various aspects of human-pathogen interaction.

Some Infectious Diseases of Humans

Amebic Dysentery (*Entamoeba histolytica*).   Amebic dysentery is most common in populations of malnourished humans living in warm climates under poor sanitary conditions. Infection usually results from ingestion of encysted amebae with food or water contaminated with feces of infected humans.

[5] Examples:

The invasiveness of pneumococci is dependent on the presence of capsules on the bacterial cells; the capsules hinder phagocytosis. The larger the capsule, the fewer the number of bacterial cells necessary for infection.

Most strains of diphtheria bacilli seem equally capable of infecting humans, but only those that are lysogenic for bacteriophage beta produce diphtheria toxin. The toxin alone can elicit the symptoms of diphtheria. Presumably, a gene necessary for toxin production is contained within the prophage.

Coagulase, an enzyme that causes chelated blood plasma to coagulate, is formed by pathogenic staphylococci and not by non-pathogenic strains. Its role, if any, in staphylococcal diseases is unknown.

Strains of dysentery amebae that form large cysts are usually pathogenic; those that form small cysts are usually non-pathogenic. There are exceptional strains of each type.

TABLE 22-2.   Microorganisms and Diseases Associated with Their Infection of Humans

Microorganism	Disease	Principal Affected Site
A. INFECTION ACQUIRED FROM SOIL, BY INHALATION, WOUND CONTAMINATION, OR CONTACT WITH SKIN		

1. Bacteria

Microorganism	Disease	Principal Affected Site
Nocardia asteroides	Nocardiosis	Lungs
Nocardia brasiliensis	Nocardiosis	Subcutaneous tissue
Clostridium tetani (also B below)	Tetanus	Nervous system
Clostridium perfringens, welchii, septicum, novyi	Gas gangrene	Wounded and adjacent tissues

2. Fungi

Microorganism	Disease	Principal Affected Site
Cryptococcus neoformans	Cryptococcosis	Lungs initially; prolonged (chronic) infection becomes generalized*
Blastomyces dermatitidis	N. American blastomycosis	
Paracoccidioides brasiliensis	S. American blastomycosis	
Coccidioides immitis	Coccidioidomycosis	
Histoplasma capsulatum	Histoplasmosis	
Sporotrichum schenckii	Sporotrichosis	Subcutaneous tissue; also skin, fascia, bone
Fonsecaea spp.		
Cladosporium sp.	Chromoblastomycosis	
Phialophora sp.		
Madurella spp.		
Allescheria sp.		
Phialophora sp.	Mycetoma	
Aspergillus nidulans		
Others		
Microsporum gypseum	Ringworm†	Cutaneous tissue
Trichophyton mentagraphytes	Dermatomycosis	Hair, skin, nails
Keratinomyces ajelloi		

B. INFECTION ACQUIRED FROM INFECTED ANIMALS OR ANIMAL PRODUCTS (E.G., MILK, MEAT); BY INHALATION, WOUND CONTAMINATION, DIRECT CONTACT, OR INGESTION		

1. Bacteria

Microorganism	Disease	Principal Affected Site
From livestock:		
Bacillus anthracis	Anthrax	Lungs; subcutaneous tissue
Brucella melitensis	Undulant fever	Generalized
Brucella spp.		
Coxiella burnetii	Q fever	Lungs, generalized
From rodents (especially rats):		
Leptospira icterohemorrhagiae	Leptospirosis	Generalized (usually includes conjunctiva)
Streptobacillus moniliformis	Rat-bite fever	Generalized (including joints and endocardium)
Spirillum minus		
From livestock, dogs, cats:		
Salmonella spp.	Salmonellosis	Gastrointestinal tract
From birds:		
Chlamydia	Psittacosis	Respiratory tract
From fish, shellfish, meat, poultry:		
Erysipelothrix rhusiopathiae	Erysipeloid	Skin

2. Fungi

Microorganism	Disease	Principal Affected Site
From dogs, cats:		
Microsporum canis	Ringworm (especially of children)	Cutaneous tissue

TABLE 22-2.   Microorganisms and Diseases (*cont.*)

Microorganism	Disease	Principal Affected Site
C. INFECTION ACQUIRED FROM FOOD OR WATER CONTAMINATED BY FECES OF INFECTED HUMANS OR ANIMALS; BY INGESTION		
1. Bacteria		
Salmonella typhosa	Typhoid fever	Gastrointestinal tract
Salmonella spp.	Enteric fevers, gastroenteritis	
Shigella dysenteriae	Bacillary dysentery	
Shigella spp.		
Vibrio cholerae (*comma*)	Cholera	Lower intestine
2. Protozoa		
Entamoeba histolytica	Amebic dysentery	Gastrointestinal tract
Balantidium coli	Ciliary or balantidial dysentery	
Isospora belli (*hominis*)	Coccidiosis	
D. INFECTION ACQUIRED FROM INFECTED HUMANS (DISEASED OR CARRIERS); BY INHALATION		
1. Bacteria		
Bordetella pertussis	Whooping cough	Respiratory tract
Corynebacterium diphtheriae	Diphtheria	Pharynx, generalized due to diffusion of toxin
Diplococcus pneumoniae	Pneumococcal pneumonia	Lungs
Haemophilus influenzae	Sinusitis, bronchitis	Respiratory tract
Listeria monocytogenes	Meningoencephalitis	Blood phagocytes, meninges; generalized in infants infected in utero
Mycobacterium tuberculosis	Tuberculosis	Lungs; other organs; bone
Mycoplasma pneumoniae	Primary atypical pneumonia	Lungs
Neisseria meningitidis	Meningococcal meningitis	Meninges
Pasteurella pestis	Pneumonic plague	Lungs
Streptococcus pyogenes (beta-hemolytic streptococci)	Several, including pharyngitis (streptococcal sore throat), scarlet fever, adenitis, otitis media, mastoiditis, streptococcal meningitis, peritonitis, pneumonia, tonsillitis— all associated with pharyngitis; puerperal sepsis (childbed fever), "blood poisoning," erysipelas, lymphadenitis; acute glomerulonephritis, erythema nodosum, rheumatic fever	Various
E. INFECTION ACQUIRED FROM INFECTED HUMANS; BY CONTACT OF SUSCEPTIBLE REGION OR OF WOUND WITH INFECTED PERSON OR DISCHARGES FROM INFECTED TISSUES OR REGIONS		
1. Bacteria		
Chlamydia	Lymphogranuloma venereum	Reproductive system, lymph nodes
Chlamydia	Trachoma	Eye
Chlamydia	Inclusion conjunctivitis	Conjunctiva
Mycobacterium leprae	Leprosy	Cutaneous tissue
Neisseria gonorrhoea	Gonorrhea	Reproductive system
Haemophilus ducreyi	Chancroid	Reproductive system
Treponema pallidum	Syphilis	Reproductive system; later internal organs; still later nervous system
Treponema pertenue	Yaws	Cutaneous tissue

TABLE 22-2.   Microorganisms and Diseases (cont.)

Microorganism	Disease	Principal Affected Site
2. Fungi (presumed by contact because the microbes are found only in humans, and especially in groups of humans)		
Epidermophyton floccosum	Dermatomycosis	Epidermis
Microsporum audouini	Ringworm	Cutaneous tissue
Trichophyton violaceum	Ringworm (in Mediterranean region)	Cutaneous tissue (scalp)
Trichophyton tonsurans	Dermatomycosis	Hair
Trichophyton rubrum	Dermatomycosis	Skin, nails
Trichophyton schoenleinii	Favus (chronic ringworm of scalp)	Hair follicles

F. INFECTION ACQUIRED FROM INFECTED ANIMALS OR HUMANS; BY BITE OF BLOOD-SUCKING INSECTS

Microorganism	Disease	Principal Affected Site
1. Bacteria		
Bartonella bacilliformis (man, via sandflies)	Oroya fever	Erythrocytes
Bartonella bacilliformis (man, via sandflies)	Verruga peruviana	Cutaneous tissue
Borrelia recurrentis (man or rodent, via ticks, lice)	Relapsing fever	Generalized
Pasteurella pestis (rats, via fleas)	Bubonic plague	Lymphatic system
Pasteurella tularensis (rodents, via various arthropods)	Tularemia	Skin; conjunctiva; respiratory tract; gastrointestinal tract
Rickettsia prowazekii (man, via body lice)	Typhus fever	Generalized
Rickettsia rickettsii (mammals, via ticks)	Spotted fevers	Generalized
Rickettsia tsutsugamuchi (rodents, via mites)	Scrub typhus	Lungs, generalized
2. Protozoa		
Plasmodium vivax, ovale, malariae, falciparum (vertebrates, via mosquitoes)	Malaria	Blood, generalized
Trypanosoma gambiense (vertebrates, via tsetse fly)	African sleeping sickness	Blood, then lymphatic system, finally nervous system
Trypanosoma rhodisiense (vertebrates, via tsetse fly)	African trypanosomiasis (Rhodesian sleeping sickness)	Blood, sometimes cerebrospinal fluid
Trypanosoma cruzi (vertebrates, via triatomid bugs)	Chagas' disease	Generalized; lymph nodes in children; internal organs in adults
Leishmania donovani (vertebrates, via sandflies)	Kala-azar	Blood, internal organs
Leishmania tropica (vertebrates, via sandflies)	Oriental sore, others	Cutaneous tissue
Leishmania brasiliensis (vertebrates, via sandflies)	Mucocutaneous leishmaniasis	Cutaneous tissue, mucous membranes

501

TABLE 22-2.   Microorganisms and Diseases (*cont.*)

Microorganism	Disease	Principal Affected Site
G. INFECTION ACQUIRED FROM AMONG INDIGENOUS PROTISTS; BY DECREASE IN HOST RESISTANCE TO INVASION ‡; EXAMPLES		
1. Bacteria		
Coliforms, pseudo-monads	Cystitis	Urinary tract, bladder
Latent *Mycobacterium tuberculosis*	Secondary (reactivation) tuberculosis	Lungs; other organs, bone
Staphylococcus aureus (also D,E above)	Localized abscesses	Various
Staphylococcus aureus	Acute staphylococcal enteritis	Intestinal tract
Viridans streptococci	Subacute bacterial endocarditis	Endocardium
2. Fungi		
Candida albicans	Candidiasis ⎫	Mouth; gastrointestinal tract; genitalia of female; respiratory tract; moist skin areas; species other than *C. albicans:* endocardium
Other *Candida* spp.	Candidiasis ⎭	
3. Mixed population		
Intestinal microor-ganisms	Peritonitis	Peritoneal cavity

* "Generalized" indicates dissemination, usually via lymphatic system and bloodstream, to various
  regions of the body. Dissemination in most instances involves the microbial cells; in a few cases,
  e.g., tetanus and diphtheria, usually only a soluble toxin is disseminated.
† "Ringworm" is a general name for similar cutaneous diseases that may be localized in scalp,
  groin, feet ("athlete's foot"), or trunk, depending on the infecting fungus and/or the site initially
  contaminated.
‡ Factors known to predispose to infectious diseases due to indigenous protists (and others of low
  pathogenicity) include wounds; radiation damage; prolonged use of corticosteroid hormones,
  narcotics, or alcohol; malnutrition; shock; obstruction of excretory organs, intestinal tract, bili-
  ary ducts, or blood vessels; debilitating, especially chronic, diseases such as cancer, diabetes
  mellitus, certain viral diseases, cirrhosis of the liver, and degenerative diseases of bone marrow
  or lymphatic tissues; and antimicrobial therapy that interferes with the usual microbial antag-
  onisms in the body.
  Diseases due to *Candida* infections are especially common as complications in debilitated patients treated chemotherapeutically; some of these diseases, e.g., vaginitis, cystitis, pneumonitis,
  septicemia, and enterocolitis, may be severe.

Intermediate carriers of contamination include hands and clothing of infected
persons, flies (cysts pass through the alimentary tract of the fly without change),
and vegetables cultivated in soil fertilized with human feces. The cysts survive
the antimicrobial action of stomach acids and enzymes and the bile salts;
excystment is stimulated by these substances and occurs in the intestines. Each
cyst gives rise to eight amebulae, each of which is capable of establishing itself
in the wall of the large intestine and initiating development of a colony.
Generally, vegetative cells (trophozoites) remain in the colon wall, and cysts
are found in the lumen and subsequently in the stools.

The growing amebae release enzymes that cause disintegration of cells of the lining of the intestine. The amebae utilize as growth substrates: the soluble and solubilized host cell components, soluble substances of dietary and microbial origin present in the intestinal contents, host blood cells, blood proteins, and fragments of discarded cells. Healthy trophozoites in the host usually do not contain ingested microbial cells, although they can be cultivated in the laboratory with coliform bacteria as their principal food.

As the amebae grow and multiply, the colony dissolves its way deeper into the intestinal wall, forming an ulcer. Eventually, the ulcer is invaded by intestinal bacteria. Blood and mucus appear in the feces; massive hemorrhage results in some patients, if the ulcer happens to hit a large artery in the intestinal wall. If the ulcer becomes perforated, adjacent body regions can be invaded by the amebae and by other intestinal microbes. The regions commonly invaded by the amebae are liver, spleen, and pericardium. Vermiform appendix, lungs, pleura, and peritoneum may also be infected by internal dissemination of the amebae; skin of the perineum and the genitalia are infected from the rectum. Tissue disintegration occurs wherever the amebae grow.

Establishment of infection and elicitation of disease are favored by:

1. Ingestion of a large number of cysts.
2. Frequent passage of amebae from host to host; in epidemics, even the trophozoites become infective, presumably because they are not killed in the stomach.
3. Slow movement of intestinal contents.
4. Ingestion by the host of only small amounts of foods during the time the amebae are present in the alimentary tract.
5. Pre-existing pathologic condition of the colon, e.g., inflammation in the intestinal wall, chronic or recurrent intestinal disorders due to bacterial infections, or intestinal blockage.
6. Malnutrition, particularly an inadequate dietary supply of B vitamins.

Transmission of the pathogens is favored by high humidity and high mean temperatures, at least partly because these conditions favor the multiplication of flies.

The majority of intestinal infections by *E. histolytica* result in only minor ulceration of the colon wall or liver abscesses; the lesions heal or scar, and the amebae disappear. Overt disease occurs in only about 10 per cent of infections. The infection and consequent symptoms can be eliminated by oral administration of chemicals including emetine, carbarsone, thioarsenites, and vioform. In cases not treated with such chemicals, the person loses weight and becomes dehydrated, but usually recovers. Recovery does not seem to increase resistance to the disease.

Histoplasmosis (Histoplasma capsulatum). *Histoplasma capsulatum* is a dimorphic[6] fungus that is widely distributed in the world in soil. It grows in soil as a septate mycelium and reproduces by formation of conidia. It is

[6]In laboratory cultures, the mycelial form develops at 25° C, the yeast form at 37° C. Abundant moisture also favors the yeast form.

particularly common in soils contaminated with the droppings of birds and bats, e.g., in barnyards, chicken coops, and bat caves, and in cities beneath trees in which birds such as starlings and pigeons nest. The droppings favor growth and are especially suitable as a medium for sporulation. The conidia are dispersed by air currents and subsequently may be inhaled by animals that are susceptible to infection; these include dogs, cats, foxes, opposums, and humans—but not birds.

Histoplasmosis in humans begins in the lungs following inhalation of conidia of *H. capsulatum*. In the lungs, the conidia germinate and give rise to yeast cells that reproduce, by budding, within phagocytic cells. The initial infection may result in mild respiratory symptoms for a short time. Healing is usually spontaneous and followed by calcification of the lung region in which the fungus multiplied. The yeast cells may appear in sputum while the infection is active, but they die quickly outside the body and are not a source of human infections.

In a small proportion of infected individuals, the infection persists and the disease becomes chronic as the yeast cells are disseminated to and multiply in various internal organs. This consequence (called disseminated histoplasmosis) of initial infection is more common among persons who are simultaneously suffering from another generalized disease such as tuberculosis or leukemia. Disseminated histoplasmosis typically involves many tissues and organs; the host is debilitated and feverish and loses weight drastically. When untreated, the disease is fatal. It is now treated successfully with the antibiotic amphotericin B, which eliminates the infection.

Tuberculosis *(Mycobacterium tuberculosis)*. Tuberculosis is primarily a pulmonary disease whose incidence, severity, and tendency to disseminate through the body are influenced by the age, sex, emotional state, and hormone content of and presence of other disease in the host. Transmission of infection is also influenced by crowding and malnutrition, but not significantly by climate. Multiple genetic factors are also involved, as evidenced by two findings: (1) the coincidence of disease in both members of a pair of twins is three times as great among identical as among fraternal twins, and (2) the disease spreads more rapidly and is more severe in populations that have not had a history of the disease. At present, approximately 3,000,000 humans die annually as a consequence of tuberculosis; about 10,000 of these deaths occur in the United States (see Table 23-3).

The tubercle bacilli are transferred from human to human mainly in droplets of material coughed out from the infected respiratory tract and in sputum; they are stable in dried mucus for several weeks if not exposed to direct sunlight, which kills them in a few hours. Small (less than 5 μm in diameter) droplets or bits of sputum can evade the ciliated epithelium defense of the respiratory tract and enter the bronchi and lungs. In the lungs, the bacilli are ingested by phagocytes, within which they are either killed or begin to multiply, depending on host characteristics. The initial infection, if established, usually results in a few granular sites of infection ("tubercles") within the lungs and adjacent lymph nodes. This stage is often not detectable by disease symptoms (is "subclinical"), and the sites of infection are too small to be detected by X-ray examination. The tubercles may remain in this condition for decades, with the tubercle bacilli within them still viable, but not multiplying. If one or more tubercles disrupt, the host can act as a source of infection for other persons, and is likely to develop symptoms of reactivation tuberculosis.

The reactivation disease is similar to disseminated ("miliary") tuberculosis, which occasionally follows the primary infection without a period of latent infection. Either occurs when viable bacilli are released from a primary tubercle and are disseminated, first in the lungs and adjacent lymphatic system and later, via lymph fluid and the bloodstream, to various internal organs. The tissues in which tubercle bacilli can multiply include nervous system (meninges), bone, spleen, kidneys, skin, prostate, and others, but not striated muscle. The intestinal tract and its associated lymphatics can be infected (primarily or following reactivation of a lung infection) by ingestion of the bacilli.

Wherever the bacilli establish colonies, adjacent tissue is dissolved and becomes non-functional. Usually the bacilli multiply first in macrophages, but as the site of infection ages, most of the bacilli are found extracellularly. Some of the tissue damage at each site is due to allergic responses of the host, which increase the intensity of inflammation; these same responses also are more or less effective (depending on host characteristics) in restricting the site and reducing the tendency of bacilli to be disseminated from the site.

Tubercular infections can now be treated successfully with drugs. One of these, isoniazid, is particularly valuable for three reasons: it is practically free of toxic side effects in the host; it is highly specific for *M. tuberculosis* and does not disturb the indigenous protists, including the mycobacteria; and—unlike other antituberculosis drugs available—it kills tubercle bacilli even when they are within phagocytes.

Typhoid Fever (*Salmonella typhosa*). Typhoid fever is the most severe of the enteric fevers and other diseases that result from infection with *Salmonella* species. It is caused by *S. typhosa;* infection with this species results from ingestion of foods or beverages contaminated with feces or by the hands of infected persons. In some cases, a mild gastrointestinal upset follows shortly after ingestion of contaminated materials, but typical symptoms of typhoid fever do not begin until one to two (or occasionally three) weeks after ingestion of the bacilli.[7]

In contrast to most enteric pathogens, the typhoid bacilli do not become established in the gastrointestinal tract during the incubation period. Except when antimicrobial therapy upsets the normal intestinal microbial population, multiplication of typhoid bacilli in the lower intestine is inhibited by the indigenous microbes throughout the course of typhoid fever. The typhoid bacilli

[7]The period between initiation of infection and onset of disease symptoms is called the **incubation period** of a disease. Determination of the incubation period aids epidemiologists in tracing the sources of infection, and knowledge of it can be used to eliminate infection before symptoms are likely to appear.

instead become established in the mesenteric lymph nodes, the Peyer's patches of the small intestine, the gall bladder and bile duct, and often also in the liver or spleen (to which they are transported principally in the lympatic system). Once established in these regions, the bacilli multiply and, usually somewhat suddenly, invade the bloodstream in large numbers. The appearance of the bacteria in the blood is coincidental with and probably responsible for the onset of disease symptoms. It also coincides with the appearance of antibodies in the blood that react with the bacilli.

Structural components of the cell cortex of typhoid bacilli are toxic for man. The presence of these substances in the bloodstream causes fever, malaise, headache, anorexia, and prostration. These symptoms are typical of typhoid fever; they continue for two to three weeks, often accompanied by "rose spots" (sites of infection in the skin), bronchitis, abdominal discomfort (although rarely diarrhea), enlargement of the spleen, and occasionally delirium. After about three weeks, the symptoms may begin to subside gradually, and the person recovers. Recovery confers immunity, although relapses may occur during convalescence. About 3 per cent of survivors recover from the disease but not the infection. The bacilli continue to inhabit the gall bladder or bile duct and are shed in the feces (as many as 10^6 to 10^9 per gram of feces). Such persons are carriers. The carrier state is difficult to eliminate by the administration of drugs; removal of the gall bladder is effective in about 90 per cent of cases, but is not a common practice.

Continuation of fever beyond the third week of symptoms often indicates that death may follow. Typhoid fever may be fatal either because the infecting strain is capable of continued multiplication in the presence of the host's antibodies (which varies with both bacterial and host characteristics), or because the wall of the upper intestine becomes perforated at the sites of bacterial multiplication. In the latter case, peritonitis results and is the proximal cause of death. Autopsies of fatal cases usually reveal that sites of infection had been established in the liver, lungs, bone marrow, and periosteum, in addition to the sites mentioned earlier. These sites usually are detectable as areas of tissue disintegration within which typhoid bacilli can be detected.

Like many other invasive pathogens, typhoid bacilli can survive phagocytosis. They apparently can multiply within certain blood phagocytes in the early stages of the disease. However, as the interaction between phagocytes and bacilli continues, the phagocytes become capable of destroying ingested bacilli. The acquisition by the phagocytes of "immunity" to the bacilli can be demonstrated by transferring such phagocytic cells from a convalescent host to a susceptible experimental host. The latter becomes temporarily resistant to infection by S. typhosa. This property of the phagocytes can be demonstrated in the absence of specific circulating antibody.

Typhoid infection of a human can be eliminated at any stage by administration of chloramphenicol. Susceptibility to infection can be reduced by artificial immunization, but this protection can be overcome when the number of ingested bacilli is large. The most effective defenses against typhoid fever are sanitation and prohibition of handling of food by typhoid carriers.

Diphtheria (*Corynebacterium diphtheriae*). Most of the pathogens discussed in this section are invasive and cause disease by damaging tissues adjacent to the sites where they multiply. Diphtheria is an exception; it is an example of infectious diseases whose principal symptoms are elicited at sites distant from the site of infection. The symptoms are elicited by soluble toxins that are released from growing cells and disseminated through the body. In the case of diphtheria, a single such substance, called diphtheria toxin, is involved. It is a protein that can enter a variety of host cells and disturb their metabolism. Specifically, it inactivates their protein-synthesizing systems and renders them fragile and non-functional.

The causative organism of diphtheria is *Corynebacterium diphtheriae,* a bacterium closely related to some of man's indigenous inhabitants. It has so far been found in nature only in humans.

The organisms are transferred from host to host in droplets of mucus from the respiratory tract. The inhaled bacteria first begin to multiply in the mucous membrane of the pharynx, or occasionally in the pharyngeal tonsils. Elaboration of the toxin destroys some of the adjacent cells, and the area becomes inflamed. A gray, membranous exudate called the "diphtheritic membrane" accumulates on the surface of the throat; it consists mainly of phagocytes and cell debris. When the membrane extends downward toward the larynx, the host may suffocate even before any of the generalized symptoms of the toxin's activities appear. When it extends upward into the nasopharynx, suffocation is less likely. In nasopharyngeal diphtheria, the generalized effects of the toxin are usually observed. The bacteria remain localized in the diphtheritic membrane; occasionally, they invade the lymph nodes of the neck, but are not found in other regions of the body, even in fatal cases.

The toxin diffuses from the throat into the bloodstream. From the bloodstream, it enters cells of various tissues. In fatal cases that have been autopsied, and in experimental animals, the effects of the toxin can be observed in lungs, kidneys, adrenal glands, heart, and liver. The nervous system may also be affected, as evidenced by the occurrence, usually late in the disease, of paralysis. Recovery occurs in many cases, but is followed by neurologic and/or cardiac complications.

Immunity usually follows recovery, but typically lasts only a few years. Whether a consequence of recovery from the disease or a result of artificial immunization with toxoid, immunity to diphtheria is invariably associated with the presence in the blood of antibodies that react with and neutralize the effects of the toxin; such antibodies are called antitoxin. Antitoxin is effective against toxin in the bloodstream, but it cannot penetrate cells, as the toxin can. Accordingly, it is effective in preventing cellular damage and disease symptoms only if it is present early in the infection. At that time, it can neutralize the small amounts of toxin that stimulate the inflammation in the pharynx and thereby prevent the development of the diphtheritic membrane and eliminate the possibility of suffocation.

In cases of diphtheria in which the toxin has reached the bloodstream, antitoxin (prepared in horses) is administered mainly to neutralize the circulating toxin. Simultaneously, antibacterial drugs, e.g., penicillin, erythromycin, and tetracyclines, may be administered to eliminate the infection and halt production of the toxin. Even with such methods available, some irreversible damage often occurs before treatment can be begun. Convalescent patients continue to shed diphtheria bacteria for as long as several weeks. Diphtheria is a disease that is much more easily prevented, by artificial immunization to the toxin, than cured.

Malaria (*Plasmodium* species). The various types of malaria in man are caused by infection with any of four species of *Plasmodium.* Of these, *P. vivax* is widely distributed and the major cause of human malaria; *P. falciparum* occurs mainly in tropical, but sometimes in temperate regions; *P. malariae* is widely distributed, but usually accounts for only a minority of infections; and *P. ovale* is principally tropical and relatively rare where it can be found. The role of mosquitoes in transmitting human malaria was suspected early in the eighteenth century, but was not demonstrated experimentally until 1899. It now seems clear that adult female mosquitoes of *Anopheles* species are entirely responsible for transmission of malaria protozoa among humans.

Sporozoites (see Fig. 15-21) of *P. vivax*[8] enter the bloodstream of a prospective human host with the saliva of a mosquito while the insect feeds on the blood. Within an hour after the insect has fed, the sporozoites disappear from the blood, a phenomenon unexplained in the study of human malaria until the late 1940's. The sporozoites leave the bloodstream and enter certain cells of the liver. Each sporozoite grows intracellularly into a large schizont, which eventually becomes multinucleate. On the ninth day after infection, about 1,500 uninucleate merozoites are formed by schizogony. These organisms are released into the bloodstream, where they enter erythrocytes. They grow within the erythrocytes, typically one per red blood cell, ingesting and utilizing cytoplasmic components, including the protein portion of the hemoglobin, as growth substrates. The pigment portion of the hemoglobin is not utilized; it accumulates within the growing protozoon as red-brown granules. Within about 46 hours, this stage undergoes merogony and forms 12 to 24 merozoites; the erythrocyte membrane ruptures, and the merozoites and cytoplasmic debris are released into the blood. Most of the merozoites enter uninfected erythroycytes within one to three hours and repeat this "erythrocytic" stage.

Beginning with the second or third erythrocytic cycle, some of the merozoites of each generation differentiate into gametocytes. If these are removed with blood by a feeding mosquito, the sexual stages of the life cycle are completed in the insect in about three weeks. The mosquito can then reinfect another human when it feeds.

When a single instance of infection occurs in a host, the pre-erythrocytic stage in liver cells and each erythrocytic cycle occur simultaneously for each clone of protozoa. The periodic release of merozoites is reflected in the perio-

[8]This description of malaria is based on the disease as associated with *P. vivax;* it is basically the same for all species, varying mainly in severity and duration of symptoms.

dicity of disease symptoms (in adults; the periodicity is less distinct in children). Symptoms may appear with the release of the first generation of erythrocyte-grown merozoites if the number of infecting sporozoites was large. If the number was relatively small, two or more generations may occur before symptoms appear. The symptoms are currently attributed to toxicity of unidentified substances released from erythrocytes with the merozoites. The symptoms may begin as headache, nausea, listlessness, aching of joints or muscles, chilliness, and occasionally vomiting. The characteristic feature of malaria is a sequence of symptoms called the paroxysm. The paroxysm includes, first, chill, usually accompanied by severe shivering, rapid pulse and respiration, headache, and nausea (with or without vomiting); this is followed by fever, which may exceed 104° F even in adults; and finally, as the fever subsides, a stage of sweating.

Paroxysm, particularly, occurs periodically. Its duration increases during the course of the disease, presumably because larger numbers of erythrocytes lyse with each generation of merozoites. Initially, the chill lasts only a few minutes, but later it lasts as long as three hours. The fever lasts for three to six hours; it is lower in early paroxysms than later. In natural infections, the disease continues in this way for two to six months, depending on host and protozoan characteristics. When this initial period of the disease has passed, symptoms may not occur for several weeks. Then the first relapse occurs, and several more may follow for at least two years after the initial infection. Relapses are ascribed to re-entry of merozoites into the bloodstream from internal organs such as liver or spleen, where the infection continues as "exoerythrocytic stages" without eliciting symptoms. During the early disease period and during relapses, the host becomes anemic, has relatively few phagocytes in his blood, and usually has an enlarged spleen.

Malaria due to *P. vivax* is usually not fatal. Its severity is increased by fatigue, malnutrition, and heat prostration of the host and addictive use of narcotics. However, its prolonged debilitation of the host results in loss of work time, which usually means loss of income, retardation of mental or physical development in children, and increased susceptibility to other infectious diseases. Malaria in pregnant women and unborn or newborn infants is more commonly fatal than it is for humans in general. In *P. falciparum* malaria, infected erythrocytes tend to clump, and capillaries of the heart, brain, adrenals, or other organs may be blocked by the clumps. Death may result from vascular collapse, heart failure, cerebral thrombosis, or adrenal insufficiency. Most fatalities among malarial humans other than pregnant women and their fetuses occur in *P. falciparum* infections.

Malaria can be treated with chemicals that eliminate the infection. Most of the chemicals known to be useful are effective against only one stage of the protozoa (e.g., paludrine against pre-erythrocytic stages; quinine, atabrine, and chloroquine against erythrocytic stages; and pentaquine and Plasmochin against exoerythrocytic stages). Accordingly, elimination of all stages of the infection, which usually coexist in a single host, requires treatment with a combination of chemicals, and usually over an extended period of time.

Combined attack on infection in humans and on the mosquito has proved effective in decreasing the incidence of malaria. This involves:

For Humans. Chemical treatment to eliminate at least the erythrocytic stages, which provide the inoculum for mosquitoes; since this also relieves symptoms, humans are usually cooperative.

For the Mosquito. (1) Prevention of feeding on human blood by the use of repellants on the skin and screens on windows; (2) elimination of breeding areas, mainly by draining of swamps or other areas of standing water; (3) elimination of the larvae from breeding areas that cannot be drained, such as by stocking the waters with larva-eating fish; and (4) attacking the mosquitoes with insecticides, the most effective of which has been DDT.

Implementation of such measures has resulted in elimination of *Plasmodium* species pathogenic for man from large segments of the earth's human population. Malaria protozoa cannot now be found among inhabitants of many regions where malaria was, only recently, a familiar disease.

Chapter 23

Protists and Technology

In the past 100 years, the scourges[1] of mankind, other than war, have been greatly reduced in potency. Pestilence takes a minor toll in some human populations, and the knowledge is available that could eliminate it in all parts of the world as a major influence in human affairs. Death has been postponed. Famine has been restricted to certain portions of the earth's population.

The studies of microbiologists that have revealed the roles of microbes in human affairs have played a prominent part in changing the character of human life during this time. Most importantly, the microbes of pestilence—the pathogens—have been identified, and their transmission to and among humans has been characterized and interrupted. Freedom from disease prolongs the life of the individual and thereby increases the probability that a newborn human will survive to maturity with his parents still living, perform some socially useful function, and, in his turn, reproduce and live to rear his children to adulthood.

The relief from pestilence has been achieved primarily through (1) sanitation and other environmental measures that reduce the number and variety of pathogens to which humans are exposed, (2) prophylactic immunization, which reduces the number of infectious diseases to which humans are susceptible, and (3) treatment, predominantly chemical, of diseased persons to relieve disease symptoms, eliminate infection, and prevent death from those diseases. Concepts and discoveries in microbiology have also led to control of diseases of plants and animals, most importantly those used as food by man; to exploitation of protistan activities with regard to soil fertility; to development of methods for reducing deterioration of foodstuffs, fabrics, and construction

---

[1] Revelations 6:1–8.

materials due to protistan activities; and to exploitation of the highly specific chemical-catalytic systems found among protists.

Microbiology and its applications have been only a part of the forces behind man's recently increased control of his environment. The methods devised for controlling and exploiting protistan activities required for their implementation concurrent developments in chemistry, physics, and engineering, and in transportation and communication, and—probably most important of all—a corps of trained personnel and an informed public.

Conversely, the continued operation of a technologically advancing society requires a reasonably healthy population—a supply of persons whose mental and physical capacities will not be reduced by malnutrition or disease, whose years of study or acquisition of skills will not be frequently interrupted by incapacitating illness, and who will live many adult years during which they can use their training.

In this chapter, some of the technologic aspects of microbiology are discussed, with particular emphasis on those applications of microbiologic principles that contribute to the physical well-being of humans.

Principles and Practices of Antimicrobiology

Protists influence their environments almost exclusively by causing chemical changes in the environment as they grow and multiply; the only technologically significant exception to this statement is the clogging with microbial protoplasm of filters or pipelines through which liquids such as water and fuel are passed. In either case, a single protist does not exert a detectable effect; sizable populations are invariably involved when microbial activities are detectable. Accordingly, protistan activities can be controlled by killing viable protists, or by inhibiting their metabolism and thereby preventing the development of populations.

Antimicrobial methods vary in the mechanisms of their effects and in the types of microbes against which they are effective. Any method (e.g., ultraviolet irradiation) that exerts antimicrobial activity by virtue of its adverse effects on genetic material is effective against the widest range of microbes, since genetic material is apparently of the same chemical composition (DNA) in all organisms. Any method (e.g., most types of chemical disinfection) whose antimicrobial activity depends on structural disorganization of protistan cells is effective against a narrower range of types, viz., those whose structural components are both susceptible and accessible to reaction with the agent. The methods (e.g., many chemotherapeutic practices) that are most specific for microbial types are those that affect metabolic processes, since these processes are more variable among protists than are structural components or genetic material.

Several widely applicable antimicrobial methods are described in the following paragraphs. A given method may be suitable for one or more of the following purposes.

Sterilization. Elimination of viable protists.
Disinfection. Reduction in the number of viable protists.
Antisepsis. Prevention of proliferation of protists.
Asepsis. Prevention of the introduction of (contamination with) viable protists (see Chap. 11).

Temperature. Each living system functions only within a narrow temperature range whose minimum is determined by the heat requirements of its catalytic proteins and whose maximum is determined by the susceptibility of its essential macromolecules to heat-catalyzed degradation. At temperatures below the minimum, the rate of metabolism is nil. At temperatures 10 to 20 C° above the maximum, heat-catalyzed damage occurs too rapidly or extensively to be repaired, and the system eventually becomes irreversibly inactivated (dies). The higher the temperature, the more rapid the inactivation.

Extremes of temperature (i.e., temperatures outside the range in which growth can occur) are generally effective antimicrobial agents. Low temperatures are widely used for retarding protistan activities in foods. Icing or mechanical refrigeration at temperatures below 10° C inhibits multiplication of all known food-borne pathogens and of many of the protists that spoil foods. However, several yeasts, some molds, and a few bacteria can grow slowly at these temperatures and cause spoilage. Freezing and cooling to temperatures below −10° C prevents all protistan activities.

High temperature (heat) is used for the disinfection and sterilization of a greater variety of materials than any other antimicrobial agent. Alternatives are sought only when the material is adversely affected by heat or is too large to permit thorough, sustained heating. In microbiologic laboratories, hospitals, and industrial processes that require sterile materials, most sterilization is effected by moist heat in an autoclave (a steam-pressure chamber) or dry heat in a hot-air oven. Protists that can survive desiccation are much more resistant to heat inactivation when dry; accordingly, the standard procedures for heat sterilization employ steam under pressure at 121° C for a time sufficient to maintain that temperature throughout the material for 15 minutes, and dry heat at 180° C throughout for two to three hours. These treatments are sufficient to inactivate bacterial endospores, which are the most heat-stable protists known. Any lesser heat treatment, such as passing live steam through a pipeline or over dishes, can be expected only to disinfect, not to sterilize.

Radiation. Organic molecules can absorb various forms of radiant energy, and such absorbed energy can cause a change in molecular structure. If a molecule of an essential constituent of a living cell absorbs radiant energy and undergoes a change that cannot be repaired or compensated for, the cell will be inactivated. Of several types of radiation that can inactivate microbial cells, only two—ultraviolet and gamma radiation—have found any significant amount of application.

Ultraviolet radiation of 200 to 300 nm wavelength can inactivate microbial cells whether they are wet or dry. It is especially useful as an agent for disinfection of air and dry surfaces. It is also used to sterilize organic materials such as pharmaceutic preparations that are inactivated by heat or made unsuitable for their intended use by addition of antimicrobial chemicals. Gamma radiation produced by radioactive cobalt-60 is currently used as a means of disinfecting some foods. In contrast to ultraviolet, gamma rays can penetrate substances such as animal flesh without significant diminution of their antimicrobial effect.

Filtration. Filtration is another alternative method for disinfection or sterilization when heat or chemical treatment is not practical. Any fluid can be disinfected or sterilized by passage through a filter that retains microbial cells. Two general types of filters are employed: filters in which retention is due to a maximum pore size smaller than bacterial cells, and filters that retain microbial cells in a maze of tortuous channels. The sand filters used in water disinfection often become inhabited by slime-producing microorganisms, and retention is aided by adhesive entrapment of microbial cells in the slime.

Filtration is used to remove microbes from a variety of fluids in addition to water. These include fruit juices, beer, preparations of pharmaceutic products that are heat- and/or ultraviolet-sensitive, air, and many laboratory preparations, including suspensions of virions ("filterable viruses").

Desiccation and High Osmotic Pressure. Depriving microorganisms of the water essential for metabolic activity is probably the oldest antiseptic method. Any material that can be dried and kept dry can be protected from microbial attack. Drying also has some disinfecting effect, since many microbes and especially vegetative cells of animal parasites other than mycobacteria do not survive prolonged dehydration. Dormant stages can usually survive lengthy periods without water, but they are relatively inactive metabolically and do not alter their environments chemically.

Reduction in water activity of a material by increasing the osmotic pressure protects it against microbial attack. This is the basis of sugaring and salting as means of food or hide preservation. The preservative effects of high osmotic pressure are attributed to dehydration of proteins in the materials, which renders them unsuitable as substrates for microbial proteolytic enzymes and thereby deprives microbes (especially bacteria) of their nitrogen source in the material. In addition, the vegetative cells of most higher protists are dehydrated in materials of high osmotic pressure and are as inactive in such environments as when dried.

The reverse of desiccation, viz., wetting, is notorious as a factor that increases the susceptibility of organic materials (fabrics, hides, lumber, foods, paint binders, and so forth) to microbial degradation.

Antimicrobial Chemicals in Disinfection and Antisepsis. Several classes of chemicals can be used to kill or inhibit microbes. Some of these are toxic for living systems in general, but others are specific for protistan types. The range of organisms affected by a given chemical is the most influential factor in determining its application.

Four classes of preparations of antimicrobial chemicals are distinguished according to the applications for which the preparations are suitable.

1a. General disinfectants can be used only for disinfection of inanimate materials that will not come in contact with human tissue or be ingested by humans.

1b. Skin disinfectants can be used to disinfect intact skin, such as in preparation for surgery, but are irritating to subcutaneous tissue.

2. Sanitizers can be used to disinfect clothing, bedding, or utensils and equipment used in preparation or serving of foods.

3. Antiseptics can be used to prevent local infection of mucous membrane or wounded tissue, but cannot be admitted directly to the bloodstream.

4. Chemotherapeutic agents can be administered internally to humans. These are considered in the following section.

A list of preparations useful in disinfection, sanitizing, and antisepsis is presented in Table 23-1.

The toxicity of a given substance is proportional to its concentration. Accordingly, a substance may be prepared as a disinfectant at one concentration and as an antiseptic at a lower concentration. This is exemplified by ethanol in Table 23-1. Also proportional to concentration is the effect on microbes. Higher concentrations may be lethal **(microbicidal),** whereas lower concentrations may only inhibit multiplication **(microbistatic);** very low concentrations may stimulate microbial growth.

A disinfectant preparation is selected for a given purpose if it meets the following criteria.

1. It is microbicidal within the time that can be allowed for it to be in contact with the material.

2. Its effectiveness is not diminished under the conditions of disinfection, e.g., temperature, pH, and presence of metal ions or organic materials. (Higher temperatures and lower pH values generally potentiate the action of disinfectant chemicals; organic materials interfere with most, and metal ions with some, disinfecting agents.)

3. It does not damage the material to be disinfected.

4. It is more toxic for the microbes likely to be present than for other organisms, especially humans.

It is further desirable in many cases that the preparation exhibit cleansing or deodorizing properties. In some cases (e.g., disinfection of floors, toilets, laboratory benches, water, and air), it is also desirable that the disinfectant leave a non-toxic, non-corrosive residue to serve as an antiseptic.

Sanitizing preparations differ from general disinfectants only in that they must be non-toxic when ingested, inhaled, or contacted by humans in the amounts they may leave as residues. The preparations suitable for this purpose are generally less efficient as microbicides, i.e., they kill more slowly, than are

TABLE 23-1. Antimicrobial Chemicals Used in Disinfection, Sanitizing, and Antisepsis

Type of Preparation	Example of Active Ingredient	Microbes Affected	Application and Effectiveness
Soaps	Unsaturated fatty acids	Gram-positive bacteria, not staphylococci	Washable surfaces, including skin; effectiveness is enhanced by aromatic oils, hexachlorophene (which affects staphylococci), and increased water temperature; cleansing properties; ions of alkaline earth metals interfere
	Saturated fatty acids	Gram-negative bacteria	
	Na-laurate	Pneumococci, streptococci, typhoid bacilli	
Detergents	Cationic: benzalkonium chloride	Gram-positive more than gram-negative bacteria; *E. histolytica* cysts	Washable surfaces, including skin; widely used to disinfect skin prior to surgery; sanitizers in food preparation; aerosols; cleansing and wetting properties; colorless, odorless, tasteless, non-corrosive, non-irritating; organic matter interferes
	Anionic: sulfated alcohols	Vegetative cells except *Pseudomonas* and *M. tuberculosis*	
Phenols and cresols	Phenol, bis-*p*-chloro-phenyl-diguanidohexane	General, including fungi	Skin disinfection, for surgery or obstetrics; phenol as an antiseptic in vaccines; aerosols; widely used to disinfect washable inanimate surfaces and public sanitary facilities; organic matter interferes
Alcohols	Ethanol	Wet vegetative microbial cells; bacterial spores when combined with dilute HCl or NaOH	At 70%, as skin disinfectant and as solvent for "tinctures" of antimicrobial agents; at 25%, as vaccine antiseptic; at 1–20%, as food preservative (antiseptic)
	Propanol	(Similar to ethanol)	
	Higher alcohols	(Similar to ethanol)	At 80%, as skin disinfectant
Organic acids	Lactic, citric, and acetic	Kills acid-sensitive, inhibits acid-tolerant microbes	Aerosols
	Benzoic acid	General, including molds	Antisepsis (preservation) of foods by acidulation; Antiseptic in acidic foods
	n-Heptyl-*p*-hydroxybenzoic acid	General, including molds	Antiseptic in beer
Heavy metals	Mercury	General	Inorganic compounds, e.g., $HgCl_2$, for disinfection of wettable surfaces; Organic compounds (mercurials) as topical antiseptics
	Silver	General	Throat disinfection
	Copper	Fungi and algae	Disinfection and antifungal antisepsis in plants; antialgal antisepsis in water

Agent class	Agent	Active against	Uses
Oxidants	Dichromates, perchlorates	General, including bacterial spores	Disinfection of wettable surfaces (in weakly acidic solutions); soluble protein interferes with these and other oxidants
	H_2O_2 (H-peroxide)	General	Skin disinfection, disinfection of aqueous solutions
	O_3 (ozone)	General, including *E. histolytica* cysts	Disinfection of water and aqueous solutions
	Halogens: Chlorine, hypochlorite, chloramines	General	Sanitizing of food-preparation equipment and utensils; principal use is in water and sewage disinfection and water antisepsis; as 1% solution, chlorine is used as a hand disinfectant; corrosive for metals; sanitizing of dairy equipment; as tincture (4.5% in 70% ethanol, with 2% KI), as skin disinfectant
	Iodine, iodophors (organic I compounds)		
	Fluorine	Fungi	
	Ethylene oxide	General	Disinfection of water- or heat-damageable surfaces; disinfection of powdered materials, e.g., talc for surgical gloves and spices
Reducing agents	Oxyquinolines	General	Antisepsis of skin and wounds
	SO_2 and H_2SO_3	Bacteria, yeasts (not wine yeasts), and filamentous fungi	Preservation of fruits and fruit juices
	HCHO (formaldehyde)	General, including bacterial spores	Vaccine antisepsis, aerosols, sanitizing, and preserving biologic specimens, including cadavers
Oils	Oil of cinnamon, oil of clove, oil of marjoram, oil of wild thyme, oil of geranium, and oil of garlic	Bacteria; some are effective against bacterial spores	Food preservatives (disinfection and antisepsis); embalming
Antibiotics (source; see Table 23-2)	Bacitracin (*Bacillus subtilis*)	Gram-positive bacteria	Antisepsis of skin, mucous membranes, and shallow wounds
	Polymyxin (*B. polymyxa*)	Gram-negative bacteria, including *Pseudomonas aeruginosa*	(Same as bacitracin)
	Tyrothricin (a mixture of gramicidin and tyrocidine)	(Same as bacitracin)	(Same as bacitracin)
	Neomycin (*Streptomyces fradiae*)	Bacteria	Given orally for disinfection of intestines prior to abdominal or rectal surgery
	Cycloheximide (*S. griseus*)	Plant pathogenic fungi	Antifungal chemotherapy in plants

general disinfectants. The sanitizer selected is usually also especially toxic for a particular type of protist, according to the need. Antifungal agents are used to sanitize clothing and other fabrics; antibacterials for food-processing equipment, dishes, and containers for food storage, as well as clothing; and antialgal preparations for equipment used in water purification, storage, and distribution.

An antiseptic should be prepared so that effective concentrations of the active chemical will remain at the site at which it is applied. The antimicrobial component should neither evaporate nor diffuse rapidly into tissue around the wound. It should not react extensively with tissue substances or be degradable by tissue enzymes. Ideally, it should not cause irritation or discoloration. In contrast to disinfectants, preparations that are microbistatic rather than microbicidal are useful as antiseptics, for two reasons: (1) their antimicrobial effect is reinforced by host defenses; prevention of microbial multiplication increases the time during which phagocytes and antimicrobial substances in the host can act to destroy the microbial cells, and (2) they are not intentionally removed from the site of application.

Chemotherapeutic Agents.   Chemotherapy is the practice of administering chemical preparations to a diseased or infected person[2] with the aim of relieving the disease symptoms or eliminating the infection. The only chemotherapeutic agents to be discussed here are those used in the treatment of infectious diseases. They are listed in Table 23-2.

Folk medicine has long made use of natural products such as herbs, bark extracts, spices, and others, mainly of plant origin, in the treatment of diseases. These methods were empirically devised and often quite effective. During the nineteenth century, as organic chemistry developed rapidly in the Western World and the germ theory of disease gained acceptance, a few medical practitioners (notably Paul Ehrlich, who coined the term "chemotherapy"), advanced the notion of selective antimicrobial chemotherapy. This concept was that certain organic molecules existed that were considerably more toxic for infecting microorganisms than for humans; the principal observation on which this idea was based was that bacterial cells had much greater affinity for certain dyes than did human cells.[3] Ehrlich tested a large number of synthetic chemicals and found that certain organic arsenic compounds were useful in treatment of spirochete infections, and that certain dyes were useful in trypanosome infections. However, he died in 1915 without finding chemotherapeutic agents selectively active against eubacterial pathogens.

Ehrlich's ideas were revived 20 years later by Domagk in Germany and Tréfouel in France. Their studies resulted in the first useful antibacterial agents, the sulfonamides. A few other useful synthetic chemicals have been found, e.g., isoniazide for antituberculosis therapy and several compounds for anti-

---

[2]For simplicity, reference in this discussion will be restricted to humans, but the principles apply as well to other animals and, with modifications, to plants.

[3]This notion has been substantiated not only by the discovery of specifically antimicrobial chemicals useful in therapy of infectious diseases, but also in the frequent correlation between susceptibility to a specific chemotherapeutic agent and gram reaction (see Chap. 13).

malaria therapy. However, most of the antimicrobial agents now in use are substances of microbial origin—the antibiotics.

Antibiotics are substances produced by living organisms (principally microorganisms) that kill or inhibit the growth of microorganisms at low concentrations. Inclusion of antimicrobial action "at low concentrations" is necessary to distinguish this type of substance from inhibitory metabolic products such as organic acids. Antibiotics are found by screening isolates for their ability to prevent growth of selected pathogens in artificial media. Hundreds of such compounds have been discovered since the 1940's, but most are toxic for humans. Some of these are used in antiseptics (see, e.g., bacitracin in Table 23-1), others as last-resort methods in persons infected with microbes resistant to less toxic drugs.

The first useful antibiotic was penicillin, discovered by A. Fleming in 1929

TABLE 23-2. Antimicrobial Agents Used in Chemotherapy

Agent	Source*	Used Principally in Treating†
Antibacterial		
Sulfonamides	Chemical synthesis	Meningococcal meningitis, trachoma; beta-hemolytic streptococcal infections in patients with rheumatic fever
Nitrofurans	Chemical synthesis	Chronic urinary tract infections
p-Aminosalicylic acid (PAS)	Chemical synthesis	Tuberculosis (with INH and/or streptomycin)
Isoniazide (INH)	Chemical synthesis	Tuberculosis
Diaminodiphenyl sulfone	Chemical synthesis	Leprosy
Penicillins	P. chrysogenum‡	All gram-positive coccal infections, diphtheria, some clostridial infections, meningococcal meningitis, gonorrhea, chancroid, syphilis, some actinomycete infections
Novobiocin	S. spheroides, S. niveus	As penicillins; also for penicillin-resistant staphylococcal infections; some Proteus and other gram-negative infections
Erythromycin§	S. erythreus	As penicillins; also for penicillin-resistant staphylococcal infections
Oleandomycin§	S. antibioticus	As erythromycin
Streptomycins‡	S. griseus	Tuberculosis (with PAS and/or INH); gram-negative infections
Kanamycin§	S. kanamyceticus	Gram-positive coccal infections, acute urinary infections
Chloramphenicol	Chemical synthesis‖	Typhoid fever, Haemophilus influenzae meningitis
Tetracyclines‡		Gram-positive chlamydial, rickettsial, mycoplasmal, and mixed bacterial infections
Chlor-	S. aureofaciens	
Oxy-	S. rimosus	
Antifungal		
Griseofulvin	P. spp.	Dermatophyte and yeast infections
Amphotericin B	S. nodosus	Cryptococcosis, disseminated histoplasmosis
Nystatin	S. noursei	Dermatophyte and yeast infections
Hydroxystilbamidine	Chemical synthesis	Blastomycosis

TABLE 23-2.   Antimicrobial Agents Used in Chemotherapy (*cont.*)

Agent	Source*	Used Principally in Treating†
Antiprotozoal		
Fumagillin	*A. fumigatus*	Amebic dysentery
Pyrimethamine, sulfonamides	Chemical synthesis	Toxoplasmosis
4-Aminoquinoline	Chemical synthesis, plant extracts	Malaria; the drugs are usually used in mixtures containing primaquine or pyrimethamine and one or more of the others
Chloroquine		
Diaminodiphenyl sulfone		
Primaquine		
Proguanil		
Pyrimethamine		
Sulfonamides		
Emetine	Chemical synthesis	Amebic dysentery
Carbarsone		
Thioarsenites		
Vioform		

*Refers to source used for commercial production; organisms listed are species of *Penicillium* (*P.*), *Streptomyces* (*S.*), and *Aspergillus* (*A.*).

†This column lists the most common uses, not the full range of therapies in which each agent is effective. Selection of a preparation for a particular infection in a given individual is determined in part by the patient's age, allergic history, general condition (especially of his heart and circulatory system), and degree of toxicity of the agent, particularly in infections that require prolonged therapy.

‡Derivatives prepared by chemical processes are also used in chemotherapy.

§Usually used for penicillin-sensitive infections in persons in whom penicillins elicit allergic reaction.

‖ Originally isolated from *S. venezuelae.*

and developed for use during World War II. The other antibiotics listed in Table 23-2 have been discovered and introduced as chemotherapeutic agents since 1944.

The useful antibiotics are highly selective in their toxicity and vary in their antimicrobial spectrums. This selectivity is an advantage in two respects: toxicity is low or nil for the host, and his indigenous microbial population is not significantly altered. It is a disadvantage, generally, in that the infecting pathogen must be definitely identified in order for the proper antibiotic to be prescribed, and, potentially, in that a single genetic mutation may confer resistance to the antibiotic on a subpopulation of the infecting pathogen. Drug resistance is the second major problem in antibiotic chemotherapy, after toxicity for humans. Wide use of any one antibiotic in a host population is known to result in selection of drug-resistant pathogen populations among those hosts.

In most infectious diseases, symptoms are relieved within hours of initiation of chemical attack on the infecting agent, whether the drug is microbicidal or, as is more common, microbistatic. Chemotherapeutic agents can also be used prophylactically to prevent infection of persons who have been in contact with an infected, diseased person, or during epidemics. However, prophylactic chemotherapy is an emergency measure and is discontinued as soon as the possibility of infection is eliminated. Generally, chemotherapy is an after-the-fact (of disease), often empiric, fingers-crossed method of controlling infec-

tious diseases in individuals. Although of undisputed value to diseased persons
and in preventing deaths from infectious diseases, it cannot protect a population
for any length of time.

The Public Health

The agent of practically every human disease that is known to be infectious
is now known, or at least its mode of transmission (see Fig. 23-1) is known.
(The infectious nature of some diseases, notably certain malignancies, is still
in doubt.) Likewise, some method for prevention of each disease is known.
This means that infectious diseases are preventable diseases, and that their
persistence among humans into the 1970's is due to lack of full implementation
of preventive measures. Implementation of most such measures requires economic and educational conditions that have not yet been achieved in some
parts of the world. Present life expectancy, frequency of cases of and deaths
due to infectious diseases, and types of prevalent infectious diseases in economically less developed areas are similar to those that prevailed a century

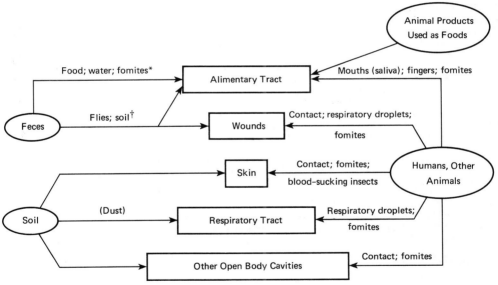

Sources and routes of transmission of microorganisms that cause diseases in humans. *Circled:*   **Figure 23-1**
sources of infective microbes. *Boxed:* body regions susceptible to infection. *Arrows:* routes,
indicating animate and inanimate carriers commonly involved.

*Fomites are inanimate materials susceptible to contamination and on or in which infective
microbes can survive. Examples include toilet articles, including facial tissues and preparations
of cosmetics; medical instruments such as hypodermic needles, catheters, and dental probes;
clothing, bedding, doorknobs, pencils.

†Soil is a carrier of some microbes that occur primarily as animal parasites, particularly those
normally present in feces; and a source of microbes that can infect humans, but occur primarily
as free-living organisms of the soil.

ago in regions now relatively advanced economically, and relatively free from pestilences. This is illustrated in Tables 23-3 and 23-4.

Preventive measures may be aimed at the environment, the potential hosts, or the pathogen (see Fig. 23-1); any one measure may serve to eliminate a source of infection or to interrupt the route of transmission of the pathogen. Environmental measures have been particularly effective as methods for controlling the spread of enteric diseases (through sanitation of milk and other foods, and of water and sewage) and of arthropod-borne diseases (by eradication of vector populations, principally with the aid of insecticides).

Immunization programs have been exclusively or largely responsible for

TABLE 23-3.   Major Causes of Death and Major Infectious Diseases in Ten Countries, 1962

	Major Infectious Diseases*	*Relative Frequency of Death Due to Infectious Disease†*	*Life Expectancy‡* *Males*	*Females*
A. MORE DEVELOPED§ REGIONS (N. AMERICA, W. EUROPE, S. EUROPE, AUSTRALIA, JAPAN)				
MAJOR CAUSES OF DEATH: INFANCY, MALIGNANCIES, ARTERIOSCLEROTIC AND DEGENERATIVE HEART DISEASES				
Sweden	Tuberculosis	1.0	71	75
U.S.A.	Tuberculosis	1.7	67‖	74‖
Japan	Tuberculosis	2.4	65	70
Hungary	Tuberculosis	2.6	65	69
Italy	Tuberculosis	3.2	66	70
B. LESS DEVELOPED§ REGIONS (LATIN AMERICA, S.E. EUROPE, NEAR EAST, AFRICA, S. AND S.E. ASIA)				
MAJOR CAUSES OF DEATH: INFANCY, COMPLICATIONS OF PREGNANCY AND CHILDBIRTH, GASTROINTESTINAL DISEASES, RESPIRATORY DISEASES				
Philippines	Tuberculosis > measles > cholera > malaria > dysentery	4.3		
Nicaragua	Malaria > whooping cough > measles > TB > typhoid fever	4.5		
Mauritius	TB > dysentery	5.0		
Chile	TB > measles > diphtheria > typhoid fever > whooping cough	7.0	50	54
U.A.R.	Measles > TB > typhoid fever > diphtheria	9.9		

*Mortality rate greater than 2.0 per 100,000 population per year.

†Calculated from *World Health Statistics Annual,* vol. 1, "Vital Statistics and Causes of Death." W.H.O., Geneva, 1965; excludes the W.H.O. category "complications of pregnancy," some of which are due to microbial infections. Sweden's mortality rate set at unity.

‡Mortality rates for all causes other than complications of pregnancy are higher for males than for females, especially in infancy and childhood, hence the shorter life expectancies for males.

§*Development* refers to general economic condition of a region as reflected in agricultural and industrial productivity of goods and nonhuman energy, normalized per capita annual income, literacy and proportion of elementary schoolteachers among the population, average intake per person per day of calories and animal protein, consumption of goods, number of motor vehicles relative to population, and amount of external trade. Not every country is comparable with the region in which it is located.

‖ This figure is 49 for migrant farm workers.

TABLE 23-4. Ten Leading Causes* of Death in the United States, 1900 and 1960

1900	1960
1. **Pneumonia** and **influenza**	Heart diseases
2. **Tuberculosis**	Malignancies
3. **Diarrhea** and **enteritis**	Cerebral hemorrhage
4. Heart diseases	Accidents
5. Cerebral hemorrhage	Premature birth
6. **Nephritis**	**Pneumonia** and **influenza**
7. Accidents	Arteriosclerosis
8. Malignancies	Diabetes
9. **Diphtheria**	Congenital malformations
10. **Meningitis**	Cirrhosis of the liver
Proportion of deaths due to the ten leading causes:	
63%	85%

*Boldface indicates diseases due to microbial or viral infections or in which infection commonly occurs as a complication leading to death.

reducing the incidence of several diseases (see below) by reducing the susceptibility of potential hosts. Such programs not only protect the immunized population from disease, but also eliminate that population as a reservoir of the disease and can halt epidemics.[4] Education of a population to personal hygienic practices and other aspects of health care further increases its resistance to infectious diseases in general.

Because many pathogens occur naturally only in hosts, the principal preventive measures aimed at the pathogen are detection of infected hosts (with or without symptoms) and elimination of their infections; animals infected with pathogens may be destroyed. Soil is the second major source of pathogens. Since this source cannot be eliminated, acquisition of infections from soil must be prevented by sanitary measures and by prompt cleansing of wounds.

Since about 1900, typhoid fever, diphtheria, measles, scarlet fever, whooping cough, and smallpox have been practically eliminated as causes of death in the United States.[4a] In addition, mortality rates have been reduced approximately 90 per cent for tuberculosis, and approximately 67 per cent for pneumonia. As the proportion of deaths due to acute diseases has decreased from more than 40 per cent to less than 10 per cent between 1900 and 1960, the proportion due to chronic diseases has increased from approximately 45 per cent to more than 80 per cent. Chronic diseases lead to death only after years of disease and are of highest frequency among the middle-aged and elderly. The life expectancy of United States inhabitants has increased from about 47 years in 1900 to almost 70 years in the 1960's.

During the twentieth century, improvement of the public health of other countries of comparable economic development has been similar to that experienced by the United States. The majority of such countries are located in

[4]A disease is considered endemic when it occurs at a constant frequency within a population; it is considered epidemic when its frequency becomes higher than normal or when it appears in a population usually free of that disease.

[4a]In 1969, no deaths and only 19 cases of poliomyelitis were reported in the United States.

temperate zones. In tropical and subtropical regions, the larger numbers and wider variety of arthropod vectors and the existence through most of the year of conditions of temperature and humidity that favor survival of pathogens outside the host pose problems for implementation of preventive measures that are not encountered in cooler climates. Thus, in those regions where resources for public health measures are more limited, the prospective costs are greater.

The two preventive measures that have proved highly effective as means of reducing or eliminating infectious diseases—sanitation and prophylactic immunization—are discussed in the following sections.

Sanitation / Water and Sewage. In 1855, John Snow concluded from his studies of outbreaks of cholera in London that the cause of cholera was a particulate agent that entered the body through the mouth, multiplied in the body, and was excreted with the feces. Any material contaminated with feces from a person suffering from cholera could transmit the agent to other persons, and water could serve to transmit the agent to large numbers of people, thereby causing epidemics. In 1884, Robert Koch isolated from cholera patients a vibrio he believed to be the cholera agent; in 1892, during a cholera epidemic in Hamburg, he isolated the same organism from the river that was used by the city as the source of its drinking water and as the depot for its sewage. Like Snow, he concluded that the causative agent could be transmitted in feces-contaminated water. During the latter half of the nineteenth century, similar interpretations of the spread of typhoid and other enteric fevers were publicized, and around 1900 bacillary dysentery was added to the list of diseases transmitted through feces-contaminated water.

Studies of outbreaks of these three diseases led to the recognition of the mouth——→feces——^{1}—→water——^{2}—→mouth route of transmission, which stimulated the development of methods for water purification and the installation of sanitary facilities in thousands of communities. The primary aim of the microbiologic aspects of water and sewage sanitation is to interrupt this chain of transmission. Sewage treatment interrupts at step 1, and water purification at step 2.

The most suitable method for providing a community with safe water is to locate an unpolluted source and protect it from fecal pollution. At present, such sources are rare; almost all surface waters in the United States that are of sufficient volume to be used as water sources for municipalities are contaminated with human or animal feces. Accordingly, water purification is generally regarded as a necessary routine measure to protect the public health.

The processing of raw water to ensure its safety with regard to microbial content involves the following basic steps.

1. Settling. The water is allowed to stand undisturbed in a tank or basin, during which time large particulate matter settles out. Settling may be accelerated by the addition to the water of aluminum sulfate, which forms a flocculent precipitate. As the alum precipitate settles, it carries down with it small particles, including microbial cells.

2. Filtration. The water from the settling tank is passed downward through beds of sand, each bed composed of a finer-grain sand than the one immediately above it. The sand filters retain up to 99 per cent of the microbial cells present before filtration.

3. Chlorination. Chlorine (as liquid or gas, as hypochlorite, or in the form of organic chlorine compounds such as chloramine) is added to the filtered water at concentrations determined according to the chlorine demand[5] of the water. Generally, sufficient chlorine is added so that a minimum of 0.2 to 1.0 mg per liter (ppm) of free chlorine will remain to serve as an antiseptic during storage and distribution to the consumer. This practice was introduced in the United States in 1908 and has been modified only in minor ways since that time.

Microbiologic analysis of water is usually carried out with samples of the raw water, the stored water, and water at various points in the distribution system. The samples are examined particularly for the presence and numbers of bacteria normally present in human feces; their presence indicates that the water has been contaminated with human feces and therefore potentially contains feces-borne pathogens. Depending on the locality, coliform bacteria, fecal streptococci, or fecal clostridia may be enumerated. Since the initiation of sanitary water control in the United States, coliform bacteria have been used as the indicators of fecal pollution, mainly because they are more easily detected than the other types. The standards for coliform content of water that are used in most States and municipalities are based on those recommended by the United States Public Health Service. Water should contain less than one viable coliform per 100 ml in order to be distributed for human consumption; undetectable levels of coliforms are the most desirable.

Sewage comprises the liquid refuse of a community. There are three principal sources of sewage; each generates a type of sewage with its particular pollutant content. (1) Sanitary (domestic) sewage carries human excrement and a variety of cleaning preparations now used in the home. (2) Industrial sewage carries a variety of inorganic and organic chemicals and occasionally animal pathogens (e.g., from slaughterhouses). (3) Storm sewage carries those pollutants that wash off a community when it rains, including air-borne chemicals and radioactivity. Ultimately, the bulk of this liquid is deposited in a natural body of water. In most communities, only the storm sewage is directed into a nearby natural body of water without treatment.

If the dilution factor *volume of sewage: volume of natural water* is low, and especially if the diluent is sea water, natural microbial and chemical processes will depollute and disinfect untreated sewage. The saprophytic microorganisms in the diluent water will oxidize organic materials, and algae and saprophytes will eventually absorb the utilizable inorganic nutrients such as

---

[5]The disinfecting action of chlorine is interfered with by organic matter. Accordingly, the greater the amount of animate and inanimate organic matter present after filtration, the greater the amount of chlorine that will be needed to disinfect the water.

nitrates, phosphates, and sulfur compounds. The natural microbial population and the general environmental conditions (e.g., high salt concentrations and low temperatures) inhibit development of microorganisms that inhabit human intestines; generally, only spore-formers survive in potentially infective numbers for longer than a few days. Disposition of sewage by dilution and dependence on natural processes for sewage purification is suitable only for sparsely populated regions. The need for artificial treatment of sewage before it is released into the nearest river, lake, ocean, stream, or bay increases with the density of the human population.

Similar methods are used in the treatment of sanitary and industrial sewage, and in some communities sewage from the two sources is mixed in the sewerage system and treated together at the municipal sanitary facilities. The aim of sewage treatment is twofold: to eliminate feces-borne pathogens, and to reduce the content of substances that support the growth of protists and higher plants (weeds) that occur in natural bodies of water. Sudden increases of nutrients in a natural body of water result in protistan and weed blooms that make the water unsuitable for growth and survival of fish, and for irrigation, recreation, or animal watering. Specific standards for microbial and chemical content of treated sewage are not commonly recommended or enforced. Generally, treated sewage is regarded as acceptable for disposal if its content of microorganisms and chemicals does not exceed that of the natural water into which it is released.

The particular method used by a community for sewage treatment is determined largely by the volume of waste that must be treated, and to a lesser extent by the types of materials in the sewage. Generally, two main steps are involved.

First, microbial degradation of organic material to CO_2 and H_2O; the microorganisms present in the sewage perform this mineralization.

Second, elimination of the microorganisms by procedures similar to those used in water purification, often including chlorination.

Two widely used methods, which differ principally in the conditions under which most of the microbial digestion of the sewage occurs, are illustrated diagrammatically in Figure 23-2. The sludge of an anaerobic digestion tank is composed of solid wastes and microbes; the predominant organisms are those especially able to multiply at the expense of the substances present in the sewage. "Activated sludge" is similar, except that the predominant microbes are aerobes that are further enriched with the active types each time some of the sludge is transferred back to undigested sewage. The trickling filter is a deep bed of rocks over which the sewage is sprayed; the filtered effluent is drained away from below the filter. A microbial population, rich in slime-producing bacteria, develops on the rocks and oxidizes organic matter still present after digestion. The microbes active in these processes are predominantly bacteria (including lithotrophs, which oxidize inorganic substances such as ammonia and sulfide), and smaller numbers of protozoa and fungi.

The principal products of these and similar methods of waste treatment are:

1. Solid wastes, which are usually dried and used as soil fertilizer.

2. Gases; these can be collected, and the methane produced in anaerobic digestion tanks can be used as fuel in the treatment plant.

3. The (chlorinated) liquid effluent, which contains oxidized inorganic salts and synthetic chemicals that are not susceptible to microbial degradation. The

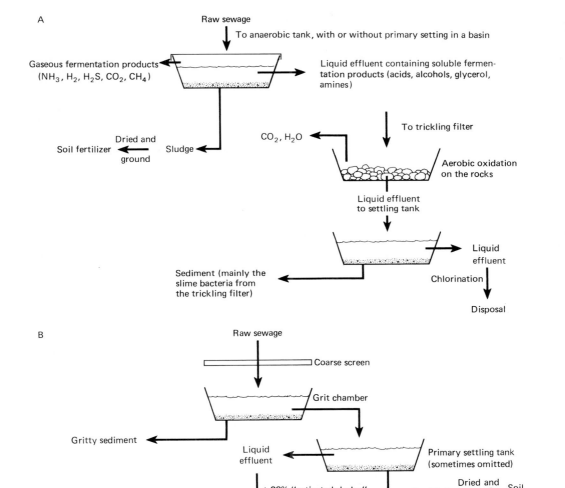

Two methods of biologic sewage treatment. *A*. Imhoff tank (anaerobic digestion). *B*. Activated sludge (aerobic digestion).

Figure 23-2

salts can be removed by inoculating the effluent with algae and allowing it to stand in a shallow, well-illuminated pond called a "stabilization pond." The algae utilize the salts as they grow and are eventually harvested from the pond and sold as livestock feed supplements. The stabilized, treated effluent is then disposed of by release into a natural body of water.

Sanitation / Foods. The public health problems associated with foods that are remedied by sanitary practices are (1) the transmission of pathogens that infect humans via the gastrointestinal tract, (2) the ingestion by humans of toxic substances produced by microorganisms that can multiply in foods, and (3) the spoilage of foods due to development in them of microbes whose growth is accompanied by undesirable changes in flavor, odor, texture, or appearance of the foods. Accordingly, microbiologic sanitary controls of foods are aimed at preventing the entry of or inactivating food-borne pathogens, and preventing microbial multiplication in foods in order to minimize food infection (by reducing dosage) and to prevent food poisonings and food spoilage.

Foods are susceptible to microbial contamination at many points between living food organism and the consumer. The major sources of microorganisms in foods are listed below.

1. The Plant and Animal Tissues. Animals acquire potential disease or spoilage organisms from their feeds, from other animals, and from soil. Plants acquire such organisms from soil and from manure used as fertilizer. Chickens transmit salmonellae through their eggs to the next generation, and to animals that eat eggs.

2. The Equipment. This includes all inanimate materials (including wash waters) used to slaughter, harvest, or milk the food organism, and in each step of processing, transporting, and packaging the killed organism or product. When food debris is left in or on the equipment between uses, the equipment may become heavily infected with microorganisms especially capable of multiplying in the type of food it processes.

3. Additives. These include water, certain spices, flour, sugar, salt, and egg and milk powders.

4. The Humans who Handle the Food at Any Step in Its Preparation. Slaughterers can acquire mild, often inapparent microbial infections from the animals they handle; they can subsequently transmit the microorganisms to uninfected animal products and to other humans. Food-handling carriers of typhoid bacilli and toxigenic staphylococci are the principal sources of these microorganisms in foods; they are also a source of infectious hepatitis virus. The enteric agents are present on feces-contaminated hands; the staphylococci are in the nasal passages and on the hands.

5. Flies. These insects carry microorganisms into foods from animal feces, animals, soil, and other foods, especially discarded portions (garbage).

6. *Dust and Air.* Microorganisms, especially the molds and bacteria that produce spores resistant to drying, are carried to foods in the air from soil, animal feces, and decaying organic materials.

Prevention of transmission of infectious food-borne diseases is the most important public health aspect of food sanitation. These diseases can be communicated by intermediates other than food. A person infected from food sheds the infective agent in his feces. Consequently, an outbreak of an infectious food-borne disease can involve many persons in addition to those who ate the contaminated food; the others acquire the infection by contact with a food-infected person or food or objects handled by him, or by ingesting water contaminated with his feces.

Food poisoning commonly occurs simultaneously in a number of persons, i.e., as outbreaks, not because it is communicable, but because it is acquired most commonly from foods that are prepared for large numbers of people. Catered foods, foods served in institutional cafeterias, and delicatessen-type foods are usually prepared some time (often several hours) before they are consumed, and especially the catered or cafeteria foods may be held at room temperature or slightly warmer during those hours. Food-poisoning organisms such as staphylococci enter the foods during preparation and multiply and release toxin during the hours the food is held without refrigeration.

Microbial spoilage of foods occurs during storage; food preservation is the practice of preventing or retarding spoilage due to the growth of microbes or to spontaneous chemical changes, particularly those due to exposure to air. In temperate climates, there has always been a need to store plant foods for use during seasons when the plants did not grow. Urbanization of human populations, which removes people from the sources of foods, requires that man preserve foods of both plant and animal origin. At the time they are eaten, stored foods must be palatable, nutritious, non-toxic, and free of viable pathogens and vermin. A change in military behavior from dependence on local residents for a food supply to dependence on military supplies has also stimulated the search for foods that can be stored indefinitely and easily transported in a soldier's pack.

Because microbial spoilage, toxicity, and infectiousness of foods are due to different microbes and involve different types of foods (see Tables 23-5 and 23-6), the specific means of preventing each may be somewhat different. However, asepsis in food handling is the single most effective means of control of all three microbial effects on foods. In addition to cleanliness, the following measures are used to protect and preserve foods.

1. *Heat- and Pressure-Processing.* Many types of moist foods are heated to kill pathogenic and/or spoilage microorganisms. Whenever possible, the food is packaged prior to heating so that it need not be handled after being disinfected. Pressure-processing is a means of heating moist foods to temperatures above the boiling point of water. It is used particularly for those foods likely to contain and allow growth of spore-forming pathogenic or spoilage bacteria.

TABLE 23-5. Principal Food Spoilage Microbes

Organism	Type of Food Affected	Characteristics of Spoilage
Bacteria		
Clostridium	Fresh, vacuum-packed, and canned meats and fish	Putrid odor, softening
	Canned vegetables	Gas, sulfide odor, sourness, with or without cheesy odor
	Fresh or canned milk	Gas, sourness
Bacillus	Fresh or canned milk	Curdling without sourness, bitter flavor
	Bread	Ropiness
	Canned meats	Softening
	Canned vegetables	Sourness, slight gas, off-odor
	Canned tomatoes, fruits	Off-odor, -flavor
Pseudomonas*	Fresh milk	Rancidity, fishy flavor
	Fresh meat	Putridity
	Cured meat	Sourness
	Fish	Discoloration
	Eggs	Greening
Serratia	Bread	Red splotches
Achromobacter*	Fish, eggs	Putridity
	Cured meat	Sourness
Lactic acid bacteria	Beer	Sourness
	Cured meat	Greening
	Concentrated fruit juice	Sourness, off-flavor
	Milk, cream	Sour curdling
	Canned tomatoes, pickles	Off-flavors
Coliform bacteria (especially Proteus)	Fresh fruits, vegetables	Softening, discoloration
	Milk	Ropiness, curdling without sourness, bitter flavor
	Eggs	Blackening, sulfide odor
	Meat	Putridity
Acetic acid bacteria	Wine	Sourness
	Concentrated fruit juice	Off-flavor
Halophilic bacteria	Fish; brined vegetables, meats and fish	Color changes, gas
Fungi*		
Osmophilic yeasts (species of Saccharomyces, Hansenula, Pichia, Candida, Torulopsis, Debaryomyces)	Canned condensed milk, jams, honey, syrups, fruit juice concentrates, etc. (sugar 40–70%)	Odor of esters, aldehydes (i.e., sweet, fruity); gas in milk
	Salted meats (bacon, ham, frankfurters), fermented olives, pickles, sauerkraut, pickled meats (salt 6–16%)	Surface growth, slimy films
Other yeasts (species of Saccharomyces, Candida, Torulopsis, Rhodotorula)	Milk, cream	Sourness, fat degradation; yeasty flavor
	Beer	Bitterness
	Wine	Turbidity, other changes in appearance
Byssochlamys fulva	Canned fruits	Disintegration of fruit tissues
Molds (Aspergillus, Penicillium, Rhizopus, Neurospora, and Geotrichum)	Milk	Sourness, fat degradation
	Bread	Musty odor; surface growth (moldiness)
	High sugar foods	Moldiness, musty odor
	Fresh fruits, vegetables	Moldiness, softening, discoloration
	Cured meat	Moldiness

*Many of these organisms are psychrophilic and slowly spoil refrigerated foods.

TABLE 23-6.   Microorganisms* of Principal Food-borne Diseases

Agent†	Type of Food	Disease
Infectious diseases from animals		
Brucella spp.	Milk	Brucellosis (undulant fever)
Mycobacterium tuberculosis	Milk	Tuberculosis
Hemolytic streptococci	Milk	Septic sore throat, scarlet fever
Coxiella burnetii	Milk	Q fever
Salmonella spp.	Animal products	Salmonellosis, gastroenteritis
Infectious diseases from food handlers		
Salmonella typhosa	Any handled food	Typhoid fever
Salmonella paratyphi	stored under re-	Paratyphoid fever
Salmonella spp.	frigeration, including milk	Salmonellosis, gastroenteritis
Shigella dysenteriae		Bacillary dysentery
Hemolytic streptococci		Septic sore throat, scarlet fever, gastroenteritis
Corynebacterium diphtheriae		Diphtheria
Infectious hepatitis virus		Infectious hepatitis
Entamoeba histolytica		Amebic dysentery
Shigella spp.		Gastroenteritis
Toxic‡ diseases from soil contamination		
Clostridium botulinum	Smoked, pickled, and canned foods	Botulism
Toxic‡ diseases from food handlers		
Staphylococcus aureus	Foods that require considerable handling and are not subsequently processed or cooked; e.g., meat salads, cream-filled pastries, creamed potatoes, canned potted meats	Gastroenteritis

*One viral disease is included in this list.

†All organisms except *Clostridium botulinum* are killed by heat disinfection at 60 to 100° C; elimination of *C. botulinum* requires pressure-processing. None can multiply at temperatures below 10° C.

‡The toxin of botulism is destroyed in a few minutes at 60 to 100° C. The toxin of *Staphylococcus aureus* is heat-stable and still active after 30 minutes of boiling.

2. Refrigeration. Maintenance of foods at 0 to 10° C dependably prevents multiplication of all known food-borne pathogens and many spoilage organisms. Some spoilage organisms, mainly yeasts, are psychrophilic and can grow in refrigerated foods. However, they usually account for only a small proportion of the microbial population initially present, and they grow more slowly than meso- or thermophilic spoilage organisms. Accordingly, refrigeration prevents food poisoning, reduces food infection, and retards spoilage.

3. Freezing. Microbial metabolism in foods stored continuously at $-10°$ C or colder is negligible, and such foods are not susceptible to microbial spoilage. The freezing process kills some of the microbes present, presumably because expansion of developing ice crystals within the cells disrupts them. Further killing occurs slowly during storage, by unknown mechanisms. Since foods are usually cleaned, but not commonly disinfected, prior to freezing, they are equivalent to clean fresh foods in microbial content, and in susceptibility to development of spoilage and disease organisms when thawed.

4. Drying. Drying in sunlight or, more commonly today, in warm-air ovens to less than 5 per cent moisture content markedly reduces the susceptibility of foods to microbial spoilage and air-catalyzed deterioration. However, it has little disinfecting action; the ultraviolet rays in sunlight disinfect only the surface of sun-dried foods. Fleshy fruits can be preserved by drying only to 15 to 50 per cent moisture; the high sugar content results in a high osmotic pressure (see 5), which inhibits microbial growth. Nevertheless, dried fruits are now also commonly heat-disinfected.

5. Sugaring, Salting, Spicing, and Addition of Chemical Preservatives. The addition of high proportions of sugar (up to 40 or 70 per cent) or salt (6 per cent, up to saturation) increases the osmotic pressure of moist foods sufficiently to prevent the growth of all food pathogens and all but a few spoilage organisms. A few fungi can grow in sugared foods, and a few others in salted foods (see Table 23-5). The value of spices as food preservatives has been known for centuries; the need for spices was one of the major stimuli of travels by Westerners to the spice-rich Orient during the age of earth exploration. However, only certain spices—cinnamon, thyme, garlic, clove—are effective antimicrobial agents (as microbicides) in foods; others, especially black pepper and coriander, are sources of large numbers of viable microorganisms in foods. ever, only certain spices—cinnamon, thyme, garlic, clove—are effective antimicrobial agents (as microbicides) in foods; others, especially black pepper and coriander, are sources of large numbers of viable microorganisms in foods.

Chemicals useful as preservatives include organic acids (usually acetic, citric, or lactic), which may occur naturally in foods or be added as purified chemicals or by fermentation of the foods; these protect the foods by lowering the pH. Ethanol may be added, as a purified chemical, as a wine (as in marination), or by fermentation; small amounts inhibit the growth of many types of microbes. Benzoic acid is added to acidic foods, in which it is an effective microbicide. Propionic acid is added to bread and some cereal products to prevent the growth of molds. Tetracycline antibiotics are now added to poultry and fish to prolong their storage life under refrigeration.

6. Miscellaneous Methods. Since World War II, several additional methods for disinfecting and protecting foods have been introduced by commercial and military food processors in the United States. These include freeze-drying, radiation pasteurization, filtration, and gaseous disinfection. Freeze-drying is drying from the frozen state, usually under vacuum; this results in less loss of flavor, texture, and microbial viability than does drying at high temperatures. Freeze-dried foods can be stored indefinitely at room temperature and weigh less than moist foods; they are especially suitable as military and space-flight foods. Gamma-irradiation is now used by some processors instead of heat to pasteurize certain types of fish and shellfish and pork products (bacon and sausage). Filtration is used by some processors instead of heat to pasteurize beer and fruit juices. Since the recognition of certain spices as sources of spoilage microbes, many food processors have begun to disinfect those spices by exposing them to ethylene oxide in the absence of air; this method results in a smaller loss of spice potency than does heat-disinfection.

The introduction in the first quarter of the twentieth century of government regulations concerning the microbial content of milk and water resulted in a rapid decrease in the incidence of diseases transmitted via the enteric route. As commercial processors took over much of food preparation and preservation from the home, the incidence of food-borne diseases, particularly food poisoning (botulism), also decreased. However, since 1946 there has been a substantial increase in food diseases, accounted for largely by salmonella infections (salmonelloses) other than typhoid fever. These infections are due to animal-harbored salmonellae, any one species of which can cause acute enteritis, chronic enteritis, or a febrile, generalized, typhoid-like disease, which may be fatal. The salmonellae need not multiply in the foods in order to cause disease, but the probability of infection is proportional to the number of salmonella cells ingested. There are two principal ways of preventing food-borne salmonelloses: sanitary practices that prevent contamination of foods and food handlers with animal feces, and disinfection of foods in which salmonellae are normally present (e.g., eggs and poultry flesh.)

By the 1960's, the rise in food infections and food poisonings due to microbes had stimulated increased surveillance of the microbial content of commercial foods and examination of outbreaks of food diseases. These studies have been carried out by health agencies and by microbiology laboratories of universities and the food industry. On the basis of such surveys, officials estimate that at present 93 per cent of the incidences of reported cases of food- and water-borne diseases originate with foods other than milk, while 4 per cent are attributed to milk and 3 per cent to water. In one study of 17 outbreaks of salmonellosis in 1962 that were traced to single sources, 15 were traced to foods (13 to poultry products, 2 to cattle products); the other 2 were traced to household pets, which, like the domesticated animals used as foods, harbor salmonellae as normal inhabitants.

Much of the problem seems directly related to sanitary conditions and precautions in the food-processing plants. High microbial counts have regularly been found in foods processed under conditions considered by public health officials to be unsanitary. High counts generally imply that the food is old, is dirty, contains pathogens, or has been held at temperatures that favor microbial development in that type of food.

It has been inferred from surveys of the microbial content of commercial foods that the increase in food diseases has resulted from the increased consumption by Americans of ready-to-eat foods that are not cooked (heat-disinfected) in the home, and of dried mixes prepared from eggs and milk, which also may not be cooked before consumption. In order to protect the public health and reverse the trend in food disease incidence, various levels of government (municipal, state, and federal) have recently enacted or proposed regulations to govern the processing and/or microbial content of foods other than milk (regulated since 1924[6]). The first foods to be covered by such regulations have been eggs, egg products, prepared mixes, and frozen ready-to-eat foods (pies, dinners, sauces, and so forth). In some localities, such foods must now be pasteurized or demonstrated to be free of salmonellae, and must have a low total count of viable microorganisms.

Prophylactic Immunization. Man recognized long ago that an individual was likely to suffer only once from a given disease. In some cases, individuals (usually children) have been intentionally exposed to diseased persons or material known to cause the disease (e.g., blankets from the bed of a diseased person or matter from a skin lesion) in order that they contract the disease and, hopefully, recover and subsequently not be susceptible to it. In 1796, the practice of vaccination (introduction of matter from a cowpox [vaccinia virus] lesion into abraded skin) was introduced in England by Edward Jenner as a means of increasing resistance to smallpox.

The practice of vaccination, in particular, led L. Pasteur to the notion that infection with a relatively weak pathogen could increase the resistance of the host to infection with a related pathogen that caused severe disease symptoms. His first extensive studies were with anthrax, a disease prevalent among livestock in nineteenth-century France. In 1881, he and his co-workers discovered that when anthrax bacilli (*Bacillus anthracis*) were repeatedly subcultured at an incubation temperature of 42 to 43° C,[7] they lost the ability to sporulate and to elicit symptoms in cattle, sheep, and goats. Within a month of the first of two injections of the attentuated bacilli, the inoculated livestock could be injected with fully pathogenic anthrax bacilli and not develop symptoms of anthrax.

Following the anthrax work, Pasteur turned his attention to rabies. It had long been known that rabies was contracted through the bite of a rabid animal, and that the incubation period was usually quite long, sometimes several months. Because the time at which exposure to the agent (the biting) is usually known to the host or its keeper, and the incubation period is long, Pasteur reasoned that there would be sufficient time to immunize an infected animal or person before the onset of disease symptoms. He developed strains attenu-

---

[6]Grade A pasteurized milk contains a maximum of 30,000 aerobic bacteria per milliliter including ten coliform bacteria per milliliter. Milk is pasteurized by heating to 62.8° C for 30 minutes or, in "flash" pasteurization, to 72.2° C for 10 to 15 seconds. This is sufficient heating to inactivate *Mycobacterium tuberculosis,* the most heat-resistant milk-borne pathogen.

[7]The optimal temperature for artificial cultivation is 35° C; the maximum is 43° C.

ated for dogs by successive subculture of the agent in rabbits. (This method of attenuation is now called serial animal passage.) Pasteur successfully immunized dogs against natural and experimental rabies by inoculating them with preparations containing dried spinal cord from rabbits infected with rabies virus. In 1885, he administered several injections of the preparation to a nine-year-old boy, Joseph Meister, beginning $2\frac{1}{2}$ days after the boy had been bitten in 14 places by a rabid dog. The boy failed to develop rabies symptoms, presumably because of Pasteur's treatment with the attenuated virus.

In honor of Jenner's work with vaccinia, Pasteur called his immunizing preparations "vaccines," a term still used for such preparations. Vaccines such as those used by Jenner and Pasteur contained infective, attenuated agents, which presumably multiplied in the vaccinated animals while inducing immunity. Similar "live" preparations are now used to immunize humans against various diseases. The agents may be attenuated by animal passage, by passage through embryonated chicken eggs or cultured animal cells, or by cultivation under conditions that have been empirically determined to reduce pathogenicity. In addition, vaccines may be prepared with pathogenic strains by inactivating the pathogens with phenol, formaldehyde, or heat. This type is referred to as a "killed" vaccine. Immunization to diseases in which the symptoms are due solely to a toxin released by the pathogen (e.g., tetanus and diphtheria) can be achieved with cell-free preparations of heat- or chemical-inactivated toxin, called toxoid.

Vaccines are available today for a number of infectious diseases of humans (and of livestock). For some of these, vaccination is the only known satisfactory method of controlling the diseases. These include diphtheria, influenza, measles (rubeola), German measles (rubella), mumps, poliomyelitis, smallpox, sylvatic yellow fever, tetanus, and whooping cough. For other diseases, artificial immunization is valuable when combined with other control measures such as water and sewage sanitation, case detection and treatment to eliminate infections, eradication of arthropod vectors, and elimination or immunization of susceptible animals. These diseases include cholera, rabies, tuberculosis, typhoid and paratyphoid fevers, typhus, and urban yellow fever. Vaccination against a few diseases is practiced only in regions or among occupational groups in which the probability of infection is high. These include brucellosis, leptospirosis, plague, and certain types of viral encephalitis. Vaccines have been sought, but are not yet available, for many diseases that are still significant public health problems, including dysenteries, venereal diseases, and diseases due to streptococcal, staphylococcal, actinomycete, fungal, and protozoan infections.

The development of an effective vaccine is only the first step in conferring immunity on a population. Several other factors are important to the success of an immunization program, including particularly the following.

1. *Cooperation of the Population.* Because the effectiveness of a vaccination program is proportional to the fraction of a population that presents itself for vaccination, it is essential that the population be informed that the vaccine

is available and that it would be valuable to the individual and the community to eliminate susceptibility to the disease. The magnitude of this problem increases with the number of doses of vaccine necessary to ensure immunization. It is greatest in regions where health services and public transportation are minimal or non-existent and vaccination stations are difficult for the population to reach even once.

2. *Cooperation of the Individual.* Children, especially, object to painful hypodermic injection. Difficulty in administering the vaccine to each individual lengthens the time required for vaccination of a large number of persons. Two methods of reducing this problem are employed whenever possible: oral administration and combination of more than one vaccine in a single preparation.

3. *Absence of Deleterious Side Effects.* Undesirable side effects are observed mainly with virus vaccines and can usually be attributed to the presence in the vaccines of components of the animal cells that produced the viruses. Components of nervous tissues (as in some rabies vaccines) and of eggs (in influenza vaccines) are known to elicit allergic reactions in some individuals.

4. *Antigenic Constancy of the Pathogen.* Different strains of pathogens may vary in their specific antigenic components that induce immunity. A vaccine should contain all known types of immunizing antigens produced by a pathogen. This is done in some cases, e.g., poliomyelitis and paratyphoid vaccines, but is not possible with influenza vaccines. New antigenic types of influenza viruses appear every few years, and a new vaccine must be developed for each type as it appears.

5. *Sustained Immunity.* In contrast to naturally acquired infections, most vaccines confer immunity for only a limited time. The duration of immunity varies with the vaccine. Most vaccines confer immunity that persists for three to seven years; vaccination against influenza is effective for only 6 to 12 months, but against yellow fever for at least 20 years.

Immunity can be prolonged by administration of a "booster" that elicits an anamnestic response; the booster usually consists of a smaller dose of the same vaccine used in the initial vaccination. Generally, immunity induced by live vaccines persists longer than that induced by killed vaccines. A mild, symptomless infection simulates natural infection in two ways that enhance the immunizing stimulus: the amount of antigen increases as the agents multiply, and the antigen is not eliminated until antibodies have been formed.

In the United States, a number of vaccines are now available and licensed by the Food and Drug Administration for immunization of the general population. Immunization with DPT vaccine (diphtheria-pertussis-tetanus), polio vaccine, smallpox (vaccinia), measles (rubeola), German measles (rubella), and mumps is recommended for infants and preschool children. In other countries where health conditions are similar to those in the United States, tuberculosis vaccine (BCG) is also recommended at about age ten. In countries with relatively inadequate health facilities, BCG is recommended for routine use in the newborn (age one month) and revaccination at age ten. In a few regions (including the state of Hawaii), most children are also vaccinated against plague, and in the tropics against yellow fever.

Commerical Uses of Protists

The notion that each microorganism has its peculiar set of physiologic properties is the foundation of exploitation of protistan activities. This idea originated in the studies of fermentations by L. Pasteur. The subsequent development of methods for the isolation of pure cultures of protists allowed the identification of physiologic properties of individual types of microorganisms.

At present, protists are employed commercially in industrial fermentations, microbiologic assays, food and beverage preparation, various agricultural practices, and waste treatment, and as dietary supplements.

Industrial Fermentations. Microbe-catalyzed processes (called "fermentations" in industry, whether aerobic or anaerobic) are employed in industry in two circumstances—when an alternative method is not available or when any alternative method available is less economical. Whenever possible, pure cultures of the most suitable organisms are employed; in many instances, mutant strains are isolated from a strain isolated from nature, screened for their relative usefulness in a process, and the most suitable mutant is subsequently employed. Suitability usually means most economical and is judged as yield of desired product per unit of substrate consumed. In a few processes, two strains or organisms are used simultaneously or in sequence, one being incubated with the substrate for a while before the second is added. All the microorganisms currently in use in industrial fermentations are either fungi or bacteria.

The substrates employed are usually industrial by-products or mass-produced mixtures of organic materials available commercially to meet demands other than those of industrial fermentations. Such preparations include yeast extract, hydrolyzed animal proteins prepared from by-products of the food industry, hydrolyzed polysaccharides from agricultural by-products such as corncobs, corn-steep liquor from cornstarch manufacturing, the solids left after the oil is removed from certain plant seeds, and grain lots unsuitable for other uses because too many kernels are damaged.

The desired product of a fermentation may be released from the microbial cells during incubation of the fermentation mixture. In such cases, the cells are removed mechanically (by sedimentation or filtration) from the mixture, and the product is purified from the liquid portion. In a minor proportion of the fermentation processes currently in use, the desired product is retained within the cells. The method most widely used to separate products from microbial cells is addition of toluene to a suspension of the organisms or directly to the fermentation mixture; the toluene disrupts the lipoprotein of the cell membrane, and the contents of the organisms are released into the suspending fluid.

A list of examples of the types of products prepared by microbial fermentations is presented in Table 23-7; the microbes employed and the uses of the products are also presented. Two of the processes listed employ microbes at only one or a few steps, the remainder of the production being by chemical synthesis (vitamin C and steroid hormones). Acetone and butanol are produced by microbial fermentations in Japan and India. These processes were once used in the United States, but since the 1950's, methods of solvent production from petrochemicals have been developed that are more economical than fermentation.

Microbiologic Assays. When a microorganism that requires a given micronutrient is cultivated in an otherwise adequate growth medium, the yield of microbial protoplasm is directly proportional (within a range) to the amount of the required micronutrient initially present in the medium (see Fig. 11-6). The growth-yield-limiting amounts are usually too small to be assayed quantitatively by chemical methods. These observations are the basis of microbiologic assay of specific organic compounds.

The necessary materials for the microbiologic assay of a given substance are (1) a microorganism whose entire nutritional requirements are known and which can therefore be cultivated in a chemically defined medium, (2) a standard curve relating the growth yield of the organisms under specified conditions to the amount (expressed as mass units such as micrograms or only as "units") of the substance to be assayed, and (3) a preparation containing an unknown amount of the substance, and not containing substances that can substitute for the substance to be assayed or inhibit the growth of the microorganism to be employed.

The microorganisms most commonly used in assays are lactic acid bacteria. Several standard strains are now available, any one of which can be used to assay more than one vitamin or amino acid. Each strain has multiple, specific micronutritional requirements; it can be used to assay any one micronutrient when all others are added to the medium as purified preparations. Protozoa have recently been introduced as assay microbes; they seem particularly suitable for assay of vitamins in human body fluids. A few unicellular algae are used in some of the vitamin assays.

Microbiologic assays are used in the pharmaceutic, organic chemical, food, and feed industries, in clinical medicine, and in nutrition research. Materials tested include purified preparations of vitamins to be used in diet supplementation or food enrichment (commercially or experimentally); samples from synthetic chemical processes and purification steps; foods such as cereals, flour, and infant foods; animal feeds and feed supplements; and body fluids (blood, serum, and urine). The possibility of employing microorganisms for the assay of trace metals has not been extensively explored, because physicochemical

TABLE 23-7. **Some Commercial Products Manufactured by Microbial Fermentations**

Product*	Microorganism	Uses of the Product
A. Antibiotics (see Tables 23-1 and 23-2)		
B. Foods and beverages (see Table 23-8)		
C. Vitamins		
B_2 (riboflavin)	*Ashbya gossypii*† or *Eremothecium ashbyii*†	Food and feed supplement
B_{12} (cobamides)	*Propionibacterium, Pseudomonas*	Food supplement, anemia therapy
D. Amino acids		
L-lysine	*Escherichia coli* mutant strain, then *Aerobacter aerogenes*	Supplement in foods prepared from cereal grains (low lysine content)
L-glutamic acid	*Micrococcus glutamicus*	Production of monosodium glutamate (MSG), a flavoring agent
E. Organic acids (non-nitrogenous)		
Lactic acid	*Lactobacillus delbrueckii* (and other lactic acid bacteria)	Acidulation of foods and beverages; deliming of hides; chemical derivatives for plastics production; fabric treatment. Ca-lactate: feed supplement, Ca vehicle in pharmaceutic preparations, baking powders. Cu-lactate: electroplating
Citric acid	*Aspergillus niger*	Acidulation of foods and beverages and pharmaceutic preparations; chelating agent; chemical derivatives as plasticizers
Gluconic acid	*Aspergillus niger*	Ca-gluconate: Ca vehicle in pharmaceutic preparations; chelating agent. Fe-gluconate: Fe vehicle in anemia therapy
Gibberellic acid	*Gibberella fujikuroi*	Stimulation of growth, seed germination, and flower and seed formation in ornamental plants‡
F. Carbohydrates		
Sorbose	*Acetobacter suboxydans*	Intermediate in synthesis of ascorbic acid (vitamin C)
G. Enzymes		
Amylase	*Bacillus subtilis*	Desizing fabrics; production of alcohol, glucose, and syrup
Invertase	*Saccharomyces cerevisiae*	Production of chocolate, invert sugar, and molasses; additive in confections to prevent crystallization

539

TABLE 23-7.   Some Commercial Products Manufactured by Microbial Fermentations (*cont.*)

Product*	Microorganism	Uses of the Product
Pectinase	Several fungi: *Sclerotinia libertina, Coniothyrium diplodiella; Aspergillus oryzae, niger,* and *flavus*	Production of fruit juices (softens fruits, clarifies juices), and concentration of coffee
Proteases	*Bacillus subtilis, Streptomyces griseus*	Production of fish solubles; meat tenderizers; removal of gelatin films on or containing metals
Takadiastase	*Aspergillus oryzae*	Bread supplement; production of syrup; digestive aid
Keratinase	*Streptomyces fradiae*	Dehairing of hides
Combinations	——	Laundry product additives, primarily as stain removers
H. Steroids	Various eubacteria, actinomycetes, and fungi; each catalyzes only one or a few steps	Intermediates in the production of steroid hormones for chemotherapy in hormone imbalance and rheumatoid arthritis
I. Flax and hemp fibers	Clostridia; molds	Separation of fibers from plant stems for use in textile and rope manufacture

*When one organism yields more than one product, a single fermentation process may yield, e.g., an antibiotic as the major product, an organic acid as a by-product, and a vitamin or enzyme extracted from the residue of cells or mycelia, which may themselves be used as feed supplements.
†This fermentation is an example of one in which the wastes require special treatment. Both the organisms used commercially are plant pathogens, and all products and wastes must be sterilized.
‡Gibberellic acid is effective in crop plants, but is considered too expensive for agricultural use.

methods are already available that are equally sensitive and that complete the assay in a fraction of the time that would be required for a microbiologic assay.

Foods and Beverages.   Man began to employ microorganisms in the preparation of foods and beverages before he began to write his own history. In particular, he used yeasts to leaven bread and to ferment fruit juices to produce wines, and bacteria-yeast mixtures to ferment milk. The fermentations were especially valued because the products, relative to the unfermented foods, resisted spoilage. However, it was not until the nineteenth century and the studies of wine and beer by L. Pasteur that the microbial basis of such fermentations was recognized.

   Several types of foods and beverages prepared with the aid of microorganisms are listed in Table 23-8. Each of these was originally prepared in the home; the inoculum for each batch was derived either from a previous batch of the same food (then called a "starter") or from the microbial population occurring naturally in or on the initial material. Usually, the initial material

TABLE 23-8. Foods and Beverages Prepared with the Aid of Microbes

Starting Material	Predominant Organism	Product
Grains		
Mashed (digested) rye, barley, corn	Distiller's yeast, beer yeast (selected strains of *Saccharomyces cerevisiae*)	Whiskeys, beer
Rice starch	*Aspergillus oryzae,* then *Saccharomyces cerevisiae*	Sake
Flour	*Saccharomyces cerevisiae*	Leavened bread
Other vegetables		
Cabbage	*Leuconostoc mesenteroides,*	Sauerkraut
Cucumbers, tomatoes, pimentoes, cauli-flower	*Lactobacillus plantarum*	Pickles
Soybean meal	*Aspergillus*	Soy sauce
Tea leaves	Mixed population: *Acetobacter xylinum* and *Saccharomyces ludwigii*	Fermented tea drink
Tea leaves	Mixed population: *Acetobacter xylinum* and *Schizosaccharomyces pombe*	Teekwass
Fruits, fruit juices		
Grape juice	*Saccharomyces cerevisiae*	Wines
Apples, oranges, peaches, apricots, berries }	Yeasts	Wines, brandies
Olives	Lactic acid bacteria	Fermented olives
Fruit juices, wines	Yeasts and acetic acid bacteria	Vinegars
Dried figs, raisins	Mixed population: *Betabacterium vermiforme* and *Saccharomyces intermedius*	Tibi
Milk products		
Milk (cow, goat, sheep, mare, buffalo, etc.)	*Streptococcus lactis* *Streptococcus thermophilus,* *Lactobacillus bulgaricus*	Cottage cheese Cultured buttermilk, Bulgarian buttermilk, acidophilus milk, yogurt, leben (Egypt), dadhi (India)
	Yeasts and lactic acid bacteria	Mazun (Armenia), kefir (Balkan countries), kumiss (S. Russia)
Sweet cream	*Streptococcus lactis*	Sour cream
Sweet or sour cream	*Streptococcus lactis* and *Streptococcus cremoris* (fermentation) and *Leuconostoc citrovorum* and *Lactobacillus dextranicum* (flavors)	Butter (the fats) and buttermilk (the liquid)
Milk proteins (curds)	Ripened by: *Propionibacterium* *Penicillium roquefortii*	Cheddar, Swiss cheeses Roquefort, other blue cheeses
	Bacterium linens Bacteria and molds	Limburger cheese Camembert cheese

was placed in a vat or crock, with or without a starter; sugar, salt, acids, herbs, or spices were added in some processes; and the mixture was allowed to stand (incubate) in a warm or cool place, depending on the conditions found to yield the most pleasing product, until the desired changes in taste, odor, and texture had taken place.

Commercial processes for preparation of fermented foods are not significantly different from home processing. The volumes are larger, and the "starters" are usually artificial cultures of known microbes (a pure culture or a mixed culture may be used) that have been selected for the dependability or quality of their product.

All the microorganisms that have been found associated with food fermentations are bacteria, yeasts, or molds, as indicated in Table 23-8. None of these is known to cause food poisoning or infection. Many of them increase the vitamin content of the foods as they grow, and most also increase the digestibility of the foods for humans. Increased digestibility may result from the production of acids that cause disintegration of plant cells so that their contents become accessible to digestive enzymes; from degradation of plant and animal proteins to release the amino acids, which, unlike the proteins, can be absorbed through the intestinal wall without further conversion; or from conversion of slowly digested or absorbed carbohydrates to compounds that are readily absorbed. Generally, the nutritional value of a food is increased by microbial fermentative processing, and the accumulation of acids or alcohols postpones or prevents its spoilage. Whether palatability is increased is solely a matter of taste.

Agricultural Uses. The discovery of bacteria in the root nodules of leguminous plants (see Chaps. 13 and 20) laid the foundation for the most valuable agricultural use of protists yet developed. This is the inoculation of legume seeds with pure cultures of rhizobia known to form effective N_2-fixing nodules on that particular strain of legume. As the seedling develops, the root hairs of practically every plant in a field become infected with rhizobia. Development of effectively nodulated plants is independent of the amount of combined nitrogen in the soil, which increases rather than decreases by the end of the growing season.

This practice is now widely employed in agriculture around the world and is being encouraged in those regions where it has not yet been adopted. Such regions are mainly within economically developing nations, many of which are in serious need of increased food supplies, particularly supplies of protein. Increased cultivation of effectively nodulated legumes could contribute to their food supply in two ways. First, as fertilizers—by increasing the fertility of their agricultural soils through N_2 fixation. Second, as foods. Many legumes are edible and have a high protein content; in contrast to grain proteins, the proteins of edible legumes are rich in certain of the amino acids required by humans.

A second type of agricultural use of protists is in pest control. This is still largely in experimental stages, but may soon be employed more widely because of the increased public concern about the use of chemical insecticides as a potential health hazard for humans, livestock, and wildlife. Theoretically, the release of an infective pathogenic agent into a pest population (e.g., of rabbits, voles, or insects) could result in eradication of that population. The major advantage of infective pathogen pesticides is the high biologic specificity they exhibit. There are still technical and theoretic problems to be solved, e.g., preparation of pathogen populations that retain infectivity until they contact a susceptible host, and possible development of immunity in pests if the dose is too low. Nevertheless, the results of field trials with a variety of pest pathogens (including bacteria, fungi, and protozoa, and viruses) have suggested that microbial and viral pest control may be a suitable substitute for control with noxious chemicals.

The third major agricultural use of protists is as animal feeds and feed supplements. In regions where livestock farms are near ocean shores, algal thalli collected from beaches or coastal rocks have been used for centuries as animal feed or, especially when dried, as supplements to stored forage and grain feeds. More recently, masses of yeast cells considered waste products of industrial and brewing processes have been used as animal feed supplements; a smaller amount of bacterial cells is used. The yeasts and bacteria have a higher protein and vitamin content than grains or forage materials, and, like those in legumes, the proteins are rich in the amino acids required by higher animals.

Waste Treatment. The role of microorganisms in the treatment of municipal wastes was described earlier in this chapter. Industries that take the responsibility for treatment of their own wastes have developed methods similar to those used in sanitary sewage treatment. Their methods vary according to the type of waste they produce (organic or inorganic) and the volume that must be treated. Because an overriding concern of industry is economy of procedure, many industrial waste treatment procedures have been adapted to yield not only waste that can be disposed of without detriment to a body of natural water, but also marketable by-products. Two examples of such methods are described below.

1. Whey, a Waste Product of Cheese Manufacture. This is inoculated with lactic acid bacteria, sometimes in combination with yeasts, and incubated for about two days in a tank. During the incubation, lime is added at intervals to neutralize the lactic acid as it forms and thereby reduce acid inhibition of microbial growth. At the end of the incubation, the mixture is fractionated and yields: calcium lactate, used as a dietary Ca supplement for treatment of rickets and for pregnant and nursing women; proteins, mostly in microbial cells, which can be used to supplement animal feeds; and purified water as the principal liquid, removed by distillation in the preparation of the calcium lactate.

2. Waste Sulfite Liquor, a Waste Product of Paper Manufacture. This is inoculated with yeasts, usually *Candida utilis* or *Saccharomyces cerevisiae,* the "food yeasts." The yeast cells are harvested and used for livestock feed supplements. In North America, approximately 50,000 tons of this material is produced annually. The solids content of the used sulfite liquor is significantly reduced by this treatment.

Protists as Foods.   The only protists that humans consume directly as foods are a few types of marine algae and the fruiting bodies of some higher fungi (truffles and mushrooms). Both green and red algae are used, particularly in the Orient, as salad components, as garnishes, or in soups. Substances extracted from algae are more widely used; most of these are polysaccharides or, more commonly, mucopolysaccharides such as agar and alginic acids. They are used as emulsion stabilizers in milk-based foods such as ice cream, as thickening agents in liquid foods such as soups, and as gelling agents (e.g., carageenin) for preparation of gels that do not, like gelatin-gelled foods, liquefy at room temperature.

In combination with starchy materials, yeasts (usually *Candida utilis*) are eaten by humans as foods. As mentioned earlier, yeast cells may be rich in vitamins (especially B vitamins) and proteins containing the amino acids needed by humans. Food yeasts, like edible legumes, could be valuable—and inexpensive—items in the diet of persons who live in regions where the food supply is inadequate for the population.

The major problem in the use of microorganisms as human foods is acceptability. Many persons do not like the taste of yeasts, and most of the persons who have participated in experimental microbial food programs report that *Chlorella* is bitter. The acceptability of unicellular algae such as *Chlorella* and *Scenedesmus* is also unlikely because of the thick cell walls of these organisms; a diet consisting largely of unicellular green algae contains too much roughage and may cause diarrhea.

The use of protists as foodstuffs will probably continue to be limited to diet supplementation, by mixing them with other foods in proportions that cause little detectable change in flavor, but are sufficient to increase the nutritional value of the food.

Bibliography

References are listed according to the part of this textbook to which they are especially relevant, although many are general works in biology or microbiology.

Part 1

Beardsley, M. C., 1966. *Thinking Straight,* 3rd ed. Prentice-Hall, Inc., Englewood Cliffs, N.J.

Brennan, J. G., 1961. *A Handbook of Logic,* 2nd ed. Harper and Row, Publishers, New York.

Brock, T. D., ed., 1961. *Milestones in Microbiology.* Prentice-Hall, Inc., Englewood Cliffs, N.J.

Bulloch, Wm., 1938. *The History of Bacteriology.* Oxford University Press, London.

Cohen, M. R., and E. Nagel, 1934. *An Introduction to Logic and Scientific Method.* Harcourt, Brace and World, Inc., New York.

Conant, J. B., 1951. *Science and Common Sense.* Yale University Press, New Haven, Conn.

Dobell, C., 1932. *Antony van Leeuwenhoek and his "Little Animals."* Staples Press, London.

Haeckel, E. H., 1866. *Generelle Morphologie der Organismen.* Reimer, Berlin.

Hayakawa, S. I., 1949. *Language in Thought and Action.* Harcourt, Brace and Co., New York.

Large, E. C., 1940. *The Advance of the Fungi.* Henry Holt and Co., New York.

Lechevalier, H. A., and M. Solotorovsky, 1965. *Three Centuries of Microbiology.* McGraw-Hill Book Co., Inc., New York.

Vallery-Radot, R., 1928. *Life of Pasteur.* Doubleday-Doran and Co., New York.

Villee, C. A., 1967. *Biology,* 5th ed. W. B. Saunders Co., Philadelphia.

Whittaker, R. H., 1969. "New concepts of kingdoms of organisms." *Science,* **163**:150.

Part 2

Bradley, D. E., 1967. "The ultrastructure of bacteriophages and bacteriocius." *Bact. Rev.,* **31**:230.

DeRobertis, E. D. P., W. W. Nowinski, and F. A. Saez, 1965. *Cell Biology,* 4th ed. W. B. Saunders Co., Philadelphia.

Jensen, W. A., and R. C. Park, 1967. *Cell Ultrastructure.* Wadsworth Publishing Co., Inc., Belmont, Calif.

Luria, S. E., and J. E. Darnell, Jr., 1967. *General Virology,* 2nd ed. John Wiley and Sons, Inc., New York.

Lwoff, A., 1957. "The concept of virus." *J. Gen. Microbiol.,* **17**:239.

Mirsky, A., and J. Brachet, eds. *The Cell,* 6 vols., 1959–1964. Academic Press, Inc., New York.

Oparin, A. I., 1957. *The Origin of Life on Earth,* 3rd ed. Academic Press, Inc., New York.

Part 3

Baldwin, E. B., 1964. *Dynamic Aspects of Biochemistry,* 4th ed. Cambridge University Press, Cambridge, England.

Fruton, J. S., and S. Simmonds, 1958. *General Biochemistry,* 2nd ed. John Wiley and Sons, Inc., New York.

White, E. H., 1964. *Chemical Background for the Biological Sciences.* Prentice-Hall, Inc., Englewood Cliffs, N.J.

Part 4

Ainsworth, G. C., and A. S. Sussman, eds. *The Fungi, An Advanced Treatise,* 3 vols., 1965–1968. Academic Press, Inc., New York.

Alexopoulos, C. J., 1962. *Introductory Mycology,* 2nd ed. John Wiley and Sons, Inc., New York.

Alexopoulos, C. J., and H. C. Bold, 1967. *Algae and Fungi.* The Macmillan Co., New York.

Bessey, E. A., 1950. *Morphology and Taxonomy of Fungi.* The Blakiston Co., Philadelphia.

Bonner, J. T., 1967. *The Cellular Slime Molds,* 2nd ed. Princeton University Press, Princeton, N.J.

Breed, R. S., E. G. D. Murray, and N. R. Smith, eds., 1957. *Bergey's Manual of Determinative Bacteriology,* 7th ed. The Williams and Wilkins Co., Baltimore.

Buchsbaum, R., 1948. *Animals without Backbones,* rev. ed. University of Chicago Press, Chicago.

Dawson, E. Y., 1956. *How to Know the Seaweeds*. Wm. C. Brown Co., Publishers, Dubuque, Iowa.

Fritsch, F. E., 1952. *The Structure and Reproduction of the Algae*. Cambridge University Press, Cambridge, England.

Gunsalus, I. C., and R. Y. Stanier, eds. *The Bacteria, A Treatise on Structure and Function,* 5 vols., 1960–1964. Academic Press, Inc., New York.

Hall, R. P., 1953. *Protozoology*. Prentice-Hall, Inc., Englewood Cliffs, N.J.

Ingold, C. T., 1967. *The Biology of Fungi,* rev. ed. Hutchinson Educational Ltd., London.

Jahn, T. L., and F. F. Jahn, 1949. *How to Know the Protozoa*. Wm. C. Brown Co., Publishers, Dubuque, Iowa.

Kudo, R. R., 1966. *Protozoology,* 5th ed. Charles C Thomas, Publisher, Springfield, Ill.

Lewin, R. A., ed., 1962. *Physiology and Biochemistry of Algae*. Academic Press, Inc., New York.

Lwoff, A., and/or S. H. Hutner, eds. *Biochemistry and Physiology of Protozoa,* 3 vols., 1951–1964. Academic Press, Inc., New York.

MacLean, R. C., ed., 1962. *Textbook of Theoretical Botany*. Langmans Press, London.

Phaff, H. J., M. W. Miller, and E. M. Mrak, 1966. *The Life of Yeasts*. Harvard University Press, Cambridge, Mass.

Prescott, G. W., 1964. *How to Know the Fresh-Water Algae*. Wm. C. Brown Co., Publishers, Dubuque, Iowa.

Round, F. E., 1965. *The Biology of Algae*. Edward Arnold (Publishers) Ltd., London.

Smith, G. M., 1950. *The Fresh-Water Algae of the United States,* 2nd ed. McGraw-Hill Book Co., Inc., New York.

Stanier, R. Y., M. Doudoroff, and E. A. Adelberg, 1970. *The Microbial World,* 3rd ed. Prentice-Hall, Inc., Englewood Cliffs, N.J.

Taylor, W. R., 1957. *Marine Algae of the Northeastern Coast of North America,* 2nd ed. University of Michigan Press, Ann Arbor.

Tiffany, L. H., 1939. *Algae: The Grass of Many Waters*. Charles C Thomas, Publisher, Springfield, Ill.

Part 5

Avery, O. T., C. M. MacLeod, and M. McCarty, 1944. "Studies on the chemical nature of the substance inducing transformation of pneumococcal types. Induction of transformation by a desoxyribonucleic acid fraction isolated from pneumococcus type III." *J. Exp. Med.,* **79:**137. (This paper, with several other articles relevant to topics treated in this textbook, can be found in J. E. Flynn, 1966. *The New Microbiology*. McGraw-Hill Book Co., Inc., New York.)

Hayes, W., 1968. *The Genetics of Bacteria and their Viruses,* 2nd ed. John Wiley and Sons, Inc., New York.

Jacob, F., and E. L. Wollman, 1961. *Sexuality and the Genetics of Bacteria*. Academic Press, Inc., New York.

Murrell, W. G., 1961. "Spore formation and germination as a microbial reaction to environment." *Symp. Soc. Gen. Microbiol.,* **11**:100.

Schwartz, V., 1965. "Einleitende Beobachtungen am Beutefang von *Didinium nasutum.*" *Zeit. f. Naturforsch.* **20b**:383.

Sinnott, E. W., L. C. Dunn, and T. Dobzhansky, 1950. *Principles of Genetics,* 4th ed. McGraw-Hill Book Co., Inc., New York.

Strickberger, M. W., 1968. *Genetics.* The Macmillan Co., New York.

Part 6

Alexander, M., 1961. *Introduction to Soil Microbiology.* John Wiley and Sons, Inc., New York.

Baumgartner, J. G., and W. Clayton, 1946. *Canned Foods, An Introduction to their Microbiology,* 2nd ed. D. van Nostrand Co., Inc., New York.

Belding, D. L., 1965. *Textbook of Parasitology,* 3rd ed. Appleton-Century-Crofts, New York.

Casida, L. E., Jr., 1968. *Industrial Microbiology.* John Wiley and Sons, Inc., New York.

Christensen, C. M., 1951. *Molds and Man.* University of Minnesota Press, Minneapolis.

Davis, B. D., R. Dulbecco, H. N. Eisen, H. S. Ginsberg, and W. B. Wood, 1967. *Microbiology.* Harper and Row, Publishers, New York.

Dublin, L. I., 1965. *Factbook on Man—From Birth to Death,* 2nd ed. The Macmillan Co., New York.

Dubos, R. J., ed., 1958. *Bacterial and Mycotic Infections of Man,* 3rd ed. J. B. Lippincott Co., Philadelphia.

Henry, S. M., ed. *Symbiosis,* 2 vols., 1966–1967. Academic Press, Inc., New York.

Mason, B., 1966. *Principles of Geochemistry,* 3rd ed. John Wiley and Sons, Inc., New York.

Odum, E. P., 1959. *Fundamentals of Ecology,* 2nd ed. W. B. Saunders Co., Philadelphia.

Prescott, S. C., C.-E. A. Winslow, and M. H. McCrady, 1946. *Water Bacteriology with Special Reference to Sanitary Water Analysis.* John Wiley and Sons, Inc., New York.

Rahn, O., 1945. *Microbes of Merit.* Jacques Cattell Press, Lancaster, Pa.

Rose, A. H., and C. Rainbow, 1963. *Biochemistry of Industrial Microorganisms.* Academic Press, Inc., London.

Rosebury, T., 1962. *Microorganisms Indigenous to Man.* McGraw-Hill Book Co., Inc., New York.

Tanner, F. W., 1944. *The Microbiology of Foods,* 2nd ed. Garard Press, Champaign, Ill.

Wilson, G. S., and A. A. Miles, eds., 1964. *Topley and Wilson's Principles of Bacteriology and Immunology,* 5th ed. The Williams and Wilkins Co., Baltimore.

Page references to illustrations are indicated by *f.*, to footnotes by *n.*, and to tables by *t.*

549

The index-glossary form is used in order to provide explanation and page references together. Index entries that are included in the glossary are printed in **boldface** type; entries that are included in the glossary of genetics terms on pages 448–49 are indicated by **G.**

Page references to illustrations are indicated by *figures:* or *f.,* to figure legends by (*f.*), to footnotes by *n.,* and to tables by *t.*

slime protists, 311
Invasiveness, pathogen, 498
Invertebrates. *See also* Animals; Arthropods
  crustaceans as food for protozoa, 284, 290
  endosymbiotic algae, 483–84
Ionization, related to pH, 393
Iron, distribution of algae, 324
  enzymes, 106
  oxidation, 179
  oxides, 184
  phosphates, 462–63
  sulfide, 182, 461
Isogamy sexual fusion of morphologically similar unicells (individuals or specialized gametes), 323,
  336 *f.*, 434–35, 439. *See also* Gamete; Sexual
  fusion
Isolate population obtained from a clone and maintained as a pure population that reproduces
  asexually, 114
Isolation, pure populations of protists, 111–17, 115 *f.*,
  435–36, 437 *f.*, 440 *f.*
Isoniazid, 505, 518, 519 *t.*
Iwanowsky, D., 69

Jenner, E., 534–35
Joblot, J., 12
Joints, mycoplasmas, 170

Kala-azar (leishmaniasis), 272, 501 *t.*
Keratin, 457
Kidney, disease, 505, 507
"Killed" vaccine immunizing preparation containing
  heat- or chemical-inactivated agents as anti-
  gens, 535–36
Killing. *See* Inactivation; Resistance
Kinetosome basal structure of the eucaryotic flagellum
  or cilium, 46 *f.*, 50, 55 *f.*, 60 *f.*, 92, 263 *t.*, 274,
  297–98, 304, 306, 354
  vestigial, 58 (*f.*), 62 (*f.*)
Kingdom (taxon), 143
Koch, R., 16, 18, 114 *n.*, 485, 524
Koch's postulates, 18

Lactic acid. *See* Acids, organic, lactic; Calcium, lactate
Lag phase, growth, 128
Larynx, 494, 507
Leaf. *See also* Plant(s)
  disease, 483
  N₂ fixation nodules, 460
  protists in/on, 225, 238, 281
Leeuwenhoek, A. van, 11–12
Legume, food, 542
  N₂ fixation, 18–19, 165, 460, 542
Leishmanial form (trypanosomes), 272–73 *f.*
Leishmaniasis (kala-azar), 272, 501 *t.*
Leprosy, 194, 500 *t.*
Leptomonad form (trypanosomes), 272–73 *f.*, 274
Leptospirosis, 499 *t.*, 535

Leukemia, 72, 504
Leukocyte, 487. *See also* Phagocytosis
Lichen symbiotic association of alga and fungus, 324,
  469–73, 471 *f.*
Life cycle events that occur between any point in the
  development of an individual and that same
  point in the development of its offspring, 102,
  414–15
  algae, 323, 325, 331, 338, 346, 374, 376, 381, 401–
  405, 402 *t.*; *figures:* 333, 340, 348, 375, 378,
  382, 401
  bacteria, 180 *f.*, 184, 185 *f.*, 191–93
  fungi, 211, 215–18, 221, 233, 236, 244, 252–53; *figures:* 210, 212, 216, 222, 224, 230, 235–36,
  241–43, 248, 253
  protozoa, 267, 272–73, 279, 284, 292–95, 310; *figures:*
  273, 293, 296
  slime protists, 314, 315 *f.*
Life expectancy, 17, 521–24, 522 *t.*
Light, energy source for growth, 105, 109, 401–405,
  435, 456
  illumination of artificial cultures, 112, 113 *t.*, 119,
  130, 176–78
  inhibition of cell division (*Chlorella*), 403, 405
  intensity, influence on growth rate, 130, 401–402
    influence on pigment content, 320 *t.*
    related to distribution of algae, 324, 378
  protection against, symbiosis, 468, 470–72
  stimulus, 134–35, 256, 314, 392 *t.*, 393, 481, 484
  wavelength, absorption by different pigments, 119,
  154
    influence on pigment content, 320 *t.*
    related to distribution of photosynthetic protists,
    154, 324, 378
Light/dark alternation, 400–405
Light scattering, 125
Lignin, 110, 457, 483
Linkage, genetic, 448 **G.**; 434, 437–38, 441–47
Lipid, 25, 29 *f.*
  bacteria, 194, 399
  oxidation, 194
  protozoa, 267
  virions, 67, 68 *t.*
Lipoprotein lipid-protein complex, 25, 29 *f.*, 50, 70
Lister, J., 16
Lithotroph, 122, 141, 526
Lithotrophy type of nutrition in which carbon is as-
  similated as CO₂, 109 *t.*
"Live" vaccine immunizing preparation containing ac-
  tive infective agents as antigens, 535–36
Liver, 295, 464–65, 487, 503, 506–508
Livestock. *See also* Animals; Poultry; Rumen
  diseases, 158, 169, 169–70, 193, 294, 464–65, 534
  food-borne pathogens, 521 *f.*, 528, 533
  protists in feeds, 324, 543–44
Living system, 4, 7–9, 19–20, 105, 453
Lobopodium one type of pseudopodium, 279, 280, 286
Locomotion, 12, 51, 92. *See also* Motility
Locule cavity within an ascostroma, containing asci,
  238
Locus, genetic, 448 **G.**